PHARMACOGNOSY AND PHARMACOBIOTECHNOLOGY

PHARMACOGNOSY AND PHARMACOBIOTECHNOLOGY

James E. Robbers, Ph.D.
Professor of Pharmacognosy
Purdue University School of Pharmacy and Pharmacal Sciences
West Lafayette, Indiana

Marilyn K. Speedie, Ph.D.
Dean and Professor of Pharmacognosy
University of Minnesota College of Pharmacy
Minneapolis, Minnesota

Varro E. Tyler, Ph.D., Sc.D.
Lilly Distinguished Professor of Pharmacognosy
Purdue University School of Pharmacy and Pharmacal Sciences
West Lafayette, Indiana

Williams & Wilkins
A WAVERLY COMPANY

BALTIMORE • PHILADELPHIA • LONDON • PARIS • BANGKOK
BUENOS AIRES • HONG KONG • MUNICH • SYDNEY • TOKYO • WROCLAW

1996

A Lea & Febiger Book

Editor: Donna Balado
Senior Managing Editor: Victoria M. Vaughn
Production Coordinator: Marette Magargle-Smith
Typesetter: Maryland Composition
Printer: Maple-Vail Book Manufacturing Group
Binder: Maple-Vail Book Manufacturing Group

Accurate indications, adverse reactions, and dosage schedules for drugs are provided in
this book, but it is possible that they may change. The reader is urged to review the package
information data of the manufacturers of the medications mentioned.

Printed in the United States of America

Library of Congress Cataloging in Publication Data

Robbers, James E.
   Pharmacognosy and pharmacobiotechnology / James E. Robbers,
Marilyn K. Speedie, Varro E. Tyler.
      p.   cm.
   Rev. ed. of: Pharmacognosy / Varro E. Tyler, Lynn R. Brady, James
E. Robbers. 9th ed. 1988.
   Includes bibliographical references and index.
   ISBN 0-683-08500-X
   1. Pharmacognosy. 2. Drugs—Biotechnology. I. Speedie, Marilyn
K. II. Tyler, Varro E. III. Tyler, Varro E. Pharmacognosy.
IV. Title.
   [DNLM: 1. Pharmacognosy. 2. Technology, Pharmaceutical.
3. Biotechnology.   QV 752 R631p 1996]
RS160.T94   1996
615'.321—dc20
DNLM/DLC
for Library of Congress   95-48963
                                                                         CIP

*The Publishers have made every effort to trace the copyright holders for borrowed material.
If they have inadvertently overlooked any, they will be pleased to make the necessary
arrangements at the first opportunity*

96 97 98 99
1 2 3 4 5 6 7 8 9 10

Reprints of chapters may be purchased from Williams & Wilkins in quantities of 100 or
more. Call Isabella Wise in the Special Sales Department, (800) 358-3583.

Preface

A book entitled *Pharmacognosy and Pharmacobiotechnology* might for some seem to be an unusual combination of terminology and disciplines. The logic behind this combination is that, on the one hand, pharmacognosy, the forerunner of all other scientific disciplines in pharmacy and which has its origins in ancient civilizations, deals with drugs produced by plants, animals, and microorganisms. It includes all drug agents produced through a biosynthetic process. On the other hand, pharmacobiotechnology involves the production of natural product drugs by application of the remarkable progress made in recent years in molecular biology. It is the newest frontier in providing innovative approaches in drug discovery and patient treatment. In essence, therefore, this book deals with both the oldest and the newest drugs, the common thread being that all are natural products.

The goal of this textbook is to provide primary knowledge of natural product drugs to the pharmacy student in the professional program of study. It will also interest those students engaged in graduate studies in natural products as well as other health professionals seeking to understand the important role natural products have in drug therapy and drug discovery. Emphasis is placed on the biology and chemistry of these drugs as they relate to drug production and pharmaceutical and medicinal use. A chapter on pharmacobiotechnology is devoted to developing an understanding of the application of molecular biology to technology in the production of recombinant protein drugs and monoclonal antibodies.

With the exception of the antibiotics and the biologics, the drugs are organized on the basis of their biosynthetic and chemical relationships; this provides the fundamental basis for the conceptual understanding of natural products as drugs. The biosynthetic processes that have evolved in living organisms have led to the formation of unique, diverse chemical structures that possess an amazing variety of biological activities. Some of these chemicals are mainstays in drug therapy, and the never-ending variety of novel pharmacophores found in natural products has served as a stimulus to the medicinal chemist to use them as prototypes for structural modification in order to improve therapeutic effect. Pharmacognosists and natural product chemists have also been stimulated to search nature to find new leads for drug discovery.

The chapter on Antibiotics includes not only natural products but semisynthetic and synthetic anti-infective agents as well. This provides a complete picture of the armamentarium of drugs used to treat infectious diseases. The chapter on Biologics and Immunomodulators is a unique aspect of the book and discusses both immunologic agents and biologics related to human blood. Many of the latter are available for drug therapy only because of the advances in pharmacobiotechnology.

The demand for information on the safety and efficacy of herbal medicines is increasing at an extremely rapid rate. Although these so-called dietary supplements are not regulated by the Food and Drug Administration nor are legal standards of identity and purity monographed in current editions of the *United States Pharmacopoeia* or the *National Formulary*, many pharmacies sell them, and it is important for pharmacists to have a working knowledge of the basic principles involved in their use. For this reason, some of the more important herbal drugs have been included and are found in the appropriate chapters according to the chemistry of their active constituents.

At the present time, the world pharmaceutical market is rapidly expanding. Numerous new drug companies are being formed along with an accompanying increase in research and development efforts. In the search for new drugs, organisms from all parts of the globe are being examined as sources for novel chemicals and bioactivity. The search ranges from plants of the tropical rain forests to animals and microorganisms from the seas. In addition, pharmacobiotechnology has had a major influence on increasing the speed of the drug discovery process by providing unique and valuable tools for drug screening, such as the cloning of receptor proteins for bioactivity assays. We believe that this book will enable the reader to understand the significant role of natural products in drug discovery and patient therapy. We hope that it will impart, at least in some small way, the excitement and awe associated with human knowledge about, and the use of, these wondrous chemicals from nature.

West Lafayette, Indiana   James E. Robbers
Minneapolis, Minnesota   Marilyn K. Speedie
West Lafayette, Indiana   Varro E. Tyler

Contents

1

Introduction to Pharmacognosy

A BRIEF HISTORY OF PHARMACOGNOSY

From the earliest days of organized pharmaceutical and medical knowledge, all of the information pertaining to drugs and their usage in Western culture was designated "materia medica" (literally, medical matter). The most famous commentary on drugs, written by the Greek pharmaco-botanist Pedanios Dioscorides in the first century A.D., is titled *De materia medica libri cinque* (Concerning medical matter in five volumes). This treatise, which covered some 600 plant drugs plus a number of animal and mineral products, remained the authority in the field for about fifteen centuries.

Gradually, as the amount of knowledge about drugs increased, specialized disciplines became a necessity. In the early nineteenth century, materia medica began to undergo division into pharmacology (the actions of drugs) and pharmacognosy (all aspects of drugs, with lesser emphasis on actions). At the time, all medicines derived from natural sources, so that qualifier is not necessary.

The word "pharmacognosy," formed from two Greek words *pharmakon* (drug) and *gnosis* (knowledge), was long thought to have been introduced by C.A. Seydler, a medical student in Halle/Saale, Germany, who used the title *Analectica pharmacognostica* for his dissertation in 1815. However, recent historical research has found an earlier usage of "Pharmacognosis." J.A. Schmidt used that title in his *Lehrbuch der Materia medica,* published in Vienna in 1811, to describe the study of medicinal plants and their properties.

Later in the nineteenth century, chemists began to synthesize large numbers of organic compounds with structures of ever-increasing complexity, some of which were useful thera-

peutic agents. Because these products were considered to fall outside the realm of pharmacognosy, the discipline of medicinal chemistry, which had remained relatively dormant since the time of Paracelsus, took on increased vigor. Thus, there came to be three basic disciplines devoted to drugs: pharmacology, which dealt with drug actions and effects; pharmacognosy, covering all information on medicines from natural sources—plants, animals, and microorganisms; and medicinal chemistry, the science of synthetic drugs.

This situation prevailed until the mid-twentieth century, at which time pharmacognosy and medicinal chemistry began to merge. The reasons were both numerous and complex and need not be dealt with here. It is sufficient to point out that, in spite of the continued utilization of a large number of significant drugs of natural origin—antibiotics, oral contraceptives, serums and vaccines, and classic medicines from higher plants—both teaching and research efforts concentrated on synthetic drugs. Many individuals who continued to work with botanicals were educated principally in chemistry and adopted the designation *natural product chemists.*

Then, in the last decades of the twentieth century, three significant events occurred which have already produced fundamental changes in the attitude of both the public and scientists toward pharmacognosy. In the first place, lay persons discovered the utility of whole plant drugs—or herbs, as they are commonly called. Dissatisfaction with the effectiveness and the cost of modern medicine, abetted by an enhanced appreciation of things "natural" and "organic," has caused millions of persons throughout the world to gain a deep appreciation of the use of classical plant drugs for the treatment of many ailments, usually of the self-limiting variety. The "green" revolution, in terms of

1

herbal medicine, has now achieved astonishing popularity in the United States. Although not yet understood or encouraged by an ultraconservative Food and Drug Administration that classifies most plant drugs as dietary supplements or food additives and places severe limitations on labeling, there is little doubt that consumer demand will promote an ever-increasing interest in classic plant drugs for use as traditional herbal remedies.

In the second place, major pharmaceutical manufacturers have recognized that plants with folkloric reputations as remedies probably provide the best source of constituents that can serve either as new drugs or as prototypes for them. Because the patent situation renders it difficult to obtain market exclusivity for many classic plant remedies long in use, the search for botanical remedies has turned to exotic plants in remote areas such as the tropical rainforests. Major pharmaceutical companies have now developed cooperative agreements with individuals or organizations seeking medicinal plants in such countries as Brazil, Costa Rica, China, Mexico, Borneo, and even Samoa. This intensive effort is certain to yield positive results in the form of new plant drugs in the reasonably near future.

And finally, the greatest revolution of all, which is still in its infancy as far as drug discovery is concerned, has begun in the field variously described as recombinant DNA technology, genetic engineering, or more specifically, pharmacobiotechnology. This involves the transfer of genetic material from one organism to another, permitting the latter to produce in quantity a component of the former that is useful as a drug. The first commercial application of the technique in pharmacognosy has been a process utilized by the Eli Lilly Company which allows the production of human insulin by a special non-disease-producing strain of *Escherichia coli* bacteria that has been genetically altered by the addition of a gene for human insulin production.

Another early commercial product resulting from this methodology was tissue plasminogen activator, alteplase or tPA, a thrombolytic agent. It is synthesized using the complementary DNA (cDNA) for natural human tissue-type plasminogen activator obtained from a line of human melanoma. This is inserted genetically into a line of Chinese hamster ovary cells which then secrete the enzyme alteplase into the culture medium from which it is recovered, purified, and marketed. These examples demonstrate the feasibility of recombinant DNA technology in the pro-

duction of commercial amounts of useful proteinaceous drugs. Details of them and other natural products produced by the technique will be discussed subsequently in this text.

In presenting this brief history of the initial development, decline, and renascence of the discipline of pharmacognosy, the comments have been purposely limited to its place in Western culture. That is not to say that drugs of plant and animal origin have played insignificant roles in the Asiatic culture represented by such countries as China and India. In China, the drug encyclopedia *Pen-ts'ao kang mu,* compiled by Li Shih-Chen and published in 1596 A.D., listed more than 2000 drugs of natural origin. Some 5000 native plants are used as medicinal herbs in that country today. The *Vedas* of India, a collection of hymns predating 1000 B.C., included more than 1000 healing herbs, many of which continue to be used in Ayurvedic medicine.

The problem is that, until now, these cultures have made only minor contributions to Western medicine. The useful plant drugs *ma-huang* (ephedra) from China and rauwolfia from India are notable exceptions. However, the philosophical precepts upon which Chinese and Ayurvedic medicines are based are entirely different from those of the West. Both of the former believe that disease is caused by an imbalance of certain "elements" or "humors" in the body reminiscent of the long-discredited four-humors doctrine of the Greek physician Hippocrates (ca. 4600 to 361 B.C.). Drug research based on such philosophical principles has not proven productive. It is only when the herbal remedies are evaluated by Western methods, as was the case with ephedra and rauwolfia, that useful drugs result. That is a task remaining to be done for many thousands of potentially useful medicinal plants.

VALUE OF NATURAL DRUG PRODUCTS

Compounds from natural sources play four significant roles in modern medicine. In the first place, they provide a number of extremely useful drugs that are difficult, if not impossible, to produce commercially by synthetic means. These include such diverse groups of compounds as the alkaloids of the opium poppy, of ergot, and of solanaceous plants; the cardiotonic glycosides of digitalis; most of the antibiotics; and all of the serums, vaccines, and related products. Natural sources also supply basic compounds that may be modified slightly to render them more effective or less toxic. The numerous variations of the morphine molecule serve as examples here. A third role of natural products is their utility as prototypes or models for synthetic drugs possessing physiologic activities similar to the originals. Procaine and similar local anesthetics are commonly cited representatives of this category. Examples of all three types of compounds and their relationships are given in Table 1–1.

There is a fourth role for natural products that is quite different from the above but is nonetheless important. Some natural products contain compounds that demonstrate little or no activity themselves but which can be modified by chemical or biological methods to produce potent drugs not easily obtained by other methods. For example, taxol may be synthesized from baccatin III, which occurs more or less abundantly in the leaves of various yew species, whereas taxol itself is found only in the bark of the scarce Pacific yew. Proper chemical and biological treatment of stigmasterol, which occurs abundantly in soybean oil, permits the large-scale production of hydrocortisone or related corticosteroids, compounds that occur in nature in only small amounts. The importance of natural products as precursors of significant drugs cannot be overemphasized.

Some 25 years have passed since the last detailed survey of the use of natural products and their constituents in medicine was conducted. However, the conclusions reached then from a survey of 1.05 billion new and refilled prescriptions are still widely quoted in the literature. It is probable that, with the exception of certain details to be mentioned later, the findings would be similar today.

In the prescriptions studied, about 25% were for drugs containing higher plant principles. Taken by itself, however, this figure can be misleading. About 10% of the total prescriptions (40% of those with plant constituents) were for hormonal principles, including progestins, corticosteroids, estrogens, and anabolic agents. Obviously, these are not isolated directly from higher plants but, instead, are produced from precursors obtained from that source. In other words, they fall into the fourth category of natural products previously discussed. Many of the narcotic analgesics are classified in the second category, namely, chemical modifications or derivatives of such compounds as morphine. The point is, the 25% figure frequently quoted does not consist of isolated plant drugs *per se* but

also includes derivatives with various related or unrelated activities prepared from plant precursors.

Nearly 12% of the total prescriptions surveyed were for microbial-derived products; about 6% were animal derived; 7% were mineral in character. The remaining 50% was composed of synthetic chemical agents. In summary, the survey indicated that approximately 50% of prescriptions filled in 1967 contained one or more natural drug products, broadly defined so as to include various molecular modifications.

No similar in-depth survey has been conducted since that time, but a 1991 prescription audit revealed little change in the overall 25% figure for prescriptions containing one or more natural products. Conclusions regarding the significance of certain medicines from natural sources may also be drawn from a general knowledge of the pharmaceutical marketplace. The 6% figure for animal-derived drugs was not and is not representative of the use of such products in the United States. Most serums, vaccines, and the like are either utilized in hospitals or administered in various types of clinics where no identifiable prescription is ever written. Various blood products also fall in this category.

In 1967, the use of antibiotics and antineoplastic agents from natural sources was much less than at present, the variety and application of such principles having increased markedly in recent years. The change of hydrocortisone from prescription to OTC status and the nearly ubiquitous use of contraceptive medication by females of child-bearing age have certainly resulted in a marked increase in the quantities of plant-derived hormones employed. Further, the advent of a fairly large number of drugs produced by pharmacobiotechnological procedures has certainly promoted an increased use of natural drug products. In addition, the therapeutic use of crude drugs (herbs) and their galenical products (phytomedicinals) by the American public has reached an all-time high. As previously explained, most of these are not technically classified as drugs in this country, but the therapeutic use and utility of many of them cannot be denied. Sales of such products in the United States in 1994 were estimated at approximately $1 billion at the wholesale level in comparison to total sales of about $55 billion by U.S. pharmaceutical manufacturers. Herbal products thus represent a small but ever-increasing percentage of the total market.

When one considers that plant-derived ste-

Table 1–1

Examples of Plant Drugs Serving as Prototypes or Models for Other Medicinals

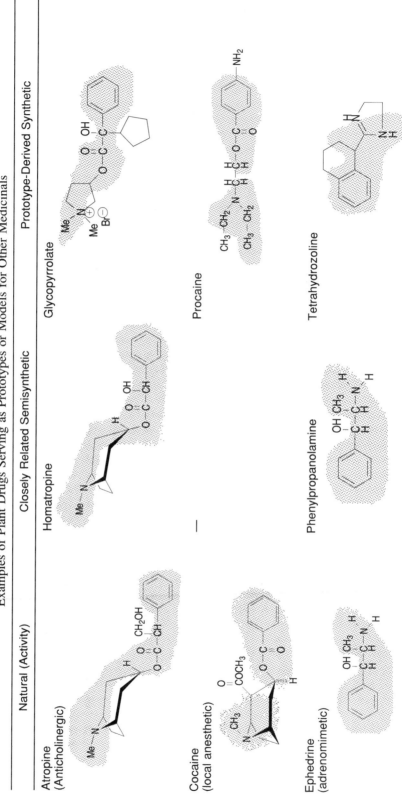

Natural (Activity)	Closely Related Semisynthetic	Prototype-Derived Synthetic
Atropine (Anticholinergic)	Homatropine	Glycopyrrolate
Cocaine (local anesthetic)		Procaine
Ephedrine (adrenomimetic)	Phenylpropanolamine	Tetrahydrozoline

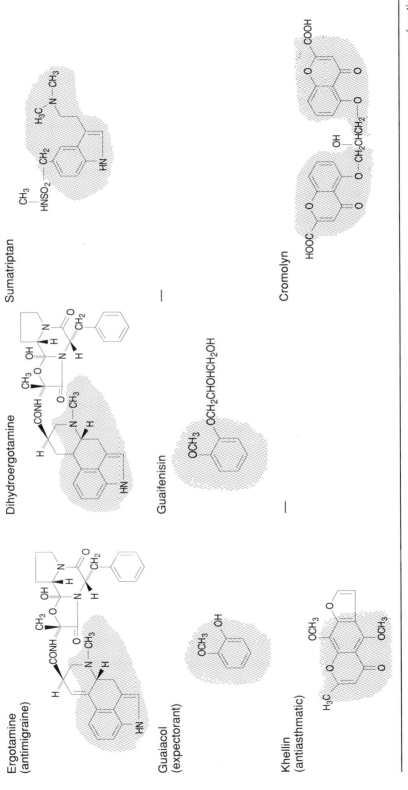

Sumatriptan

Dihydroergotamine

Guaifenisin

Cromolyn

Ergotamine
(antimigraine)

Guaiacol
(expectorant)

Khellin
(antiasthmatic)

(continued)

Table 1–1

Examples of Plant Drugs Serving as Prototypes or Models for Other Medicinals—*(Continued)*

Natural (Activity)	Closely Related Semisynthetic	Prototype-Derived Synthetic
Morphine (narcotic analgesic)	Hydromorphone	Propoxyphene
Physostigmine (cholinergic)		Neostigmine
Podophyllotoxin (antineoplastic)	Etoposide	

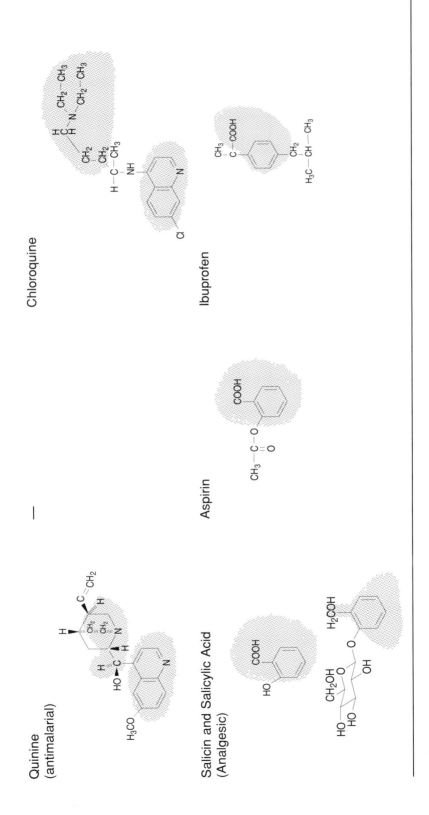

Quinine
(antimalarial)

Chloroquine

Aspirin

Ibuprofen

Salicin and Salicylic Acid
(Analgesic)

roids alone account for about 15% ($22 billion) of the $150 billion world pharmaceuticals market, that the annual market for taxol is estimated to reach $1 billion by the year 2000, that the antineoplastic agents vinblastine and vincristine have sales amounting to $100 million per year, that the market for psyllium seed products amounts to some $300 million annually, and that nicotine and scopolomine patches now have combined sales of more than $1 billion per year, it is obvious that natural products continue to play important economic as well as therapeutic roles in modern medicine. Based on figures of this nature, it must be concluded that natural drugs from higher plants, microbial sources, and animals have at least held firmly to the 43% market share they enjoyed in 1967. If one considers expanded OTC usage, they have probably increased their numerical share of the total drug market, even considering the large increase in synthetic drugs currently available.

In any case, research developments have blurred the dividing line between natural and synthetic products. The naturally occurring alkaloid ephedrine is now usually produced by chemical synthesis involving the reductive condensation of L-l-phenyl-l-acetylcarbinol with methylamine. Diazepam, a benzodiazepine tranquilizer, long thought to be of purely synthetic origin has since been found to occur naturally in small amounts in both plants and animals. This erosion of rigid classificational limits is one of the factors that has caused instruction in pharmacognosy to be combined with that in medicinal chemistry in many educational programs in American colleges and universities. Still, it must not be forgotten that a healthy market share approaching 50% of the significant drugs utilized in medicine today are natural in origin. It is the function of this volume to discuss the significant features of these important medicines.

PRODUCTION OF NATURAL DRUG PRODUCTS

Because of their diverse origin from plant, microbial, and animal sources, the production of natural drug products takes many different forms. Higher plants may be collected in the wild (wildcrafted), or cultivated, or both. In the case of those obtained from our ever-dwindling natural resources, special attention must be paid to quality control. Collectors, for the most part, are relatively uneducated individuals, not versed

(and sometimes not caring) about the details of plant taxonomy. Their produce is sometimes misidentified or adulterated. It may also be harvested at the wrong time of year for maximum yield of desired constituents, improperly dried and stored, and subject to insect or rodent infestation. Obviously, quality control is important in such cases.

However, it is not always easy to determine the quality of plant materials. If they are maintained in whole form, identification is simple; but if they are finely comminuted, even qualified experts have difficulty, especially with mixtures. Once the plant material has been extracted, only suitable analytical techniques will give a true picture of quality. Such procedures may be chemical, physical, or biological in nature. Various chromatographic procedures that enable the analyst to compare the profile of the sample being tested with that of a product of known quality are most useful.

Unless wildcrafting is carefully and conscientiously carried out, natural reserves tend to become depleted. This is the situation that now exists in much of the United States, Western Europe, and even parts of Asia with respect to popular drug plants. This phenomenon ultimately results in the commercial cultivation of drug plants, but this industry is also beset with problems.

In the first place, the market is generally quite limited; and it often requires special techniques and procedures that are difficult to conduct, especially on a limited scale. Unless mechanization can be effected—a difficult task in small-scale crop production—it is labor intensive and therefore not feasible in technologically advanced nations where wages are high. For this reason, only a few such specialty crops are cultivated presently in the United States.

One of these is American ginseng, a shade-grown root crop that because of its high price lends itself to small scale production even in this country. Used primarily by inhabitants of the Asian rim nations, ginseng is becoming popular as a kind of tonic in both Europe and America. In the United States it is approved by the FDA only as a food for beverage purposes; but it is extensively cultivated here, especially in Wisconsin. Ginseng exports from this country in 1992 amounted to approximately $90 million.

Another plant drug grown extensively in the United States is ginkgo leaves. One plantation of 10 million trees, grown as bushes so the leaves can be harvested mechanically, occupies more than 1000 acres in South Carolina. The leaves are dried and shipped to Europe for processing. Ginkgo biloba extract (GBE) is a best-selling drug there.

Volatile-oil-producing plants, such as peppermint, are also extensively cultivated in parts of the United States, especially in Indiana and the Pacific Northwest. All of the operations involved, including the initial distillation of the oil from the harvested plant material, are highly mechanized to reduce labor costs. As is the case with other drug plants, cultivation permits selection of high-yielding varieties and also allows the time of harvest to be controlled to maximize yields.

Nevertheless, most of the drug plant cultivation takes place outside the United States. Even a specialty crop, such as ergot, that involves mechanical inoculation of rye plants with spores of a selected fungus, is produced in Eastern Europe. This kind of field cultivation must necessarily compete successfully on an economic basis with saprophytic production of the alkaloids obtained by growing the organism in submerged culture. Large fermenters are employed for this purpose in a manner analogous to antibiotic production.

An alternative method of drug plant cultivation involves production of the desired secondary constituents by cell-culture techniques. Although this method may be utilized in certain specialized cases, there are many limitations, including slow growth of the cells, expensive media and production facilties, low yields of desired metabolites, and a tendency to store desired constituents in the cells rather than to excrete them into the media where they may be more easily recovered. Studies have shown that stress conditions, such as interaction with an appropriate pathogen, may stimulate the production of certain desired constituents in plant-cell suspension cultures, but slow growth of the cell biomass is still a problem. Probably this method of drug production will not become truly useful until the plant genes that code for enzymes catalyzing the desired biosynthetic reactions can be transferred into more rapidly growing bacterial or fungal cells.

Microbial metabolites used as drugs, especially the antibiotics and related antineoplastic agents, are produced by fermentation. This usually involves growing the desired organism in aerated tanks holding thousands of gallons of a sterilized nutrient medium. At the proper time, the cell growth is separated from the culture broth, the latter is extracted, and the extract is then purified to yield the desired component. In some cases, such as with the cephalosporins, the constituent produced by fermentation is subjected to various chemical reactions to produce by semisynthesis the desired drug product.

Production of genetically engineered drugs is basically quite similar to the fermentation techniques used for antibiotics. The principal difference is that a gene controlling the formation of the desired component is transferred from its original source to a fast-growing microbial or animal cell line, thereby allowing quantity production in a relatively short period of time. Because the technique is relatively new and considerable experimentation is required to develop a single commercial product, most drugs produced by recombinant DNA technology are quite costly, a factor that tends to limit their use.

In addition to desired components, undesirable constituents may also be synthesized by genetically modified organisms. This was vividly demonstrated in 1989 when tryptophan produced by a Japanese manufacturer using a strain of bacteria so modified was implicated in 1,400 cases of eosinophilia myalgia syndrome, a serious blood disorder. At least 19 deaths were recorded. Subsequent investigation revealed the tryptophan was not the causative agent. Instead, two toxic contaminants produced by the modified organisms and not removed during the purification procedure were at fault. Nevertheless, the FDA acted to remove tryptophan from the dietary supplement market. This episode points up the necessity for thorough testing of all genetically engineered foods and drugs prior to marketing.

In the specialized sense, the term *biologics* refers to animal derivatives, such as serums, antitoxins, and globulins or to microbial products, such as vaccines, toxins, and tuberculins that confer protection against pathogenic microorganisms. Products in the first category are prepared from the blood of animals, usually following some sort of special treatment designed to increase the concentration of desired components. Those of the second type are produced by inoculating an appropriate culture medium, which in some cases may consist of living tissue, with the proper pathogen. After appropriate purification, the product is ready for drug use. Even though they may lack immunizing activity, human blood and its various fractions or derivatives are usually considered to be biologics.

A whole spectrum of natural drug products exists, and their precise method of production is highly individualized. In the United States, where medical practice is oriented toward the use of single chemical entities, most natural drugs are processed to yield one or more active constituents. Morphine from opium, ergotamine from ergot, and digoxin from digitalis leaf are typical examples. Hydroalcoholic tinctures, fluidextracts, or extracts of plant material are now infrequently utilized in medical practice here. While such products may present some advantage in providing a number of different types of physiologically active constituents, they are often difficult to standardize, making precise dosage impossible. Nevertheless, such galenical preparations are commonly employed in many other countries and have regained some popularity here as a result of the resurgence of interest in herbal medicine. With rare exceptions, standards of quality are now lacking for galenicals in the United States, so any such preparations should be obtained from a producer with a reputation for quality work. On the other hand, purified natural products are required to adhere to standards established in *The United States Pharmacopeia* or *The National Formulary,* so quality in such cases is not a significant concern.

CHEMISTRY OF NATURAL DRUG PRODUCTS

The living organism may be considered a biosynthetic laboratory not only for chemical compounds (carbohydrates, proteins, fats) that are utilized as food by humans and animals but also for a multitude of compounds (glycosides, alkaloids, terpenoids) that exert a physiologic effect. These latter chemical compounds give plant and animal drugs their therapeutic properties. Drugs are used as such in their crude form; or they may be extracted, the resulting principles being employed as medicinal agents. It is obvious, therefore, that any study of pharmacognosy must embrace a thorough consideration of these chemical entities. The usual term of these entities is **constituents;** however, because the plant or animal is composed of many chemical compounds, it is common practice to single out those compounds that are responsible for the therapeutic effect and call them **active constituents.**

The active constituents are differentiated from **inert constituents,** which also occur in plant and animal drugs. Cellulose, lignin, suberin, and cutin are usually regarded as inert matter in plant drugs. In addition, starch, albumin, coloring

matters, and other substances may have no definite pharmacologic activity and also are considered inert constituents. In animal drugs, keratin, chitin, muscle fiber, and connective tissue are regarded as inert. Often the presence of inert substances may modify or prevent the absorbability or potency of the active constituents. To eliminate the undesirable effects of inert matter in the crude drug or its preparations, active principles are extracted, crystallized, and purified for therapeutic use. These constituents have been referred to as ''secondary'' plant substances.

There has long been a controversy regarding the utility of such compounds to the plants that produce them. One school of thought believes them to be little more than metabolic errors—that is, principles that are without value, except possibly as a substitute for an excretory method lacking in plants which would ''lock up'' unneeded metabolites in more or less permanent form.

A more popular hypothesis at present views such compounds as conferring survival value on the plant. Just as sharp thorns discourage predators from grazing on the plants bearing them, so does a poisonous alkaloid or an astringent tannin help preserve a specimen by rendering it unpalatable. While this postulation seems reasonable, the student in applying it must be careful to avoid teleological thought. Lacking any kind of of a central nervous system, plants cannot be imbued with purpose. At best, such constituents must be thought of as metabolic accidents that confer survival value, allowing their hosts to reach maturity and to reproduce.

Pharmacologically active constituents are responsible for the therapeutic activity of the drug. They may be either single chemical substances or mixtures of principles, the separation of which is neither practical nor advantageous. The single chemicals are exemplified by glycosides, terpenoids, steroids, phenylpropanoids, alkaloids, and peptides. The mixtures include gums, fixed oils, fats, waxes, volatile oils, resins, and resin combinations.

The secondary constituents of drug plants are influenced by three principal factors: heredity (genetic composition), ontogeny (stage of development), and environment. Genetic effects induce both quantitative and qualitative changes, but those caused by environmental influences are primarily quantitative. Plants of the same species that resemble one another closely in form and structure (phenotypically) may, nevertheless, be quite different in genetic composition (genotypically). This often results in distinct differences in chemical composition, particularly with reference to secondary constituents. Such plants are said to belong to different chemical races.

Perhaps the best-known pharmacognostic examples of chemical races are found in the ergot fungus *Claviceps purpurea*. Individual strains have been isolated representing chemical races that produce superior yields of single desired alkaloids, e.g., ergotamine, instead of the usual small concentrations of complex mixtures of alkaloids. Other examples include chemical races of certain species of *Eucalyptus* that exhibit large variations in the content of cineole and related constituents in the volatile oils. Chemical races of *Strophanthus sarmentosus* differing markedly in the content of glycosides and sapogenins have also been reported.

Ontogeny also plays a significant role in the nature of the active constituents found in medicinal plants. Although it might be expected that the concentration of secondary metabolites would increase with the age of the plant, it is not generally appreciated that the identity of these constituents may also vary according to the stage of development. The cannabidiol content of *Cannabis sativa* reaches a peak early in the growing season and then begins to decline. When this decline occurs, the concentration of tetrahydrocannabinol begins to increase reciprocally and continues until the plant approaches maturity. Old plants, as well as stored plant material, are characterized by high concentrations of cannabinol. In the opium poppy, *Papaver somniferum,* the morphine content of the capsules is highest 2 to 3 weeks after flowering. If the latex is harvested earlier, related alkaloids such as thebaine and codeine predominate. On the other hand, if harvesting is delaying too long, the morphine decomposes.

Environmental factors that can produce variations in secondary plant constituents include soil, climate, associated flora, and methods of cultivation. Because all these factors are more or less related, they are difficult to evaluate individually. For example, many alkaloid-containing plants accumulate higher concentrations of such constituents in moist regions than in arid lands. However, this may actually be related to the soil, which is usually poor in nitrogen in arid regions, and rich nitrogen sources are usually required for good yields of alkaloids. This is not always the case with volatile-oil-bearing plants because excess nitrogen does not necessarily

cause an increase in their yields. Indeed, such plants abound in dry areas as opposed to moister habitats.

One phase of pharmacognosy that has assumed a role of importance in recent years is the study of the biochemical pathways leading to the formation of secondary constituents used as drugs. This study is commonly referred to as **drug biosynthesis** or **biogenesis.** Just as an understanding of the chemical synthesis of phenobarbital or other synthetic drugs is of fundamental importance to the student of medicinal chemistry, a knowledge of the biochemical synthesis of drugs of natural origin is of equal importance to the student of pharmacognosy.

The biosynthetic pathways leading to the formation of secondary constituents used as drugs have been a subject of scientific investigation throughout most of the twentieth century. As early as 1912, the Swiss chemist G. Trier postulated that amino acids and their simple derivatives served as precursors of structurally complex alkaloids. However, it was not until isotopically labeled organic compounds became readily available in the second half of this century that positive confirmation of this and other ''paper chemistry'' hypotheses could be achieved.

Some of these fundamental reaction sequences leading to the different types of secondary constituents used as drugs will be presented in the chapters dealing with the individual drugs and their constituents, but to facilitate a general understanding of the pathways involved and their interrelationships, they are summarized in Figure 1–1.

THE ORIGIN OF DRUGS

Most consumers purchasing over-the-counter (OTC) prescription drugs today have no idea of their origin. As far as they are concerned, drugs come from a bottle, just as milk comes from a plastic jug and beer from a can. Yet, with few exceptions, drug development has often followed a logical progression from an unmodified natural product, usually extracted from an herb, to a synthetic modification of that natural chemical entity, to a purely synthetic compound apparently showing little relationship to its natural forebears. It will be instructive to select one of these latter compounds and to trace back its origins.

Ibuprofen or (±)-2-(4-isobutylphenyl) propionic acid, is presently a very widely used nonste-

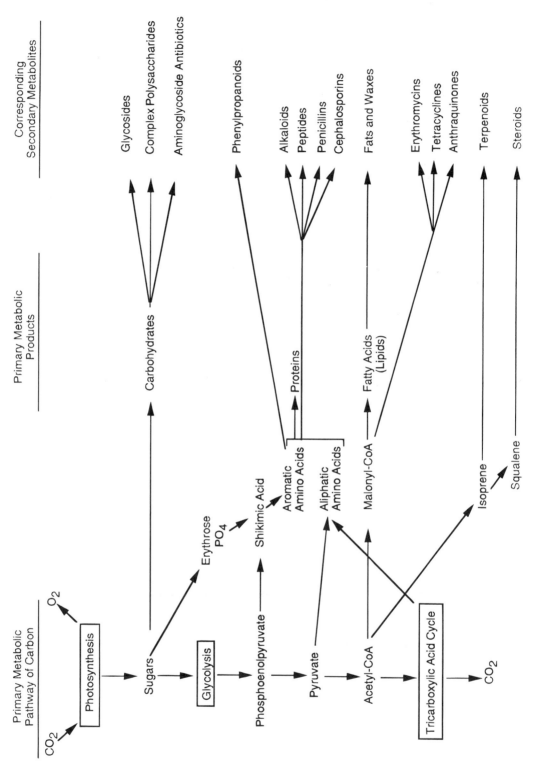

Fig. 1–1.   Interrelationships of biosynthetic pathways leading to secondary constituents in plants.

roidal anti-inflammatory drug (NSAID), analgesic, and antipyretic. It was introduced to the American market in 1974 under the name of Motrin. Looking at its structure in Table 1–1, it seems at first glance to be an entirely new chemical entity without an obvious close relationship to previously available drugs. However, on closer inspection, it will be observed that the structure features an aromatic ring and a side chain with a terminal carboxyl group. These same features are found in aspirin (acetylsalicylic acid), long used for the same therapeutic effects as ibuprofen. Other characteristics shared by these two compounds include:

1. A flat configuration enabling them to fit a specific receptor site on an enzyme;
2. Acidic and strongly ionized at a physiological pH;
3. Aqueous solubility, allowing them to concentrate in plasma and extracellular water;
4. Sufficient lipid solubility to allow them to penetrate biological membranes easily.

Aspirin does not occur in plants nor was it the original NSAID. That recognition goes to salicin (salicyl alcohol glycoside) that was first isolated from the bark of the willow true (*Salix* sp.) by the French pharmacist H. Leroux in 1829. The first modern reference to the use of willow bark in treating feverish conditions dates from 1763; however, both Hippocrates and Celsus were familiar with the virtues of this plant. After its isolation, salicin was shown to be a pro-drug that was converted to the active principle, salicylic acid, in the intestinal tract and liver following consumption. In the meantime, salicylic acid had itself been isolated from other sources, including meadowsweet, then known as *Spiraea ulmaria* L. [now properly referred to as *Filipendula ulmaria* (L.) Maxim.]. Because of this origin it was named *spirsaüre* in German, or spiric acid in English.

Salicylic acid was found to possess excellent anti-inflammatory, analgesic, and antipyretic properties, but even its sodium salt was difficult to consume for lengthy periods because of the irritation and damage it produced in the mouth, esophagus, and particularly the stomach. After all, salicylic acid is an essential ingredient in corn and wart removers because of its keratolytic effects. Then, prior to 1899, a chemist named Felix Hoffman at the Bayer Co. in Germany took from the shelf a bottle of acetylsalicylic acid and administered a quanity of it to his rheumatic father who could no longer take sodium salicylate. It proved to be both effective and well tolerated. Thus, aspirin (*acetyl spiric* acid) was introduced into medicine.

Over the years, numerous modifications of the salicylic acid molecule have been made synthetically in attempts to improve its action and reduce its side effects. Acetanilide proved too toxic; phenacetin was carcinogenic; acetaminophen is used as an analgesic but lacks anti-inflammatory properties; and the newer NSAIDs, such as ibuprofen, all have advantages and disadvantages but are generally quite effective.

It is interesting to consider how a worldwide industry of enormous proportions devoted to the relief of pain and inflammation grew from the common willow tree. This is just one of numerous examples that could be cited to show the many ramifications of a single plant drug and how much the modern pharmaceutical industry owes to its natural-product heritage.

THE FUTURE

The future of drug development does not lie in the search for new traditional drugs in the rainforest, the screening of their extracts for various physiological activities, and the isolation of active chemical constituents or prototypes that can be made into useful drugs by semisynthesis or mimicked by total synthesis. The future also does not lie in the random screening of newly synthesized organic chemicals in the hope that one will cure cancer or prevent the rejection of a transplanted liver. No, the future lies, as molecular biologists are prone to remind us, in the identity of the nature of receptor sites on and within cells in the brain or in other organs or tissues and the customized synthesis of agents that will occupy those sites to promote some desirable effect or to prevent an undesirable one.

However, contrary to that oft-repeated phrase, "The future is now," in drug development at least, the future is not yet here. It will come, but it will come slowly and in pieces, not all at once. So, until the day when pharmacobiotechnological developments can be made with sufficient ease to permit the marketing of its products at affordable costs, or the day when all those receptor sites are known and appropriately fitting drugs can be readily synthesized, we must rely on the classic empirical methods for the discovery of new drugs. Certainly the plant kingdom is a tried and true source. If we are able to curb the naturally rapacious nature of an ever-expanding human population, perhaps a considerable number of those potentially useful species may be examined scientifically and clinically before being trampled, burned, or plowed into extinction. There are certain to be some good, new drugs out there remaining to be discovered, but to find them has become a race against time.

One of the first drug plants to be rendered extinct in the ancient world was silphium (*Ferula* sp.), a birth-control agent highly valued by the ancient Romans. Its employment as a contraceptive was so widespread that this difficult-to-cultivate plant no longer existed in the Mediterranean area, or anywhere else, after the third century A.D. This paradox serves as an important lesson to all who seek to improve the destiny of human beings by making use of materials from the kingdom of the plants.

In advancing our own cause, we must be ever mindful not to destroy that which helps us to advance. Plants have been faithful servants to humans from the beginning of time. It is difficult to imagine pharmacy or medicine without the digitalis glycosides, the opium alkaloids, the tetracycline antibiotics, or, for that matter, even the senna anthraquinones. Yet without plants neither these nor many other widely used drugs would ever have existed. It is time to express our thanks by helping plants to continue to occupy their rightful place in the world—a world in which botanicals existed long before *Homo sapiens*. If we fail in this conservation effort, both pharmacy and humanity will be the losers.

SUGGESTED READINGS

Andrews, T.: *A Bibliography on Herbs, Herbal Medicine, "Natural" Foods, and Unconventional Medical Treatment.* Littleton, Colorado, Libraries Unlimited, 1982.

Bisset, N.G., ed.: *Herbal Drugs and Phytopharmaceuticals.* Stuttgart, medpharm, 1994.

Collier, H.O.J.: Aspirin. Sci. Am., 209:97–108, 1963.

Crellin, J.K., Philpott, J.: *Herbal Medicine Past and Present.* Vols. 1 and 2. Durham, North Carolina, Duke University Press, 1990.

Der Marderosian, A.: The 1990s: The Status of Pharmacognosy in the United States, pp. 221–225 in *Natural Resources and Human Health—Plants of Medicinal and Nutritional Value.* S. Baba, O. Ak-erle, Y. Kawaguchi, eds., Amsterdam, Elsevier, 1992.

Duke, J.A.: *Handbook of Phytochemical Constituents of GRAS Herbs and Other Economic Plants.* Boca Raton, Florida, CRC Press, 1992.

Farnsworth, N.R.: Drugs from Higher Plants. Tile and Till, 55:32–36, 1969.

Ganzinger, K.: Über die Termini "Pharmacognosis" und "Pharmacographia," ein Beitrag zur Geschichte der Pharmazeutischen Wissenschaften. Medizinhistorisches J., 14:186–195, 1979.

Glasby, J.S.: *Dictionary of Plants Containing Secondary Metabolites.* London, Taylor and Francis, 1991.

Harborne, J.B., Baxter, H.: *Phytochemical Dictionary: A Handbook of Bioactive Compounds from Plants.* London, Taylor and Francis 1993.

Herbert, R.B.: *The Biosynthesis of Secondary Metabolites,* 2nd ed., London, Chapman and Hall, 1989.

Kinghorn, A.D., Balandrin, M.F., eds.: *Human Medicinal Agents from Plants.* Washington, D.C. American Chemical Society, 1993.

Magner, L.N.: *A History of Medicine.* New York, Marcel Dekker, 1992.

Meacham, Jr., R.: Assessing analgesics: An overview of the fight against pain. Hazleton Laboratories Pharmaceutical Newsletter 3(2):1–6, 1992.

Mitra, R.: *Bibliography on Pharmacognosy of Medicinal Plants.* Lucknow, India, Economic Botany Information Service, 1985.

Principe, P.P.: The Economic Significance of Plants and their Constituents as Drugs. *Economic and Medicinal Plant Research,* vol. 3. H. Wagner, H. Hikono, N.R. Farnsworth, eds., London, Academic Press, 1989; 1–117.

Riddle, J.M., Estes, J.W.: Oral contraceptives in ancient and medieval times. Am. Sci., 80:226–233, 1992.

Simon, J.E., Chadwick, A.F., Craker, L.E.: *Herbs: An Indexed Bibliography.* 1971–1980, Hamden, CT, 1984.

Tyler, V.E.: *Herbs of Choice: The Therapeutic Use of Phytomedicinals.* Binghamton, New York, Pharmaceutical Products Press, 1994.

Tyler, V.E.: Medicinal Plant Research: 1953–1987. Planta Med., 95–100, 1988.

Tyler, V.E.: Plant Drugs in the Twenty-First Century. Econ. Bot., 40:279–288, 1986.

Werbach, M.R., Murray, M.T.: *Botanical Influences on Illness.* Tarzana, California, Third Line Press, 1994.

Williams, D.H., Stone, M.J., Hauck, P.R., Rahman, S.K.: Why are Secondary Metabolites (Natural Products) Biosynthesized? J. Nat. Prod., 52: 1189–1208, 1989.

Zito, S.W., ed.: *Pharmaceutical Biotechnology.* Lancaster, PA, Technomic Publishing Co., 1992.

2

Pharmacobiotechnology

INTRODUCTION AND HISTORY

Biotechnology can be defined as the use of organisms or enzymes for the production of useful materials. This is a very broad definition that encompasses many processes, such as wine and cheese making and fermentation processes that yield antibiotics, which precede recombinant DNA technologies. The advent of recombinant DNA techniques in 1973, primarily the ability to clone human (and other) genes and express their encoded proteins in microorganisms, revolutionized biotechnology and drastically increased its importance to many areas of our lives. While the impact of biotechnology can be felt in agriculture, food technology, environmental science, and many other areas, one of its major impacts is in the area of drugs, diagnostics, and vaccines. We have chosen the term **pharmacobiotechnology** to refer to the application of biotechnology to pharmaceuticals.

Biotechnology is often thought of in terms of using microorganisms to produce useful products, and although that is a major component of the technology, the field does, in fact, go beyond the use of microbes to include tissue culture, isolated enzymes, and even genetically engineered cows and goats who produce foreign proteins in their milk. Plants are also being genetically engineered for resistance to disease or to produce certain desirable compounds, and these also fall under the broad definitions of biotechnology. The impact of recombinant techniques on medicine and pharmaceuticals is felt well beyond our ability to produce new drugs. Our knowledge of the molecular basis of the pathophysiology of diseases and of drug action has grown immensely due to these tools, and they also have enabled the identification and production of isolated drug targets (i.e., receptors and

enzymes) for use in drug discovery and drug design.

The basic technique that revolutionized biotechnology was described by Herbert Boyer and Stanley Cohen in 1973 and involved the specific transplantation of a functional unit of DNA (a gene) from one organism to another, forming "recombinant" organisms. Although the transfer of DNA between organisms was nothing new, the ability to specifically transfer a specific piece of DNA and control its expression was dramatically new, and its potential for revolutionizing molecular biology and biotechnology was recognized quickly. The strategy Boyer and Cohen devised for gene cloning was, of course, based on a number of molecular biology enzymes and other tools that other scientists had discovered, but they were able to put them all together to create the revolutionary strategy. The potential was soon exploited, and by 1978, human insulin, the first pharmaceutical produced as a result of genetic engineering, was available. In the years since then, many new biotechnology-derived products have entered the pipeline. A 1994 report from the Pharmaceutical Research and Manufacturers of America showed 21 products on the market derived from recombinant DNA technology and more than 150 in various stages of clinical trials. Perhaps even more important, but less quantifiable, is the dramatic increase in knowledge of the molecular basis of a number of previously untreatable diseases that will lead to even more new drug therapies in the future.

TOOLS OF BIOTECHNOLOGY

Recombinant DNA (rDNA) is constructed outside the living cell using enzymes called "restriction enzymes" to cut DNA at specific sites

15

and enzymes called "ligases" to insert the cleaved piece of DNA (the "insert") into "vector" DNA, i.e., plasmid or viral DNA that will be able to enter a "host" cell or microorganism. Once the foreign DNA enters the host organism, it is called a "recombinant organism."

Restriction enzymes or restriction endonucleases digest DNA into short pieces at very specific sites determined by a four base or greater stretch of specific DNA sequence. They serve as our molecular scissors. The longer the number of bases required to specify a cleavage site for a specific enzyme, the less often it will cut a long piece of DNA. The DNA sequences specifying restriction sites are palindromic as seen in Figure 2-1, in that the sequence is observed on both strands of DNA (in the 5' to 3' direction) and the bases in positions 1, 2, and 3 on one strand of a six-base site will be complementary to bases in positions 6, 5, and 4, respectively, of the same strand. Restriction enzymes are produced by bacteria as a way of protecting themselves from foreign DNA. They protect the sites in their DNA corresponding to the enzymes they produce by methylating those sites. Restriction enzymes are named by the first letter of the genus name combined with the first two letters of the species name (e.g., an enzyme from **Proteus vulgaris** is called *Pvu*I). A strain may designated by a capital letter (e.g., *Eco*RI) or an arabic numeral and a capital letter (e.g., *Sau*3AI), and Roman numerals follow to specify individual enzymes when a given microbe has more than one. Most restriction enzymes leave "sticky ends," single strand extensions that will base pair with the opposite strand of another piece of DNA cleaved by the same enzyme, but some leave blunt ends. Figure 2-1 shows some examples of restriction enzyme sites.

DNA pieces cleaved with the same enzyme will have complementary or sticky ends that will

anneal under appropriate conditions when the pieces are mixed together. These annealed pieces will have single strand breaks (called "nicks") at the sites at which they were cleaved. Treatment of these mixed pieces with an enzyme called **DNA ligase** (usually T4 ligase from a bacteriophage named T4) will result in phosphodiester bond formation at the ends of the DNA strands that are already held together by complementary base pairing, thus creating an intact piece of recombinant DNA. In gene cloning procedures (i.e., genetic engineering), a gene corresponding to a specific protein will be joined with a **cloning vector** so that it can be transferred into a host cell. A cloning vector can be a plasmid or a bacteriophage. Plasmids are self-replicating, double-stranded, circular DNA molecules that are usually maintained in the host cell as an independent extrachromosomal moiety. Plasmids will be characterized by size, host specificity (which organisms it can exist in), and copy number, i.e., the number of copies of a given plasmid usually found in a cell. Ones used for cloning purposes often have genetic elements such as antibiotic resistance genes that can be used to determine which cells have the plasmid, promoters that can be used to express the recombined gene in large amounts, and multicloning sites, regions of DNA that have overlapping restriction enzyme sites that can be used to insert DNA cut with a variety of enzymes. Plasmids enter the host cell through a process called transformation, which allows intact DNA to fuse with and cross the cell membrane. Plasmids are usually designated with a small **p** and two or three letters that designate the researchers or laboratory in which the plasmid was developed, followed by a numerical designation with some meaning to the researchers (e.g., pBR322 was created by F. **B**olivar and R. **R**odriquez). Antibiotic resistance genes are particularly useful on plasmids used for cloning purposes because they allow selection of plasmid-bearing organisms (transformants). Non-plasmid bearing cells will be killed by the antibiotic leaving only those cells which received a plasmid and are expressing the protein that confers antibiotic resistance. An example of the genetic map for a plasmid used in cloning is illustrated in Figure 2-2.

Bacteriophages (viruses that infect bacteria) are also used as cloning vectors, and foreign DNA is inserted into the viral genome in an analogous manner. Viral DNA (carrying an insert) gets into cells by viral infection, and the genes

Enzyme	Producing organism	Cleavage Site
*Pvu*1	*Proteus vulgaris*	.....CGATCG..... GCTAGC
*Hpa*1	*Haemophilus parainfluenzae*	.....GTTAAC..... CAATTG
*Eco*R1	*Escherichia coli*	.....GAATTC..... CTTAAG
*Sau*3A1	*Staphylococcus aureus*	.....GATC..... CTAG

Fig. 2–1. Examples of restriction endonucleases.

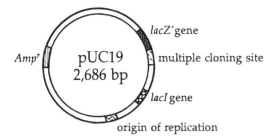

Fig. 2–2. Genetic map of plasmid pUC19. The plasmid contains an ampicillin resistance gene which allows selection of plasmid-bearing organisms. The multiple cloning site has several restriction enzyme sites and occurs within the *lacZ'* gene that encodes beta-galactosidase. *LacZ'* is induced by isopropylthiogalactoside (IPTG) which interferes with the binding of the repressor protein encoded by *lacI* to the *lacZ'* promoter, thus derepressing the *lacZ'* gene leading to its transcription and translation. Foreign genes inserted into the multiple cloning site will interfere with the production of beta-galactosidase activity but will be expressed themselves, either from the lacZ' promoter or from the promoter belonging to the gene.

are expressed as the viral genome is expressed. Copies of the recombinant virus genome will be packaged into the many copies of virus produced during the viral infection process, and the bacteria carrying the phage will be killed, creating a plaque or clear spot on a plate of bacteria corresponding to the infected cells. Within the plaque are many copies of the infecting virus. Sometimes bacteriophage will have genes removed to create a vector that can infect cells but not go through a lytic cycle (not kill the infected cell), and then the DNA can be stably expressed within the recipient bacterial cell. This same general kind of procedure can be used to transfect eucaryotic cells either in tissue culture or *in vivo* (see the discussion of gene therapy).

Hybridization probes are another essential tool for genetic engineering. A probe is a complementary sequence of DNA that is labeled either with radioactivity or with a fluorescent or chromogenic material. DNA that is being probed will be bound to a solid support (nylon or nitrocellulose) and heated in a mixture with the probe DNA. As the strands separate and reanneal, the probe will hybridize with its complementary sequence. The probe will bind (hybridize) to the DNA to which it is complementary and indicate the presence of that segment of DNA by making the hybridized DNA either radioactive, chromo-

genic, or fluorescent. Probes can be synthetic oligonucleotides or larger segments of DNA or even whole plasmids. It takes a minimum of 11 identical bases in a row or an 80% match within a segment of 50 bases for a probe to stably hybridize to a complementary DNA sequence, although this varies with conditions of temperature and salt concentration (''stringency'') and with the positioning of mismatched bases. The DNA can come from whole colonies or from DNA cut and spread on an agarose gel by electrophoresis. The process is called **Southern blotting**. An analogous procedure in which an oligonucleotide probe is used to detect a specific RNA sequence is called **Northern blotting**. Specific proteins can be detected by complementary antibodies, leading to a color reaction, in a process called **Western blotting**. These tools are very powerful identifiers of specific pieces of DNA, RNA, or protein.

We now can look at the overall cloning process for inserting a known gene into a host organism as illustrated in Figure 2-3. The gene to be inserted is cut with restriction enzymes and mixed with plasmid DNA that has been cut with the same enzyme. Ligase is used to anneal the nicks, creating an intact plasmid that is subsequently transformed into the host organism. Antibiotic selection is used to select recipient hosts that have the plasmid, and those plasmid-bearing colonies, which have the desired inserted gene, can be detected either through detection of the enzyme activity encoded by the inserted gene, by Western blotting of cell extracts to detect the new protein, or by hybridization with a DNA probe complementary to the inserted gene. One or more colonies (clones) carrying the desired gene and expressing the desired protein will be selected and grown in large fermentation to produce the desired protein in large quantities. The recombinant cells will be lysed, and the protein will be purified and used.

How, then, does one find the gene that one wants to clone and overexpress through the process just described? The answer depends on what is already known about the gene and its protein and in what organism it occurs. The process begins with creating and screening a library. A **library** is a collection of recombinant organisms, each of which contains a different fragment of DNA from the organism which naturally has the gene of interest in its chromosome. Libraries are created by cutting the total DNA of a donor organism with a given restriction enzyme and then using the previously described

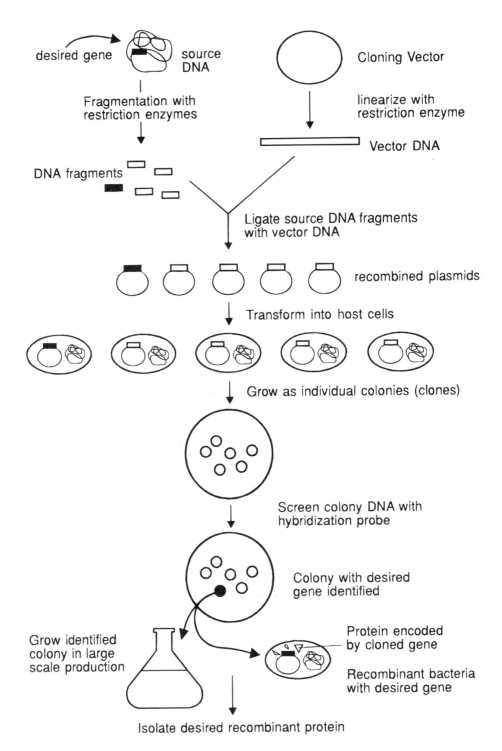

Fig. 2–3. Overall cloning process.

procedure to ligate the various fragments into a vector and introduce the vectors into the host organism. [For complex donor organisms (e.g., humans) other approaches are used to limit the number of DNA fragments cloned into the library, and some of those approaches are described later.] Each colony (clone) of the host organism potentially has a different piece of the donor DNA, and the entire chromosome should be represented in the library of clones. Because a donor's chromosome will be cut into thousands of fragments, a method of screening for the one clone containing the desired gene is essential. If the sequence of the gene is known, a hybridization probe can be synthesized and used to identify the colonies with the desired gene. Similarly, if the protein sequence is known, a corresponding oligonucleotide probe can be synthesized using either a ''best guess'' of codon usage (a ''guessmer'') or a mixture of oligonucleotides corresponding to the degenerate codons. Sometimes one relies on the gene being expressed in

the host organism, and the protein is identified through the characteristics it confers on the host cell or by antibody detection of the protein. Many genes will have **homology** (similarity) to comparable genes in other organisms, and the desired clone can be detected by using a homologous gene sequence as a probe.

As mentioned, for human genes, the chromosome is too large to generate a library and screen it as described. Also, eucaryotic organisms have their genes on the chromosome as a series of exons and introns (intervening sequences) so that the messenger RNA (mRNA) must be spliced before protein synthesis can occur. *E. coli* and other procaryotic host organisms do not splice DNA, so the DNA cloned into *E. coli* must have already had the intervening sequences removed. As illustrated in Figure 2-4, a typical approach for cloning and expressing DNA encoding a desired human protein would involve isolating mRNA from human cells expressing the protein of choice, preferably in large quan-

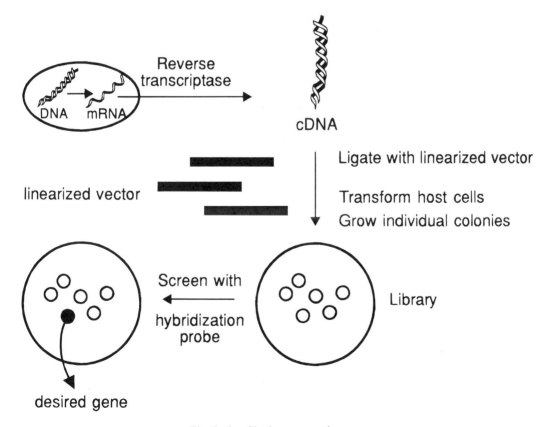

Fig. 2–4. Cloning eucaryotic genes.

tities (e.g., a pancreatic insulinoma was used to obtain mRNA for human insulin). mRNA can be treated with an enzyme called **reverse transcriptase,** which performs the reverse of transcription—it synthesizes a DNA strand complementary to the mRNA (called ''cDNA'' for complementary DNA). The cDNA fragments can be ligated into a vector and used to create a library to be screened in the same manner as previously described.

Another approach developed in recent years involves a technique called **PCR** for **polymerase chain reaction**. PCR is an *in vitro* procedure that involves amplification of a specific gene sequence . It requires some knowledge of the sequence of the gene one wants to amplify because

the process involves the use of short oligonucleotide ''primers'' that are complementary to the desired gene. However, the sequence for these primers can come as best guesses of codon usage corresponding to the protein sequence or from homologous genes from other species, much as described. The basic process, as shown in Figure 2-5, involves three steps: denaturation, annealing, and extension. The strands of DNA that contain the gene of interest are separated by high temperature (e.g., 90 to 95°C) and mixed with a pair of primers that are short pieces of synthetic DNA corresponding to a small portion of the sequence of the desired gene, one on each strand. As the temperature is lowered, the primers anneal to the target DNA. Then a heat-stable DNA

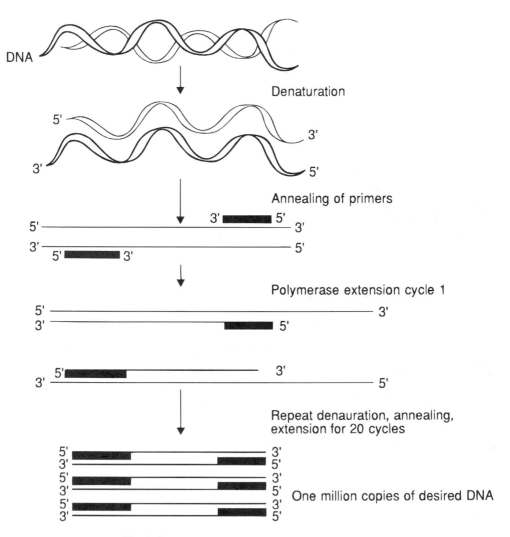

Fig. 2–5. Polymerase chain reaction (PCR) process.

polymerase is added (e.g., from a thermophilic bacterium *Thermus aquaticus*) along with the four deoxyribonucleotides, the temperature is raised to 75°C, and two daughter strands are synthesized by extending the primers. As the cycle is repeated 20 to 30 times, the region between the two primers is amplified exponentially, producing a million or more copies. The amplified DNA can be isolated and cloned into a vector for transformation and expression in a host cell. This will not, of course, be useful for cloning a human gene that requires splicing directly into *E. coli* for expression, but it is useful under many other circumstances. PCR also plays an extremely important role in diagnosis of infectious diseases and diseases caused by genetic mutations such as cystic fibrosis because it can detect very precise gene sequences.

PRODUCTION OF RECOMBINANT PROTEINS AND PEPTIDES

Once a gene is isolated, cloned, and sequenced, it must be expressed in a suitable expression system, either bacterial, fungal, insect tissue culture, or mammalian tissue culture. An expression system includes a host organism as well as a specific vector, a promoter that will give high yields of protein, and sometimes manipulations that will yield a secreted protein. The choice of expression system will depend on many factors, some concerning the structure of the protein being produced and some economic. Bacterial systems (e.g., *E.coli*) will, in general, be the least expensive, but they do not always yield an active protein. Any steps that reduce expensive processing once the protein is produced will be extremely desirable. Scale-up of production to commercial levels will have to be performed, and procedures for large-scale purification of the desired protein will have to be developed. Each step is accompanied by many analytical tests to ensure that the proper protein is being produced.

One of the key issues is whether the protein of choice must be glycosylated to have proper activity. Eucaryotic proteins that are normally secreted or inserted in membranes pass through the endoplasmic reticulum and golgi apparatus in the eucaryotic cell and are glycosylated during the process. *N*-glycosylation occurs at asparagine residues that are part of the sequence . . Asn–X–Ser . . or . . Asn–X–Thr . . and *O*-gly-

cosylation occurs on serines or threonines in the protein sequence. The oligosaccharides that are attached to asparagine residues are complex, consisting in part of a core oligosaccharide that is attached as the protein passes into the endoplasmic reticulum. The core oligosaccharide is modified and new sugar residues added as the protein moves on through the golgi apparatus. A variety of monosaccharide units are incorporated in the final oligosaccharide structure, and the specific structures are protein and organism specific. Glycosylation contributes substantially to the molecular weight of many mammalian glycoproteins. One of the structural features of most importance to pharmacobiotechnology is the sialic acid residue that sometimes is the terminal residue on an oligosaccharide. Sialic acid is *N*-acetylneuraminic acid (Fig. 2-6), and it serves as a cap to protect proteins from receptors in the plasma membrane of liver cells that remove asialylated proteins from the bloodstream. The half-life of sialylated proteins in humans is substantially longer than the comparable protein without sialic acid.

The role of glycosylation is still being unraveled. Some glycoproteins are unable to bind to their receptors or elicit the appropriate activity when they are produced in a non-glycosylated form, and others function normally without the sugar residues. Roles in cell–cell recognition and adhesion are some of the functions of glycoproteins that are becoming better understood.

A recombinant protein that must have proper glycosylation for its activity must be produced in eucaryotic cells. Yeast (*Saccharomyces cerevisiae*) tend to hyperglycosylate and may attach oligosaccharides containing more than 100 mannose residues (compared to 8 to 13 in high mannose mammalian glycoproteins). Alternatives to mammalian cell culture include other species of yeast (e.g., *Pichia pastoris*) or insect cells that have been transfected with a baculovirus expression system.

Structural features in addition to glycosylation influence the choice of expression system. Some structural features that may not be accomplished in a bacterial system include proper disulfide folding and proper *N*-terminal processing. Bacterially produced proteins will have an *N*-formylmethionine (f-Met) at the *N*-terminus because that is the signal for translation initiation, unless a cleavage site is introduced or the protein is secreted and cleaved in the process.

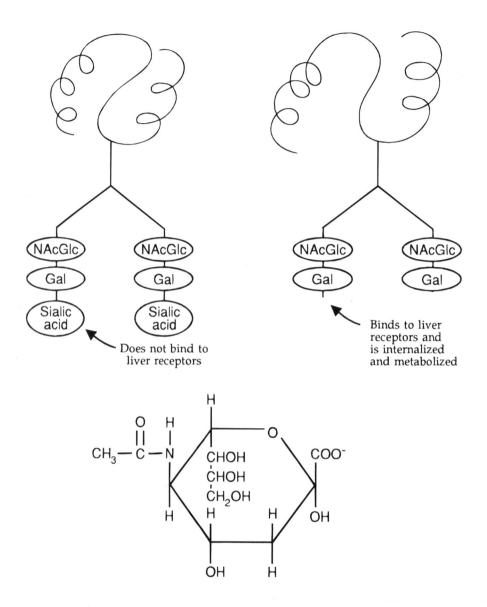

N-Acetylneuraminic acid = Sialic acid

Fig. 2–6. Sialic acid and its role in protein metabolism.

Sometimes that methionine residue will interfere with the normal functioning of the protein. Also, sometimes other *N*-terminal modification (e.g., acetylation) is needed for a given protein's activity or stability and that will not be accomplished in *E. coli*. When proteins are overexpressed in *E. coli*, they tend to aggregate in intracellular bodies called inclusion bodies. These can be helpful or harmful for protein recovery. They precipitate out from the cytoplasm when cells are lysed, and if the overproduced protein is able to be easily denatured with urea or guanidine hydrochloride and then refolded properly with dilution and dialyzation, recovery is fairly simple. Unfortunately, not all proteins will survive such treatment, and many are not recovered from inclusion bodies. Another alternative for production in *E. coli* is to attach a signal sequence to the protein that directs it into the periplasmic space of the bacteria where it is recovered in relatively pure form by gentle removal of the cell wall and outer membrane. Human insulin is produced in this manner today, using a proinsulin gene attached at the *N*-terminus to a beta-lactamase signal sequence that directs the secretion of the protein and with the signal sequence cleaved off during secretion. Proinsulin is then further processed with a proteolytic enzyme to yield active insulin.

Mammalian tissue culture expression systems (e.g., Chinese hamster ovary cells) are usually transfected with a viral vector. They are more expensive to use for protein production because of more complex media requirements, slower growth, and lower yields. However, many proteins are not produced accurately otherwise, and there is great interest in further development of stable, efficient mammalian tissue culture systems to bring the cost down.

Identification of the produced protein and determination of purity requires substantial testing. In addition to bioassays to determine bioactivity, proteins will be tested by polyacrylamide electrophoresis for molecular weight (which will reveal any proteolytic cleavages), by isoelectric focusing electrophoresis for charge (which should help reveal any amino acid substitutions), by high performance chromatography for changes in charge or hydrophobicity reflective of folding errors, and sometimes by x-ray crystallography to confirm identity with the initially identified protein. Capillary electrophoresis and injection for pyrogenicity will help determine purity. Stability under specified storage conditions will be repeatedly tested.

Once a protein is produced for clinical trial and receives FDA approval, any changes in the production or purification procedures require reapproval. Therefore, companies are often reluctant to change the expression system or downstream processing procedures.

IMPACT OF BIOTECHNOLOGY ON PHARMACY PRACTICE

The impact of biotechnology on pharmacy practice has been multifold. The first (and probably foremost) of these effects is that many drugs are now proteins and peptides that require different consideration for stability, formulation, administration, storage, and side effects than small molecule drugs. Secondly, the choice between products may involve consideration of the expression system and the minor differences in structure that result from the use of different expression systems. Thirdly, there are many new drug classes on the market as we are able to understand the pathophysiology of and devise therapies for diseases that were previously untreatable. Finally, there are many new modes of diagnostic agents, many of which are available through pharmacies. All of these developments lead to a series of pharmacoeconomic and ethical issues of substantial interest to the profession. Each of these impacts will be considered in turn.

Proteins and Peptides as Drugs

The administration of peptides and proteins as drugs raises issues of drug delivery, stability, antigenicity, pharmacokinetics, and the basis of comparison of similar products.

Proteins and peptides do not, for the most part, cross the intestinal membrane intact and thus are not suitable for oral administration. Other factors limiting an oral route of administration are the proteolytic enzymes found in the stomach and intestine and the acidic pH of the stomach. All of the currently approved biotherapeutic agents except one are formulated for delivery via injection. The exception, dornase alfa (Pulmozyme), is administered via nebulizer directly to its site of action in the lungs. While parenteral administration is fine for drugs used for acute diseases, it is less desirable for chronic diseases in ambulatory patients. Research is progressing on ways to get proteins into the blood stream via inhalation, nasal sprays, etc., as well as by the preferred route of oral administration, but applications of this work are still in the future. Implantable slow-release polymers or pumps may allow chronic delivery for some proteins, much as the insulin pumps are being used now.

Formulation of proteins in injectable form requires substantial consideration of the stability of proteins. The formulation may be sold as a liquid solution or as a powder that requires reconstitution. Usually the formulation contains a buffer, since proteins are pH sensitive, and sometimes a bacteriostat, since any microbial contamination will express proteases and destroy the product. Albumin is often added to intravenous preparations since proteins in small concentrations will stick to the plastic of the intravenous bags and the tubing leading into the patient. Albumin, an inert protein, will occupy most of the non-specific binding sites on the plastic and allow the drug molecules to enter the patient. The stability of many proteins in solution is often less than in a dry state; a pharmacist must be aware of the length of time a given product can be stored. Often storage is recommended at refrigerator temperatures since freezing causes some proteins to denature. Vigorous shaking will also cause some proteins to oxidize and lead to instability. In general, particulate matter in a protein solution is a sign that the protein has aggregated, or some other denaturation has occurred. A pharmacist should be able to answer questions about storage and stability for each product under a number of scenarios (e.g., the patient leaves a product unrefrigerated overnight). Because these products are often very expensive, a patient may be unwilling to discard the drug remaining in single-use vials or otherwise try to use drug products that may be inactive.

Proteins vary in their stability depending on the specific amino acid residues and the number of disulfide bonds holding the tertiary structure in place, as well as the degree of electrostatic, hydrogen and hydrophobic bonding stabilizing the active conformation. Proteins are denatured through a variety of physical and chemical changes. Chemical instability can involve cleavage of peptide bonds, disulfide exchange of paired cysteines, deamidation of the terminal amide of glutamine and asparagine residues (leaving glutamate or aspartate), oxidation of methionine to methionine sulfoxide, oxidation of thiol groups of cysteine to sulfonic acid, and beta-elimination of thiol, hydroxyl, or amino groups on the side chains of cysteine, serine or threonine, and lysine, respectively. Peptide bonds normally are considered relatively stable, but aspartic acid residues, particularly when they are next to proline residues, can lead to a proteolytic hot-spot with increased lability of the Asp-Pro peptide bond. Many of these changes occur more rapidly under slightly acidic or alkaline conditions, reinforcing the importance of buffering protein solutions. The changes will often lead to loss of biological activity.

Physical instability can involve denaturation, aggregation, and precipitation. Denaturation is the unfolding of the protein (loss of tertiary structure) due to disruption of the bonds holding the native conformation. This may be caused by temperature, pH, or a variety of salts or organic solutes. It is sometimes, but not always, reversible. Protein molecules may self-associate into dimers, tetramers, and larger aggregates. Aggregation is affected also by pH and solvent composition and is hastened by partial denaturation. When aggregation reaches a macroscopic level, the protein will actually come out of solution and form a visible precipitate. Physical instability can sometimes be prevented by the addition of specific salts or polyalcohol substances such as glycerol or sugars. Nonionic detergents such as Tween may also help to stabilize proteins against physical instability.

The use of site-directed mutagenesis to replace particularly labile amino acid residues or to introduce additional disulfide bonds is another approach to increasing the stability of a protein. Site-directed or site-specific mutagenesis is a process by which the gene is altered at a specific site to change the codon corresponding to one amino acid into one encoding a different amino acid. One cannot immediately assume that a change can occur without change in biological activity because the change of one amino acid residue can often have long-ranging effects on the overall protein secondary and tertiary structure and activity, even when it is not at the active site. However, this approach has been used successfully; for example, a variant form of GM-CSF (granulocyte/macrophage-colony stimulating factor) has had a major proteolytic site altered from arginine to leucine to decrease susceptibility to protease cleavage. In another example, human beta interferon expressed in *E. coli* had a disappointing 10% of the activity of the authentic protein. Researchers discovered that the protein had three cysteine residues; two were involved in a cystine dimer, but one was available for intermolecular disulfide bonding leading to aggregation or intramolecular mispairing. The unpaired cysteine was altered by site-directed mutagenesis to a serine, the amino acid closest in structure to cysteine, and the serine-17 variant had activity similar to the native interferon and did not form multimeric complexes.

Site-directed mutagenesis has also been used to alter other characteristics of proteins. For example, human growth hormone has been rationally mutagenized to alter its relative specificity for binding to the growth hormone receptor versus the prolactin receptor. In another example, the gene for tissue plasminogen activator was mutagenized to replace asparagine residues with glutamines, thus blocking glycosylation and increasing the half-life of the protein in the body. One must always be concerned that alteration of structure may create a protein that the body recognizes as foreign, thus leading to antibody development and antigenicity, but the potential for creating derivatives of known proteins with desirable activity characteristics and stability is enormous.

Another mode of altering characteristics of proteins is to covalently attach polyethylene glycol (PEG) to them. These ''pegylated'' proteins (e.g., pegademase is adenosine deaminase conjugated to polyethylene glycol, an inert polymer) have a substantially longer half-life in the body (3 to 6 days with pegademase) than the nonmodified protein. This alteration greatly improves the usefulness of adenosine deaminase for the treatment of severe combined immunodeficiency disease (SCID), a genetic disorder that is fatal if left untreated.

Proteins serve as antigens; the body recognizes foreign proteins and develops antibodies to them. This process may lead to allergic reactions or may just lead to inactivation of subsequent doses of a proteinaceous drug by antibody binding. Certainly allergenicity limited the use of non-human proteins before the development of recombinant DNA technology that allowed us to produce human proteins as drugs. Even with human protein drugs, the body may form antibodies to alterations in amino acid side chains or glycosylation patterns. Removal of sugar groups may reveal an antigenic epitope that is not available in the native protein. Administering a protein such as Factor VIII clotting factor to a hemophiliac, who does not normally produce that protein and whose body has never seen the protein, may lead to a gradual loss of efficacy and a need for increased doses as the body produces inactivating antibodies. Also, there is always some danger of contaminating proteins from the producing host organism, and products such as GM-CSF produced from *E. coli* are labeled with a warning that the product should be administered with caution to anyone who has demonstrated allergenicity to other *E. coli*-produced proteins (although it is not clear that a patient would know such a fact).

Another issue of both scientific and clinical interest is the difficulty in measuring blood and tissue levels of proteins administered as drugs to determine pharmacokinetic parameters. Antibody-based methods may be our best way of detecting specific proteins, but one does not always know whether the antibody is detecting the active protein or some metabolite that retains an active epitope and is therefore antibody-detectable, but is inactive. This is clearly an area that requires future development if we are to monitor dosing and blood levels as we do for small molecule drugs and to understand the effect of various protein modifications on the absorption, distribution, metabolism, and elimination of protein drugs.

New Drug Classes

Table 2-1 shows the recombinant DNA products approved by the FDA by mid-1994. Among them are two hormones, a vaccine, an antibody, and three enzymes. Of particular note are the five interferons, three growth factors, and an interleukin. Most of these products provide access to therapy for previously untreatable conditions or diseases. Our knowledge of immunology and immunotherapies has grown enormously in the decade since the discovery of recombinant DNA technology, and it is this area of therapy that is undergoing the greatest revolution in response to development of recombinant biotechnology. The immune system is enormously complex, and we are just beginning to understand the roles of the various cytokines. It is likely that our ability to treat a variety of immunologically based diseases, including those with an autoimmune component such as multiple sclerosis and arthritis, will grow rapidly. Health professionals trained before this burst of knowlege about the immune system and pharmacological intervention with it will require continuing education if they are to provide adequate medical and pharmaceutical care in this area. The specific products listed in Table 2-1 will be discussed in detail in later chapters.

New Diagnostic Agents

The development of monoclonal antibodies and hybridization methods has opened up many new avenues of diagnosis of disease. Monoclonal antibodies have many potential uses in addition to diagnosis. Therefore, a general overview of their production and characteristics, followed by specific discussion of their use in diagnosis, is included here. Later in the chapter, other uses of monoclonal antibodies will be presented.

Antibodies are specific proteins that are produced by mammalian cells called B lymphocytes in response to immunological challenge. In an

Table 2–1
Approved Recombinant Proteins

Generic Name	Brand Name	Therapeutic Use (Year Approved)
Human insulin	Humulin (Lilly) Novolin (Novo Nordisk)	Insulin dependent diabetes (1982)
Human growth hormone	Protropin (Genentech) Humatrope (Lilly) Nutrophin (Genentech)	Growth hormone deficiency in children (1985); growth retardation in chronic renal disease (1993).
Hepatitis B vaccine	Engerix-B (SmithKline Beecham) Recombivax HB (MSD)	Hepatitis B prevention (1986)
Interferon alfa-2a	Roferon-A (Hoffman-LaRoche)	Hairy cell leukemia (1986); AIDS related Kaposi's sarcoma (1988)
Interferon alfa-2b	Intron-A (Schering-Plough)	Hairy cell leukemia (1986); AIDS related Kaposi's sarcoma (1988); Chronic hepatitis, types B (1992) and C (1991); condylomata acuminata (1988)
Muromonab-CD3	Orthoclone OKT3 (Ortho)	Acute allograft rejection in renal transplant patients (1986) and cardiac transplant patients (1993)
Alteplase	Activase (Genentech)	Acute myocardial infarction (1987); pulmonary embolism (1990)
Epoetin alfa	Epogen (Amgen) Procrit (Ortho)	Anemias of chronic renal disease (1989), AIDS (1991) and cancer chemotherapy (1993).
Interferon alfa-n3	Alferon N (Interferon Sciences)	Condylomata acuminata (1989)
Interferon gamma-1b	Actimmune (Genentech)	Chronic granulomatous disease (1990)
Filgrastim	Neupogen (Amgen)	Neutropenias due to myelosuppressive chemotherapy (1991); myeloid reconstitution after bone marrow transplantation (1994).
Sargramostim	Leukine (Immunex)	Myeloid reconstitution after bone marrow transplantation (1991)
Aldesleukin	Proleukin (Chiron)	Metastatic renal cell carcinoma (1992)
Antihemophiliac factor	KoGENate (Miles) Recombinate (Baxter)	Hemophilia A (1992)
Interferon beta-1b	Betaseron (Berlex)	Multiple sclerosis (1993)
Dornase alfa	Pulmozyme (Genentech)	Cystic fibrosis (pulmonary complications) (1993)
Imiglucerase	Cerezyme (Genzyme)	Type 1 Gaucher's disease (1994)

animal, the body will react to a foreign protein (called an "antigen") by producing a variety of antibody proteins that combine with various discrete regions (called epitopes or antigenic determinants) of the foreign protein. The mixture of antibody molecules produced in response to a given invading protein is called a "polyclonal" antibody. Each of the distinct antibodies within the polyclonal mixture will react with one part (epitope) of the invading protein and is called a "monoclonal" antibody when it is produced in quantity by itself.

The technique for producing monoclonal antibodies was described in the mid 1970s and is illustrated in Figure 2-7. Spleen cells from a mouse that has been immunized with the foreign protein are isolated and fused in culture with myeloma cells that are not producing antibodies.

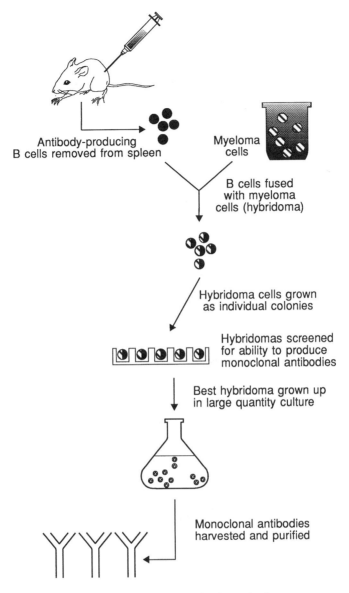

Fig. 2–7. Monoclonal antibody production.

The myeloma cells have been mutated to make them require a functional enzyme from spleen cells to grow on a selective medium, so only the fused myeloma-spleen cells (called "hybridomas") will survive. These cells are distributed into plastic microtiter plates and screened for their ability to produce antibodies which react with the immunizing protein or a specifc epitope of it. The screening test involves precoating a plastic microtiter dish with the target antigen. The culture medium from each of the fused cells is distributed into the microtiter wells where appropriate antibody will bind to the antigen. After washing to remove unbound antibody, another antibody is added that will react with all mouse antibodies. This second antibody has been conjugated with an enzyme that yields a colored reaction product. In a positive test, the hybridoma antibody will have bound to the antigen in the wells, and the anti-mouse antibody ("secondary antibody") will bind to the hybridoma antibody and give a positive color reaction when

1. Bind sample to support

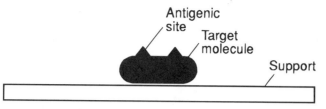

2. Add primary antibody; wash; antibody binds if antigen is present.

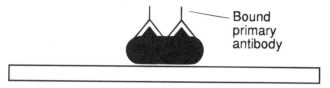

3. Add secondary antibody-enzyme conjugate; wash; secondary antibody binds if primary antibody has bound.

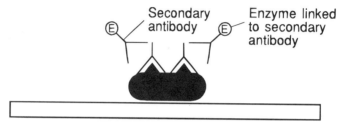

4. Add substrate; see colored reaction product from bound enzyme.

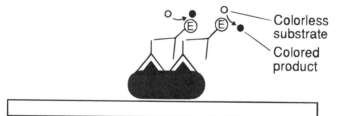

Fig. 2–8.   ELISA reaction (*E*nzyme-*l*inked *i*mmuno*s*orbent *a*ssay).

enzyme substrate is added. This type of test is called an ELISA for "enzyme-linked immunosorbant assay" and is illustrated in Figure 2-8. Once the hybridoma cells are identified that are producing antibodies (which are now monoclonal since all antibodies produced by a given fused hybridoma will be identical), they can be grown continuously in culture to produce quantities of the antibody.

The ELISA reaction is the general reaction used diagnostically. The antigen that the monoclonal antibody recognizes can be a specific protein or can be a small molecule that was conjugated to a protein as a "hapten" during the production of the antibody. Monoclonal antibodies also can be used to detect proteins on the surface of pathogenic organisms that are characteristic of that pathogen and proteins on the surface of other cells (e.g., receptors). Because the monoclonal antibody is raised to a distinct site on the molecules it is detecting, it can be very specific compared to polyclonal antibodies. This is important for diagnostic purposes since one needs to reduce false positive reactions. Table 2-2 lists many targets for which diagnostic monoclonal antibodies have been developed.

Table 2–2
Targets of Diagnostic Monoclonal Antibodies

Hormones
   human chorionic gonadotropin   (pregnancy)
   human lutenizing hormone   (ovulation)
Tumor markers
   Prostate-specific antigen   (prostate
                                   cancer)

Infectious diseases
   Chlamydia
   Herpes (HSV-1 and HSV-2 antigens)
   Rubella
   HIV

Most of these tests are sensitive, simple, and specific for the target antigen. Many of the antibodies are sold as kits for over-the-counter purchase. Pharmacists need to be aware that the enzymes used in these kits have a limited stability, and the shelf-life and storage conditions recommended for each should be followed.

An antibody molecule consists of two heavy peptide chains and two light peptide chains held together by disulfide bonds (Fig. 2- 9). The variable regions (the amino terminii) of the four chains are the binding site for the antigen, and the constant regions are species specific but constant for all antibodies of a given species. When mouse antibodies are used for pharmacological purposes in humans, the body will sometimes recognize them as foreign proteins and develop antibodies to them. This will result in inactivation of the foreign, exogenously administered antibody over time. To surmount this limitation, "humanized" antibodies are being produced. Humanized antibodies are hybrid ("chimeric") antibodies that have been produced through genetic engineering by combining the DNA sequence for the variable regions of a mouse antibody with the DNA sequence for the constant region of human antibodies and then cloning the chimeric construct into an expression vector and transfecting B-lymphocytes. Another approach to generating human antibodies that is in preliminary experimental stages is the use of transgenic mice that produce human antibodies in response to antigenic challenge.

Another recent development in antibody tech-

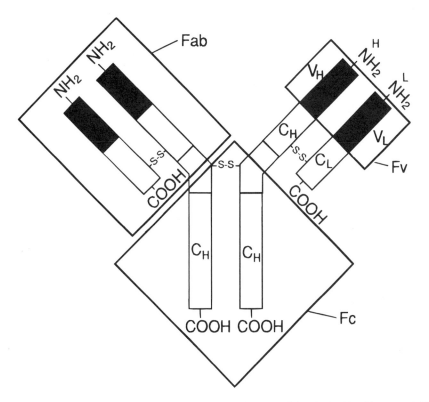

Fig. 2–9. Generalized antibody structure. H = heavy chain, L = light chain; V_H, V_L = variable regions for heavy and light chains, C_H, C_L = constant regions for heavy and light chains, respectively.

nology is the development of antibodies produced in *E. coli*. Hybridoma cells grow relatively slowly, do not attain high cell densities, and require a complex, expensive growth medium. Therefore, the ability to express an antibody in a bacterial system is highly desirable. Antibodies are expressed in *E. coli* by isolating mRNA from mouse or human B-lymphocytes and forming cDNA. The light and heavy chains are amplified by PCR and cloned into one bacteriophage vector. The expression of the many light and heavy chains in the bacteriophage yields what is called a "combinatorial library" of 10^6 to 10^8 different antibodies, and each bacteriophage plaque will have a different combination. These can be rapidly screened for binding to the target antigen and the correct bacteriophage grown in quantity. Generally the DNA sequences corresponding to the desired antibody chains are transferred from the phage vector to a plasmid vector for large-scale antibody production in *E. coli*.

For some applications, the constant region of the heavy chains (the Fc region) is dispensable, and in fact, a smaller molecule has better pharmaceutical properties. It was found that antigen-binding single-chain antibodies can be made by linking the two variable chains together with a linker fragment (V_L-linker-V_H) such that the two variable regions can assume a correct conformation. The DNA sequence for the entire chain can be cloned and expressed in *E. coli*. These single-chain antibodies are being studied to determine their utility in various situations. A question that remains to be answered is the extent to which these single-chain antibodies will be recognized as foreign proteins by the human body. If so, they would be substantially less useful for therapeutic purposes than the humanized antibodies discussed.

Hybridization probes are also very useful for diagnostic purposes, especially of infectious diseases. To be effective, the DNA sequence used in the probe must be highly specific to avoid false positive reactions. The probe can be used to identify target DNA in clinical samples of feces, urine, blood, throat washings, and tissue samples without extensive DNA purification. It permits rapid identification of a pathogen without the need to culture, grow, and identify the organism. If the target sequence is rare in the working sample, PCR can be used to amplify it prior to hybridization. Probes can be labeled with phosphorus-32, but non-radioactive proce-

dures in which the DNA is linked to chromogenic or chemiluminescent substrates are gaining popularity. Examples of available diagnostic hybridization probes include *Plasmodium falciparum* (causes malaria), *Legionella pneumophila* (causes Legionnaire's disease), and enteropathogenic *E. coli* (causes gastroenteritis).

PCR methods have also been devised to provide sensitive detection of mutations in specific genes that lead to genetic diseases. Sometimes a specific mutation will lead to a change in the restriction sites within a gene, and PCR amplification followed by restriction enzyme digestion will reveal such a mutation. Other mutations can be detected using sensitive techniques to detect mismatches between the patient's DNA and a probe corresponding to the non-mutated gene. The specific mutation that leads to genetic diseases such as cystic fibrosis can now be identified in each patient.

Our increased ability to definitively diagnose genetic diseases or predisposition to diseases even before symptomology is evident raises many interesting and important ethical issues. How widespread testing should be and who should have access to the information are issues which society needs to address. The implications for insurance companies are obvious, but such information may have positive effects in allowing individuals with a predisposition to certain diseases to alter lifestyle or undertake other preventative measures to intervene with the disease process.

BIOTECHNOLOGY-DERIVED PHARMACEUTICALS OF THE NEAR FUTURE

Monoclonal antibodies have therapeutic uses in addition to the diagnostic uses described. Therapeutically administered antibodies can be used to bind to and block sites within the body. They also have been proposed and studied for use in delivering toxins or other drugs to specific sites within the body. One example of a monoclonal antibody drug that has been approved by the FDA and which nicely illustrates the principle of using monoclonal antibodies therapeutically is **OKT3** or **Muromonab CD3**. OKT3 is a mouse monoclonal antibody that binds to CD3 receptors on mature T-lymphocytes. Cytotoxic T-cells are responsible for the inflammation and destruction of transplanted tissues (allografts), and treatment with OKT3 depresses T-cell function and increases the survival of the transplanted tissue. It has been approved for renal transplant and cardiac transplant patients and is used preventively, although it also has some efficacy in reversal of transplant rejection. The drug is administered intravenously daily for 10-14 days. Other immunosuppressants can be given concurrently and may decrease the likelihood of development of antibodies to the mouse antibody, which would decrease efficacy, particularly in a second course of treatment. Most patients experience some side effects especially upon receiving the first dose. The side effects of fever, dyspnea and chills, which are often characteristic of protein drugs, can be reduced by coadministration of antipyretics, antihistamines, and/or corticosteroids.

Tumor cells carry very specific proteins on their surfaces, and many antitumor agents are very toxic compounds. It is reasonable then to think that chemically linking antitumor agents, radioactivity, or toxins to monoclonal anitbodies raised against tumor antigens will result in delivery of the drug to the tumor and spare normal cells, resulting in a highly selective antitumor therapy. This approach has been tested with a variety of tumor-binding monoclonal antibodies and conjugated molecules, but no therapeutic agents have yet been approved for use. The approach is simple and elegant in concept but difficult in execution since ways must be devised to conjugate drug to antibody without destroying the antibody efficacy, and obtaining release and uptake of the toxin or drug at the site of the tumor may be problematic. Nevertheless, this is an active area of research and should yield useful products in the near future.

Other drugs besides antitumor agents may also be more effective or less toxic when targeted to a specific site. An example is the conjugation of tissue plasminogen activator (tPA) to antifibrin antibodies. tPA is approved for use in dissolving blood clots in heart attacks or emboli and works by activating the enzyme plasminogen that is circulating in the body to break down fibrin, the protein that forms the matrix of a blot clot. However, plasminogen also breaks down fibrinogen, the precursor to fibrin, and activation of it may lead to general bleeding. Researchers reasoned that linking tPA to antifibrin antibody would localize the plasminogen activity at the site of the clot and reduce general bleeding. This approach has been shown to work under experimental conditions, but clinical trials have not yet been completed.

Antisense oligonucleotides are another form of biotechnology-derived therapeutic agent that may be expected to result in useful therapeutic agents in the near future. Again the concept is simple, but the execution of the concept involves several hurdles. The concept is illustrated in Figure 2-10. Antisense therapy is designed to prevent, or at least lower, expression of a specific gene. An oligonucleotide that has a sequence that is complementary to the mRNA of the target gene is introduced into the cell. It will bind to the mRNA of the target gene and block translation of the message into protein. It may bind to DNA in the nucleus, blocking transcription, or to the transcript during its processing and transport from the nucleus to the cytoplasm; all these interactions would reduce expression of the gene. Hurdles to be overcome include getting the oligonucleotides into the cell, making them stable to ribonucleases in the cell, and gaining selective inhibition of the desired gene.

The approach has been used commercially in the production of the Flavr-Savr tomato. The antisense sequence to the polygalacturonase gene was introduced into the DNA of the tomato resulting in reduced expression of the enzyme. Polygalacturonase is an enzyme which results in degradation of the cell walls during ripening, resulting in a softening of the tomato. Tomatoes traditionally have been picked and shipped in an unripe state to prevent crushing during shipping, and normal ripening with development of the ripe flavor and color has been difficult to achieve once they reach their destination. With the down-regulation of the expression of the polygalacturonase enzyme, tomatoes can be allowed to develop the proper ripe flavor and color on the vine and then picked and shipped, with softening proceeding at a slower pace and reaching proper consistency once the tomatoes have reached their destination.

Although antisense DNA sequences may also be introduced into the human genome with expression of the antisense messenger RNA occurring in the cell, it is more likely that antisense oligonucleotides will be administered as drugs and transported into the cell from the bloodstream. Analogs of nucleotides with alterations in the sugar-phosphate backbone are being used to create oligonucleotides that are stable to ribonucleases. A minimum length for antisense oligonucleotides in order to get specific binding is

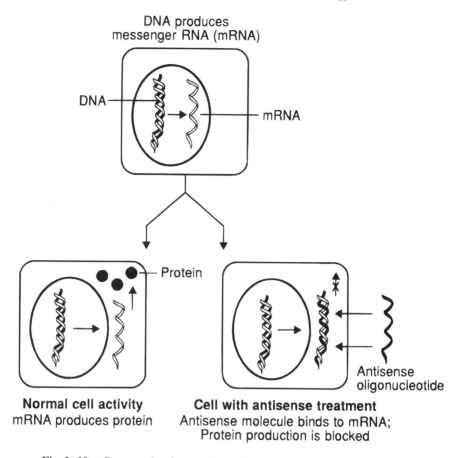

Fig. 2–10.   Concept of antisense oligonucleotide inhibition of gene expression.

11 bases, but most being tested are in the 15-25 base range. The chemistry that is being tested includes the synthesis of phosphorothioates (Fig. 2-11) and methyl phosphonates (Fig. 2-11), among others. These derivatives are resistant to nucleases, and the methyl phosphonates are uncharged and therefore more lipophilic than native DNA or RNA and may penetrate the cells better. However, solubility may be a problem with methyl phosphonates, and the doses of methyl phosphonates are high because they become bound to membranes and less of a dose is available to bind to mRNA. Therefore, phosphorothioates have gained favor with several companies. At least one company is working on a promising alternative strategy of synthesizing oligonucleotides with a 2'-5' linkage instead of the natural 3'-5' linkage in the sugar-phosphate backbone. Approaches to getting the antisense oligonucleotides into cells include liposomal en-

capsulation and linking the oligonucleotide to molecules for which there are cell transport receptors on the surface of cells.

Most of the target genes thus far are in the anticancer or antiviral area. The targets that will be most profoundly affected by low doses of antisense oligonucleotides are those for which only a few transcript (mRNA) molecules exist in the cell at any one time. Antisense oligonucleotides have been effective at the tissue culture level in inhibiting the expression of P-glycoprotein which renders cancer cells resistant to many anticancer agents, in inhibiting the expression of HIV envelope protein and thus inhibiting viral replication, and in inhibiting expression of the *ras* oncogene. Other targets under experimentation include other viral infections (herpes virus, cytomegalovirus), cancers (especially those that appear to be oncogene-linked), and inflammatory and autoimmune disorders.

There are many problems yet to be worked

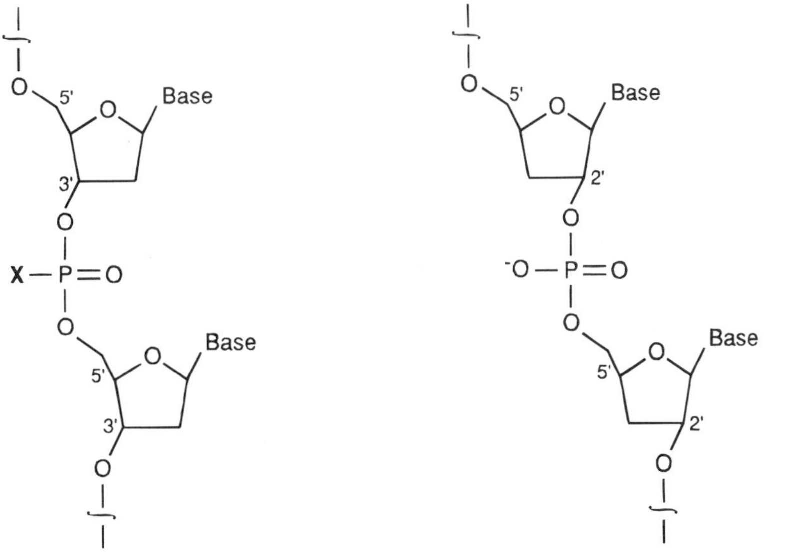

X	Phosphate group
−O	Phosphodiester
−S	Phosphorothioate
−CH₃	Methyl phosphonate

Fig. 2–11. Chemistry of oligonucleotide analogs being tested as antisense therapeutics.

out in getting from tissue culture level to the clinical therapeutic level, not the least of which is producing these synthetic drugs in large quantities at a reasonable cost. Also, researchers will have to determine the fate of the drugs in the cell, the length of time inhibition persists, whether or not they are antigenic, and how selective they are *in vivo*. Nevertheless, there are a number of companies investing in bringing this concept of therapy to reality, and one can anticipate that at least some antisense drugs will become useful therapeutic agents.

Gene therapy is another therapeutic modality that is rapidly moving from the lab bench to the clinic. In contrast to antisense oligonucleotides which are used to turn off genes, gene therapy is used to replace missing or defective genes. It also can serve as a type of drug delivery system for protein drugs which are synthesized *in vivo* instead of being delivered to the body as proteins.

To get genes into the cells, a vector is required. This may be a plasmid or defective virus, and some success has been achieved with naked DNA (no vector) introduced into cells via physical methods such as electroporation, liposomal fusion, and even direct microinjection. Adenoviruses have been used to introduce genes into

lung tissue, and retroviruses have been explored. The advantage to retroviral vectors is that the DNA stably integrates into the host chromosome; the danger is that it may integrate randomly and disrupt needed genes. When the introduction of the DNA occurs in the body, the therapy is termed "*in vivo*," and when cells (usually lymphocytes) are removed from the patient, transfected with the genetic material and grown in culture, and then reintroduced into the body, the therapy is called "*ex vivo*." Circulating lymphocytes that are expressing a protein from an inserted gene will provide that protein for the lifetime of that cell. This is an enormous advantage compared with daily (or more frequent) administration of a missing protein as the protein itself. Figure 2-12 illustrates an *ex vivo* gene therapy procedure.

Potential targets for gene therapy are many and varied. Some of the genetic diseases for which gene therapy is being considered and tested are adenosine deaminase (ADA) deficiency (severe combined immunodeficiency disease), cystic fibrosis, hypercholesterolemia, and hemophilia. In some cases the gene is introduced in circulating lymphocytes (ADA deficiency); in others another tissue is targeted, especially when the protein being replaced is part of the cell and

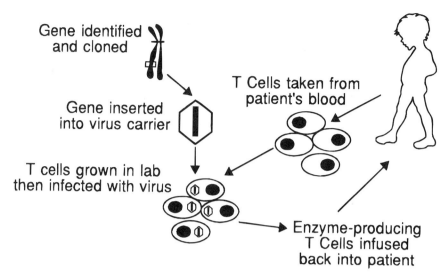

Fig. 2–12. Example of ex-vivo gene therapy.

not a circulating protein. For example, in cystic fibrosis, the mutated gene product is improperly processed and is not inserted into the cell membrane and does not function in lung tissue; the replacement gene is targeted to the lung tissue using an adenovirus vector. There is substantial interest in inserting genes into stem cells in the bone marrow so that all subsequent blood cells would carry the gene of interest and produce the missing protein. This has proven difficult to accomplish and needs to be approached with some caution. A patient who had a bad reaction to the inserted gene or its product could only have it removed by sterilization of the patient's bone marrow and subsequent transplant, a serious procedure. Even more serious to contemplate is the possibility of correcting a genetic defect in the germ cells so the individual would not pass a defect on his/her offspring. The long-term effects of an error are so great that germ cell gene therapy is considered unethical at this point in time. All proposed gene therapy protocols requesting government funding are subject to review by the Recombinant DNA Advisory Committee which serves as an advisory group to the National Institutes of Health, and the FDA Center for Biologics Evaluation and Research must grant approval to all gene therapy protocols prior to initiation of human trials.

Many scientists feel that because of the difficulties involved in administering proteins and peptides, most of these biotherapies will eventually be reduced to small molecules, called **peptidomimetics**, which mimic the interaction of a protein with its receptor and induce the same pharmacological effect as the larger protein drug. The overall process of getting from the protein drug to the peptidomimetic is called **rational drug design** and usually involves examination of the interaction of parts of the protein molecule with functional groups at the active site of the receptor using computational chemistry and molecular modeling approaches. The peptidomimetic may involve amino acids and peptide-like linkages or may involve completely new chemistry that places functional groups at the correct location to interact with the receptor molecule.

One peptidomimetic is on the market. It is called octreotide (Sandostatin), and it is a peptidomimetic of the peptide hormone somatostatin. Somatostatin has several activities in the body, but the one of therapeutic importance is inhibition of the GI endocrine secretion of vasoactive intestinal peptide (VIP) and other GI hormones. The HIV virus has a segment which mimics VIP and binds to mucosal cells, causing diarrhea in AIDS patients. Both somatostatin and octreotide help control the symptoms (severe diarrhea and flushing) of patients with metastatic carcinoid or VIP-secreting tumors and of AIDS patients. Octreotide is a synthetic eight amino acid peptide analog of the fourteen amino acid somatostatin, and contains a number of D-amino acids which slow down proteolytic metabolism. The advantages of octreotide over somatostatin are that octreotide can be administered subcutaneously (compared to intravenous administration of somatostatin), it has greater potency than the native hormone, and the peptidomimetic has a longer half-life because it is not metabolized as rapidly.

BIOTECHNOLOGY AND DRUG DISCOVERY

Biotechnology is having a profound effect on drug discovery, both in terms of natural products and synthetic mixtures of peptides and oligonucleotides, in that biotechnology tools can be used to produce millions of molecules of a therapeutically important target molecule (e.g., a receptor). These can be bound to solid supports or produced on the surface of cells. When they are exposed to complex mixtures of materials [either mixtures of natural product extracts or randomly produced ("combinatorial") mixtures of peptides or oligonucleotides], only the molecules that bind to the receptors will be bound to the solid support or the cells. These compounds can be selectively eluted and identified.

SUGGESTED READING

Bird, R.E., Walker, B.W.: Single chain antibody variable regions. Trends Biotechnol., 9:132, 1991.

Blundell, T.L.: Problems and solutions in protein engineering—toward rational design. Trends Biotechnol., 12:145, 1994.

Buckholtz, R.G., Gleeson, M.A.G.: Yeast systems for the commercial production of heterologous proteins. Biotechnology, 9:1067, 1991.

Bud, R.: *The Uses of Life: a History of Biotechnology.* Cambridge University Press, Cambridge. 1993.

Clackson, T., Wells, J.A.: In vitro selection from protein and peptide libraries. Trends Biotechnol., 12: 173, 1994.

Cunningham, B.C., Wells, J.A.: Rational design of receptor specific variants of human growth hormone. Proc. Natl. Acad. Sci. USA, 88:3407, 1991.

Erlich, H.S., Gelfand, G., Sninsky, J.J.: Recent advances in the polymerase chain reaction. Science, 252:1643, 1991.

Fray, R.G., Grierson, D.: Molecular genetics of tomato fruit ripening. Trends Genet., 9:438, 1993.

Gibaldi, M.: Human gene therapy. Pharmacotherapy 13:79, 1993.

Glick, B.R., Pasternak, J.J.: *Molecular Biotechnology: Principles and Applications of Recombinant DNA.* Washington, D.C., American Society for Microbiology Press, 1994.

Goldspiel, B.R., Green, L., Calis, K.A.: Human gene therapy. Clin. Pharm., 12:488, 1993.

Hodgson, J.: Making monoclonals in microbes. Biotechnology, 9:421, 1991.

Johnson, I.S.: Human insulin from recombinant DNA technology. Science, 219:632, 1983.

Kingsbury, D.T.: DNA probes in the diagnosis of genetic and infectious diseases. Trends Biotechnol., 5:107, 1987.

Kohler, G., Milstein, C.: Continuous cultures of fused cells secreting antibody of predefined specificity. Nature, 256: 495, 1975.

Kuppuswamy, M.N., Hoffman, J. W., Kasper, C. K., Spitzer, S.G., Groce, S.L., Bajaj, S.P.: Single nucleotide primer extension to detect genetic diseases. Experimental application to hemophilia B (factor IX) and cystic fibrosis genes. Proc. Natl. Acad. Sci., 88:1143, 1991.

Manning, M.C., Patel, K., Borchardt, R.T.: Review of the stability of protein pharmaceuticals. Pharm. Res., 6:903, 1989.

Miller, L.K.: Baculoviruses as gene expression vectors. Ann. Rev. Microbiol., 42:177, 1988.

Mossinghoff, G.J.: Biotechnology medicines in development. Pharmaceutical Manufacturer's Association, 1993.

Sambrook, J., Fritsch, E.F., Maniatis, T.: *Molecular Cloning: A Laboratory Manual*, 2nd ed., Cold Spring Harbor Laboratory, Cold Spring Harbor, N.Y., 1989.

Thayer, A.M.: Companies designing genetic code blocking drugs to treat disease. Chem. Eng. News, December 3, 1990, p17.

Tolbert, W.R.: Manufacture of biopharmaceutical proteins by mammalian cell culture systems. Biotech. Adv., 8:729, 1990.

Voet, D., Voet, J.G.: *Biochemistry*, 2nd ed., New York, John Wiley and Sons, 1995.

Waldmann, T.A.: Monoclonal antibodies in diagnosis and therapy. Science, 252:1657, 1991.

Zito, S. W., editor: *Pharmaceutical Biotechnology: A Programmed Text*, Technomic Publishing Company, Lancaster, PA, 1992.

3

Complex Polysaccharides

Polysaccharides are polymers of monosaccharides (sugars) linked together through glycosidic (ether) linkages and represent a structurally diverse class of biological macromolecules. The structural diversity of these compounds arises from the many different sugars and sugar derivatives such as uronic acids found in polysaccharides and because each sugar can be covalently linked to other sugars through several different positions on the sugar ring. In addition, the glycosidic linkages can have either an α or β configuration due to the stereochemistry of the sugars, and both types of linkages can exist in the same molecule.

In systematic nomenclature polysaccharides are given the ending "-an," and another word for polysaccharide is the generic term glycan. If only one type of monosaccharide unit is present, the polysaccharide is a homoglycan but a heteroglycan if more than one kind of monosaccharide is involved. A more precise differentiation of polysaccharides utilizes nomenclature that indicates the nature of the monosaccharide building unit and the position and configuration of the glycosidic linkage. For example, cellulose which is a homoglycan can also be designated as β-1,4-D-glucan. In this case, the combining unit is D-glucose that has the β configuration at the anomeric carbon atom (C-1) which is linked to C-4 of the next repeating unit of D-glucose. In the case of heteroglycans, the different monosaccharides generally appear in an ordered arrangement. For example, linear diheteroglycans are composed of two kinds of monosaccharides arranged in an alternating and regular manner. A commonly occurring heteroglycan is D-gluco-D-mannan, composed of D-glucose and D-mannose. When more than two types of sugars are combined to produce a polysaccharide, they usually form a branched chain structure.

The complex polysaccharides are represented by starch, inulin, and the celluloses. These polysaccharides can usually be hydrolyzed to a component hexose sugar. Starch, which yields glucose, is a glucan; and inulin, which yields fructose, is a fructan. Sugars and starch are important products in the economy of mankind. They are used extensively as foods and pharmaceuticals.

Cellulose forms the primary cell wall in plants. Other substances, such as the hemicelluloses, also occur with cellulose. These are also high–molecular-weight polysaccharides but are considerably more soluble and more easily hydrolyzed than cellulose. Closely related to the hemicelluloses are the gums and mucilages, which constitute an important group of drugs both from the pharmaceutic and the therapeutic viewpoint. Also associated with cellulose are the pectins, which have some pharmaceutic application.

No summary of the polysaccharides is complete without mentioning the pentoses and pentosans. The pentoses arabinose, xylose, and ribose are products resulting from the hydrolysis of the pentosans. Xylan, which occurs in the wood of deciduous trees, is an example of a pentosan. Pentoses also result from the hydrolysis of gums and mucilages.

HOMOGLYCANS

Starch

Starch is produced in large quantities in green leaves as the temporary storage form of photosynthetic products. As a permanent reserve food material for the plant, starch occurs in seeds and in the pith, medullary rays, and cortex of the stems and roots of perennials and other plants. It constitutes from 50 to 65% of the dry weight of cereal seeds and as much as 80% of the dry matter of potato tubers.

In the United States, more than 95% of marketed starch is made from corn. Although starch is distributed widely in the plant kingdom, few plants provide starch on a large scale. Corn and other cereals, such as rice, sorghum, and wheat, contribute to the world's supply. Commercial starch is also obtained from potato tubers, maranta rhizomes, and cassava roots. Starch occurs in granules (or grains) that have characteristic striations. These striations and the size and shape of the granules are more or less characteristic in many species of plants and may be used as a microscopic means of identifying the botanic origin of the starch. In this manner, the identity of many food and drug products of vegetable origin may be established.

Starch is generally a mixture of two structurally different polysaccharides. One component, termed **amylose**, is a linear molecule composed of 250 to 300 D-glucopryanose units uniformly linked by α-1,4 glucosidic bonds, which tend to cause the molecule to assume a helixlike shape. The second component, **amylopectin**, consists of 1000 or more glucose units that are also connected with α-1,4 linkages. However, a number of α-1,6 links also occur at branch points. These links amount to about 4% of the total linkages, or one for approximately every 25 glucose units.

Because of these structural differences, amylose is more soluble in water than is amylopectin, and this characteristic may be used to separate the two components. More efficient separations are affected by complexing and precipitating the amylose with suitable agents, including various alcohols or nitroparaffins. Amylose reacts with iodine to form a deep blue complex; amylopectin gives a blue-violet or purple color.

Most starches have a similar ratio of amylose to amylopectin, averaging about 25% of the former to 75% of the latter. Certain waxy or glutinous starches contain either no amylose or small amounts (less than 6%).

α-**Amylase** (α-1,4-glucan 4-glucanohydrolase), an enzyme present in pancreatic juice and saliva, hydrolyzes starch by a random splitting of α-1,4-glucosidic linkages. Amylose thus gives rise to a mixture of glucose, maltose, and amylopectin, a mixture of branched and unbranched oligosaccharides containing α-1,6 bonds.

β-**Amylase** (α-1,4-glucan maltohydrolase) produces its effect by removing maltose units from the nonreducing ends of polysaccharide molecules. The end product in the case of amylose is nearly pure maltose. The hydrolytic action of β-amylase on the α-1,4 linkages of amylopectin continues until a branch point is approached. Because the enzyme lacks the capacity to hydrolyze α-1,6 bonds, the reaction stops, leaving polysaccharide fragments known as dextrins as the product of incomplete hydrolysis.

Hydrolysis of starch by mineral acids ultimately produces glucose in nearly quantitative yields. The course of hydrolysis may be conveniently followed by the iodine reaction, which changes successively from blue-black to purple to red to no reaction.

Starches form colloidal sols rather than true solutions. If a suspension of starch in cold water is added to boiling water while stirring, the opaque granules swell and finally rupture to give a translucent sol. If this sol is somewhat concentrated, it sets to a firm jelly when cooled. Cold, concentrated aqueous solutions of the caustic alkalies, of chloral hydrate, of ammonium thiocyanate, or of hydrochloric acid also cause the swelling and ultimate rupture of the starch granules to form pastes.

Biosynthesis of the amylose fraction of starch is affected by enzymes known as transglycosylases. The reaction involves the lengthening of priming chains of identical composition by the addition of single glucose residues. In certain microorganisms, glucose 1-phosphate is the glucose donor, and the enzyme that catalyzes the transfer is phosphorylase. Various sugar nucleotides, such as UDP-glucose and ADP-glucose, function as glycosyl donors in higher plants. Primer is essential to the reaction and must be a chain of at least three α-1,4-linked glucose units. The following equations illustrating this reaction show UDP-glucose as the source of the glucose residues:

$$(\text{Glucose})_n + \text{UDP-glucose}$$
$$\rightarrow (\text{Glucose})_{n+1} + \text{UDP}$$
$$(\text{Glucose})_{n+1} + \text{UDP-glucose}$$
$$\rightarrow (\text{Glucose})_{n+2} + \text{UDP, etc.}$$

Amylopectin, the branched component of starch, is formed from amylose by the action of a transglycosylase designated Q-enzyme. This enzyme affects the splitting of a monosaccharide chain containing at least 40 glucose units into two fragments. The fragment that carries the newly exposed reducing end first forms an enzyme-subtrate complex and, in this form, is transferred to an appropriate acceptor chain, establishing an α-1,6 branch. This is illustrated diagrammatically in Figure 3-1.

Starch, as the term is used in pharmaceutic circles, consists of granules separated from the mature grain of corn, *Zea mays* Linné (Fam.

Poaceae), the mature grain of wheat, *Triticum aestivum* Linné (Fam. Poaceae), or from tubers of the potato, *Solanum tuberosum* Linné (Fam. Solanaceae). Starches obtained from different botanic sources may not exhibit identical properties for specific pharmaceutic purposes, such as tablet disintegration, and they should not be interchanged unless performance equivalency has been ascertained.

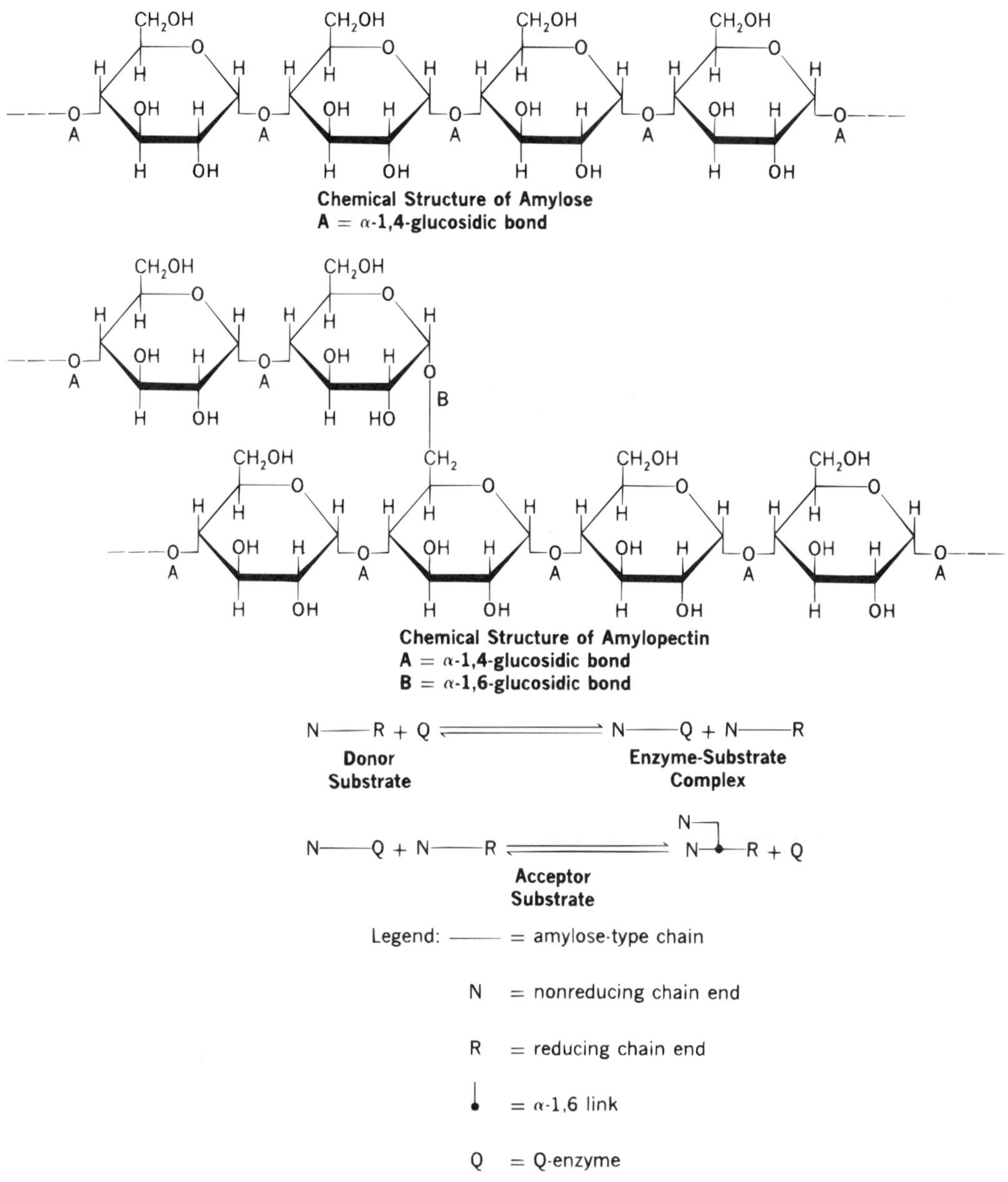

Fig. 3–1. Formation of α-1,6 branch in amylopectin (diagrammatic).

Preparation of starch involves disruption of the plant cells to release the starch granules, and appropriate manipulations are necessary in the case of corn and wheat to eliminate tacky proteins (glutens), which impede free flow of the starch and lipids from the embryo (germ), causing the embryo to become rancid. The separated embryos contain vitamin E and can be processed to yield useful oils.

Starch is used as an ingredient in dusting powders and as a pharmaceutic aid. The latter applications include use as a tablet filler, binder, and disintegrant. Purified **starch amylose** is also particularly useful for such purposes. A starch suspension may be swallowed as an antidote for iodine poisoning. Starch has many commercial uses, such as paper sizing, cloth sizing, and laundry starching. It is the starting material from which liquid glucose (corn syrup), dextrose, dextrins, and high-fructose sweeteners are made.

Hetastarch is a semisynthetic material that is prepared in such a manner that it is approximately 90% amylopectin, and seven or eight hydroxyethyl substituents are present for each ten glucose units. A 6% solution of hetastarch is used as a plasma expander.

It is adjunct therapy in treatment of shock caused by hemorrhage, burns, surgery, sepsis, or other trauma. The duration of the improved hemodynamic status is 24 to 36 hours. The polymer is degraded, and molecules with molecular weights of less than 50,000 are eliminated rapidly by renal excretion.

Inulin is a D-fructan in which residues are linked in a linear manner by β-2,1 bonds. It is obtained from the subterranean organs of members of the family Asteraceae. It is particularly abundant in taraxacum, inula (elecampane), lappa (burdock root), echinacea (cone flower), and chicory (succory or blue dandelion root). Inulin occurs in the cell sap and, by immersing the fresh rhizome or root in alcohol for some time, the inulin usually crystallizes in sphaerite aggregates. Inulin is used in culture media as a fermentative identifying agent for certain bacteria and in special laboratory methods for the evaluation of renal function. It is filtered only by the glomeruli and is not excreted or reabsorbed by the tubules.

Dextran is an α-1,6-linked polyglucan that is formed from sucrose by the action of a transglucosylase enzyme system (dextran sucrase) present in *Leuconostoc mesenteroides*. This reaction can be summarized in the following equation:

$$n\text{Sucrose} + (\text{Glucose})_x$$
$$\text{Primer}$$

$$\rightarrow (\text{Glucose})_{x+n} + n\text{Fructose}$$
$$\text{Dextran}$$

Dextrans of the desired size are prepared by controlled depolymerization (acid hydrolysis, fungal dextranase, or ultrasonic vibration) of native dextrans or by controlled fermentation, including use of a cell-free enzyme system. At present, dextrans with clinical utility have average molecular weights of 40,000, 70,000, and 75,000. The two larger dextrans are used in 6% solutions as plasma expanders in cases of shock or pending shock caused by hemorrhage, trauma, or severe burns; dextran is not a substitute for whole blood when the latter is indicated. These dextran preparations are well suited for their intended uses because their osmolarity and viscosity resemble those of plasma; they are serologically indifferent and relatively nontoxic, and their effectiveness is prolonged by the slow metabolic cleavage of the 1,6-glucosidic linkage.

The low–molecular-weight dextran crosses extravascular space and is excreted readily, but a 10% solution can be used as an adjunct in the treatment of shock. It is also employed to reduce blood viscosity and to improve microcirculation at low flow states. Dextrans interfere with some laboratory tests and may significantly increase clotting time.

Cellulose

Cellulose is the most abundant organic compound on earth. Most of the cellulose used for industrial purposes originates from wood (40-50% cellulose) and cotton fibers (98% cellulose). Cellulose is the principal structural element of higher plant cell walls and occurs as very fine threads called microfibrils that are cylinders made up of about 40 pairs of cellulose chains consisting of several hundred β-1,4-linked D-glucose molecules (β-1,4-glucan). Two other types of components of the cell wall are hemicelluloses, which are usually heteroglycans containing two to four different types of sugars (xyloglucans, rhamnogalacturonans, arabinogalactans) and pectins, which are principally α-1,4 polymers of galacturonic acid. The microfibrils are held together by hydrogen bonds between hemicellulose molecules, which in turn are cross linked to pectin. Pectin molecules are joined by calcium ion bridges, and protein molecules weave through the matrix linking the molecules that compose the matrix. By this complex system, the cellulose microfibrils are interlinked and embedded into an amorphous matrix of pectins and hemicelluloses like a steel fabric woven into concrete.

The β glycosidic linkage of the cellulose polymer is not hydrolyzed by mammalian enzyme systems, an important consideration in the application of many cellulose derivatives, but is hydrolyzed by cellulase, which is produced by many microorganisms, including the rumen microflora of herbiverous animals.

Purified cotton is the hair of the seed of cultivated varieties of *Gossypium hirsutum* Linné or of other species of *Gossypium* (Fam. Malvaceae) that is freed from adhering impurities, deprived of fatty matter, bleached, and sterilized in its final container. Purified cotton is also referred to as **absorbent cotton**. *Gossypium*, the ancient name for the cotton plant, is from the Arabic *gos*, meaning a soft silky substance; *hirsutum* is from the Latin, meaning rough or hairy.

G. hirsutum, as cultivated in the southern United States, is an annual herb that attains a maximum height of about 4 feet and yields most of the commercial cotton known as American Upland Cotton; *G. barbadense* Linné, a somewhat larger plant, is cultivated in South Carolina and Georgia along the sea coast and yields Sea Island Cotton.

The plants produce capsules (bolls) that open along longitudinal sutures when ripe and reveal a mass of white hairs attached to the brownish seeds. The mass of hairs (cotton fibers) and seeds is collected and ''ginned,'' a machine process for removing the seeds. To render cotton absorbent and suitable for surgical use, it is first carded (combed) to remove gross impurities and short hairs (linters). The cotton is then washed with a weak alkali solution to remove fatty materials, bleached with chlorinated soda, washed with weak acid, washed with water, and finally dried and recarded into flat sheets. After the absorbent cotton is packaged, it is usually sterilized.

Cotton for textiles is spun into thread and then woven; or, it may be treated with various chemicals, thereby yielding such fabrics as mercerized cotton, rayons, and others. The United States produces about half the world's supply of cotton. Cotton is also produced in Egypt and other tropical parts of Africa, India, the West and East Indies, and South America.

Cotton has been known since remotest antiquity. It has been cultivated in India for more than 3000 years. Egypt had a well-developed cotton industry 4000 years ago. Cotton has been found in the mounds of the Aztecs in Mexico.

Purified cotton is employed as a surgical dressing; it serves as a mechanical protection to absorb blood, mucus, or pus and to keep bacteria from infecting wounds. Commercially, cotton is employed for textiles and is a source of pure cellulose in the manufacture of explosives, cellulose acetate, and other materials. Absorbent gauze, microcrystalline cellulose, purified rayon, and such cellulose derivatives as carboxymethylcellulose, cellulose acetate phthalate, ethylcellulose, hydroxyethylcellulose, hydroxypropylcellulose, hydroxypropylmethylcellulose, methylcellulose, oxidized cellulose, and pyroxylin find special applications in pharmacy and medicine.

Powdered cellulose is purified, mechanically disintegrated cellulose prepared by processing α-cellulose obtained as a pulp from fibrous plant materials. The purity of cellulose is defined by measurement of its solubility in sodium hydroxide solution. Cellulose remaining insoluble is termed α-cellulose, and the greater the quantity of α-cellulose present, the higher the quality of the material. It exists in various grades and exhibits degrees of fineness ranging from a free-flowing dense powder to a coarse, fluffy, nonflowing material. It is used as a self-binding tablet diluent and disintegrating agent.

HETEROGYLCANS

Gums

Gums are natural plant hydrocolloids that may be classified as anionic or nonionic polysaccharides or salts of polysaccharides. They are translucent, amorphous substances that are produced frequently in higher plants as a protective after injury. Many plants that grow under semiarid conditions produce **exudate gums** in copious quantities when their bark is damaged which serves to seal the wound and prevent dehydration of the plant. **Seed gums** are hydrocolloids contained in some seed embryos where they serve as polysaccharide food reserves. Various algae contain **marine gums** as components of cell walls and membranes or in intracellular regions where they serve as reserve food material. Selected microorganisms produce **microbial gums** in fermentation, and these exopolysaccharides can be isolated from the fermentation broth. A number of semisynthetic cellulose derivatives are used for their hydrophilic properties, and they can be considered as specialized hydrocolloid gums.

Gums are typically heterogeneous in composition. Upon hydrolysis, arabinose, galactose, glucose, mannose, xylose, and various uronic acids are the most frequently observed components. The uronic acids may form salts with calcium, magnesium, and other cations; methyl ether and sulfate ester substituents further modify the hydrophilic properties of some natural polysaccharides.

Gums find diverse applications in pharmacy. They are ingredients in dental and other adhesives and in bulk laxatives. But their most frequent contribution is as agents of pharmaceutic necessity. These hydrophilic polymers are useful as tablet binders, emulsifiers, gelating agents, suspending agents, stabilizers, and thickeners. When problems are encountered in the utilization of hydrocolloids, some alteration in the hydration of the polymer is usually involved; for example, gums are precipitated from solution by alcohol and by lead subacetate solution.

An effort has been made to distinguish between mucilages and gums on the basis that gums readily dissolve in water, whereas mucilages form slimy masses. Some investigators have tried to distinguish between them on the basis that mucilages are physiologic products and gums are pathologic products. However, these classifications have not been successful. Knowledge of the nature of the polysaccharide polymers is increasing, and it now seems advantageous to abandon extensive use of such designations and to focus on those features that are associated with useful physical properties. The hydrocolloids may be linear or branched, and they may have acidic, basic, or neutral characteristics. Basic polymers have limited commercial importance; acidic and neutral hydrocolloids are widely used, and some generalizations can be made about their properties.

Gums consisting of linear polymers are less soluble than those with branched constituents, and linear hydrocolloids yield solutions with greater viscosity. These features are related to the increased possibility for good alignment and considerable intermolecular hydrogen bonding among linear molecules. This tendency for intermolecular associations also explains why solutions of linear polysaccharides are less stable (tend to precipitate), especially with reductions in temperature, than solutions of branched molecules. This observation could significantly influence the shelf life of product formulations. When linear polymers contain uronic acid residues, columbic repulsion reduces intermolecular associations and gives more stability to solutions. However, hydrocolloids with acid groups also have the potential for anionic-cationic interaction to give precipitation or to alter the hydrophilic properties in another manner.

Branched hydrocolloids form gels rather than viscous solutions at higher concentrations. They tend to be tacky when moist, a feature that is advantageous for adhesive purposes, and to rehydrate more readily than linear hydrocolloids, a property of importance in drug formulations that must be reconstituted immediately before use.

Plant exudates have been the traditional gums for pharmaceutic purposes, and they still find significant application; however, preparation of these gums is labor-intensive and carries a premium price, and their use will probably continue to decline. Marine gums are widely used as utility gums at the present time, and their competitive position appears stable. Guar gum is obtained from an annual legume that is adaptable to modern agricultural practices and will likely join various cellulose derivatives and the microbial gums as those hydrocolloids whose applications are expanding. Recently, by using recombinant DNA technology in microbial gum production, a recombinant plasmid was constructed that is capable of enhancing xanthan gum production through gene augmentation.

Tragacanth

Tragacanth is the dried, gummy exudate from *Astragalus gummifer* Labillardière, or other Asiatic species of *Astragalus* (Fam. Fabaceae). It is commonly known as **gum tragacanth**. The name tragacanth is from the Greek *tragos* (goat) and *akantha* (horn) and probably refers to the curved shape of the drug; *astragalus* means milk-bone and refers to the exuding and subsequent hardening of the drug; *gummifer* is from the Latin and means gumbearing. The plants are thorny branching shrubs about 1 meter in height and are abundant in the highlands of Asia Minor, Iran, Syria, the former Soviet Union, and Greece. When the plant is injured, the cell walls of the pith and then of the medullary rays are gradually transformed into gum. The gum absorbs water and creates internal pressure within the stem, thus forcing it to the surface through the incision that caused the injury. When the gum strikes the air, it gradually hardens owing to the evaporation of the water. The nature of the incision governs the shape of the final product. The gum exuding from natural injuries is more or less wormlike and is twisted into coils or is shaped like irregular tears of a yellowish or brownish color. The better grade comes from transverse incisions made with a knife in the main stem and older branches. The gum from such incisions is known as ribbon gum and flake gum, depending on the shape of the solidified exudate. The gum usually shows longitudinal striations caused by small irregularities in the incision. The metamorphosis occurs only at night, and the tragacanth ribbons exhibit transverse striations that show the amount that exudes each night. The shorter the drying time, the whiter and more translucent the ribbons. Tragacanth was known to Theophrastus (300 B.C.) and Dioscorides and seems to have been used during the Middle Ages.

Tragacanth contains 60 to 70% of bassorin, a complex of polymethoxylated acids, which swells in water but does not dissolve. Bassorin has an elongated molecular shape and forms a viscous solution. Tragacanthin, which is probably demethoxylated bassorin, composes about 30% of the gum and is the more water-soluble component.

A more precise chemical analysis of the gum provides an acidic component termed tragacanthic acid and a nearly neutral arabinogalactan. The arabinogalactan is highly branched with interior chains of D-galactopyranose units linked $1\rightarrow6$ and $1\rightarrow3$ with side chains of L-arabinofuranose residues linked $1\rightarrow2$, $1\rightarrow3$, and $1\rightarrow5$. Tragacanthic acid is essentially a linear chain of $(1\rightarrow3)$-linked α-D-galacturonic acid residues with occasional insertions of $1\rightarrow2$-L-rhamnopyranose. Approximately one-half of the remaining units are neutral sugars present as short side chains in the form of β-D-xylopyranose, β-D-galactopyranose-$(1\rightarrow2)$-β-D-xylopyranose, and α-L-fucopyranose $(1\rightarrow2)$-β-D-xylopyranose, with the β-D-xylopyranose residues attached to the O-3 position of the galacturonic acid units of the linear chain.

Tragacanth is employed pharmaceutically as a suspending agent for insoluble powders in mixtures, as an emulsifying agent for oils and resins, and as an adhesive. Tragacanth is the most resistant of the hydrocolloids to acid hydrolysis and thus is preferred for use in highly acidic conditions. It is employed in cosmetics (hand lotions) as a demulcent and an emollient and in cloth printing, confectionery, and other processes.

Acacia

Acacia is the dried, gummy exudate from the stems and branches of *Acacia senegal* (Linné) Willdenow or of other related African species of *Acacia* (Fam. Fabaceae). It is commonly known as **gum arabic**. *Acacia* is from the greek *akakia*, coming from *ake*, meaning pointed and referring to the thorny nature of the plant; *senegal* refers to its habitat. The name ''gum arabic'' seems to be a misnomer because little acacia is produced on the Arabian peninsula and none is exported. The name may reflect the drug's extensive use by the early Arabian physicians.

Acacia plants are thorny trees about 6 meters in height that grow in the Sudan and in Senegal. Most of the official drug comes from cultivated trees in the Sudanese province of Kordofan. The trees are tapped by making a transverse incision in the bark and peeling it both above and below the cut, thus exposing an area of cambium 2 to 3 feet in length and 2 to 3 inches in breadth. In 2 or 3 weeks, the tears of gum formed on this exposed surface are collected; the average annual yield of gum per tree is 900 to 2000 g. The formation of the gum may be caused by bacterial action or by the action of a ferment. No trace of metamorphosed cell walls is found in the gum; therefore, the gum must be formed from cell contents. The gum is occasionally exposed to and bleached by the sun. Numerous minute cracks often form in the outer portion of the tears during the bleaching process, thus giving them a semiopaque appearance. The tears are garbled and graded by hand, then packed and shipped via Port Sudan.

Acacia has been an article of commerce since remote times. The tree and heaps of gum are pictured during the reign of Ramses III and in later inscriptions. It was exported from the Gulf of Aden 1700 years before Christ. Theophrastus mentioned it in the third century B.C. under the name of ''Egyptian gum.'' During the Middle Ages, acacia was obtained from Egypt and Turkey. The West African gum (Senegal) was imported by the Portuguese during the fifteenth century.

Acacia consists principally of arabin, which is a complex mixture of calcium, magnesium, and potassium salts of arabic acid. Arabic acid is a branched polysaccharide that yields L-arabinose, D-galactose, D-glucuronic acid, and L-rhamnose on hydrolysis. 1,3-Linked D-galactopyranose units form the backbone chain of the molecule, and some of the D-galactopyranose units bear side chains at the C-6 position consisting of two 1,6-linked β-D-galactopyranose units terminated by a 1,6-linked β-D-glucuronic acid unit. Some of the L-arabinofuranose and L-rhamnopyranose residues occur in single or branched side chains attached to primary side-chain D-galactopyranose units. Other L-rhamnopyranose units are linked to the C-4 position of D-glucuronic acid which is linked to D-galactopyranose units of the primary backbone chain. Acacia contains 12 to 15% of water and several occluded enzymes (oxidases, peroxidases, and pectinases) that can cause problems in some formulations.

Acacia is unusually soluble for a hydrocolloid and can form solutions over a wide range of concentrations. It remains in solution at alcohol concentrations below 60%, a property that is useful in some drug formulations. Solutions of acacia have low viscosity and good stability over the pH range of 2 to 10; these properties contribute to the gum's use as an excellent emulsifying agent.

Acacia is also used as a suspending agent. It possesses useful demulcent and emollient properties and finds application as an adhesive and binder in table granulations.

Ghatti gum or Indian gum is a product that is sometimes used as a substitute for acacia. It is an exudate from *Anogeissus latifolia* (Fam. Combretaceae), a tree indigenous to India and Sri Lanka. It is a branched hydrocolloid consisting of units of D-galactopyranose, L-arabinofuranose, L-arabinopyranose, and D-glucopyranosyluronic acid grouped in side chains which are attached to D-mannopyranose residues of a main chain of alternating 1,4-linked β-D-glucopyranosyluronic acid and 1,2-linked D-mannopyranose residues. It readily forms dispersions with cold water; the dispersions are more viscous than those of acacia.

Karaya Gum

Karaya gum or sterculia gum is the dried, gummy exudate from *Sterculia urens* Roxburgh, *S. villosa* Roxburgh, *S. tragacantha* Lindley, or other species of *Sterculia* Linné (Fam. Sterculiaceae), or from *Cochlospermum gossypium* DeCandolle or other species of *Cochlospermum*

Kunth (Fam. Bixaceae). These trees are native to India and are widely scattered in the Indian forests. They may attain a height of 10 meters, but the trunks are large, soft, and corky. Sterculia is from the Latin *sterculius*, the deity that presided over manuring, and refers to the fetid odor of the trees. The gum exudes naturally or from incisions made to the heartwood and is collected throughout the year, mostly from March to June. The incisions produce knoblike masses of gum that are collected frequently for 9 months. The tree should then be allowed to rest for 2 to 3 years. Three commercial grades are collected in the central provinces of India and exported from Bombay; the various meshes of granular and powdered karaya are produced in the United States.

Karaya gum consists of an acetylated, branched heteropolysaccharide with a main chain of 1,4-linked α-D-galacturonic acid and 1,2 linked L-rhamnopyranose units having short D-glucopyranosyluronic acid containing side chains attached 1→3 to the main chain D-galacturonic acid residues. Varying amounts of pigmented impurities are also present in commercial grades of this gum; its color ranges from pale yellowish to pinkish brown. Karaya gum is one of the least soluble of the exuded plant gums. It absorbs water, swells to several times its original bulk, and forms a discontinuous type of mucilage.

Karaya gum is used as a bulk laxative, as an agent for forming emulsions and suspensions, and as a dental adhesive. It is used extensively in wave set solutions and in skin lotions, in the textile and printing industries, in the preparation of food products, and in the preparation of composite building materials.

Sodium Alginate

Sodium alginate or algin is the purified carbohydrate product extracted from brown sea weeds by the use of dilute alkali. It is chiefly obtained from *Macrocystis pyrifera* (Turn.) Ag.(Fam. Lessoniaceae). Algin is found in all species of brown seaweeds (Class Phaeophyceae), and some commercial algin has been obtained from, among other sources, species of *Ascophyllum, Ecklonia, Laminaria*, and *Nereocystis. Macrocystis pyrifera* is harvested from several temperate zones of the Pacific Ocean; the area off Southern California is a major producing site.

Algin consists chiefly of the sodium salt of

alginic acid, a linear polymer of L-guluronic acid and D-mannuronic acid. Mannuronic acid is the major component, but there is some variation with the algal source. The alginic acid molecule appears to be a copolymer of 1,4-linked mannopyranosyluronic acid units, of 1,4-linked gulopyranosyluronic acid units, and of segments where these uronic acids alternate with 1,4-linkages.

Sodium alginate occurs as a nearly odorless and tasteless coarse or fine powder and is yellowish white in color. It is readily soluble in water, forming a viscous, colloidal solution. It is insoluble in alcohol, ether, chloroform, and strong acid.

Sodium alginate is a suspending agent. It is also used in the food industry (ice cream, chocolate milk, salad dressings, icings, confectionery), for suspending cosmetic preparations, as a sizing, and for other industrial purposes.

Alginic acid is relatively insoluble in water, but it is used as a tablet binder and thickening agent. Useful gel-forming properties are associated with salts of various polyvalent cations and alginic acid. Calcium alginate has found application for a number of gelation purposes, including the formation of a firm gel for preparing dental impressions. The propylene glycol ester of algin has been prepared and is especially useful in formulations that require greater acid stability than that possessed by the parent hydrocolloid.

Agar

Agar is the dried, hydrophilic, colloidal substance extracted from *Gelidium cartilagineum* (Linné) Gaillon (Fam. Gelidiaceae), *Gracilaria confervoides* (Linné) Greville (Fam. Sphaerococcaceae), and related red algae (Class Rhodophyceae). Agar is sometimes referred to as **Japanese isinglas**.

These algae grow along the eastern coast of Asia and the coasts of North America and Europe. Most of the commercial supply comes from Japan, Spain, Portugal, and Morocco. Mexico, New Zealand, South Africa, and the United States are also significant producers.

Agar is prepared in California as follows: the fresh seaweed is washed for 24 hours in running water, extracted in steam-heated digesters with dilute acid solution and then with water for a total period of about 30 hours. The hot aqueous extract is cooled and then congealed in ice machines. The water from the agar almost completely separates as ice. The 300 lb agar ice block

(containing about 5 lb of dry agar) is crushed, melted, and filtered through a rotary vacuum filter. The moist agar flakes are dried by currents of dry air in tall cylinders. The fully dried product can be reduced to a fine powder.

Agar usually occurs as bundles consisting of thin, membranous, agglutinated strips or in cut, flaked, or granulated forms. It may be weak yellowish orange, yellowish gray to pale yellow, or colorless. It is tough when damp, brittle when dry, odorless or slightly odorous, and has a mucilaginous taste. Agar is insoluble in cold water, but if one part of agar is boiled for 10 minutes with 65 times its weight of water, it yields a firm gel when cooled.

Agar is predominantly the calcium salt of strongly ionized, acidic polysaccharides. It can be resolved into two major fractions, agarose and agaropectin. The structures of these constituents have not been fully established, and they are probably variable. The primary carbohydrate component appears to consist of alternating, 1,3-linked D-galactopyranosyl and 3,6-anhydro-L-galactopyranosyl units. Most of the anhydrogalactose residues in agaropectin have a sulfate ester substituent, but agarose is characterized by a low sulfate content.

Agar hydrates to form a smooth, nonirritating bulk that favors normal peristalsis and is used as a laxative. Agar is also used as a suspending agent, an emulsifier, a gelating agent for suppositories and surgical lubricants, and a tablet excipient and disintegrant. It is extensively used as a gel in bacteriologic culture media and as an aid in food processing and other industrial processes.

Agarose also finds special application in clinical diagnostics. It is used as a matrix for immunodiffusion, for electrophoretic separation of globulin and other proteins, and for techniques involving gel filtration and gel chromatography.

Carrageenan

Carrageenan is a term referring to closely related hydrocolloids that are obtained from various red algae or seaweeds. *Chondrus crispus* (Linné) Stackhouse and *Gigartina mamillosa* (Goodenough and Woodward) J. Agardh (Fam. Gigartinaceae) are major sources of carrageenan; these algae are commonly known as chondrus or Irish moss.

These plants are common along the northwestern coast of France, the British Isles, and the coast of Nova Scotia. The plants are collected chiefly during June and July, spread out on the beach and bleached by the action of the sun and dew, then treated with salt water, and finally dried and stored. The chief points of collection in the United States are located 15 to 25 miles south of Boston, where *Chondrus crispus* is gathered and used in the manufacture of carrageenan. *Gigartina mamillosa* is most abundant north of the *Chondrus crispus* region; thus, it rarely occurs in the drug collected in the United States, though it is not unusual in the imported chondrus.

Chondrus is an allusion to the cartilage-like character of the dry thallus; *Gigartina* is an allusion to the fruit bodies that appear as elevated tubercles on the thallus. The specific name, *crispus*, pertains to the curled fronds; *mamillosa* to the small, breastlike, stalked fruit bodies or cystocarps.

The carrageenan hydrocolloids are galactans with sulfate esters and physically resemble agar. The carrageenans differ chemically from agar because they have a higher sulfate ester content. Carrageenan polysaccharides consist of chains of 1,3-linked β-D-galactose and 1,4-linked α-D-galactose units which are variously substituted and modified to the 3,6-anhydro derivative. Carrageenans can be separated into several components, including k-carrageenan, i-carrageenan, and λ-carrageenan.

There are some differences in the specific properties and applications of the individual carrageenans. For example, k- and i-carrageenans tend to orient in stable helices when in solution, but λ-carrageenan does not. Consistent with these properties, k- and i-carrageenans are good gelating agents, and the nongelling λ-carrageenan is a more useful thickener.

Carrageenans are widely used to form gels and to give stability to emulsions and suspensions. The firm texture and good rinsability of these hydrocolloids are particularly desirable in toothpaste formulations. They are also used as a demulcent, a bulk laxative, and an ingredient in many food preparations.

Furcellaria fastigiata (Huds.) Lamour., a red alga, yields an extract called furcellaran or Danish agar. This hydrocolloid is similar to k-carrageenan, and it finds some use, especially in Europe, as a gelating and suspending agent.

Plantago Seed

Plantago seed, psyllium seed, or plantain seed is the cleaned, dried, ripe seed of *Plantago psyllium* Linné or of *P. indica* Linné (*P. arenaria* Waldstein et Kitaibel), known in commerce as Spanish or French psyllium seed; or of *P. ovata* Forskal, known in commerce as blonde psyllium or Indian plantago seed (Fam. Plantaginaceae). *Plantago* is from the Latin and means sole of the foot, referring to the shape of the leaf; *psyllium* is from the Greek and means flea, referring to the color, size, and shape of the seed (fleaseed); *arenaria* is from the Latin *arena* and means sand, referring to the sandy habitat of the plant. *Ovata* refers to the ovate shape of the leaf.

P. psyllium is an annual, caulescent, glandular, pubescent herb native to the Mediterranean countries and extensively cultivated in France, which yields the bulk of the American imported psyllium seed.

P. ovata is an annual, caulescent herb native to Asia and the Mediterranean countries. The plant is cultivated extensively in Pakistan.

In France, the seeds are planted in March and harvested in August, when they are about three-quarters mature. The fields are mowed about dawn, when the dew is heaviest, to prevent scattering of the seed. The plants, partially dried in the sun, are threshed, and the seeds are cleaned and bagged and allowed to dry fully. In Europe, the seeds have been a domestic remedy since the 16th century, but only since 1930 have they been extensively used in America as a popular remedy for constipation.

Commercially, the most important plantago product is the husk of the seed of *P. ovata*. It is produced in Pakistan and further purified and processed in the United States. However, **psyllium husk** may be prepared from any of the three commercial *Plantago* species. A physicochemical process is used to separate the mucilaginous layer of the seed coat.

Plantago seeds contain 10 to 30% of hydrocolloid, which is localized in the outer seed coat. The hydrocolloid material can be separated into acidic and neutral polysaccharide fractions, and, upon hydrolysis, L-arabinose, D-galactose, D-galacturonic acid, L-rhamnose, and D-xylose are obtained. The exact compositions of the polymers have not been determined. Solutions of the purified gum are thixotropic; the viscosity decreases as shear rate increases, a property that is of potential value.

Plantago seed husk is a cathartic. Its action is caused by the swelling of the gum of the seed coat, thus giving bulk and lubrication. It should be taken with a considerable amount of water.

By taking up water in the gastrointestinal tract

the volume of feces is increased and peristalsis promoted. It is a particularly effective agent when excessive straining must be avoided following anorectal surgery or in the management of hemorrhoids. It is also used in the treatment of diverticular disease or the irritable bowel syndrome.

In drug preparations psyllium husk (psyllium hydrophilic mucilloid) is combined with various chemicals such as powdered anhydrous dextrose, sodium bicarbonate, monobasic potassium phosphate, citric acid, and others (Metamucil).

Guar Gum

Guar gum or guaran is the powdered endosperm of the seed of *Cyamopsis tetragonolobus* (Linné) Taubert (Fam. Fabaceae), an annual plant that is readily cultivated in dry climates. Texas is a major producing area. Use of this gum is expanding rapidly, and there is no practical limit on the amount of gum that can be produced by modern agricultural practices to meet the demand. Guar gum and the related locust bean gum are obtained by milling the seeds to obtain the endosperm that serves as the crude gum. This can be further refined by water extraction and then recovery by alcohol precipitation.

The hydrocolloid is a galactomannan. In it, 1,4-linked D-mannopyranosyl units form a linear chain; single 1,6-linked D-galactopyranosyl residues are attached to alternate mannose moieties. This molecular structure gives properties that are intermediate between those typically associated with branched and linear hydrocolloids. The gum hydrates in cold water and is stable in acidic formulations.

Guar gum is used as a bulk-forming laxative and as a thickening agent, a tablet binder, and a disintegrator in pharmaceuticals. The food processing and paper industries are large users of this gum.

Locust Bean Gum

Locust bean gum is the hydrocolloid-containing powdered endosperm of the seed of *Ceratonia siliqua* Linné (Fam. Fabaceae), a tree native to the Mediterranean region. The slow development of the tree (approximately 15 years for initial seed production) restricts the prospects for increasing the supply of the gum to meet expanding demands for hydrocolloids.

A "flour" or powder made from the flesh of the mature seed pods of the tree is the carob, which is currently popular with natural food advocates. This material resembles chocolate and can be used in a variety of food products. It is also known as carob pulp or St. John's bread, the latter name from its legendary use as the food of St. John the Baptist.

Locust bean gum is a galactomannan and is similar to guar gum. The structural distinction is locust bean gum's lesser frequency of galactose substituents on the linear mannose chain of the locust bean polymer; every fourth or fifth mannose residue is substituted. Locust bean gum has properties slightly more typical of linear hydrocolloids; it is incompletely dispersed in cold water.

Locust bean gum can be used in pharmaceuticals as a thickener and stabilizer and in other manufacturing processes where a hydrocolloid is indicated. It, along with guar gum, has the capacity to form gels in association with other polysaccharides such as agarose, carrageenan, and xanthan gum.

Xanthan Gum

Xanthan gum is a high-molecular-weight microbial gum prepared by the action of *Xanthomonas campestris* on suitable carbohydrates. The exocellular gum is recovered from the fermentation broth by precipitation with isopropyl alcohol.

Recombinant DNA technology has been applied to the production of xanthan gum. Genomic banks of *X. campestris* have been constructed in *Escherichia coli* using mobilized broad-host-range cosmids as the vectors. Following conjugal transfer of the genes from *E. coli* into nonmucoid *X. campestris*, wild-type genes were recovered by their ability to restore mucoid phenotype. Some of the cloned plasmids resulted in wild-type strains of *X. campestris* with enhanced xanthan gum production.

Commercial gums with various genetically controlled compositions and molecular weights are available. Xanthan gum is marketed as the sodium, potassium, or calcium salt.

Xanthan gum consists of 1,4-linked β-D-glucan backbone substituted at O-3 of every second glucose residue by the trisaccharide β-D-mannopyranose (1→4)-β-D-glucopyranosyluronic acid (1→2)-α-D-mannopyranose (1→). The mannose sugars are acetylated and pyruvylated at specific sites but in varying degrees. The gum dissolves in hot and cold water to give high viscosity solutions, and it has good compatibility with a wide range of salts. The viscosity is independent of temperature between 10 and 70° C.

Xanthan gum is used in pharmaceuticals for its excellent emulsifying and suspending properties. The pseudoplastic properties of this gum enable toothpastes and ointments both to hold their shape and to spread readily.

PECTIN

Pectin is a general term for a group of polysaccharides present in the primary cell walls of all seed-bearing plants and are located particularly in the middle lamella. These polysaccharides function in combination with cellulose and hemicellulose as an intercellular cementing material. The parent substance protopectin is insoluble but is easily converted to pectin by restricted hydrolysis using dilute acid extraction of the inner portion of the rind of citrus fruits or from apple pomace. Pectin is from the Greek and means congealed or curdled. It is a natural hydrophilic colloid consisting chiefly of partially methoxylated polygalacturonic acids; the main carbohydrate component is a linear, 1,4-linked D-galacturonan. Many of the carboxyl groups of the galacturonan are esterified with methanol. In addition, the neutral polysaccharides arabinan, galactan, and arabinogalactan have been isolated, the amounts of each being dependent upon the plant source. The molecular weight of pectin ranges from 100,000 to 250,000. Pectin yields not less than 6.7% of methoxyl groups and not less than 74% of galacturonic acid. The gelling power and viscosity of solutions depend on the number of galacturonic acid units in the molecule.

Pharmaceutic pectin differs from "commercial" pectin because it does not contain sugars of organic acids. Pharmaceutic pectin is pure pectin to which no additions have been made.

Pectin may be standardized to the convenient "150 jelly grade" by the addition of dextrose or other sugars. It sometimes contains sodium citrate or other buffer salts. Much of the commercial pectin is obtained as a by-product of the citrus canning industry. Citrus peel is a rich source of pectin, the amount varying with the season and the variety. Approximately half of the pectin made in the United States is derived from lemon peel.

Pectin in fruit is found in an insoluble form known as protopectin; it is converted to the soluble form by heating the fruit with dilute acid.

This solution of pectin can be precipitated by alcohol or by "salting out." It is then washed and dried.

Pectin is a coarse or fine powder, yellowish white in color, almost odorless, and has a mucilaginous taste. It is completely soluble in 20 parts of water, and the solution is viscous, opalescent, colloidal, and acidic to litmus paper. One part of pectin heated in nine parts of water forms a stiff gel.

Pectin is classified as a protectant and a suspending agent and is an ingredient in many antidiarrheal formulations (Kaopectate). As a colloidal solution, it has the property of conjugating toxins and enhancing the physiologic functions of the digestive tract through its physical and chemical properties. In the upper intestinal tract, pectin possesses a surface area composed of ultramicroscopic particles(micelles) that have the property of colloidal absorption of toxins. The efficacy of pectin in the gastrointestinal tract is largely owing to this colloidal action.

SUGGESTED READINGS

Aspinall, G.O., ed.: *The Polysaccharides*. Vols. 1-2. New York, Academic Press, Inc., 1982-1983.

Colwell, R.R., Pariser, E.R., Sinskey, A.J., eds.: *Biotechnology Marine Polysaccharides*. Washington, Hemisphere Publishing Corporation, 1985.

Davidson, R.L., ed.: *Handbook of Water-Soluble Gums and Resins*. New York, McGraw-Hill Book Co., 1980.

Dey, P.M., Harborne, J.B.,eds.: *Methods in Plant Biochemistry*,Vol 2: *Carbohydrates*. San Diego, Academic Press Inc., 1990.

Hoppe, H.A., Levring, T., Tanaka, Y., eds.: *Marine Algae in Pharmaceutical Science*, Vols 1-2. Berlin, Walter de Gruyter, 1979-1982.

Loewus, F.A., Tanner,W.: *Encyclopedia of Plant Physiology*, Vol.13A: *Plant Carbohydrates I*. Berlin, Springer-Verlag, 1982.

Phillips, G.O., Williams, P.A., Wedlock, D.J., eds.: *Gums and Stabilisers for the Food Industry 6*. Oxford, Oxford University Press, 1992.

Pigman, W.W., Wolfram, M.L., Tipson, R.S., Horton,D., eds.: *Advances in Carbohydrate Chemistry and Biochemistry*, Vols. 1-42. New York, Academic Press, Inc., 1945-1984.

Preiss, J.,ed.: *The Biochemistry of Plants*, Vol 3. *Carbohydrates: Structure and Function*. New York, Academic Press, Inc. 1980.

Roehrig, K.L:. *Carbohydrate Biochemistry and Metabolism*. Westport, Connecticut, The AVI Publishing Co., Inc,. 1984.

Tanner, W., Loewus, F.A.: *Encyclopedia of Plant Physiology*,Vol 13B: *Plant Carbohydrates II*. Berlin, Springer-Verlag, 1981.

Walter, R.H.,ed.: *The Chemistry and Technology of Pectin*. San Diego, Academic Press, Inc. 1991.

Whistler, R.L.,ed.: *Industrial Gums, Polysaccharides and Their Derivatives*, 2nd.ed., New York, Academic Press, Inc., 1973.

Whistler, R.L., BeMiller, J.N.,eds.: *Methods in Carbohydrate Chemistry*, Vols. I-VIII. New York, Academic Press, Inc., 1962-1980.

Whistler, R.L., BeMiller, J.N., Paschall, E.F., eds.: *Starch: Chemistry and Technology*, 2nd. ed., Orlando, Academic Press, Inc. 1984.

Yalpani, M., ed.: *Progress in Biotechnology*, Vol.3. *Industrial Polysaccharides*. Amsterdam, Elsevier Science Publishers B.V., 1987.

4

Glycosides

Glycosides are compounds that yield one or more sugars among the products of hydrolysis. The most frequently occurring sugar is D-glucose, although rhamnose, digitoxose, cymarose, and other sugars are components of glycosides. In addition, several glycosides are known in which the sugar moiety is not a true sugar but a sugar derivative such as glucuronic acid or galacturonic acid. The sugars or sugar derivatives exist predominantly as cyclic hemiacetals corresponding to an intramolecular reaction between the aldehyde group of C-1 and a hydroxyl group on a carbon atom in the same molecule. Depending on which hydroxyl group undergoes cyclization, D-glucose, for example, can exist as either a five-membered (glucofuranose) or six-membered (glucopyranose) cyclic hemiacetal. Because the cyclic structures have one more chiral center, two diastereoisomers differing in configuration about the anomeric carbon (C-1) can exist. These diastereoisomers are called anomers and are designated α and β. If the hydroxyl group on the anomeric carbon is down in relation to the cyclic structure, it is the α-D anomer. If the hydroxyl is up, it is the β-D anomer.

Chemically, the glycosides are usually mixed acetals in which the hydroxyl group on the anomeric carbon atom is replaced by a moiety possessing a nucleophilic atom. In the case of O-glycosides, the nucleophilic atom is most commonly oxygen present in an alcohol, a phenol, or a carboxyl. The sugar hemiacetal may react with a hydroxyl group of another sugar to form a disaccharide, and the reaction can be repeated to yield polysaccharides (Chapter 3). When the nucleophilic atom is sulfur, such as in a thiol group, S-glycosides are obtained. N-Glycosides such as nucleosides are formed when the nucleophilic atom is nitrogen, and rarely the nucleophilic atom is carbon in the form of a carbanion giving rise to C- glycosides. The nonsugar component of a glycoside is known as the **aglycone;** the sugar component is called the **glycone**. Both α and β glycosides are possible, depending on the stereoconfiguration at the anomeric carbon atom (Fig. 4-1). However, primarily β forms occur in plants. Emulsin and most other natural enzymes hydrolyze only the β varieties.

In the nomenclature of glycosides the trivial names have an ''in'' ending, and the names indicate the source of the glycoside, for example, digitoxin from *Digitalis*, salicin from *Salix*, and prunasin from *Prunus*. The systematic names are usually formed by replacing the ''ose'' suffix of the parent sugar with ''oside.'' The anomeric prefix (α- or β-) and the configurational prefix (D or L) immediately precede the sugar stem name, and the chemical name of the aglycone precedes the name of the sugar. For example the systematic name of salicin is o-hydroxymethylphenyl β-D-glycopyranoside.

From the biologic viewpoint, glycosides play an important role in the life of the plant and are involved in its regulatory, protective, and sanitary functions. Among such a variety of compounds one finds many therapeutically active agents. Some of our most valuable cardiac specifics are glycosides from digitalis. Laxative drugs, such as senna, aloe, rhubarb, cascara sagrada, and frangula, contain anthraquinone glycosides, and sinigrin, a glycoside from black mustard, yields allyl isothiocyanate, a powerful local irritant.

The classification of glycosides is a difficult matter. If the classification is based on the sugar group, a number of rare sugars are involved; if the aglycone group is used as a basis of classification, one encounters groups from probably all classes of plant constituents. A therapeutic classification, although excellent from a pharmaceutic viewpoint, omits many glycosides of pharmacognostic interest.

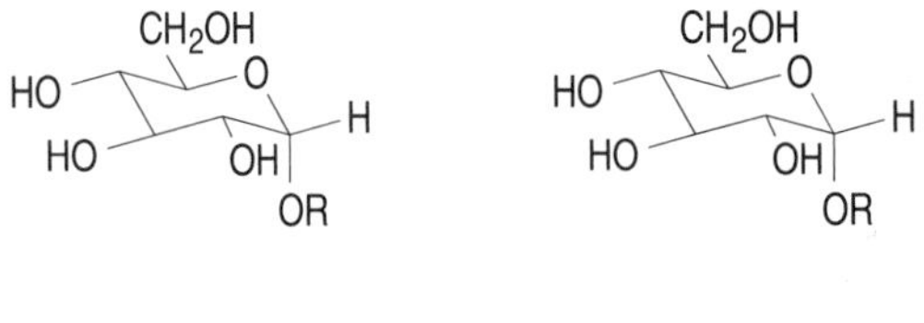

α-anomer   β-anomer

Fig. 4–1. Structures of the diastereoisomers of D-glucopyranosides. R = aglycone.

Some glycosides contain more than one saccharide group, possibly as di- or trisaccharides. Upon proper conditions of hydrolysis, one or more of the saccharide groups can be removed from such compounds, resulting in glycosides of simpler structure (see amygdalin).

All natural glycosides are hydrolyzed into a sugar and another organic compound by boiling with mineral acids; however, they vary in the ease with which this hydrolysis is performed. In most cases, the glycoside is hydrolyzed easily by an enzyme that occurs in the same plant tissue, but in different cells from those that contain the glycoside. Injury to the tissues, the germination process, and perhaps other physiologic activities of the cells bring the enzyme in contact with the glycoside, and the hydrolysis of the latter takes place. A large number of enzymes have been found in plants. Many of these enzymes hydrolyze only a single glycoside; however, two enzymes, namely **emulsin** of almond kernels and **myrosinase** of black mustard seeds, each hydrolyze a considerable number of glycosides. Glycosides that are derivatives of rhamnose require a special enzyme known as rhamnase for their hydrolysis.

BIOSYNTHESIS OF GLYCOSIDES

Consideration of glycoside (heteroside) biosynthesis necessarily consists of two parts. The general reactions couple a sugar residue to an aglycone. Presumably this transfer reaction is similar in all biologic systems. This contrasts with the pathways for biosynthesis of the various types of aglycones, which tend to be diverse and must be considered individually.

The principal pathway of glycoside formation involves the transfer of a uridylyl group from uridine triphosphate to a sugar 1-phosphate. Enzymes catalyzing this reaction are referred to as uridylyl transferases (1) and have been isolated from animal, plant, and microbial sources. Phosphates of pentoses, hexoses, or various sugar derivatives may participate. The subsequent reaction, mediated by glycosyl transferases (2), involves the transfer of the sugar from uridine diphosphate to a suitable acceptor (aglycone), thus forming the glycoside.

$$UTP + Sugar\text{-}1\text{-}P \rightleftharpoons UDP\text{-}Sugar + PPi \quad (1)$$

$$\begin{aligned} UDP\text{-}Sugar \ + \ &Acceptor \\ &(Glycoside) \\ \rightleftharpoons \ &Acceptor\text{-}Sugar \ + \ UDP \quad (2) \end{aligned}$$

Once such a glycoside is formed, other enzymes may transfer another sugar unit to the monosaccharide moiety, converting it to a disaccharide. Enzymes occur in various glycoside-containing plants that are capable of producing tri- and tetrasaccharide moieties of the glycosides by analogous reactions.

To illustrate the biosynthesis of an aglycone moiety and the stereospecificity that can be involved in the glycosyl transferase reaction, the formation of cyanogenic glycosides is an interesting case to note. The process of glycoside formation is shown in Figure 4-2 for prunasin, a cyanogenic glucoside. The amino acid phenylalanine, which arises from the shikimate pathway, is the starting precursor. An aldoxime, a nitrile, and a cyanohydrin are involved as intermediates in the pathway. The presence of a chiral center in mandelonitrile provides the opportunity for two β-glucosides to occur. In wild cherry, *Prunus serotina*, prunasin [(R)-mandelonitrile glucoside] is formed. The isomeric sambunigrin [(S)-mandelonitrile glucoside] is formed in *Sambucus nigra*. Apparently, these compounds do not occur in the same species, further confirming the stereospecificity of the glycosyl transferases that catalyze their formation.

When the chemical nature of the aglycone group is used as a basis of systematization, the classification of the glycoside-containing drugs follows this scheme: (1) cardioactive steroid group; (2) anthraquinone group; (3) saponin group; (4) cyanophore group; (5) glucosinolate or isothiocyanate group; (6) flavonol group; (7) alcohol group; (8) aldehyde group; and (9) phenol group.

ANTHRAQUINONE GLYCOSIDES

A number of glycosides with aglycones related to anthracene are present in such drugs as

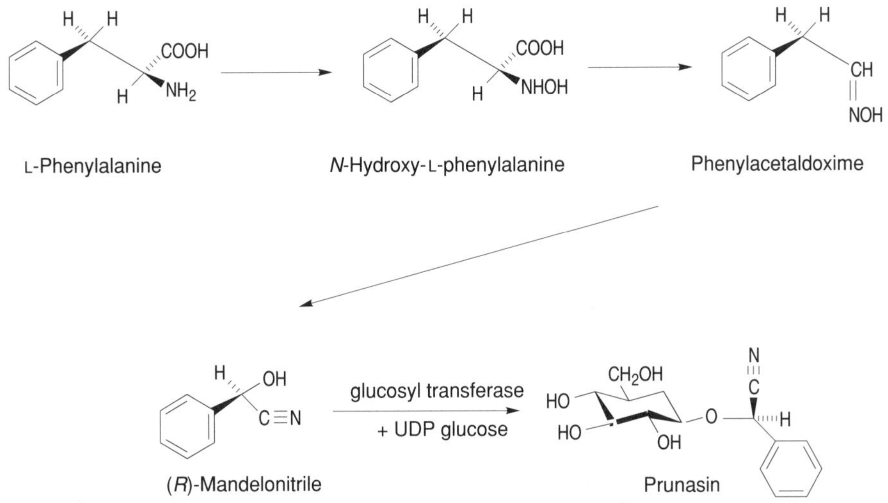

Fig. 4–2. The biosynthetic pathway for the cyanogenic glycoside prunasin.

cascara sagrada, frangula, aloe, rhubarb, and senna. These drugs are used as cathartics. The glycosides, upon hydrolysis, yield aglycones that are di-, tri-, or tetrahydroxyanthraquinones or modifications of these compounds. A typical example is frangulin A, which hydrolyzes to form emodin (1,6,8-trihydroxy-3-methylanthraquinone) and rhamnose. The structural relationships of emodin are shown in Figure 4-3.

Glycosides of anthranols, dianthrones, and oxanthrones (reduced derivatives of anthraquinones) also occur in the plant materials, and they make significant contributions to the therapeutic action of these natural products.

The anthraquinone and related glycosides are stimulant cathartics and exert their action by increasing the tone of the smooth muscle in the wall of the colon and stimulate the secretion of water and electrolytes into the large intestine.

After oral administration, the anthraquinone glycosides are hydrolyzed in the colon by the enzymes of the microflora to the pharmacologically active free aglycones which usually produce their action in 8 to 12 hours after administration. These agents are indicated for constipation in patients who do not respond to milder drugs and for bowel evacuation before investigational procedures or surgery. Stimulant laxatives

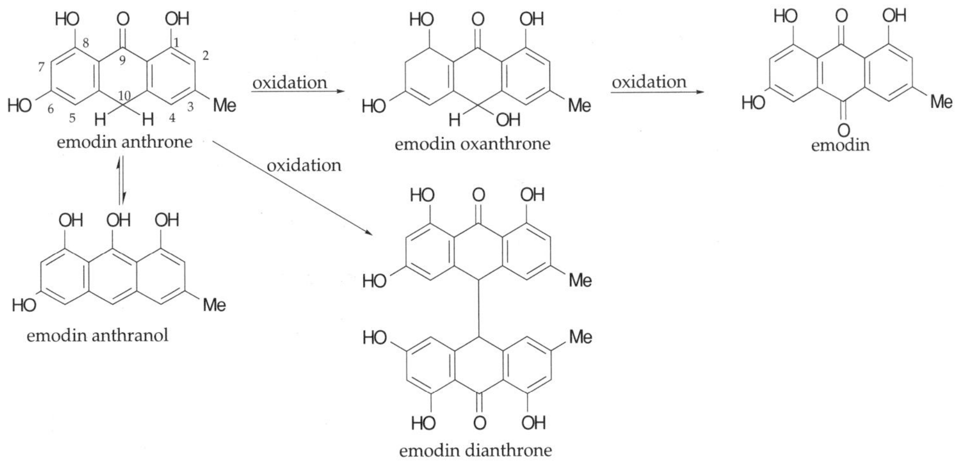

Fig. 4–3. Structure relationships of derivatives of emodin.

are habit-forming, and long-term use may result in laxative dependence and loss of normal bowel function. Glycosides of anthranols and anthrones elicit a more drastic action than do the corresponding anthraquinone glycosides, and a preponderance of the former constituents in the glycosidic mixture can cause discomforting griping action. The drugs of choice are cascara sagrada, frangula, casanthranol, and senna. Aloe and rhubarb are not recommended because they are more irritating which increases the chance for the griping action.

BIOSYNTHESIS OF ANTHRAQUINONE GLYCOSIDES

Much of our knowledge of the biosynthesis of anthraquinones has been obtained from studies of microorganisms. Feedings of labeled acetate to *Penicillium islandicum*, a species that produces several anthraquinone derivatives, have revealed that the distribution of radioactivity in these compounds is consistent with formation via a head-to-tail condensation of acetate units. A poly-β-ketomethylene acid intermediate is probably first produced and then gives rise to the various oxygenated aromatic compounds after intramolecular condensations. Anthranols and anthrones are likely intermediates in the formation of anthraquinones. Presumably, the emodin-like anthraquinones are formed in higher plants by a similar pathway. The transglycosylation reaction, which creates a glycoside, probably occurs at a late stage in the pathway after the anthraquinone nucleus has been formed.

Cascara Sagrada

Cascara sagrada or rhamnus purshiana is the dried bark of *Rhamnus purshianus* DeCandolle (Fam. Rhamnaceae). The species epithet was formerly spelled *purshiana*, and that form is retained in one of the titles applied to the drug. It should be aged for at least 1 year before use in medicinal preparations. Reduced forms of the emodin-type glycosides are present in the fresh bark; during the minimum 1-year storage period, these glycosides are converted to monomeric oxidized glycosides, which exhibit a milder cathartic activity.

The name cascara sagrada is Spanish for sacred bark; *Rhamnus* is the ancient classical name for buckthorn; *purshianus* was given in honor of the German botanist, Friedrich Pursh. The plant is a tree that attains a height of 10 meters and is indigenous to the Pacific Coast of North America. Most of the present-day market supply comes from Oregon, Washington, and southern British Columbia. Collections are made during the summer, beginning at the end of May and continuing until the rainy season starts. The wild trees are scattered in the native forests on the mountains. The bark is stripped from the tree by making longitudinal incisions and peeling off sections that tend to roll into large quills. The trees are often felled, and the bark is removed from the larger branches. The bark is sacked and conveyed to suitable places, often sawmill platforms, for sun drying. The inner surface is not exposed to the sun, however, to retain the yellow color. After the large quills are dried, they are run through a "breaker" and broken into small transversely curved pieces.

Two types of anthracene compounds have been reported: normal *O*-glycosides (based on emodin), about 10 to 20%, and aloinlike *C*-glycosides, representing about 80 to 90% of the total. About a dozen such compounds have been identified. Two of the *C*-glycosides are barbaloin and deoxybarbaloin (chrysaloin). The main active principals are four glycosides designated as cascarosides A, B, C, and D. Cascarosides A and B are based on optical isomers of barbaloin and cascarosides C and D on optical isomers of chrysaloin. All four of the cascarosides, being primary glycosides of barbaloin and chrysaloin, are actually both *O*- and *C*-glycosides. The remaining four to six anthracene derivatives identified in the drug are normal *O*-glycosides, based mostly on emodin. Dried medicinal quality cascara bark yields not less than 7% of total hydroxyanthracene derivatives, calculated as cascaroside A. The cascarosides should make up at least 60% of this total.

Cascaroside A	R = OH, (10*S*)
Cascaroside B	R = OH, (10*R*)
Cascaroside C	R = H, (10*S*)
Cascaroside D	R = H, (10*R*)

Cascara sagrada is a cathartic. Its principal use is in the correction of habitual constipation, where it not only acts as a laxative but restores natural tone to the colon. Cascara sagrada extract, fluidextract, and aromatic fluidextract are obtained by percolating and evaporating coarse powder of the bark. The bitter taste and the activity are considerably reduced by treating cascara sagrada extracts with alkaline earths or magnesium oxide.

Casanthranol is a purified, water-soluble mixture of the anthranol glycosides extracted from cascara sagrada. Each gram of casanthranol contains not less than 200 mg of total hydroxyanthracene derivatives, calculated as cascaroside A, of which not less than 80% of the derivatives consists of cascarosides.

Frangula

Frangula or buckthorn bark is the dried bark of *Rhamnus frangula* Linné. This plant is a shrub that grows in Europe and western Asia. Its laxative effect is due to the presence of anthraquinone glycosides, principally frangulins A and B and the related glucofrangulins A and B. Like cascara, frangula bark should be aged 1 year before use to allow the reduced forms of the glycosides with harsh action to be oxidized to milder forms. The activity of frangula bark corresponds to that of cascara sagrada, and it finds a comparable use in Europe and the Near East. Products from the dried, ripe fruits of *R. catharticus* Linné are also used in these areas for their cathartic action. Other *Rhamnus* species contain anthraquinone glycosides but are not employed in medicine.

Frangulin A   R = H
Glucofrangulin A   R = β-D-glucopyranose

Frangulin B   R = H
Glucofrangulin B   R = β-D-glucopyranose

Aloe

Aloe or aloes is the dried latex (juice) of the leaves of *Aloë barbadensis* Miller (*A. vera*

Linné), known in commerce as Curacao aloe, or of *A. ferox* Miller and hybrids of this species with *A. africana* Miller and *A. spicata* Baker, known in commerce as Cape aloe (Fam. Liliaceae). Aloe yields not less than 50% of water-soluble extractive. *Aloe* is from the Arabic *alloeh* or the Hebrew *halal*, meaning a shining, bitter substance; *vera* is from the Latin *verus*, meaning true. *Barbadensis* refers to the Barbados Islands; *ferox* is from the Latin meaning wild or ferocious; *africana* refers to the habitat of the plant, southern Africa; and *spicata* refers to the flowers in spikes.

About 300 species of *Aloë* are known, most of which are indigenous to Africa. Many have been introduced into the West Indies and Europe. The aloes are typical xerophytic plants that have fleshly leaves, usually have spines at the margins, and resemble to some extent the agave or century plant (*Agave americana* Linné, Fam. Amaryllidaceae).

Aloë barbadensis is a native of northern Africa but was introduced into the Barbados Islands in the 17th century. *A. chinensis*, a variety of *A. barbadensis (A. vera)*, was introduced into Curacao from China in 1817. The drug was cultivated to a considerable extent in Barbados until the middle of the 19th century, but since that time the industry apparently has died out. Curacao aloe, which is often called Barbados aloe, comes from the Dutch islands of Aruba and Bonaire. The leaves are cut in March and April and placed cut-end down on a V-shaped trough. The latter is inclined so that the latex contained in specialized cells just beneath the epidermis of the leaf can be led into the vessel. The latex is evaporated in a copper kettle and, when of the proper consistency, is poured into metal containers and allowed to harden. At the present time, the principal areas of production are Aruba, Bonaire, Haiti, Venezuela, and South Africa. Curacao aloe is the most important form occurring in the United States.

Aloe occurs on the market as opaque masses that range from reddish black to brownish black to dark brown in color. The taste of each variety of aloe is nauseating and bitter. The characteristic odor is disagreeable. This drug is totally different from the colorless mucilaginous gel (aloe vera gel) obtained from the central portion of aloe leaf that is used as a wound healing agent and to treat burns.

Aloe contains a number of anthraquinone glycosides, the principal ones of which are aloins

A and B (formerly designated barbaloin and iso-barbaloin, respectively).

The active constituents of aloe vary qualitatively and quantitatively according to the species from which the drug is obtained.

Aloin A = (10*R*)
Aloin B = (10*S*)

In addition to these physiologically active compounds (10 to 30%), aloe contains inactive ingredients including large amounts (16 to 63%) of a resinous material plus a volatile oil.

Aloe is a pharmaceutic aid for Compound Benzoin Tincture and is also used as a cathartic. Aloe glycosides elicit a drastic cathartic action, and some authorities advocate a preferential use of other cathartic substances.

Aloe Vera Gel

The fresh mucilaginous gel contained in the parenchymatous tissue in the center of the leaves of *Aloë barbadensis (A. vera)* has been used for years in the treatment of burns, abrasions, and other skin irritations.

Commonly referred to as aloe vera gel, a so-called stabilized product is now prepared from the central leaf tissue by many different proprietary or patented methods, some of which involve expression or solvent extraction under harsh conditions. The resulting product is consequently extremely variable. Thus, while scientific studies have substantiated the cell-proliferative (wound-healing) properties of the fresh gel, they have not verified such activity in the "stabilized" product.

Rhubarb

Rhubarb, rheum, or Chinese rhubarb consists of the dried rhizome and root that are deprived of periderm tissues of *Rheum officinale* Baillon, of *R. palmatum* Linné, of other species (except *R. rhaponticum* Linné, the common garden rhubarb plant), or of hybrids of *Rheum* Linné (Fam. Polygonaceae) that are grown in China.

Indian rhubarb or Himalayan rhubarb consists of the dried rhizome and root of *R. emodi* Wallich, of *R. webbianum* Royle, or of some related *Rheum* species that are native to India, Pakistan, or Nepal.

The principal constituents of medicinal rhubarbs are rhein anthrones. Rhubarb has been used in cathartic preparations; the cathartic action is drastic, and the use of other cathartic substances has largely been adopted.

Senna

Senna or senna leaves consists of the dried leaflet of *Cassia acutifolia* Delile, known in commerce as Alexandria senna, or of *C. angustifolia* Vahl, known in commerce as Tinnevelly senna (Fam. Fabaceae). Modern taxonomists tend to lump both species together under one name *Senna alexandrina* Mill. The name *Senna* is from the Arabic *sena,* the native name of the drug; *Cassia* is from the Hebrew *qetsiah,* meaning to cut off, and refers to the fact that the bark of some of the species was once peeled off and used (the application of the name *cassia* to cinnamon barks should be noted); *acutifolia* is Latin and refers to the sharply pointed leaflets; and *angustifolia* means narrow-leaved. The plants are low-branching shrubs; *C. acutifolia* grows wild near the Nile River from Aswan to Kordofan, and *C. angustifolia* grows wild in Somalia, the Arabian peninsula, and India. Most of the commercial supply of the drug is collected from plants cultivated in southern India (Tinnevelly); some material is also produced in the Jammu district of India and in northwest Pakistan.

Alexandria senna is harvested in April and in September by cutting off the tops of the plants about 15 cm above the ground and drying them in the sun. Afterward, the stems and pods are separated from the leaflets by using sieves. The portion that passes through the sieves is then "tossed." The leaves work to the surface, and the heavier stalk fragments sink to the bottom. The leaves are then graded and baled or packed in bags. This process of collection and separation accounts for the large number of broken leaves in Alexandria senna. This drug was formerly shipped via Alexandria but is now distributed through Port Sudan on the Red Sea.

Tinnevelly senna is gathered by hand and dried in the sun, then carefully baled and shipped primarily from the port of Tuticorin. It is cultivated in nearby areas to which the term "Tinnevelly" is applied. Senna is cultivated on wet lands resembling rice paddies; in fact, rice is often one crop of the season, and senna is a later crop of the same season. The poorer grades of senna are grown on dry land without irrigation. Senna is graded according to the size of the leaf and the color of the leaflets: blue-green leaves are best, yellowish leaves are poorest.

Sennoside A

Senna was introduced into European medicine in the 9th or 10th century by the Arabians. Its native use seems to antedate historical record. According to Isaac Judaeus, a native of Egypt who lived about 850 to 900 A.D., senna was brought to Egypt from Mecca.

The principal active constituents of senna are dimeric glycosides whose aglycones are composed of aloe-emodin and/or rhein. Those present in greatest concentration are sennosides A and B, a pair of stereoisomers whose aglycones are rhein dianthrone (sennidin A and B). Small quantities of monomeric glycosides and free anthraquinones are also present. Senna pods also contain useful, active glycosides; some of the primary glycosides in the pods have as many as ten sugar molecules attached to a rhein dianthrone nucleus. Although senna is not as mild in laxative action as cascara, producing more griping action, it is widely used because it is less expensive.

A concentrate of the active constituents and an isolated mixture of sennosides, which may be prepared from either the leaves or the pods, are used in various products, some of which contain a senna component combined with a hydrocolloid or a surfactant.

SAPONIN GLYCOSIDES

This group of glycosides is widely distributed in the higher plants. Saponins form colloidal so-

lutions in water that foam upon shaking; they have a bitter, acrid taste, and drugs containing them are usually sternutatory and otherwise irritating to the mucous membrane. They destroy red blood corpuscles by hemolysis and are toxic, especially to cold-blooded animals. Many saponins are used as fish poisons. Upon hydrolysis they yield an aglycone known as a "sapogenin." The sapogenin portion can be one of two possible chemical classes either steroid or triterpenoid. Triterpenoid saponins are the most widely distributed in nature with more than 360 different sapogenins representing 750 different glycosides. Because these aglycones have a large number of carbon atoms (C_{27} to C_{30}) making them lipophilic, the saponin molecule due to the water-soluble sugars has a hydrophilic/hydrophobic asymmetry that results in the compounds lowering surface tension in aqueous solution, hence, the foaming upon shaking. The sapogenins form readily crystallizable compounds upon acetylization. This process can be used to purify sapogenins.

Much of the research conducted on the saponin-containing plants was motivated by the attempt to discover precursors for the partial synthesis of steroid hormones. Because animal sources for the steroid hormones are in limited supply, academic, industrial, and governmental research agencies have examined many species of plants, particularly those containing steroidal sapogenins. After many years of investigation, the most important plant steroids for the partial synthesis of steroid hormones are diosgenin and botogenin from the genus *Dioscorea*; hecogenin, manogenin, and gitogenin from species of *Agave*; sarsasapogenin and smilagenin from the genus *Smilax*; and sitosterol from crude vegetable oils.

The more poisonous saponins are often called "sapotoxins." Many are toxic to insects and mollusks, and some have been used for controlling schistosomiasis snails. From the medicinal viewpoint, the most widely used saponin-containing drugs are glycyrrhiza and ginseng.

Glycyrrhiza

Glycyrrhiza is the dried rhizome and roots of *Glycyrrhiza glabra* Linné, known in commerce as Spanish licorice, or of *G. glabra* Linné var. *glandulifera* Waldstein et Kitaibel, known in commerce as Russian licorice, or of other varieties of *G. glabra* Linné that yield a yellow and sweet wood (Fam. Fabaceae). *Glycyrrhiza* is of Greek origin and means sweet root; *glabra* means smooth and refers to the smooth, pod-like fruit of this species. The fruit in the variety *glandulifera* has gland-like swellings. Glycyrrhiza is also called **licorice root.**

At the end of the third or fourth year, the rhizome and roots are dug, preferably in the autumn and from plants that have not borne fruit, thereby ensuring maximum sweetness of the sap. The washed material is air-dried (4 to 6 months) and packed into bales or cut and tied into short cylindric bundles. The large thick roots of Russian licorice are peeled before drying. In Turkey, Spain, and Israel, a considerable amount of the crop is extracted with water, the liquid is clarified and evaporated, and the resulting black pilular extract is molded into sticks or other forms. Glycyrrhiza contains a saponinlike glycoside, glycyrrhizin (glycyrrhizic acid),

Glycyrrhizin

which is 50 times as sweet as sugar. Upon hydrolysis, the glycoside loses its sweet taste and is converted to the aglycone glycyrrhetic acid (glycyrrhetinic acid) plus two molecules of glucuronic acid. Glycyrrhetic acid (3β-hydroxy-11-oxoolean-12-en-29-oic acid) is a pentacyclic triterpene derivative of the β-amyrin type. Other constituents include flavonoid glycosides, (liquiritin, isoliquiritin, liquiritoside, isoliquiritoside, rhamnoliquiritin, and rhamnoisoliquiritin), coumarin derivatives (herniarin and umbelliferone), asparagine, 22,23-dihydrostigmasterol, glucose, mannitol, and about 20% of starch. Reports of estrogens in the plant appear to be based on low-level estrogenlike activity of other constituents.

Glycyrrhiza possesses demulcent and expectorant properties. It is used considerably as a flavoring agent and masks the taste of bitter drugs such as aloe, ammonium chloride, quinine, and others; the surfactant property of the saponins may also facilitate absorption of poorly absorbed drugs, such as the anthraquinone gly-

cosides. Commercially, licorice is added to chewing gums, chocolate candy, cigarettes, smoking mixtures, chewing tobacco, and snuff; when it is added to beer, it increases the foaminess; when it is added to root beer, stout, and porter, it imparts a bitter taste.

Pharmacologic studies of licorice have been extensive in recent years, particularly in Europe. As a result, glycyrrhetic acid is used there in dermatologic practice for its anti-inflammatory properties, and licorice root extract is employed in the treatment of peptic ulcer and Addison's disease (chronic adrenocortical insufficiency).

Glycyrrhizin increases fluid and sodium retention and promotes potassium depletion. Persons with cardiac problems and hypertension should avoid consumption of significant quantities of licorice.

Ginseng

Ginseng is the root of the perennial herbs *Panax quinquefolius* Linné and *Panax ginseng* C.A. Mey (Fam. Araliaceae). The former is known as American ginseng. It grows in rich woods in the eastern United States and Canada; the latter, designated Asian ginseng, is indigenous to the mountainous forests of eastern Asia. The roots are gathered from 3- to 6-year-old plants and carefully cleaned and dried.

American ginseng has been collected from wild plants and from cultivated stands and has been exported to China since the early 1700s. A ship sailed from Boston for China in 1773 with 55 tons of ginseng. The plant is now an endangered species in the United States. Its collection and sale are subject to registration, permits, reports, and an official ginseng season. Collector education is also mandatory. Cultivated Asian ginseng is produced in Korea, Japan, and the former Soviet Union. American ginseng is grown in the United States, primarily in Wisconsin, and in Canada.

Ginseng contains a complex mixture of triterpenoid saponins that can be either steroidal triterpenes or pentacyclic related to oleanoic acid. These glycosides have been categorized into three series: the ginsenosides, the panaxosides, and the chikusetsusaponins. Ginsenoside Rg_1, one of the major saponins found in ginseng, is an example of a glycoside with a steroidal triterpene aglycone, (20S)-protopanaxatriol. One or more of these groups of glycosides appear to account for the biologic properties of ginseng.

Ginseng is a favorite remedy in Chinese medicine and is considered to have tonic, stimulant, diuretic, and carminative properties. It reportedly has adaptogenic (antistress) activity and also acts favorably on metabolism, the central nervous system, and endocrine secretions. It is employed in the Orient in the treatment of anemia, diabetes, insomnia, neurasthenia, gastritis, and, especially, sexual impotence.

Ginsenoside Rg₁

Western interest in the drug has vastly increased, and ginseng has become widely available in ''health-food'' outlets. Widespread use has been accompanied by a veritable deluge of literature pertaining to the product and its purported activity.

Pharmacologically speaking, ginseng is classified as an adaptogen because some studies in animals suggest that it may help the body adapt to stress and correct adrenal and thyroid dysfunctions. Such effects, if real, are subtle but are apparently a function of the ginsenoside saponin glycosides contained in the root. Ginseng is also heavily promoted as an aphrodisiac and a performance and endurance enhancer. The drug is administered in such forms as powders, extracts, and teas.

Because of the high cost of ginseng products and almost total lack of quality control in the ''health food'' industry, studies performed have shown great variations in the ginsenoside glycoside content of various preparations. In view of such problems, persons purchasing ginseng products are best advised to obtain dosage forms standardized on the basis of their ginsenoside content. The FDA found no evidence of enhanced sexual experience or potency resulting from its use, but these findings are a result of lack of data submitted to that agency for evaluation.

CYANOGENIC GLYCOSIDES

Several glycosides yielding hydrocyanic acid (HCN) as one of the products of hydrolysis are commonly found in plants. They are designated as cyanogenic glycosides and are accompanied in the plant by enzymes (β-glucosidases) that catalyze the hydrolysis.

Some common cyanogenic glycosides are derivatives of mandelonitrile (benzaldehyde-cyanohydrin). The group is represented by amygdalin, which is found in large quantities in bitter almonds, in kernels of apricots, cherries, peaches, plums, and in many other seeds of the Rosaceae, and also by prunasin, which occurs in *Prunus serotina*. Both amygdalin and prunasin yield (*R*)-mandelonitrile as the aglycone. Sambunigrin from *Sambucus nigra* liberates (*S*)-mandelonitrile as its aglycone.

The enzymatic hydrolysis of amygdalin takes place in three steps (Fig. 4-4). The β-glucosidase emulsion has been separated into three different enzyme activities, amygdalin hydrolase that catalyzes the breakdown of amygdalin to glucose and prunasin, prunasin hydrolase that hydrolyzes prunasin to glucose and mandelonitrile, and mandelonitrile lyase that catalyzes the dissociation of mandelonitrile to HCN and benzaldehyde.

Cyanogenesis has been demonstrated in over 3,000 plant species belonging to 110 plant families. In these plants, β-glucosidases and the cyanogenic glycosides are present in different cellular compartments. The compartmentalization has to be disrupted for the enzyme and the substrate to come in contact and lead to cyanogenesis. This suggests that cyanogenesis is a chemical defense response to organisms damaging the plant tissue when feeding on intact plant parts or attacking the plant through a site of injury.

Preparations from plant materials containing cyanogenic glycosides are widely employed as flavoring agents. Anticancer claims have also been made for an amygdalin-containing preparation known as laetrile or vitamin B₁₇, and the possibility for control of sickle cell anemia with cyanogenic glycosides has been noted. The FDA has not recognized the efficacy of laetrile for treatment of cancer.

Wild Cherry

Wild Cherry is the carefully dried stem bark of *Prunus serotina* Ehrhart (Fam. Rosaceae). *Prunus* is the classic name of the plum tree; *sero-*

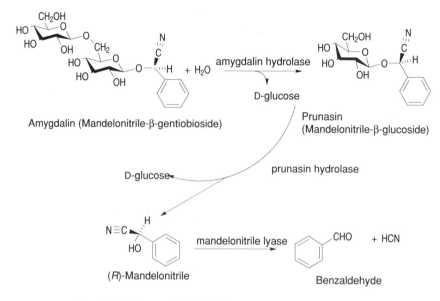

Fig. 4–4. Enzymatic hydrolysis (cyanogenesis) of amygdalin.

tina means late or backward, referring to the time of flowering and fruiting of the species. Wild Cherry is known as **prunus virginiana** and as **wild black cherry tree**.

The plant is a tree that grows to a height of 30 meters or more in the eastern United States and Canada. The commercial supplies of the drug come chiefly from Tennessee, Mississippi, Virginia, and North Carolina.

Wild cherry bark was used by the Indians, and no doubt the early settlers learned its use from them. It has long enjoyed popular usage in domestic medicine.

Wild cherry bark contains a cyanogenic glycoside, prunasin [(*R*)-mandelonitrile glucoside], a compound formed by the partial hydrolysis of amygdalin (Fig. 4-4).

Other constituents include the hydrolytic enzyme prunase, *p*-coumaric acid, trimethyl gallic acid, starch, and traces of a volatile oil. The yield of hydrocyanic acid varies from 0.23 to 0.32% in inner bark, 0.03% in trunk bark, and varies even in bark of the same thickness from the same tree.

Wild cherry, in the syrup form, is used as a flavored vehicle, especially in cough remedies. It has been considered a sedative expectorant.

Apricot Pits

Kernels of varieties of *Prunus armeniaca* Linné (Fam. Rosaceae), commonly referred to as *apricot pits*, are sold in "health food" stores throughout the United States as a source of laetrile or amygdalin, which exists to the extent of about 3%. Technically, laetrile and amygdalin are not synonymous; the former is supposedly (−)-mandelonitrile-β-glucuronoside. However, because the product now offered as an anticancer agent is primarily amygdalin, the two names can be used interchangeably.

Controversy of an emotional and political nature has raged in recent years regarding the effectiveness of laetrile in treating cancer patients, particularly those who are terminally ill. Its purported mechanism of action, a selective release of cyanide or a toxic cyanide-containing compound in the cancer cells without injury to other normal cells or tissues, has never been proved. The FDA banned laetrile from interstate commerce in 1971; however, a number of states have since declared that intrastate production and sale are legal.

In 1981, the results were published of an extensive study conducted by the National Cancer Institute in collaboration with four major U.S. medical centers. They found laetrile and natural products containing it, such as apricot pits, were an ineffective treatment for cancer.

Still the use of laetrile continues to a limited extent. Because of the federal ban, pure amygdalin for drug purposes is not readily available in the United States. As a consequence, patients have turned to the acquisition and use of apricot kernels as a source of the drug. This is a dangerous practice for, in addition to the amygdalin, the pits contain emulsin, an enzyme that hydrolyzes the glycoside, releasing toxic cyanide as detailed in Figure 4-4. Deaths have been reported from the ingestion of apricot pits. Although the emulsin may be inactivated by heating, complete inactivation is always uncertain. Even if inactivation is accomplished, the user may not realize that other sources of emulsin, e.g., almonds, must be avoided. Further, evidence now obtained from small-animal experimentation indicates that amygdalin alone, without the action of exogenous β-glycosidases, causes cyanide toxicity.

Because the treatment is ineffective and carries considerable potential danger, the use of apricot pits as an anticancer drug must be considered irrational. Their use should be avoided.

ISOTHIOCYANATE GLYCOSIDES

The seeds of several mustard family plants contain glycosides, the aglycones of which are isothiocyanates. These glycosides are also termed **glucosinolates** and represent a group of bound toxins, like the cyanogenic glycosides. Upon hydrolysis by the enzyme myrosinase, glucosinolates yield D-glucose and a labile aglycone that spontaneously rearranges with the loss of sulfate to give an isothiocyanate as the major product. The significant features of the structure of glucosinolates (Fig. 4-5) are a sulfur atom conjugated to glucose as the *S*-glycoside and a second sulfur present in a sulfonated oxime grouping. The aglycones may be either aliphatic or aromatic derivatives formed from amino acids in the plant. The currently accepted biosynthetic pathway involves *N*-hydroxylation and oxidative decarboxylation to yield an aldoxime intermediate.

Glucosinlates have a distribution limited to a few plant families and are characteristic constituents of the mustard family (Brassicaceae) which includes oilseeds (rapeseed), condiments (mustard and horseradish), and vegetables (broccoli, cabbage, and turnips). In plants they play a major role as feeding deterrents against both insects and mammals.

Mustard family vegetables have been found to have anticarcinogenic properties. For example, indole-3-carbinol derived from indolylmethyl glucosinolate which is widely distributed in mustard family vegetables has been shown to reduce risk of estradiol-linked mammary cancer. In addition, 4-methylsulfinyl isothiocyanate isolated from broccoli has been shown to induce anticarcinogenic protective enzymes.

Principal among the glycosides are sinigrin from black mustard, sinalbin from white mustard, and gluconapin from rape seed. When hydrolyzed by the enzyme myrosinase, they yield the mustard oils. Although the fixed oil content of these seeds exceeds the amount of the volatile oil developed on hydrolysis, the activity is caused by the latter.

Mustard

Black mustard, sinapis nigra, or brown mustard is the dried ripe seed of varieties of *Brassica nigra* (Linné) Koch or of *B. juncea* (Linné) Czerniaew or of varieties of these species (Fam. Brassicaceae). *Brassica* is from the Celtic *bresic*, meaning cabbage; *juncea* is from the Latin, meaning rush or reed; and *nigra* is from the Latin, meaning black. The term *mustard* is believed to be derived from the use of the seed as a condiment. The sweet *must* of old wine was mixed with crushed seeds to form a paste called "mustum ardens" (hot must); hence the name "mustard."

The plants are annual herbs that have slender erect stems, yellow flowers, pinnatifid leaves, and somewhat four-sided siliques with short

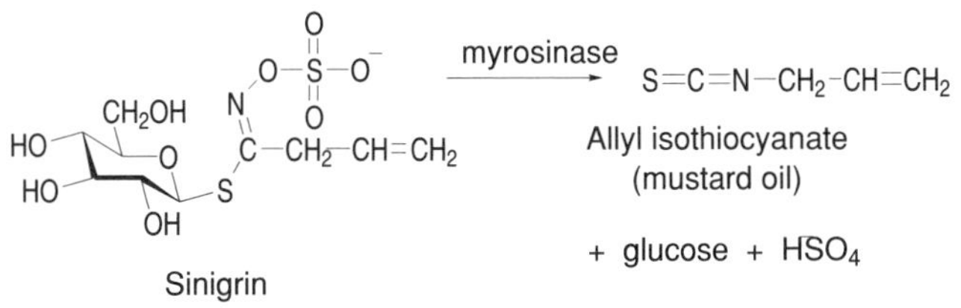

Fig. 4–5. Hydrolysis of sinigrin.

stalks. They are native to Europe and southwestern Asia but are naturalized and cultivated in temperate climates in many countries and show considerable variations in form. *B. nigra* is cultivated in England and on the continent, and *B. juncea* is cultivated in India. Black mustard is mentioned in an edict of Diocletian (301 A.D.) as a condiment, and both Theophrastus and Pliny mention its use in medicine. During the Middle Ages it was an accompaniment to salted meats. The popularity of mustard as a condiment has by no means diminished.

Although black mustard contains fixed oil (30 to 35%), its principal constituent is the glycoside sinigrin, which is accompanied (probably in adjacent cells) by the enzyme myrosinase. Upon the addition of water to the crushed or powdered seeds, the myrosinase effects the hydrolysis of the sinigrin, as shown in Figure 4-5. The allyl isothiocyanate produced is volatile; it is commonly called volatile mustard oil.

Black mustard is a local irritant and an emetic. Externally, the drug is a rubefacient and vesicant. Commercially, it is used as a condiment.

White Mustard

White mustard or sinapis alba consists of the dried, ripe seeds of *Brassica alba* (Linné) Hooker filius (Fam. Brassicaceae). White mustard is as commercially important as black mustard. The plant resembles that of *B. nigra* but is usually considerably shorter, and its siliques are more rounded and tapered. Like black mustard, it is cultivated in temperate climates all over the world.

White mustard contains the enzyme myrosinase, and a glucoside, sinalbin, which, upon hydrolysis, yields *p*-hydroxybenzyl isothiocyanate, a pungent-tasting but almost odorless oil that is much less volatile than allyl isothiocyanate. It also contains 20 to 25% of fixed oil.

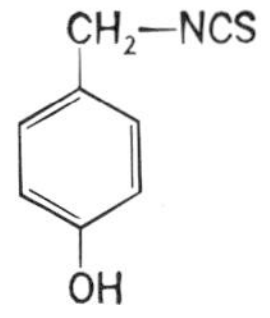

P-Hydroxybenzyl isothiocyanate

OTHER ORGANOSULFUR DRUGS

Garlic

Garlic consists of the bulb of *Allium sativum* Linné (Fam. Liliaceae) and has been consumed both as a food and a medicine since the time of the Pharaohs. The intact cells of garlic contain the odorless, sulfur-containing amino acid derivative (+)-*S*-allyl-L-cysteine sulfoxide. This compound is commonly known as alliin and occurs in garlic in a concentration of up to 1.2% of fresh weight. When the cells are crushed, it comes into contact with the enzyme alliinase which is stored in vacuoles within the cell and is converted to allicin (diallyl thiosulfinate) as illustrated in Figure 4-6. Allicin has potent antibacterial activity. Unfortunately, it is also the compound responsible for the characteristic odor and flavor of garlic, decomposing readily in the presence of air and water to yield diallyl disulfide, diallyl trisulfide, and the correspond-

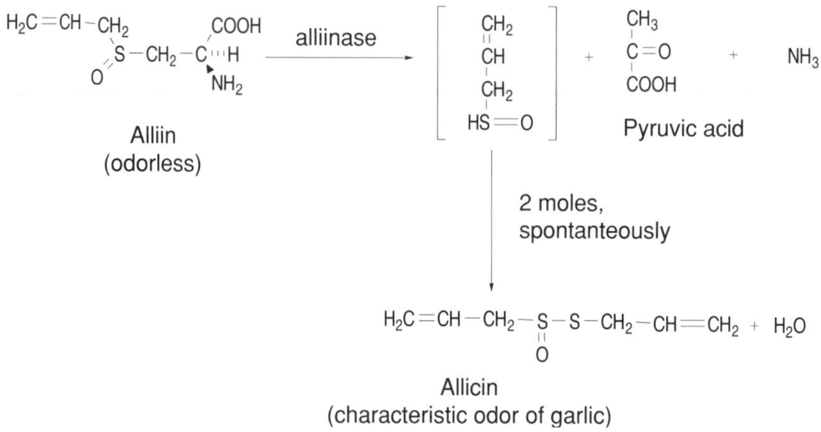

Fig. 4–6. Formation of allicin in *Allium* species.

ning polysulfides, all of which are strong smelling compounds. In addition to antibacterial activity, garlic possesses antihyperlipidemic activity and enhances blood fibrinolytic activity and inhibits platelet aggregation. (*E*)-Ajoene and (*Z*)-ajoene are formed from allicin and have antithrombotic properties with the *Z* isomer being the more bioactive. Studies indicate the mode of action involves inhibition of fibrinogen receptors on blood platelets.

Most authorities agree that the best measure of the total activity of garlic is its ability to produce allicin which, in turn, results in the formation of other active principles. There is some debate as to the daily amount of fresh garlic required to achieve a beneficial therapeutic effect. Daily doses with a range of one to five cloves (4 g fresh weight per clove) have been recommended. With commercial garlic preparations there is a great variation in their ability to yield allicin because the mode of preparation greatly influences the stability of alliin and alliinase. Enteric coated tablets or capsules have enhanced activity because stomach acid inactivates alliinase, thus preventing the conversion of the inactive alliin to the bioactive products. A recent study in Germany of garlic preparations available in that country revealed that only about one-quarter produced an allicin yield equivalent to 4 g of fresh garlic (one clove).

(*Z*)-Ajoene

2-Propenyl 3-(2-propenylsulfinyl)-1-propenyl disulfide

ALCOHOL GLYCOSIDES

Salicin

Salicin is a glycoside obtained from several species of *Salix* and *Populus*. Most willow and poplar barks yield salicin, but the principal sources are *Salix purpurea* and *S. fragilis*. The glycoside populin (benzoylsalicin) is also associated with salicin in the barks of the Salicaceae.

Salicin   Saligenin

Salicin is hydrolyzed into D-glucose and saligenin (salicyl alcohol) by emulsin. Salicin has antirheumatic properties. Its action closely resembles that of salicylic acid, and it is probably oxidized to salicylic acid in the human system. Recognition of the properties of salicin clarifies many folkloric uses of poplar and willow barks.

ALDEHYDE GLYCOSIDES

Vanilla is a drug that has an aldehydic aglycone as its chief constituent. **Vanillin** is the aglycone developed during the curing of vanilla beans. Vanillin is methylprotocatechuic aldehyde.

Vanilla

Vanilla or vanilla bean is the cured, full-grown unripe fruit of *Vanilla planifolia* Andrews, often known in commerce as Mexican or Bourbon vanilla, or of *V. tahitensis* J. W. Moore, known in commerce as Tahiti vanilla (Fam. Orchidaceae). *Vanilla* is from the Spanish *vania*, sheathlike pod, and *illa*, meaning small; *planifolia* is from the Latin *planus*, meaning flat, and *folium*, meaning leaf; *tahitensis* refers to Tahiti, its adopted home.

The plants are perennial, climbing, dioecious epiphytes attached to the trunks of trees by means of aerial rootlets. The plant is native to the woods of eastern Mexico but is cultivated in tropical countries where the temperature does not fall below 18° C and where the humidity is high.

The plant usually propagated by means of cutting and , after 2 to 3 years, reaches the flowering stage. It continues to bear fruit from 30 to 40 years. The flowers, approximately 30 on each plant, are hand pollinated, thus producing larger and better fruits. The fruits are collected as they ripen to a yellow color, 6 to 10 months after pollination, and are cured by dipping in warm water and repeated sweating between woolen blankets in the sun during the day and packing in wool-covered boxes at night. This requires about 2 months, during which time the pods lose from 70 to 80% of their original weight and take on the characteristic color and odor of the commercial drug. The pods are then graded, tied into bundles of about 50 to 75, and sealed in tin containers for shipment.

The Spaniards found that the Aztecs of Mexico used vanilla as a flavoring for cocoa and consequently introduced its use into Europe. Cultivation began in Réunion and Madagascar in 1839, and shortly after, other countries adopted this practice.

Green vanilla contains two glycosides, glucovanillin (avenein) and glucovanillic alcohol. Glucovanillin is hydrolyzed by an enzyme during the curing process into glucose and vanillin, and glucovanillic alcohol is similarly hydrolyzed into glucose and vanillic alcohol, which is, in turn, oxidized to vanillic aldehyde (vanillin). Vanillin is the principal flavoring constituent. Vanilla also contains about 10% of sugar, 10% of fixed oil, and calcium oxalate. Vanilla, in the form of vanilla tincture, is used as a flavoring agent and as a pharmaceutic aid. It is a source of vanillin.

Coniferyl alcohol   Vanillin   Isoeugenol

Vanillin is 4-hydroxy-3-methoxybenzaldehyde or methylprocatechuic aldehyde. It may be obtained from vanilla or prepared synthetically from other sources: (1) coniferin, a glycoside present in the cambium sap of pine trees; (2) eugenol, a phenol present in clove oil; and (3) lignin, a by-product of the pulp industry. Most of the vanillin in commerce is made from lignin.

Vanillin consists of fine, white to slightly yellow, needle-like crystals that have an odor and a taste resembling vanilla. It is slightly soluble in water and glycerin and is freely soluble in alcohol, chloroform, and ether. Vanillin is employed as a flavoring agent.

PHENOL GLYCOSIDES

The aglycone groups of many of the naturally occurring glycosides are phenolic in character. Thus, arbutin, found in uva ursi, chimaphila, and other ericaceous drugs, yields hydroquinone and glucose upon hydrolysis. Hesperidin, which occurs in various citrus fruits, may be classified as a phenol glycoside. Phloridzin, found in the root bark of rosaceous plants, baptisin from *Baptisia*, and iridin from *Iris* species are additional examples of phenol glycosides.

Arbutin   Hydroquinone   Glucose

Uva Ursi

Uva ursi or bearberry is the dried leaf of *Arctostaphylos uva-ursi* (Linné) Sprengel or its varieties *coactylis* or *adenotricha* Fernald and MacBride (Fam. Ericaceae). The plant is a procumbent evergreen shrub indigenous to Europe, Asia, and the northern United States and Canada.

In addition to the glycoside arbutin, the leaves contain corilagin, pyroside, several esters of arbutin, quercitin, gallic acid, elagic acid, and ursolic acid.

Uva ursi has a long history of use for its antiseptic and astringent properties. Extract of uva ursi was formerly an ingredient in some proprietary formulations, but its use in prescription medications has been replaced by more effective urinary antiseptics. The inclusion of uva ursi and diuretic materials in various products intended for weight reduction is without recognized merit.

SUGGESTED READINGS

Anon: Aloe update. Lawrence Rev. Nat. Prod., 3:81, 1982.

Britton, G.: *The Biochemistry of Natural Pigments.* Cambridge, Cambridge University Press, 1983.

Cheeke, P.R., ed.: *Toxicants of Plant Origin,* Vol.II. Boca Raton, Florida, CRC Press, Inc., 1989.

Ciba Foundation Symposium: 140, *Cyanide Compounds in Biology.* Chichester, UK, John Wiley & Sons Ltd., 1988.

Cutler, H.G., ed.: *Biologically Active Natural Products: Potential Use in Agriculture.* Washington, DC, American Chemical Society, 1988.

Esen, A., ed.: *β-Glucosidases: Biochemistry and Molecular Biology.* Washington, DC, American Chemical Society, 1993.

Glasby, J. S.: *Encyclopedia of the Terpenoids*, Vols. I-II. Chichester, England, John Wiley & Sons Ltd., 1982.

Hiller, K.: New Results on the Structure and Biological Activity of Triterpenoid Saponins. In *Biologically Active Natural Products.* Hostettmann, K., and Lea, P.J., eds. Oxford, Oxford University Press, 1987.

Mussinan, C.J., Keelan, M.E., eds.: *Sulfur Compounds in Foods.* Washington, DC, American Chemical Society, 1994.

Poulton, J.E.: Cyanogenic Compounds in Plants and Their Toxic Effects. In *Handbook of Natural Toxins*, Vol. 1. Keeler, R.F., Tu, A.T., eds. New York, Marcel Dekker, Inc., 1983.

Shibata, S., Tanaka, O., Shoji, J., Saito, H.: Chemistry and Pharmacology of *Panax*, In *Economic and Medicinal Plant Reseach*, Vol. 1. Wagner, H., Hikino, H., Farnsworth, N.R., eds., Orlando, Academic Press, Inc., 1985.

Thomson, R.H.: *Naturally Occurring Quinones,* 2nd ed. New York, Academic Press, Inc., 1971.

Thomson, R.H.: *Naturally Occurring Quinones III, Recent Advances.* London, Chapman and Hall Ltd., 1987.

5

Lipids

Lipids (fixed oils, fats, and waxes) are esters of long-chain fatty acids and alcohols, or of closely related derivatives. The chief difference between these substances is the type of alcohol; in fixed oils and fats, glycerol combines with the fatty acids; in waxes, the alcohol has a higher molecular weight, e.g., cetyl alcohol.

Fats and fixed oils are obtained from either plants (olive oil, peanut oil) or animals (lard). Their primary function is food (energy) storage. The fixed oils and fats are important products used pharmaceutically, industrially, and nutritionally. Waxes may also be of plant or animal origin. Many drugs contain fixed oils and fats as their principal constituents; the fixed oils and fats are often separated from the crude vegetable drugs (by expression) or the crude animal drug (by rendering or extraction) and are employed as drugs in the refined state.

Fixed oils and fats differ only as to melting point; those that are liquid at normal temperatures are known as fatty or fixed oils; whereas those that are semisolid or solid at ordinary temperatures are known as fats. Although most vegetable oils are liquid at ordinary temperatures and most animal fats are solid, there are notable exceptions, such as coconut oil, which is a solid vegetable oil in temperate climates and a liquid in its tropical region of origin, and cod liver oil, which is a liquid animal fat.

The United States Pharmacopeia includes several tests that determine the identity, quality, and purity of fixed oils. These tests are based on the chemical constitution of the fatty acids. The **acid value** or **acid number** (the number of milligrams of potassium hydroxide required to neutralize the free fatty acids in 1 g of the substance) indicates the amount of free fatty acids present in the oil; the **saponification value** indicates the number of milligrams of potassium hydroxide required to neutralize the free acids and

saponify the esters contained in 1 g of the substance; and the **iodine number** (the number of grams of iodine absorbed, under prescribed conditions, by 100 g of the substance) indicates the degree of unsaturation. Other physical constants, such as melting point, specific gravity, and refractive index, also serve as identity, purity, and quality tests.

Fixed oils and fats of vegetable origin are obtained by expression in hydraulic presses. If the expression is carried out in the cold, the oil is known as a ''virgin oil'' or a ''cold-pressed oil.'' In contrast, if the expression is carried out in heat, the oil is known as a ''hot-pressed oil.'' Sometimes organic solvents are used for the extraction of oils. Animal fats are separated from other tissues by rendering with steam, with or without pressure. The heat melts the fat, which rises to the top and may be separated by decantation. Oils may be further clarified by filtration and bleached with ozone. Stearins are often removed by chilling and filtration.

Vegetable oils and fats may occur in various parts of the plant, but as a general rule, seeds contain larger quantities of fats and oils than other plant parts. Seeds are the usual source of fixed oils; as a few examples, the following might be mentioned: cottonseed, linseed, sesame seed, rapeseed, coconut, castor beans, almond, and others. In a few instances, other plants parts yield considerable quantities of fixed oil (pericarp of the olive).

Chemically, the fixed oils and fats are composed predominately of triacylglycerols which have different or identical fatty acids esterified to the three hydroxyl positions on the glycerol molecule. These compounds are also known as triglycerides, but this designation is discouraged because taken literally it connotes that three glycerol residues are present, and this is not the

Table 5–1

Names, Structures, and Symbols for Important Higher Fatty Acids

Trivial Name	Systematic Name	Structure	Symbol
Lauric acid	Dodecanoic acid	$Me(CH_2)_{10}COOH$	12:0
Myristic acid	Tetradecanoic acid	$Me(CH_2)_{12}COOH$	14:0
Palmitic acid	Hexadecanoic acid	$Me(CH_2)_{14}COOH$	16:0
Stearic acid	Octadecanoic acid	$Me(CH_2)_{16}COOH$	18:0
Oleic acid	(Z)-9-Octadecenoic acid		18:1 (9Z) or (n-9)
Linoleic acid	(Z,Z)-9,12-Octadecadienoic acid		18:2 (9Z,12Z) or (n-6)
α-Linolenic acid	(Z,Z,Z)-9,12,15-Octadecatrienoic acid		18:3 (9Z,12Z,15Z) or (n-3)
γ-Linolenic acid	(Z,Z,Z)-6,9,12-Octadecatrienoic acid		18:3 (6Z,9Z,12Z) or (n-6)
Arachidonic acid	(Z,Z,Z,Z)-5,8,11,14-Eicosatetraenoic acid		20:4 (5Z,8Z,11Z,14Z) or (n-6)
Erucic acid	(Z)-13-Docosenoic acid		22:1 (13Z) or (n-9)
Ricinoleic acid	[R-(Z)]-12-Hydroxy-9-octadecenoic acid		—

case. The general formula of acylglycerols is as follows:

$$CH_2—O—CO—R$$
$$|$$
$$CH—O—CO—R'$$
$$|$$
$$CH_2—O—CO—R''$$

If R, R', and R'' are the same fatty acid radical, the compound is a simple triacylglycerol. Because triacylglycerols are named on the basis of the acyl moieties, if oleic acid contributes the acyl moiety, for example, the compound is named either trioleoylglycerol, glycerol trioleate, or triolein, the first name being preferred. If R, R', and R'' are different fatty acids, a mixed compound results, and if the position of substitution on the three carbons of glycerol is known, it is indicated in the name, for example, 1,2-dipalmitoyl-3-stearoylglycerol where two molecules of palmitic acid and one of stearic acid contribute the acyl moieties. The composition of the triacylglycerols in any fixed oil or fat is influenced by the amount of various fatty acids that are present during formation. Thus, the composition of fixed oils and fats from any source can vary within certain limits.

The term **fatty acid** designates any one of the aliphatic monocarboxylic acids that can be liberated by hydrolysis from naturally occurring fats and oils. The major fatty acids can be saturated or unsaturated with an unbranched even-numbered carbon chain. Some of the more common fatty acids are illustrated in Table 5–1. The saturated fatty acids—lauric, myristic, palmitic, and stearic; and the unsaturated fatty acids—oleic, linoleic, and linolenic together account for almost all of the fatty acid content of commercial fats and fixed oils. Usually, the triacylglycerols of unsaturated fatty acids are liquid, whereas the triacylglycerols of saturated fatty acids of sufficient chain length are solid. The predominance of either type in an oil determines whether the mixture is liquid or solid.

Many fatty acids have common names derived from the source of the oil or fat from which the fatty acid was originally isolated. Thus, palmitic acid is named after palm oil, and oleic acid is named after olive oil. All of the fatty acids have systematic names based on the Greek for the number of carbon atoms present. In addition, a shorthand nomenclature is in common usage for fatty acids. It is written as two numbers separated by a colon. The number before the colon indicates the carbon chain length, and the figure after corresponds to the number of double bonds. Additional letters in parentheses show the position of double bonds and the letters Z and E show whether the bond is *cis*-olefinic or *trans*-olefinic, respectively. In a systematic name, the position of the double bond is defined by numbering the carbons from the carboxyl end; however, in medical research the distance between the methyl end of the carbon chain and the first double bond is of utmost importance. This information is included in the shorthand designation using the $(n-x)$ symbol where x is the first unsaturated carbon from the methyl end. In older literature, the Greek omega symbol was used for this designation. For example, n-3 was designated $\omega 3$.

Besides triacylglycerols, other constituents are also present in lipids to varying degrees, depending on the maturity and physical condition of the natural source (e.g., seed, fruit, animal tissue) at the time of lipid extraction. These constituents include mono- and diacylglycerols, as well as unesterified fatty acids. Although these compounds are intermediates in the biosynthesis of triacylglycerols and can occur naturally in small amounts, the presence of larger quantities is an indication of lipolytic activity in immature, damaged, or germinated seeds and damaged animal tissue. Also present in small amounts are more polar lipids such as phospholipids and glycolipids. The phospholipids are characterized by a phosphate ester joined to either choline, ethanolamine, inositol, or serine, attached to the C-1 position of glycerol and fatty acid groups esterified to the C-2 and C-3 positions. In the case of glycolipids, there are only a few in plants, and diacylgalactoglycerol and diacylgalabiosylglycerol are important to the plant because they play a role in chloroplast metabolism.

BIOSYNTHESIS OF LIPIDS

In the biosynthesis of lipids, the fatty acid moieties are formed from acetyl-CoA and malonyl-CoA involving several reactions. These reactions were first studied in cell-free extracts of *Escherichia coli* where they are catalyzed by independent enzymes. In plants individual enzymes catalyze fatty acid formation in chloroplasts; however, in animals, except for the first reactions involving the synthesis of malonyl-CoA from acetyl-CoA, fatty acid biosynthesis occurs on a multienzyme complex known as

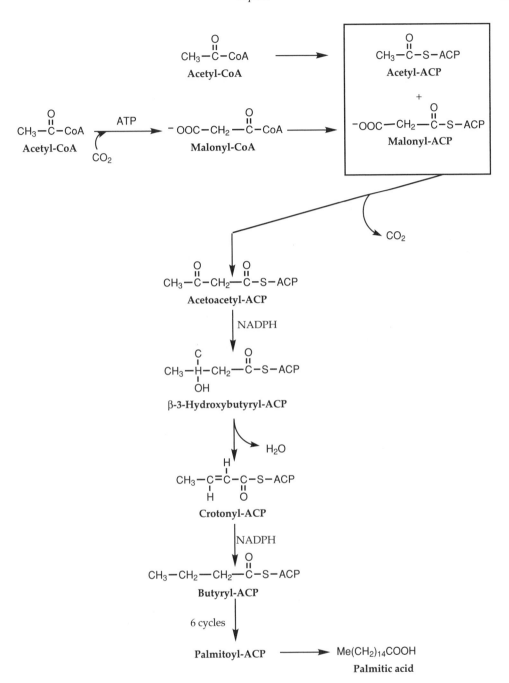

Fig. 5–1. Biosynthesis of fatty acids.

fatty acid synthase (Fig. 5–1). Intermediates in the biosynthesis are covalently linked to the sulf-hydryl groups of an acyl-carrier protein (ACP), which carries all the intermediates during the synthesis. The growing fatty acid chain is elon-gated by the sequential addition of two carbon units derived from acetyl-CoA, but the activated donor of these units is malonyl-ACP. The energy that drives the chain elongation process is cou-pled to the ATP-dependent carboxylation of acetyl-CoA to form malonyl-CoA and the subsequent decarboxylation of the malonyl group in the condensation reaction. In this reaction, a four-carbon unit, acetoacetyl-ACP, is formed from a two-carbon unit, acetyl-ACP, and a three-carbon unit, malonyl-ACP, with a release of CO_2. The next three steps involve a reduction, a dehydration, and a second reduction to convert the keto group at C-3 of acetoacetyl-ACP to a methylene group producing butyryl-ACP which completes the first elongation cycle.

In the second round of elongation, butyryl-ACP condenses with another malonyl-ACP to form a C_6-β-ketoacyl-ACP, and the reactions of the first cycle are repeated on the C_6 substrate. The elongation cycles continue until palmitoyl-ACP is formed. This intermediate is not a substrate for the condensing enzyme, and it is hydrolyzed to yield palmitic acid (16:0) and ACP.

Palmitic acid is the precursor of longer chain saturated and unsaturated fatty acids through the actions of elongases and desaturases. Elongation involves the successive condensation of malonyl-CoA with acyl-CoA. These reactions are each followed by NADPH-associated reductions similar to those catalyzed by fatty acid synthase, the only difference being that the CoA derivative rather than the ACP derivative is involved.

Unsaturated fatty acids are produced by desaturases. Whereas plants produce a large variety of polyunsaturated fatty acids, mammals cannot desaturate between the C-9 position and the methyl end of an acyl chain. Thus, mammals have a dietary requirement for linoleic acid [18:2 (9Z, 12Z)] and linolenic acid [18:3 (9Z, 12Z, 15Z)] which are essential components of phospholipids in membranes and precursors to eicosanoids (C20 signal molecules such as prostaglandins). Arachidonic acid [20:4 (5Z, 8Z, 11Z, 14Z)] is formed in mammals from linoleic acid by the action of elongase and desaturases. This fatty acid is important as a precursor of the prostaglandins, thromboxanes, and leukotrienes.

Triacylglycerols are synthesized from fatty acyl-CoA esters and glycerol-3-phosphate or dihydroxyacetone phosphate. In both cases, through the action of acyl transferases, lipophosphatidic acid is first formed. Lysophosphatidic acid is converted to triacylglycerol by the successive actions of 1-acylglycerol-3-phosphate acyltransferase to form phosphatidic acid, phosphatidic acid phosphatase to form diacylglycerol, and diacylglycerol acyltransferase to form triacylglycerol. The intermediate phosphatidic acid and diacylglycerol can also be converted to phospholipids. The acyltransferases are not completely specific for particular fatty acyl-CoAs, either in chain length or degree of unsaturation; therefore, different fatty acids can be attached to different positions of the glycerol moiety.

Little is known about the biosynthetic pathways leading to other pharmaceutically important lipids. The higher alcohol esters of waxes are probably formed from smaller fatty acid units in a manner analogous to fatty acid biosynthesis. Hydrocarbon compounds of lipids may arise by reduction of squalene or a metabolic equivalent.

Fixed oils are sometimes classified into **drying oils, semidrying oils,** and **nondrying oils.** This classification is based on their ability to absorb oxygen from the air. Oxygen saturates the double bonds to form oxides that may polymerize to form hard films. This property of drying oils is of great importance in the paint industry. The double bonds in the unsaturated fatty acids also take up hydrogen under the proper conditions. **Hydrogenation** of the liquid oils produces semisolid fats that are extensively used as cooking fats and shortenings.

Fixed oils may be **hydrogenated** by passing hydrogen, in the presence of nickel or palladium, through the oil heated to 160 to 200°C. The unsaturated glycerides are more or less converted to saturated glycerides, which are solid at room temperature and stable. Many such oils are used for culinary purposes.

Vegetable oil sources account for about 70% of the world's edible fat production, the rest coming from animal fats (28%) and marine oil (2%). Clinical and epidemiological medical research has shown that an increased blood cholesterol in the form of low density lipoprotein (LDL) is an important risk factor for cardiovascular disease caused by atherosclerosis and its complications. In addition, it has been found that dietary fat rich in saturated fatty acids, especially lauric acid (12:0), myristic acid (14:0), and palmitic acid (16:0), raises blood cholesterol levels. Monounsaturated fatty acids in the diet, such as oleic acid (18:1), and polyunsaturated fats, such as linoleic acid (18:2), have a cholesterol reducing effect (Table 5–2). Because of these effects on serum cholesterol, it is recommended that total fat in the human diet should not exceed 30% of total caloric intake and saturated fat intake should be limited to less than 10% of total daily calories.

Fixed oils and fats are employed in pharmaceuticals for their emollient properties. They

Table 5-2
Fatty Acid Composition (%) of Some Important Dietary Vegetable Oils

Fixed Oil	Lauric (12:0)	Myristic (14:0)	Palmitic (16:0)	Stearic (18:0)	Oleic (18:1)	Linoleic (18:2)
Saturated Oils						
Coconut oil	41–50*	13–23	4–12	1–5	6–8	1–4
Palm kernel oil	46–52	15–17	6–9	1–3	13–19	1–2
Palm oil	—	1–6	32–51	2–8	38–52	5–11
Monounsaturated Oils						
Olive oil	—	—	8–20	1–4	53–86	4–20
Peanut oil	—	—	7–14	1–5	33–71	12–47
Rapeseed oil (Canola oil)	—	—	4–5	1–2	55–63	20–31
Polyunsaturated Oils						
Corn oil	—	—	8–14	1–4	19–50	32–62
Soybean oil	—	—	9–12	1–4	27–60	25–56
Cottonseed oil	—	1–3	18–45	1–9	10–32	31–53
Sunflower oil	—	—	5–7	3–7	15–37	52–74
Safflower oil	—	—	2–10	1–10	7–42	55–81

* Range of values influenced by different cultivars, maturity, storage, processing treatments, and environmental conditions.

may also serve, either in their natural form or in emulsions, as vehicles for other medicaments. A few, such as castor oil, have special therapeutic properties; the prostaglandins are other lipid metabolites that have recently attracted considerable attention for their physiologic properties and therapeutic potential. In the arts and in industry, fats and oils are used in the manufacture of soaps (sodium and potassium salts of the fatty acids), as drying oils in the manufacture of paints and varnishes, and as lubricants. Lipids also form an important class of foods; their high caloric value and low osmotic pressure make them important agents in enteral and parenteral nutrition. Parenteral nutrition is generally used only when it is impossible to meet nutritional requirements by the enteral route. Intravenous lipid emulsions are used to prevent or correct essential fatty acid deficiency and to provide calories in high-density form during prolonged total parenteral nutrition procedures.

SATURATED FIXED OILS

Coconut Oil

Coconut oil is the fixed oil obtained by expression or extraction from the seed kernels of the coconut palm, *Cocos nucifera* Linné (Fam. Arecaceae). This tall, stately tree rises to a height of 30 meters, has a tuft of leaves at the top, and bears 100 or more fruits (coconuts) each year.

The oil consists of a mixture of triacylglycerols in which 80 to 85% of the acids are saturated (Table 5–2); it is a semisolid at 20°C. Lauric and myristic are the major fatty acids. These low molecular-weight acids give the oil a high saponification value, and coconut oil yields quality soaps and shampoos.

Coconut oil also contains acylglycerols of caprylic (8:0) and capric (10:0) acids. A lipid fraction containing these medium chain triacylglycerols is used when conventional food fats are not well digested or absorbed. Coconut oil and medium-chain triacylglycerols are ingredients in a number of combination products for oral administration that are described as balanced dietary supplements for enteral nutrition therapy.

Palm Oil

Palm oil is the fixed oil obtained from the fleshy part (mesocarp) of the fruit of *Elaeis guineenss* Jacquin (Fam. Arecaceae), a palm native to western Africa but now grown in countries of Asia and Central and South America. The genus *Elaeis* is derived from the Greek word elaion meaning oil and *guineensis* indicates its origin is the Guinea Coast of Africa. Palm oil has had a long history of food use dating back to over 5,000 years. It is one of the world's most widely consumed edible oils, next only to soybean oil, and is mostly used as shortening, margarine, and frying fat. Well-known nonfood uses are in soap and candle manufacture.

The oil consists of a mixture of triacylglycerols whose component acids are almost equal proportions of saturated and unsaturated fatty acids (Table 5–2).

Palm Kernel Oil

Palm kernel oil is obtained as a minor product during processing of oil palm fruit. It is obtained from palm kernels after separation, drying, and cracking of the shell of the nut. Palm kernel oil is characterized as a hard oil and closely resembles coconut oil with which it is easily interchangeable. It is composed mostly of saturated fatty acids (Table 5–2) and is solid at ambient temperatures in temperate climates. Palm kernel oil is used in cooking oil, margarine, and shortening formulations, confectionery and baking products, and in the preparation of ice cream and mayonnaise.

MONOUNSATURATED FIXED OILS

Castor Oil

Castor oil is the fixed oil obtained from the ripe seed of *Ricinus communis* Linné (Fam. Euphorbiaceae). *Ricinus* is Latin and means a tick or a bug, referring to the seed's resemblance to some bugs in shape and markings.

The plant is an annual in temperate climates, or a tree, attaining the height of 15 meters, in the tropics. There are many forms of the plant, with variations in the shape of the leaves and the color, size, and markings of the seeds. The fruit is a 3-celled spiny capsule, each cell containing an ovoid albuminous seed. The plant is indigenous to eastern Africa. It is extensively cultivated in India, Brazil, other South and Central American countries, the former Soviet Union, various parts of Africa, southern Europe, and the southern United States. The seeds have been found in Egyptian tombs. The oil apparently had only technical use until the 18th century, when its medicinal use began.

Castor seeds contain from 45 to 55% of fixed oil; about 20% of protein substances consisting of globulin, albumin, nucleoalbumin, glycoprotein, and **ricin** (a toxic lectin or hemagglutin); an alkaloid, ricinine; and several enzymes. Ricin is not removed in the extraction of the castor oil but remains in the oil cake. It is poisonous to cattle but does not affect poultry.

Castor bean pomace contains an allergen that causes allergic reactions in hypersensitive individuals. This powerful allergen is in the nontoxic protein polysaccharide fraction.

Deactivation of toxic substances and removal of the allergenic fraction are problems that must be solved in castor oil production.

Castor oil is prepared by passing the seed through a decorticator, which has rollers with sharp cutting edges that break the testae but do not injure the kernel. The testae are then separated by sieves and compressed air, and the kernels are subjected to pressure. The oil is steamed to destroy albumins, is filtered, and is bleached.

The yield of the "cold-pressed" oil separated by hydraulic pressure is 60% and represents a light-colored, good grade. The remainder of the oil from the seed is solvent extracted, yielding a darker, lower grade oil.

Castor oil is a pale yellowish or almost colorless, transparent, viscid liquid. It has a faint, mild odor and a bland, characteristic taste.

Castor oil is composed of a mixture of triacylglycerols, about 85% of which is triricinoleoylglycerol. The remainder consists of diricinoleoylglycerols with the third acyl group, representing either oleic, linoleic, dihydroxystearic, or a saturated (palmitic or stearic) acid. Triricinoleoylglycerol is hydrolyzed by pancreatic lipase in the duodenum to release ricinoleic ([R-(Z)] 12-hydroxyoctadec-9-enoic) acid, which exerts a cathartic effect.

Castor oil is a stimulant cathartic that usually should be reserved for total colonic evacuation, such as prior to surgery or radiologic, sigmoidoscopic, or proctoscopic procedures; the usual dose is 15 to 60 ml. The oil is also used externally for its emollient effect and as a plasticizer in flexible collodion. Commercially, castor oil is employed in the manufacture of soaps and as a lubricant for internal combustion engines. Hydrogenated castor oil is used as a stiffening agent in some pharmaceutic formulations.

Olive Oil

Olive oil is the fixed oil obtained from the ripe fruit of *Olea europaea* Linné (Fam. Oleaceae). Olive oil is sometimes called **sweet oil**. The generic name *Olea* is from the Latin *oliva*, meaning olive or from the Greek *elaion*, meaning oil.

The olive tree is a small evergreen tree that attains a great age but seldom exceeds 10 meters in height. It was apparently a native of Palestine and has been widely cultivated in the Mediterranean countries from remote antiquity. It is now also cultivated in the southwestern United States and many other subtropical localities. There are a large number of cultivated varieties of the olive, the fruit of which vary in size, color, and yield of oil.

The fruit is a drupe, usually purple when ripe. The full-grown but green fruit, as well as the ripe fruit, when pickled in brine, is widely used as a condiment. The olive ''stone'' or endocarp enclosing the seed has been finely comminuted and used as an adulterant of spices and certain powdered drugs.

Olive oil is offered on the market in several grades of purity. **Virgin oil** is obtained by gently pressing the peeled pulp free from the endocarp. First and second grades of edible oil are pressed from crushed pulp, the first grade with less pressure, the second grade from the same pulp with more pressure. Hand-picked olives are used, and the oil is obtained promptly before decomposition produces fatty acids, Finally, the pulp, mixed with hot water, is pressed again for technical oil; or, the pulp is extracted with carbon disulfide to obtain ''sulfur'' olive oil of inferior quality. The fallen, decomposed, or refuse olives that are allowed to ferment furnish a low grade ''tournant oil,'' which contains large amounts of free fatty acids.

Olive oil is a pale yellow or light greenish yellow, oily liquid whose odor is slight but characteristic and whose taste is bland to faintly acrid. Upon chilling, olive oil tends to become cloudy, and at 0° C it usually forms a whitish granular mass. The composition of olive oil seems to vary rather widely and is given in Table 5–2.

Olive oil is classed as a pharmaceutic aid. It is used as a setting retardant for dental cements and in the preparation of soaps, plasters, and liniments. It is also a demulcent, an emollient, and a laxative. Olive oil is a nutrient and is widely used as a salad oil and a cooking oil.

Peanut Oil

Peanut oil is the refined fixed oil obtained from the seed kernel of one or more of the cultivated varieties of *Arachis hypogaea* Linné (Fam. Fabaceae). The plant is a low, annual herb with imparipinnate leaves and yellow papilionaceous flowers. It is native to Brazil but is extensively cultivated in the southern United States, India, China, and other localities with similar climates. The fruit is not a true nut because the immature pod penetrates the soil and ripens underground. It contains from one to six reddish brown seeds. When ripe, the plants with the fruits are raked from the soil into windrows. When dry, the pods are machine separated and sacked for shipment, or the dried plants are threshed to separate and clean the seeds. For human consumption, the fruits are roasted, passed between rollers, andthe seeds are separated. The kernels contain about 45% of fixed oil, 20% of protein, and a high content of thiamine; hence, they are highly nutritious and are extensively used as food, both whole and when ground into a paste (**peanut butter**).

Peanut oil is sometimes referred to as **arachis oil**. It is a colorless or a yellowish liquid with a slightly nutlike odor and a bland taste.

Peanut oil consists of a mixture of triacylglycerols with component acids as illustrated in Table 5–2. Other minor acids include stearic (18:0), arachidic (20:0), behenic (22:0), and lignoceric (24:0) acids. It closely resembles olive oil and is used as a pharmaceutic aid. Its principal use is as a food oil. It is nondrying and therefore has no value in paints but does have value as a lubricant. The oil saponifies slowly but yields an excellent, firm, white soap. Peanut oil is a solvent for intramuscular injections.

Rapeseed Oil

Rapeseed oil is the fixed oil obtained from the seeds of *Brassica campestris* Linné, *B. juncea* Czerniakowka & Cosson, and *B. napus* Linné (Fam. Brassicaceae). *B. campestris* and *B. napus* are the two most important sources grown in North America and Europe. *B. juncea* and *B. campestris* are grown in India and the Far East.

The oil consists of a mixture of triacylglycerols that are rich in unsaturated fatty acids (Table 5–2). Prior to 1970, commercial rapeseed oil contained up to 50% erucic acid (22:1). Because of some indications that erucic acid has antinutritional properties, varieties of rapeseed have been developed in which the level of erucic acid is much reduced (0.2 to 2.0%). Oil obtained from these rapeseed varieties is termed **canola oil.** Refined canola oil has a bland taste and resists clouding at refrigeration temperature; therefore, it is extensively used as a salad oil. Other edible uses are for shortenings, margarines, and as a frying oil. Rapeseed oil with high erucic acid content has specific industrial uses based on the characteristics of this fatty acid.

POLYUNSATURATED FIXED OILS

Soybean Oil

Soybean oil is the refined, fixed oil obtained from the ripe seed of *Glycine soja* Siebold et Zaccarini (Fam. Fabaceae), an important food and forage crop. The plant is an annual with trifoliate, hairy leaves, rather inconspicuous, pale blue to violet flowers, and broad pods containing 2 to 5 seeds. The seeds are more or less compressed, spheroidal or ellipsoidal, and vary in color from nearly white to yellow-green or brownish black. The seeds contain about 35% of carbohydrates, up to 50% of protein substances, up to 20% of fixed oil, and the enzyme urease.

Soybeans are used as a general food for humans and livestock, and soybean is presently the world's most important oilseed in terms of total production.

Soybean oil is obtained by expression, and the yield seldom exceeds 10%. It consists of a mixture of triacylglycerols as illustrated in Table 5–2.

Soybean oil is consumed principally as salad oil, shortening, and margarine. The oil is usually hydrogenated chemically to reduce the content of linolenic acid (18:3) from about 8% to 3% or less which results in a longer shelf life.

Soybean oil is an ingredient in parenteral nutrients and is a source of lecithin. **Lecithin** is an ingredient in a number of proprietary products that are useful in controlling deranged lipid and cholesterol metabolisms. Stigmasterol, obtained from the lipid fraction of soybeans, can be used as a precursor for steroidal hormones. The oil is used extensively in the manufacture of varnishes, insulators, and other products.

Partially hydrogenated soybean oil is an ingredient in a number of combination products for oral administration that are described as balanced dietary supplements.

Cottonseed Oil

Cottonseed Oil is the refined, fixed oil obtained from the seed of cultivated plants of various varieties of *Gossypium hirsutum* Linné or of other species of *Gossypium* (Fam. Malvaceae). The cottonseed, after ginning off the fibers, is decorticated and cleaned of hulls. The kernels are steamed and pressed at about 1500 lb pressure to yield about 30% of oil. The oil, thus obtained, is turbid and reddish in color. It is refined by filtering, decolorizing, and "winter chilling," which removes the stearin.

Cottonseed oil is a pale yellow, oily liquid. It is odorless and has a bland taste. The oil consists of a mixture of triacylglycerols with the component fatty acids, indicated in Table 5–2.

Cottonseed oil is employed pharmaceutically as a solvent for a number of injections. A considerable quantity is hydrogenated and used to make substitutes for lard. A large amount is also used in the manufacture of soap.

Sesame Oil

Sesame oil, teel oil, or benne oil is the refined, fixed oil obtained from the seed of one or more cultivated varieties of *Sesamum indicum* Linné (Fam. Pedaliaceae).

Sesamum is from the Greek *sesamon*, the original name of the plant; *indicum* refers to its habitat, India. The plant is an annual herb attaining a height of about 1 meter. It is native to southern Asia but is cultivated from Africa to the East Indies, in the West Indies, and in the southern United States.

The seeds are small, flattened, oval or ovate, smooth and shiny, and whitish, yellow, or reddish brown. Their taste is sweet and oily. They contain 45 to 55% of fixed oil, 22% of proteins (aleurone), and 4% of mucilage. These seeds are nutritious and form an important food in India. In Europe and America they are used like poppy seeds on bread and rolls. The fixed oil is obtained by expression and is a pale yellow, oily liquid, almost odorless and bland tasting.

Sesame oil consists of a mixture of triacylglycerols with the following component acids: approximately equal parts of oleic and linoleic (about 43% of each), palmitic (9%), and stearic (4%). The excellent stability of the oil is owing to the phenolic constituent, sesamol, which is produced by hydrolysis of sesamolin, a lignan present in the unsaponifiable fraction of the oil.

Sesame oil is classed as a pharmaceutic aid and is used as a solvent for intramuscular injections. It has nutritive, laxative, demulcent, and emollient properties. Sesamolin, contained in the unsaponifiable fraction of the oil, is an effective synergist for pyrethrum insecticides.

Almond Oil

Almond oil, expressed almond oil, or sweet almond oil is the fixed oil obtained by expression from the seed kernels of different varieties of *Prunus amygdalus* Batsch (Fam. Rosaceae). *Prunus* is the classic name of the plum tree; *amygdalus* is from the Greek *amygdolos*, meaning almond tree; *amara* and *dulcis*, the variety designations, are Latin and mean bitter and sweet, respectively.

The tree is native to Asia Minor, Iran, and Syria and is cultivated and naturalized in all tropical and warm-temperature regions. The presence of amygdalin in the bitter almond and its bitter taste distinguish it from sweet almond. The oil is obtained mostly from Sicily, southern Italy, Spain, China, and California.

Both bitter and sweet almonds are expressed for their fixed oil (45 to 50%). Practical economic considerations favor the use of bitter almonds or sweet almonds of inferior quality. Bitter almonds, after maceration to permit hydrolysis of amygdalin, also yield a volatile oil that is used as a flavoring agent. Sweet almonds are extensively used as a food, but bitter almonds are not suitable for this purpose. The seeds of the bitter almond were known to be poisonous in the days of antiquity. The sweet almond is mentioned early in the Old Testament (Genesis 43:11) as one of the fruits Israel commanded his sons to carry from Palestine as a gift to Egypt. Theophrastus makes several references to the almond. Charlemagne (812 A.D.) introduced the tree on the imperial farms, and, in the 14th century, the almond was an important item of Venetian trade.

Almond oil consists of a mixture of glycerides with component acids of the following approximate composition: oleic (77%), linoleic (17%), palmitic (5%), and stearic (1%). Expressed almond oil is an emollient and an ingredient in cosmetics

Persic Oil

Persic oil, apricot kernel oil, or peach kernel oil is the oil expressed from the kernels of varieties of *Prunus armeniaca* Linné (apricot kernel oil) or from the kernels of varieties of *P. persica* Siebold et Zuccarini (peach kernel oil) (Fam. Rosaceae).

Persic oil is prepared in the same manner as is expressed almond oil. Its characteristics closely resemble those of expressed almond oil, and it is used as a vehicle and pharmaceutic necessity.

Corn Oil

Corn oil is the refined oil obtained from the embryo of *Zea mays* Linné (Fam. Poaceae).

The oil-rich embryos (often called germs) are separated by a flotation process during the preparation of cornstarch. After the embryos are washed free of starch and gluten, they are subjected to pressure and heat to express the oil. The germ oil cake that remains is ground and sold as cattle feed. The crude oil is clarified by filtering and settling and refined by removing the fatty acids, refrigerating, filtering, and sterilizing. Corn oil is a clear, light yellow, oily liquid that has a faint characteristic odor and taste.

The oil consists of a mixture of triacylglycerols with component acids as indicated in Table 5–2.

Corn oil is used as a solvent for injections; it is also a solvent for irradiated ergosterol. It is an edible oil and, as such, is used in salads and in the preparation of food. An emulsion containing 67% of corn oil is used as a high-calorie dietary supplement. Corn oil is also an ingredient in a number of combination products for oral administration (e.g., Ensure) that are described as balanced dietary supplements in enteral nutrition therapy. When hydrogenated, the oil becomes semisolid and is used as a margarine.

Safflower Oil

Safflower oil is the fixed oil obtained from the seed of *Carthamus tinctorius* Linné (Fam. Asteraceae), which is mainly grown in India, Mexico, and the United States.

The oil consists of a mixture of triacylglycerols whose component acids are largely unsaturated. The oil is widely used as a cooking oil, salad oil, hydrogenated fat, margarine, and mayonnaise. Because of its high content of unsaturated fatty acids, it is a drying oil and used in paints and varnishes.

An emulsion containing 50% of safflower oil is used orally as a high-calorie dietary supplement. Safflower oil is also an ingredient in products that are balanced dietary supplements for enteral nutrition therapy.

Sunflower Oil

Sunflower oil is the fixed oil obtained from the seeds of cultivated varieties of *Helianthus annuus* Linné (Fam. Asteraceae). Russia ranks first in the world in the production of sunflower with Argentina ranking second. There are two types of sunflowers: the oil-seed type which represents over 90% of total sunflower production and the edible-seed type which is consumed as whole roasted seeds.

The oil consists of a mixture of triacylglycerols that are rich in unsaturated acids (Table 5–2). The polyunsaturated acid content of sunflower oil is influenced by climate as well as genetics. The oil is used as an alternative to corn oil and safflower oil for culinary purposes, and it is an ingredient in a number of specialty dietary supplements.

Linseed Oil

Linseed oil or Flaxseed oil is the fixed oil obtained from the dried, ripe seed of *Linum usitatissimum* Linné (Fam. Linaceae). The generic name *Linum* is from the Latin *linea,* meaning thread and refers to the use of flax fibers; *usitati-*

ssimum is from the Latin and means "most useful." The plant is an annual which is cultivated in all temperate and tropical regions either for the fiber (flax) or for the seed.

Linseed oil is a yellow liquid having a distinct odor and a disagreeable taste. When exposed to air it gradually thickens and darkens in color. The oil consists of a mixture of triacylglycerols with the following fatty acid composition: 52% linolenic acid (18:3), 15% linoleic acid (18:2), 19% oleic acid (18:1), 7% stearic acid (18:0), and 6% palmitic acid (16:0). The high content of linolenic acid makes it unsuitable for edible purposes, but it is an important drying oil in the paint and varnish industry.

Cod Liver Oil

Cod liver oil is the partially destearinated, fixed oil obtained from the fresh livers of *Gadus morrhua* Linné and other species in the family Gadidae. The generic name *Gadus* is from the Greek *gados*, meaning codfish, and *morrhua* is the Latin name of the codfish.

Codfish inhabit the northern Atlantic Ocean, and cod liver oil is a by-product of the fishing industry. The livers are removed during the fish processing, taking care to exclude the gallbladders, and frozen until subjected to a steaming process to remove the oil. The steaming takes place in closed containers in a carbon dioxide atmosphere to prevent oxidation. The separated oil is chilled to a temperature below minus 5° C; the precipitated stearin is separated from the lighter vitamin-containing oil by decantation and filtration. Finally, the oil is adjusted to a definite vitamin content by admixture, if necessary, of different lots with higher or lower vitamin levels.

Cod liver oil is a thin, oily liquid that has a distinctive, slightly fishy but not rancid odor and a fishy taste. Medicinal-grade cod liver oil must contain, in each gram, not less than 255 μg (85 units) of vitamin D. It may be flavored by the addition of not more than 1% of a suitable flavoring agent or a mixture of such substances. The oil also contains glyceryl esters of unsaturated (about 85%) and saturated (about 15%) fatty acids. (A sterile solution of the sodium salts of the fatty acids, sodium morrhuate injection, is employed as a sclerosing agent.) Myristic and palmitic acids are the major saturated acids; only traces of stearic acid remain in the oil. The unsaturated acids include 22% oleic [18:1(n-9)], 12% palmitoleic [16:1 (n-7)], 12% gadoleic [20:1 (n-11)] and gondoic [20:1 (n-9)], 11% cetoleic [22:1 (n-11)], 7% (Z,Z,Z,Z)- 5,8,11,14,17-eicosapentaenoic [20:5 (n-3)], and 7% (Z,Z,Z,Z,Z,Z)-4,7,10,13,16,19-docosahexaenoic [22:6 (n-3)] acid. The last two n-3 polyunsaturated acids, which are also found in other ocean fish, may decrease the risk of heart disease because they decrease blood platelet aggregation. Bile salts and the alkaloids, morrhuine and aselline, should be absent; presence of the former indicates contamination of the livers with gallbladders, and presence of the latter indicates decomposition.

Cod liver oil was introduced into medicine during the middle of the 18th century. Fish liver oils were the predominant therapeutic sources of vitamin A and D for years. Pure, laboratory-prepared vitamins A and D have substantially replaced the fish liver oils, but cod liver oil still finds some use as a dietary supplement. The oil may also be used in formulating oleovitamin A and D products and topical emollients containing these vitamins.

FATS AND RELATED COMPOUNDS

Theobroma Oil

Cacao seeds or cacao beans are the roasted seeds of *Theobroma cacao* Linné (Fam. Sterculiaceae). *Theobroma* is Greek and means "food of the gods"; *cacao* is from the Aztec name of the tree; "chocolate" is from the Nahuatl. It has long been highly esteemed by the Aztecs, the Mexicans, and later by the Europeans, who explored the Americas.

The plant is a tree attaining the height of about 12 meters and is indigenous to Mexico but widely cultivated in tropical countries. The flowers arise from the older branches or trunk and develop into large, ovoid, fleshy fruits that are 10-furrowed longitudinally, are yellow or reddish, and contain 5 rows of seeds, 10 or 12 in each row. Cacao was known to Columbus and Cortez. Most of the cacao seed on the market is obtained from Ecuador, Columbia, Dominican Republic, Malaysia, Curacao, Mexico, Trinidad, Central America, Brazil, West Africa (Nigeria, Côte d'Ivoire, Cameroons, and Ghana), Sri Lanka, and the Philippine Islands.

The seeds are separated from the ripe pod and allowed to cure. During the process, they change from white to dark reddish brown due to the action of polyphenoloxidase on epicatechins, and at the same time biochemical transformations take place within the seed that lead to the formation of flavor precursors. They are then roasted (not above 140° C) to lose water and develop their characteristic odor and taste. The flavor of chocolate is a result of a complex combination of over 300 chemical compounds, many of which are formed during the curing and roasting process. The curing is essential because the uncured seed does not develop any chocolate flavor when roasted. The roasted seeds are passed through a "nibbling" machine to crack the seed coats (cacao shells), which are separated from the kernels by winnowing. The broken kernels are called "nibs," and when ground between hot rollers, they yield a paste containing up to 50% of fat, **cacao butter.** The paste congeals at room temperature to form **bitter chocolate. Sweet chocolate** is bitter chocolate to which sugar and vanilla or other flavoring substances have been added. After expressing cacao butter, the marc, which retains some oil, is powdered and is known as **prepared cacao** or **breakfast cocoa.** Some brands of cocoa contain alkali to render it "soluble"; it is, of course, not soluble, but the alkali partially saponifies the fat at the surface of each minute particle, resulting in a smoother and more complete suspension of the cocoa in water or milk.

Cacao seeds contain 35 to 50% of a fixed oil, about 15% of starch, 15% of proteins, 1 to 4% of theobromine, and 0.07 to 0.36% of caffeine. When the seeds are roasted, the theobromine in the kernel passes into the shell. The shell is a commercial source of this xanthine derivative.

Theobroma oil or cocoa butter is the fat obtained from the roasted seed of *T. cacao*. It is a yellowish white solid that has a faint, agreeable odor and a bland, chocolatelike taste. It melts between 30 to 35° C.

Theobroma oil consists of a mixture of triacylglycerols with component acids of the following approximate composition; oleic (37%), stearic (34%), palmitic (26%), linoleic (2%). The relatively sharp melting point of the fat and its comparative brittleness and nongreasiness are owing to its peculiar acylglycerol structure. 1-Palmitoyl-2-oleoyl-3-stearoylglycerol and 1,3-distearoyl-2-oleoylglycerol are its major constituents. Cocoa butter is used pharmaceutically as a suppository base.

Lanolin

Lanolin is the purified, fatlike substance from the wool of the sheep, *Ovis aries* Linné (Fam.

Bovidae). It contains between 25 and 30% of water and therefore is commonly called **hydrous wool fat.**

Lanolin is a yellowish white, ointmentlike mass that has a slight, characteristic odor. When heated on a steam bath, it separates at first into two layers. Continued heating with frequent stirring drives off the water that makes up the lower layer.

Chemically, it consists largely of fatty acid esters of cholesterol, lanosterol, dihydrolanosterol, and aliphatic alcohols. The esterified acids are of several series, including normal acids, iso and anteiso acids, and acids hydroxylated in the α and ω positions. The chains contain 7 to 41 carbon atoms. The aliphatic alcohols are similar in chain length and degree of branching, and several diols have been reported.

Lanolin is used as a water-absorbable ointment base. It is employed for the external administration of remedies locally or by inunction. Lanolin is an ingredient in many skin creams and cosmetics. As such, however, it may act as an allergenic contactant in hypersensitive persons.

Anhydrous Lanolin

Anhydrous lanolin is lanolin that contains not more than 0.25% of water. After lanolin has been purified and bleached, it is dehydrated. Anhydrous lanolin is usually referred to as **wool fat.**

Anhydrous lanolin is a water-absorbable ointment base. It is more readily absorbed through the skin than any other known fat and is therefore valuable as a base for therapeutic agents that are administered by inunction. In addition, it possesses emollient properties.

WAXES

Waxes are usually defined as esters resulting from the condensation of high-molecular-weight, straight-chain acids and high-molecular-weight, primary, straight-chain alcohols. Such esters, of course, exist in waxes, but, in reality, waxes are better defined as mixtures of different molecular weight acids and alcohols. In addition, waxes may also contain paraffins.

In plants, waxes are found in connection with the outer cell walls of epidermal tissue, particularly in fruits and leaves. The function of wax appears to be protection against the penetration or loss of water. Insects also secrete waxes for various purposes. Carnauba wax and bayberry wax are examples of vegetable waxes, and lac wax and beeswax are examples of insect waxes.

Waxes are employed in pharmaceuticals to ''harden'' ointments and cosmetic creams. They are also used in the preparation of cerates. In industry and the arts, waxes are used for protective coatings.

Spermaceti

Spermaceti, a waxy substance obtained from the head of the sperm whale [*Physeter macrocephalus* Linné (Fam. Physeteridae)], was formerly recognized as a quality emollient and a desirable ingredient in cold creams and other cosmetics. However, the sperm whale is an endangered species, and spermaceti is no longer available. Efforts to find a substitute have led to the use of a synthetic spermaceti or hydrogenated jojoba oil.

Synthetic spermaceti or cetyl esters wax is a mixture consisting primarily of esters of saturated fatty alcohols (C_{14} to C_{18}) and saturated fatty acids (C_{14} to C_{18}).

Jojoba Oil

Jojoba oil is a liquid wax expressed from seeds of *Simmondsia chinensis* (Link) Scheider (Fam. Buxaceae). The plant is a bushy shrub native to the arid regions of northern Mexico and to the southwestern United States.

Jojoba seeds contain 45 to 55% of an ester mixture (not triacylglycerols) that is a liquid at ambient temperatures. It is a liquid wax which is unique in the plant kingdom and has a close resemblance chemically and physically to sperm whale oil, which is no longer available in the United States. The major components identified upon hydrolysis of the ester mixture are (Z)-11-eicosenoic acid [20:1(*n*-9)], (Z)-13-docosenoic acid 22:1(*n*-9)], (Z)-11-eicosen-1-ol, and (Z)-13-docosen-1-ol. Hydrogenation of the oil yields a crystalline wax that has the appearance and properties of spermaceti.

Jojoba oil and its hydrogenated derivatives are useful emollients and agents of pharmaceutic necessity.

Beeswax

Yellow wax or beeswax is the purified wax from the honeycomb of the bee, *Apis mellifera* Linné (Fam. Apidae). Wax is secreted in cells on the ventral surface of the last four segments of the abdomen of the worker bees. The wax excretes through pores in the chitinous plates and is employed by the young worker bees in the construction of the comb.

The honeycomb, after separation from the honey, is melted in water, then cooled and remelted, and finally strained and allowed to harden in molds.

Beeswax is a solid varying in color from yellow to grayish brown. It has an agreeable, honeylike odor and a faint, characteristic taste. When cold, beeswax is somewhat brittle and exhibits a dull, granular, noncrystalline fracture.

The wax consists principally of alkyl esters of fatty and wax acids (about 72%), chiefly myricyl palmitate $C_{15}H_{31}COOC_{30}H_{61}$, myricyl cerotate $C_{25}H_{51}COOC_{30}H_{61}$, myricyl hypogaeate $C_{13}H_{27}CH{=}CHCOOC_{30}H_{61}$, and ceryl 2-hydroxypalmitate, $C_{14}H_{29}CH(OH)COOC_{26}H_{51}$; fatty wax acids (about 11%), especially cerotic acid and its homologs; hydrocarbons (15%); and other minor constituents, including moisture, pollen, and propolis (bee glue). The latter two materials are responsible for most of the color of the wax.

Yellow wax is a stiffening agent and is an ingredient in yellow ointment. It is also used as a base for cerates and plasters. Commercially, the largest markets are in the manufacture of candles and cosmetics, and it is contained in a number of polishes.

White wax is bleached, purified wax from the honeycomb of the bee, *A. mellifera* Linné (Fam. Apidae). The bleaching process is accomplished by allowing the melted wax to flow slowly over revolving wetted cylinders, upon which it hardens in thin, ribbonlike layers. These layers are removed and exposed to sunlight and air until they are bleached. (The process usually is repeated). The bleached wax is finally melted and cast into cakes of various shapes. White wax is sometimes referred to as bleached beeswax.

White wax is employed pharmaceutically in ointments and in cold creams.

Carnauba Wax

Carnauba wax is obtained from the leaves of *Copernicia prunifera* (Mueller) H.E. Moore [*C. cerifera* (Arruda da Camara) Martius] (Fam. Arecaceae), a palm growing from northern Brazil to Argentina. The wax consists of alkyl esters of wax acids (80%), chiefly myricyl cerotate; free monohydric alcohols (10%); a lactone;

resin; and other minor constituents. It is used in the manufacture of candles, wax varnishes, leather and furniture polishes, and in place of beeswax.

PROSTAGLANDINS

Prostaglandins are C_{20} lipid metabolites formed in the body from essential, unsaturated fatty acids of the diet. The most important dietary precursor of the prostaglandins is linoleic acid [18:2 (9Z, 12Z)] which is converted by elongation and desaturation in the liver to arachidonic acid [20:4 (5Z, 8Z, 11Z, 14Z)]. Arachidonic acid is released from cell-membrane phospholipids by the enzyme phospholipase A_2 and is then metabolized by two major pathways, one involving the key enzyme cyclooxygenase and the other involving lipoxygenases. Prostaglandins, thromboxanes, and prostacyclin are products of the cyclooxygenase pathway, and leukotrienes are products of the lipoxygenase pathway. Because arachidonic acid and most of its metabolites contain 20 carbon atoms, they are referred to as **eicosanoids**. Prostaglandins apparently occur in nearly all mammalian tissues, but they are present in low concentrations. The major prostaglandins have been grouped into three main classes designated as prostaglandins A, E, and F. All prostaglandins (PG) have a cyclopentane ring with two aliphatic side chains, and they are related to prostanoic acid.

Prostanoic acid

The three classes (A, E, and F) are distinguished on the basis of the functional groups around the cyclopentane ring: the A type has an α,β-unsaturated keto group, the E type has a β-hydroxyketone, and the F series compounds are 1,3-diols. Subscript numerals refer to the number of double bonds in the side chains, and the subscript α refers to the configuration of the 9-hydroxyl group with the hydroxyl group projecting down from the plane of the ring.

Concerning the physiologic roles of prostaglandins, attention was initially attracted to these substances in 1930 when it was observed that constituents in human semen could produce contraction and relaxation of the human uterus. A large body of biologic knowledge, especially regarding members of the PGE and PGF series, has been accumulated. Mammalian cells and tissues may respond differently (stimulation or inhibition of a biologic process) to individual prostaglandins; in some instances, this response may be a concentration factor. Prostaglandins appear to act at the level of the cell membrane, and they may modulate the transmission of hormonal or other extracellular stimuli into cyclic AMP for the internal regulation of cellular functions. Actions of this type seem consistent with the pharmacologic effects that have been noted with the prostaglandins. Pharmacologic effects of these compounds involve contraction or, in some cases, relaxation of smooth muscles of the female reproductive system, of the cardiovascular system, of the intestinal tract, and of the bronchi. They also influence gastric secretion and renal function.

Securing a feasible source of the various prostaglandins was a major deterrent to the early exploration of their biologic properties and therapeutic potential. Much of the explosion of knowledge about these compounds during the past decade is a result of several achievements that have resolved the supply problem. Key accomplishments include the development of an enzymatic synthesis that uses prostaglandin synthetase from sheep seminal vesicles, the discovery of prostaglandin materials in *Plexaura homomalla* (sea fan or sea whip), which is a coral found in reefs off the Florida coast, and the development of several procedures for total chemical synthesis.

The prostaglandins have diverse pharmacologic effects, and some enthusiasts believe that their therapeutic potential transcends that of the steroids. The use of PGE_2 or 15-methyl-$PGE_{2\alpha}$ for termination of second trimester pregnancies and the use of PGE_2 for ripening an unfavorable cervix in pregnant women at or near term with a medical or obstetrical need for labor induction; the use of PGE_1 for palliative therapy to maintain temporarily neonates with patent ductus arteriosus and certain congenital heart defects; and the use of misoprostol, a synthetic PGE_1 analog, as a gastric antisecretory and gastroprotective agent are the only applications that have received FDA approval at this time. However, experimental studies have revealed potential for therapeutic use of various prostaglandins to prevent premature labor (PGE), to induce menstruation (PGE), to increase fertility in certain conditions (PGE), to manage some types of hypertension (PGE$_1$ and PGE$_2$), to control certain cardiac arrhythmias (PGE$_{2\alpha}$), to correct some defects in red blood cells (PGE), to exert antithrombogenic and thrombolytic activity (PGE$_1$), to control asthmatic seizures (PGE$_1$), and to treat several other conditions. The multiple effects of the prostaglandins and the diverse response to individual prostaglandins by various body tissues are factors that give above-average chances for undesirable side effects in any therapeutic use of these compounds; this appears to be a problem, but its full significance remains to be evaluated in most situations. Because prostaglandins are formed in situ in most body tissues, the potential for use of prostaglandin synthetase inhibitors is also receiving investigational attention.

(15*S*)-Methylprostaglandin F$_{2\alpha}$

(15*S*)-Methylprostaglandin F$_{2\alpha}$, (15*S*)-methyl-PGF$_{2\alpha}$ or carboprost is the 15-methyl analog of PGF$_{2\alpha}$ and stimulates contractions of the gravid uterus that are similar to the contractions of the full term uterus at labor and is used in terminating second trimester pregnancy. Side effects are usually related to its contractile effect on smooth muscle including the gastrointestinal tract, producing vomiting and/or diarrhea, and the vascular system, causing elevation in blood pressure.

PGF$_{2\alpha}$ is rapidly inactivated (serum half-life of 10 minutes or less) in the lungs and other body tissue. A major pathway for inactivation is through the oxidation of the 15-hydroxy group to a keto function. The 15-methyl substituent of (15*S*)-methyl-PGF$_{2\alpha}$ prevents metabolic inactivation via oxidation of the 15-hydroxyl group and permits administration of this derivative as the tromethamine salt by deep intramuscular injection as opposed to slow injection into the amniotic sac for PGF$_{2\alpha}$.

(15*S*)-Methylprostaglandin F$_{2\alpha}$

Prostaglandin E$_2$

Prostaglandin E$_2$, PGE$_2$, or dinoprostone is another uterine stimulant that has been ap-

proved for termination of second trimester pregnancy. PGE$_2$ differs from PGF$_{2\alpha}$ only in that the 9-oxygen substituent is a keto group. PGE$_2$ is available for this purpose as a vaginal suppository that should be stored at a temperature below minus 20°C.

The pharmacologic effects of PGE$_2$ are similar to those of PGF$_{2\alpha}$; a notable exception is the lack of vasoconstriction and resulting hypertension with high doses of PGE$_2$. Frequently encountered adverse reactions include vomiting, pyrexia, diarrhea, nausea, headache, and chills. PGE$_2$ is also administered vaginally as a gel to ripen the cervix before the membranes are ruptured and to induce labor at term.

Prostaglandin E$_2$

Prostaglandin E$_1$

Prostaglandin E$_1$, PGE$_1$, or alprostadil differs from PGE$_2$ only in the reduction of the unsaturated bond at position 5. PGE$_1$ produces vasodilation, inhibits platelet aggregation, and stimulates intestinal and uterine smooth muscle. The vasodilation property underlies its use for palliative therapy to maintain temporarily neonates with patent ductus arteriosus and congenital heart defects that restrict the pulmonary or systemic blood flow. The dilated ductus arteriosus facilitates blood oxygenation and body perfusion pending surgical correction of the congenital defects.

Prostaglandin E$_1$

PGE$_1$ is metabolized rapidly (up to 80% on the first pass through the lungs) by oxidation of the 15-hydroxyl group, and the drug is administered by continuous intravenous infusion of the lowest dosage that maintains the desired response.

(16*R,S*)-Methyl-16-hydroxyprostaglandin E$_1$ Methyl Ester

(16*R,S*)-Methyl-16-hydroxyprostaglandin E$_1$ methyl ester, (16*R,S*)-methyl-16-hydroxy-

PGE$_1$ methyl ester, (16*R,S*)-methyl (13*E*)-11, 16-dihydroxy-16-methyl-9-oxoprost-13-enoate, or misoprostol is a synthetic analog of PGE$_1$. Prostaglandins of the E series have a role in protecting the gastrointestinal mucosa from ulceration by inhibiting gastric acid secretion and by an independent cytoprotection of mucosal cells. The ulcerogenic effects of aspirin and other nonsteroidal anti-inflammatory drugs (NSAIDs) have been attributed to the inhibition of prostaglandin synthesis. Misoprostol is used orally in patients that are at high risk for developing ulcers during NSAID therapy. It is rapidly absorbed and metabolized to its active form which is the free acid. The addition of the 16-methyl group to PGE$_1$ prevents rapid metabolic inactivation which is a problem with the oral administration of PGE$_1$. Like other prostaglandins misoprostol produces uterine contractions that may endanger pregnancy by causing abortion.

(16*R,S*)-Methyl-16-hydroxyprostaglandin E$_1$ Methyl Ester

SUGGESTED READINGS

Dimick, P.S., ed.: *Proceedings of the Cacao Biotechnology Symposium.* University Park, Pennsylvania, Department of Food Science, Pennsylvania State University, 1986.

Gunstone, F.D., Harwood, J.L., Padley, F.B.: *The Lipid Handbook.* London, Chapman and Hall, 1986.

Hickey, M. S.: *Handbook of Enteral, Parenteral, and ARC/AIDS Nutritional Therapy.* St. Louis, Mosby-Year Book, Inc., 1992.

Kolattukudy, P.E., ed.: *Chemistry and Biochemistry of Natural Waxes.* New York, Elsevier Scientific Publishing Co., 1976.

Mead, J.F., Alfin-Slater, R. B., Howton, D.R., Popjak, G.: *Lipids: Chemistry, Biochemistry and Nutrition.* New York, Plenum Press, 1986.

Murphy, R.C.,Fitzpatrick, F.A., eds.: *Methods in Enzymology: Arachidonate Related Lipid Mediators,* Vol. 187. San Diego, Academic Press, 1990.

Rattray, J., ed.: *Biotechnology of Plant Fats and Oils.* Champaign, Illinois, American Oil Chemists' Society, 1991.

Röbbelen, G., Downey, R. K., Ashri, A., eds.: *Oil Crops of the World.* New York, McGraw-Hill, Inc., 1989.

Salunkhe, D. K., Desai, B. B.: *Postharvest Biotechnology of Oilseeds.* Boca Raton, Florida, CRC Press, Inc., 1986.

Salunkhe, D. K., Chavan, J. K., Adsule, R. N., Kadam, S. S.: *World Oilseeds: Chemistry Technology, and Utilization.* New York, Van Nostrand Reinhold, 1992.

Sammuelsson, B., Paoletti, R., eds: *Advances in Prostaglandin, Thromboxane, and Leukotriene Research,* Vols. 1-21. New York, Raven Press, 1976-1991.

Vance, D. E., Vance, J. E., eds.: *New Comprehensive Biochemistry: Biochemistry of Lipids, Lipiproteins, and Membranes,* Vol. 20. Amsterdam, Elsevier Science Publishers B.V., 1991.

Willis, A. L., ed.: *CRC Handbook of Eicosanoids: Prostaglandins and Related Lipids,* Vols. I-II. Boca Raton, Florida, CRC Press, Inc., 1987.

Wood, G. A. R., Lass, R. A.: *Cacao.* London, Longman Scientific & Technical, 1987.

6

Terpenoids

TERPENOIDS

Terpenoids are widely distributed in nature and are found in abundance in higher plants. In addition, fungi produce a range of interesting terpenoids; marine organisms are a prolific source of unusual terpenoids, and terpenoids are found as insect pheromones and in insect defense secretions. Terpenoids are defined as natural products whose structures may be divided into isoprene units; hence, these compounds are also called **isoprenoids.** In addition, this class of compounds is also collectively called the terpenes; however, the -oid suffix is more logical, as used for alkaloids, flavonoids, etc. The -ene suffix should be restricted to the unsaturated hydrocarbons of the class. The isoprene units arise biogenetically from acetate via mevalonic acid and are branched-chain, five-carbon units containing two unsaturated bonds.

$$CH_3$$
$$|$$
$$CH_2{=}C{-}CH{=}CH_2$$

Isoprene
C_5H_8

During the formation of terpenoids, the isoprene units are usually linked in a head to tail manner, and the number of units incorporated into a particular unsaturated hydrocarbon terpenoid serves as a basis for the classification of these compounds. **Monoterpenoids** are composed of two units and have the molecular formula, $C_{10}H_{16}$. **Sesquiterpenoids**, $C_{15}H_{24}$, contain three isoprene units. **Diterpenoids**, $C_{20}H_{32}$, have four isoprene units. **Triterpenoids**, $C_{30}H_{48}$, are composed of six isoprene units, and **tetraterpenoids** or **carotenoids**, $C_{40}H_{60}$, have eight units. The concept that terpenoids are built

from isoprene units is known as the "biogenetic isoprene rule" and is illustrated in Figure 6–1.

Terpenoids can be named systematically according to the general International Union of Pure and Applied Chemistry (IUPAC) rules of nomenclature; however, names derived in this manner are long and cumbersome. For this reason, the trivial names of terpenoids are still used for naming the more common compounds.

The terpenoids are further categorized as acyclic (open chain), monocyclic (one ring), bicyclic (two rings), tricyclic (three rings), etc. and can be not only isoprene oligomers but also saturated or partially saturated isomers as well as oxygenated derivatives such as alcohols, aldehydes, ketones, phenols, ethers, and esters.

In addition to the terpenoids discussed, there are many other natural products of mixed biosynthetic origin that are constructed from isoprene and nonisoprenoid units. Such compounds have been designated **meroterpenoids.** For example, among the alkaloids there are compounds that contain an isoprene unit (ergot alkaloids) or a monoterpenoid unit (quinine). Other examples of natural product classes of meroterpenoids are the cannabinoids, phylloquinones such as Vitamin K, and tocopherols such as Vitamin E.

The number of different terpenoids isolated from nature is approximately 20,000 and far exceeds that of any other group of natural products. The plant terpenoids have dominated the subject of chemical ecology, and terpenoids have been assigned roles as phytoalexins, insect antifeedants and repellents, pollination attractants, defense agents against herbivores, pheromones, allelochemicals, plant hormones, and signal molecules. Terpenoid molecules have been implicated in almost every possible interaction between plant and animal, plant and plant, or plant and microorganism.

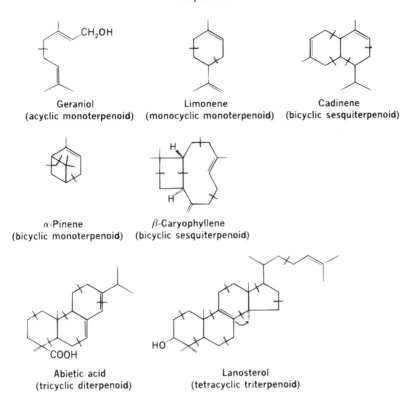

Fig. 6–1. Representative terpenoids showing the isoprene units in each molecule.

Biosynthesis of Terpenoids

In the biosynthesis of terpenoids as outlined in Figure 6–2, three units of acetyl-CoA are involved in the early stages of the pathway and transformed in two steps to yield (3S)-3-hydroxyl-3-methylglutaryl-CoA (HMG-CoA). Next, reduction of HMG-CoA by a two step NADPH-dependent process catalyzed by HMG-CoA reductase generates (3R)-mevalonic acid. In the following steps, mevalonic acid is phosphorylated twice in sequence to give mevalonate 5-pyrophosphate, which is then decarboxylated to form isopentenyl pyrophosphate (IPP), the C_5 building unit of terpenoid biosynthesis termed **active isoprene.** The isomerization of isopentenyl pyrophosphate to 3,3-dimethylallyl pyrophosphate with subsequent head-to-tail condensation of these two C_5 units under the influence of prenyltransferase gives rise to geranyl pyrophosphate (C_{10}). Geranyl pyrophosphate serves as the substrate for the various monoterpenoid synthases (cyclases) and represents the key precursor of monoterpenoid biosynthesis. Geranyl pyrophosphate may also undergo further elongation with the sequential addition of IPP by head-to-tail coupling to give farnesyl pyrophosphate (C_{15}) and geranylgeranyl pyrophosphate (C_{20}) through the action of the corresponding prenyltransferases and these intermediates give rise to the sesquiterpenoids and diterpenoids, respectively. Head-to-head dimerization of farnesyl pyrophosphate affords the triterpenoids (C_{30}) and steroids while a similar dimerization of geranylgeranyl pyrophosphate provides the 40 carbon tetraterpenoids and carotenoids. Additional IPP units added to geranylgeranyl pyrophosphate result in the formation of polyterpenoids such as the *cis*-polyisoprene known as rubber.

MONOTERPENOIDS

More than 1,000 naturally occurring monoterpenoids are presently known, most of which have been isolated from higher plants. More recently, however, a number of halogenated monoterpenoids have been isolated from marine organisms, and monoterpenoids are occasionally found in defense and pheromonal secretions of insects. Characteristic features of monoterpen-

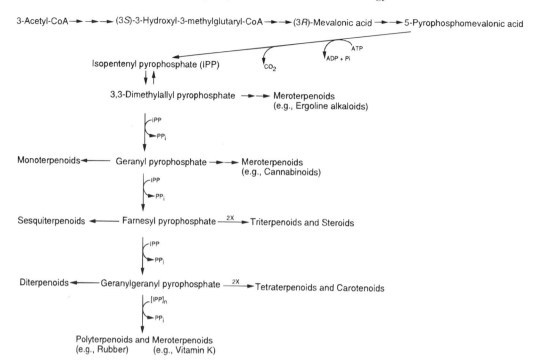

Fig. 6–2. General scheme of terpenoid biosynthesis.

oids are their volatility and intensely pungent odors, and they are the most common components in plants responsible for fragrance and flavor. As a consequence, there is a great commercial interest in these compounds for the production of volatile oils in the perfume and fragrance industry and in the production of species and culinary herbs for the food and seasoning industry.

The monoterpenoids are structurally diverse and have been classified into over 35 different structural types. The structural types that occur most frequently are the acyclic myrcane, the monocyclic *p*-menthane, and the bicyclic bornane, carane, fenchane, pinane, and thujane. Although many monoterpenoid derivatives of these classes occur naturally in optically pure form, in some plants both enantiomers may be found. For example, (+)-and (−)-α-pinene are present in all species of *Pinus*. Representative chemical structures of monoterpenoids are illustrated in Figure 6–3.

Biosynthesis of Monoterpenoids

Monoterpenoid biosynthesis diverges from the pathways leading to other isoprenoids at the acyclic, C_{10} intermediate geranyl pyrophosphate

(Fig. 6–2). Following the formation of geranyl pyrophosphate, the cyclic compounds are formed through the action of different specific monoterpenoid synthases also known as cyclases. Geranyl pyrophosphate itself cannot cyclize directly to form a six- membered ring because of the *trans*-geometry of the double bond at C-2. However, the monoterpenoid synthases isomerize geranyl pyrophosphate to a bound intermediate with the *cis*-geometry, which is thought to resemble linalyl pyrophosphate and which is then able to cyclize. Representative products of cyclization reactions are illustrated in Figure 6–4, and after the initial cyclizations these compounds can undergo a variety of subsequent enzymatic transformations including oxidations, reductions, isomerizations, and hydrations leading to a diverse array of final products. A volatile oil produced by a particular plant species may have only a few major constituents; however, it may have up to 50 other monoterpenoids present in lesser amounts.

Camphor

Camphor is a ketone obtained from *Cinnamomum camphora* (Linné) Nees et Ebermaier (Fam. Lauraceae) or produced synthetically.

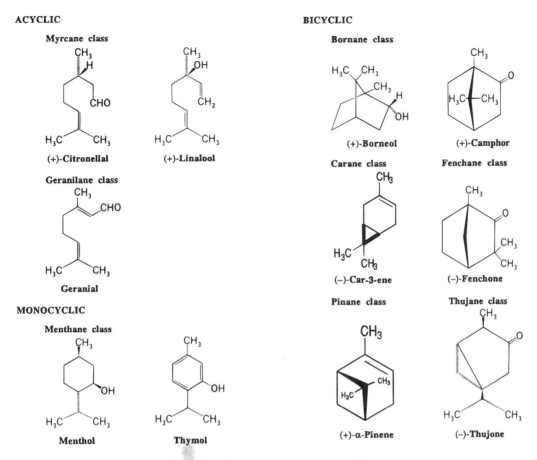

ACYCLIC

Myrcane class

(+)-Citronellal   (+)-Linalool

Geranilane class

Geranial

MONOCYCLIC

Menthane class

Menthol   Thymol

BICYCLIC

Bornane class

(+)-Borneol   (+)-Camphor

Carane class   Fenchane class

(−)-Car-3-ene   (−)-Fenchone

Pinane class   Thujane class

(+)-α-Pinene   (−)-Thujone

Fig. 6–3. Representative monoterpenoids.

Camphora is from the Arabic *kafur*, meaning chalk. The plant is a large evergreen tree indigenous to eastern Asia but naturalized in the Mediterranean region, Sri Lanka, Egypt, South Africa, Brazil, Jamaica, Florida, and California. Early references to camphor do not pertain to the laurel camphor but rather to the Borneo camphor (borneol), which reached Arabia in the 6th century and Europe in the 12th. Laurel camphor appeared in Europe in the 17th century. When Japan annexed Taiwan (Formosa), a government monopoly was created (1900). From that time until World War II, about 80% of the world's supply of natural camphor (about 4 million kg per year) was produced in Taiwan (Formosa), where the tree occurs naturally in abundance and is also extensively cultivated; the remaining 20% was produced largely in Japan and southern China. Since 1945, the production of synthetic camphor has gradually lessened the demand for the natural product; nevertheless, Japanese and Taiwanese camphors still are found on the market.

Natural camphor occurs as a crystalline product in clefts in the woody stems and roots and, to a greater extent, dissolved in volatile oil. The wood is chipped and distilled with steam, and 1 lb of crude camphor is obtained from 20 to 40 lb of chips. The crude camphor is then freed of oil by centrifugation and pressing into the familiar cakes.

Synthetic camphor is made from pinene, the principal constituent of turpentine oil. The starting point is the stumps of felled pine trees previously used in turpentining. A number of complex methods have been used for producing synthetic camphor, but all are based on (1) converting pinene into bornyl esters, which are (2) hydrolyzed to isoborneol, and (3) finally oxidized to camphor.

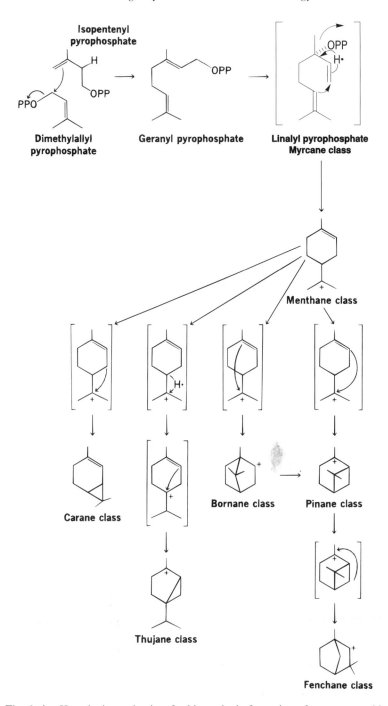

Fig. 6–4. Hypothetic mechanism for biosynthetic formation of monoterpenoids.

The specific rotation of natural camphor is between $+41°$ and $+43°$. Synthetic camphor is the optically inactive racemic form.

Camphor is a topical antipruritic in concentrations of 0.1 to 3%. In higher concentrations of up to 11% it is used as a counterirritant for fibrositis and neuralgia associated with inflamed joints, sprains, and other inflammatory conditions. Camphor stimulates the nerve endings in the skin and induces relief of pain by masking deeper visceral pain with a milder pain arising from the skin at the same level of innervation. Camphor has been shown to be safe and effective for reducing cough when externally applied to the chest and throat of young children. Inhalation of the aromatic vapors causes a local anesthetic action.

Cineole

Cineole or eucalyptol is found in eucalyptus and several other volatile-oil-yielding drugs. It is also called cajuputol because it occurs in cajuput.

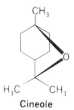

Cineole

Cineole is obtained from eucalyptus oil and from other sources. Eucalyptus oil is the volatile oil distilled with steam from the fresh leaves of *Eucalyptus globus* Labillardiere or from other species of *Eucalyptus* (Fam. Myrtaceae). This tree is indigenous to eastern Australia and Tasmania and is cultivated in southern Europe and in California. The oil contains about 70–85% cineole, which is a colorless liquid that has a characteristic, aromatic, camphoraceous odor and a pungent, cooling, spicy taste. Cineole may be obtained (1) from eucalyptus oils by fractional distillation and subsequent freezing of the distillate or by treating eucalyptus oil with phosphoric acid and subsequently decomposing the cineole-phosphoric acid with water, or (2) from terpin hydrate as a dehydration product on treatment with acids.

Cineole is classed as a flavor. It has properties similar to those of eucalyptus oil, and both are employed in a variety of products, such as nasal inhalers and sprays for antiseptic and mild anesthetic action to the nose and throat. They have also been used, often by steam inhalation, as stimulating expectorants in bronchitis.

Menthol

Menthol or menthan-3-ol is as alcohol obtained from diverse mint oils or prepared synthetically. Menthol may be levorotatory [(−)-menthol], from natural or synthetic sources, or racemic [(±)-menthol], produced synthetically.

Menthol is usually prepared from Japanese peppermint oil by refrigeration (−22°C), during which the menthol crystallizes. The liquid portion is poured off, and the crystallized menthol is pressed between filter papers and subsequently purified by recrystallization. Japanese peppermint oil is obtained by steam distillation of the flowering tops of *Mentha arvensis* Linné var. *piperascens*. Synthetic racemic menthol is produced by hydrogenation of thymol. Menthol may also be prepared from pinene.

Menthol occurs as colorless, hexagonal crystals that are usually needlelike, as fused masses, or as a crystalline powder. It has a pleasant, peppermintlike odor.

When applied to the skin in concentrations of 0.1 to 1%, menthol dilates the blood vessels causing a sensation of coldness followed by a depression of sensory cutaneous receptors resulting in an antipruritic action. For this reason it is found in preparations used to treat minor burns and sunburns, poison ivy rash, douche powders, and athlete's foot. When used in higher concentrations (1 to 16%), it acts as a counterirritant, and for this purpose it is usually combined with other agents such as camphor.

In addition, menthol is combined with camphor and eucalyptus oil (cineole) in ointments, cough drugs, nasal sprays, and inhalants to relieve symptoms of bronchitis, sinusitis, and nasal congestion. In small doses by mouth, menthol has a carminative action; however, larger doses will have a depressant effect on the heart.

Terpin Hydrate

Terpin hydrate or terpinol is formed by the action of nitric acid on rectified turpentine oil in the presence of alcohol. It is *cis-p*-menthane-1,8-diol hydrate.

Terpin hydrate is a stimulant to mucous membranes; therefore, it is used as an expectorant in the form of terpin hydrate elixir.

Thymol

Thymol is a phenol obtained from thyme oil (*Thymus vulgaris* Linné), from horsemint oil (*Monarda punctata* Linné), from Oswego tea oil (*Monarda didyma* Linné), from ajowan oil (*Carum copticum* Bentham et Hooker), or it may be prepared synthetically from *m*-cresol or *p*-cymene. The oil may be treated in two ways to obtain thymol crystals: (1) it may be subjected to freezing temperatures causing the thymol to crystallize, or (2) it may be treated with sodium hydroxide solution, the aqueous solution of sodium thymol being separated and decomposed with acid, thus liberating the thymol, which is subsequently purified.

Thymol occurs as large colorless crystals or as a white crystalline powder. It has an aromatic thymelike odor and a pungent taste. Thymol may be readily microsublimed.

Thymol is an antifungal and antibacterial agent. It is more powerful than phenol, but its use is limited by its low solubility in water, irritancy, and susceptibility to protein. It is included in topical antiseptic and analgesic preparations in concentrations ranging from 0.1 to 1% in personal-care products, and in mouthwashes for its antiseptic action, but such preparations have limited germicidal efficacy.

SESQUITERPENOIDS

The **sesquiterpenoids** have a wide distribution in nature and form the largest class of terpenoids. Among the first sesquiterpenoids isolated from nature were β-cadinene from oil of cade (juniper tar) and β-caryophyllene from clove oil (Fig. 6–1). Abscisic acid is a sesquiterpenoid that is an essential plant hormone controlling growth and development.

Sesquiterpenoid lactones are chemically distinct from other members of the sesquiterpenoid group through the presence of an α-methylene-γ-lactone system. Many of them also contain α,β-unsaturated carbonyls as well as epoxides. These functional groups represent reactive receptor sites for biological nucleophiles such as thiol and amino groups of enzymes. As a consequence, a wide spectrum of biological activities has been reported for these compounds, for example, antimicrobial and antitumor activity, and some are highly toxic to mammals.

Sesquiterpenoid lactones can be classified according to their carbocyclic skeleton, and of these, three major groups are germacranolides with a ten-membered ring, eudesmanolides with two fused six-membered rings, and guaianolides with a five-membered ring fused to a seven-membered ring (Fig. 6–5).

Artemisinin

Artemisinin or qinghaosu is a sesquiterpenoid lactone isolated from the leaves and flowering tops of *Artemisia annua* Linné (Fam. Asteraceae), an herb that has traditionally been

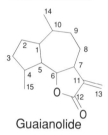

Germacranolide

Eudesmanolide

Guaianolide

Fig. 6–5. Major skeletal types of sesquiterpenoid lactones without stereochemical designations.

used in China for the treatment of malaria for over a thousand years. However, the active principal was not isolated and characterized until 1972, when Chinese scientists showed it to be a novel antimalarial compound with an internal peroxide linkage which is essential for activity.

To overcome the poor solubility of artemisinin in water, a number of dosage forms and routes of administration have been utilized , and several more potent derivatives with more suitable pharmaceutical properties have been developed. The most promising include the methyl ether derivative **Artemether,** which is more lipid soluble and more potent and the sodium salt of the hemisuccinate ester, **sodium artesunate,** which is soluble in water allowing intravenous administration.

Artemisinin and its derivatives are potent and rapidly acting blood schizontocides in the treatment of malaria. They are active against *Plasmodium vivax* and against both chloroquine sensitive and chloroquine-resistant strains of *Plasmodium falciparum*. They produce a more rapid clearance of parasites than quinine or chloroquine which has been encouraging in the treatment of cerebral malaria; however, high rates of reoccurrence necessitates combination therapy with other antimalarials.

Artemisinin

Chamomile

The dried flower heads of *Matricaria recutita* Linné (Fam. Asteraceae) constitute the drug known as **German chamomile** or **matricaria.** A related plant, *Chamaemelum nobile* (Linné) All., known as **Roman chamomile,** contains similar constituents and is similarly employed. Chamomile is extensively cultivated in Europe, where it is widely utilized in folk medicine for its carminative, spasmolytic, and anti-inflammatory effects. The most common form of the drug is a tea, but various extracts and volatile-oil-containing preparations are also available. In fact, chamomile is so highly regarded and so extensively used that it might be labeled the ''ginseng'' of Europe. Recently, chamomile has become one of the most popular herbal teas in the United States.

As might be expected, such a renowned plant has been the subject of a large number of botanic, agronomic, chemical, and pharmacologic studies. In essence, the latter have revealed definite anti-inflammatory and antispasmodic properties in chamomile, owing primarily to constituents of the volatile oil, especially the sesquiterpenoids $(-)$-α-bisabolol, $(-)$-α-bisaboloxides A and B, and the guaianolide lactone matricin (prochamazulene), chemical name 8α-acetoxy-4α-hydroxyguaia-1(10),2-dien-12,6α-olide. Flavonoids and coumarin derivatives add to the spasmolytic effects.

Unfortunately, an infusion (tea) contains only about 10 to 15% of the volatile oil present in the plant material, and the ingredients in the volatile oil provide most of the anti-inflammatory activity. Whole plant extracts or preparations containing quantities of the volatile oil are certainly much more effective. In spite of the relatively low concentrations of lipid-soluble active ingredients in the tea, one authority believes that, when the tea is used over a long period of time, a cumulative beneficial effect may result. This belief is attested to by the centuries-old use of chamomile as a home remedy and healthful beverage in Europe and by its increasing popularity for these purposes among the laity in the United States.

Feverfew

The leaves of *Tanacetum parthenium* (L.) Schultz-Bip. (Fam. Asteraceae), known as **feverfew,** have been used for centuries as an antipyretic or febrifuge. Recently, however, double-blind placebo-controlled clinical trials have shown that feverfew is effective in the prophylaxis of migraine by substantially reducing the frequency and severity of the headache.

The principal primarily responsible is parthenolide, a sesquiterpenoid lactone of the germacranolide type with the chemical name 4α,5β-epoxygermacra-1(10),11(13)-dien-12,6α-olide. Parthenolide acts as a serotonin antagonist resulting in an inhibition of the release of serotonin from blood platelets.

Feverfew has been used simply by chewing the fresh leaves of the plant; however, dried preparations either as tablets or capsules are available. For these to be effective, it is recommended that they contain a minimum concentration of 0.2% parthenolide. The usual dose of dried leaves of good quality is 125 mg daily.

Parthenolide

Valerian

Valerian consists of the dried rhizome and roots of *Valeriana officinalis* Linné (Fam. Valerianaceae). It has been employed as an antianxiety agent and sleep aid for more than 1,000 years. The drug contains from 0.3 to 0.7% of an unpleasant-smelling volatile oil containing bornyl acetate and the sesquiterpenoids, valerenic acid, valerenolic acid, and acetoxyvalerenolic acid. Also present is a mixture of lipophilic iridoid principals known as valepotriates. These bicyclic monoterpenoids are quite unstable and occur only in the fresh plant or in material dried at temperatures under 40°C. Although the specific active principal(s) of valerian have not been determined, it is possible that a combination of the sesquiterpenoids and the valepotriates may be involved.

The drug may be administered as a tea prepared from 2 to 3 g of the dried herb or equivalent amounts of a tincture or extract may be employed.

DITERPENOIDS

The **diterpenoids** comprise a large group of non-volatile C_{20} compounds derived from geranylgeranyl pyrophosphate. Although mainly of plant or fungal origin, they are also formed by some marine organisms and insects. Some acyclic diterpenoids are known, but the vast majority are carbocyclic compounds containing as many as five rings. Diterpenoids at many different states of oxidation ranging from hydrocarbons to highly oxygenated compounds are known and are usually isolated as optically active solids that can exist in both the normal and the antipodal stereochemical configurations. The normal series has an A/B ring fusion stereochemically related to that of the steroids, and those in which the ring fusion is antipodal are known as the *ent* series; examples of each series may occur in the same plant species.

The diterpenoids have a wide range of different biological activities. The resin acids such as abietic acid (Fig. 6–1) are exuded from the wood of trees, especially conifers, and protect the tree from infection and insect attack. The gibberellins are plant hormones that stimulate plant growth, whereas podolactones are plant growth inhibitors. Diesters of phorbal have been extensively used in pharmacological investigations on carcinogenesis because of their ability to promote tumor formation. In contrast to the triterpenoids, the diterpenoids are rarely combined with sugars to form glycosides; however, an exception is stevioside which is a glycoside about 300 times sweeter than sucrose and used as a sweetening agent in Japan.

Forskolin

Forskolin or colforsin is a labdane diterpenoid isolated from the roots of the Indian herb *Coleus forskohlii* (Poir.) Briq. (Fam. Lamiaceae). *Coleus* is from the Greek *coleos*

meaning sheath, referring to the fused filaments of the flower that form a staminal sheath around the style. The epithet *forskohlii* commemorates the Finnish botanist Forskal. The plant is distributed over the subtropical to temperate climatic zones in the mountains of Africa, Burma, Nepal, Sri Lanka, and Thailand and grows on the sunny, dry hill slopes between an altitude of 300 and 1800 meters. It is under cultivation in India.

Forskolin is 7β-acetoxy-8,13-epoxy-1α,6β, 9α-trihydroxylabd-14-en-11-one and was discovered via a screening program in India of plants used in Hindu and Ayurvedic traditional medicine. It has been shown to be a prototype for a novel class of drugs that activates cyclic AMP-generating systems through an ability to stimulate adenylate cyclase in a receptor-independent manner. As a consequence, it has become as important research tool in cyclic AMP-related studies. In addition, forskolin has a high therapeutic potential in diseases such as congestive cardiomyopathy and bronchial asthma in which the repeated use of β-adrenergic agonist drugs leads to desensitization of the receptors and a loss of drug efficacy. It also has potential for use in glaucoma and hypertension.

Forskolin

Ginkgo

A concentrated acetone-water extract of the dried leaves of *Ginkgo biloba* Linné (Fam. Ginkgoaceae) is currently a popular drug in Europe for the treatment of peripheral vascular disease, particularly cerebral circulatory disturbances and other peripheral arterial circulatory disorders. The plant is a dioecious tree growing to 30 meters in height and has been described as a living fossil, having survived unchanged in eastern Asia for some 200 million years. There is debate as to whether or not it still grows in the wild, but it is thought to have been preserved by priests in China and Japan who cultivated it on temple grounds.

Plantations of ginkgo trees have been established in the southeastern United States to supply the market with dried leaves. The trees are severely pruned to shrub height to allow mechanical picking. The acetone-water extract of the dried leaves is dried and adjusted to a potency of 24% flavone glycosides and 6% terpenoids.

The extract is a complex mixture of constituents, and more than one agent may be responsible for the therapeutic effect. The flavone glycosides of the rutin type reduce capillary fragility and reduce blood loss from the capillary vessels which may prevent ischemic brain damage. Probably more important is the presence of diterpenoid lactones known as ginkgolides. Ginkgolides A,B,C, and M have been shown to inhibit platelet-activating factor (PAF). PAF, produced by a variety of body tissues, not only induces aggregation of the blood platelets but also causes bronchoconstriction, cutaneous vasodilation, chemotaxis of phagocytes, hypotension, and the release of inflammatory compounds. All of these actions are blocked by the ginkgolides, resulting in an increase in blood fluidity and circulation.

Although the extract is sold in Europe as an approved drug, it has not been approved in the United States; however, ginkgo extract is sold as a dietary supplement in the United States in the form of tablets containing 40 mg of the extract.

Ginkgolide A

Taxol

Taxol or paclitaxel is a diterpenoid obtained from the bark of *Taxus brevifolia* Nutt. (Fam. Taxaceae), also known as the Pacific yew. The plant is a small, slow-growing evergreen tree native to the northwestern United States. Taxol is one of the most promising antineoplastic drugs to emerge from the antitumor screening of natural products in recent years. The mode of action is unique in that it enhances the polymerization of tubulin, the protein subunit of the spindle microtubules and induces the formation of stable, nonfunctional microtubules. As a consequence, taxol disrupts the dynamic equilibrium within the microtubule system and blocks cells in the late G_2 phase and M phase of the cell cycle, inhibiting cell replication.

A major obstacle in the development of taxol has been the limited supply of the drug. Because of taxol's complex chemistry, it is not economically feasible to synthesize the drug, and in harvesting the bark the tree is destroyed. Efforts are under way to increase supplies by utilizing semisynthetic methods where taxol precursors are extracted from needles of abundant ornamental *Taxus* species. For example, 10-desacetylbaccatin III, isolated from the needles of *Taxus baccata*, can be converted to taxol and related active agents by a relatively simple synthetic procedure. Needles, in contrast to bark, can be harvested without damage to the plant and are, therefore, a more rapidly renewable resource of the drug.

Taxol is a complex diterpenoid with a taxane ring system and a four-membered oxetane ring. An ester side chain at position 13 of the taxane ring is essential for the drug's cytotoxic activity. In addition, the presence of an accessible hydroxyl group at position 2′ of this ester side chain enhances the activity. Taxol is hydrophobic; therefore, the injectable concentrate preparation for intravenous infusion is solubilized in polyoxyethylated castor oil. Before injection, it must be diluted in sodium chloride or dextrose solution or combinations thereof.

Taxol is used in the treatment of metastatic carcinoma of the ovary after failure of first-line or subsequent chemotherapy and in the treatment of breast cancer after failure of combination chemotherapy for metastatic disease or relapse within 6 months of adjuvant chemotherapy.

Taxol

TRITERPENOIDS

The **triterpenoids** are formed biosynthetically from six isoprene units and share in common the C_{30} acyclic precursor squalene. Different types of ring closure in squalene can give rise to many different skeletal types of triterpenoids. In fact, over 4,000 natural triterpenoids have been isolated, and more than 40 skeletal types have been identified. The triterpenoids can be divided into two main classes: the tetracyclic compounds and the pentacyclic compounds.

Also, in the later stages of biosynthesis small carbon fragments may be removed to produce molecules with less than 30 carbon atoms, for example, the C_{27} steroids (Chapter 7). Most triterpenoids are alcohols and can combine with sugars to form glycosides, which is the case with saponins (Chapter 4). Free triterpenoids are often components of resins, latex, or cuticle of plants.

Triterpenoids that are ecologically significant include the cucurbitacins and quassinoids which have a bitter taste that may be a defense against herbivory, and the saponins which are toxic to cold-blooded animals such as molluscs. The limonoids, a group of tetranortriterpenoids, have insect antifeedant properties. For example, the neem tree *Azadirachta indica* produces the limonoid azadirachtin which is one of the most potent insect antifeedant compounds known. Another group of triterpenoids is the phytoecdysones that disrupt metamorphosis in insects that are feeding on plants. Triterpenoids that are used as drugs are discussed in the chapter on glycosides.

TETRATERPENOIDS AND CAROTENOIDS

The **carotenoids** comprise an important and ubiquitous class of C_{40} tetraterpenoids. Many of the yellow, orange, red, and purple colors seen in living organisms are due to the presence of these compounds. Their biosynthesis takes place in the chloroplasts of plants or chromatophores of bacteria and fungi. The precursor, geranylgeranyl pyrophosphate, undergoes a head-to-head dimerization to give prephytoene pyrophosphate and then phytoene, the central intermediate in the formation of C_{40} carotenoids. In some microbes additional isopentenyl groups may be added onto the tetraterpenoid backbone to produce C_{45} and C_{50} carotenoids, the homocarotenoids. The C_{40} carotenoids may also be oxidized to carotenoids containing less then 40 carbons, the apocarotenoids.

Approximately 600 carotenoids have been described that occur naturally. The largest structural variety is found in those isolated from marine organisms, including some with acetylenic groups. Well known carotenoids are either simple unsaturated hydrocarbons based on lycopene or their oxygenated derivatives, known as **xanthophylls.** The chemical structure of lycopene consists of a long chain of eight isoprene units joined head-to-tail, giving a conjugated system

of alternate double bonds, which is the chromophore responsible for imparting color to the molecule. Cyclization of lycopene at both ends of the molecule produces the bicyclic hydrocarbon **β-carotene,** the most common carotenoid in higher plants.

In plants and microorganisms, carotenoids function as photoprotective agents, as photosynthetic accessory pigments, and as membrane stabilization components. In animals, carotenoids serve as a source of vitamin A and other retinoids and as photoprotective and cancer prevention agents. These protective functions of carotenoids appear to be due to their ability to quench free radicals and singlet oxygen, acting as antioxidants and preventing oxidative damage to cells.

There is a large commercial market for carotenoids as colorants for foods, animals feeds, pharmaceuticals, and cosmetics. Carotenoids for this purpose are obtained by chemical synthesis, extraction of natural products such as carrots, and fermentation. Biotechnology is now playing a major role in improving carotenoid production with the use of directed mutagenesis, carotenogenic enzymes, immobilized enzyme systems, and bioreactors.

Vitamin A

Vitamin A is a term applied to all derivatives of β-ionone, other than the carotenoids, that possess the biologic activity of all-*trans* retinol. Retinol is the major natural form of the vitamin, but known forms include the acetate and palmitate esters of the alcohol and such oxidation products as retinol, retinoic acid, and 3-dehydroretinol. The ester forms have good stability characteristics, and the acetate and palmitate esters of synthetically prepared all-*trans* retinol are the major commercial forms of vitamin A.

Vitamin A Alcohol (Retinol)

Retinol is readily absorbed (80 to 90%) from the normal intestinal tract and is stored in body tissues, especially the liver. An estimated one third of the ingested vitamin A is stored under normal circumstances. Fish liver oils are the richest known natural sources of the vitamin and formerly were its primary commercial sources.

Common dietary sources of vitamin A are animal organs (heart, kidney, liver), eggs, dairy products, and fish. Vitamin A activity is also derived from some plant carotenoids that occur in carrots and green leafy vegetables. Only carotenoids that possess at least one unhydroxylated β-ionone ring (α-, β-, and γ-carotene and cryptoxanthin) can be converted to vitamin A. β-Carotene and related carotenoids (provitamin A substances) are cleaved by β-carotene oxygenase in mucosal cells of the intestine to yield retinal, most of which is promptly reduced in the presence of NADH to retinol.

Vitamin A is involved in vision, growth, and tissue differentiation. A deficiency of this vitamin can result in a variety of conditions, including nyctalopia (night blindness), xerophthalmia, hyperkeratosis of the skin, growth retardation, and decreased resistance to infection. Activation of the visual pigment rhodopsin involves retinol (retinol is probably oxidized in situ). The function of vitamin A in tissue differentiation may relate to the synthesis of specific glycoproteins (cell receptors or regulators); retinyl phosphate plays an essential role in transferring sugars to glycoprotein. Evidence suggests that vitamin A is biochemically involved in many other essential processes, but details of its molecular involvement need clarification. For example, observations suggest that a deficiency of vitamin A prompts a decline in the plasma level of a macroglobulin that is an inhibitor of collagenases and other proteinases in the cornea; the consequence can be the development of corneal lesions.

Vitamin A is indicated specifically for the treatment of a deficiency of this vitamin, a situation rarely encountered in practice. The vitamin is used primarily for prophylactic purposes when normal dietary intake is inadequate or when normal absorption is compromised.

Vitamin A is usually taken orally, but it may be administered intramuscularly. Therapy may be discontinued when liver storage of the vitamin is determined to be adequate. Vitamin A equivalent to an adult requirement for 2 years is normally stored in the hepatic tissues of persons receiving a balanced diet.

Tretinoin or all-*trans* retinoic acid is available in several formulations (cream, gel, and solution) for topical purposes. It appears to increase epidermal cell mitosis and epidermal cell turnover and is used to treat acne vulgaris.

Isotretinoin or 13-*cis* retinoic acid is available for oral use in special situations. It is approved for use in severe recalcitrant cystic acne. It is also used sometimes in keratinization disorders of the skin, which are frequently preneoplastic. Use of the drug must be closely monitored since adverse reactions are common and may require its discontinuation. It should not be used by women who are pregnant, and contraception should be continued for at least one month after termination of therapy.

Beta-Carotene

Beta-carotene, in addition to being a provitamin A substance, is effective in reducing photosensitivity in individuals with erythropoietic protoporphyria. It does not act as a sunscreen in normal individuals and should not be used for that purpose. However, β-carotene does provide a novel and safe approach to the treatment of a specific type of photosensitivity. When ingested over a period of several weeks, the drug produces carotenemia, a yellowing of the skin often first observed in the palms of the hand or on the soles of the feet. The mode of action has not been established, but it is no doubt related to the pigmentation of the skin. During the course of therapy, elevated blood carotene levels are observed, but vitamin A levels do not rise above normal.

VOLATILE OILS AND SPICES

Volatile oils are the odorous principals found in various plant parts. Because they evaporate when exposed to the air at ordinary tempera-

β-Carotene

tures, they are called **volatile oils, ethereal oils,** or **essential oils.** The last term is applied because volatile oils represent the "essences" or odoriferous constituents of the plants. **Spices** are dried, fragrant, aromatic, or pungent plant parts that contain a volatile oil and are used primarily in food as a seasoning rather than for nutrition (Table 6.1).

Depending on the plant family, volatile oils may occur in specialized secretory structures such as glandular hairs (Lamiaceae), modified parenchymal cells (Piperaceae), oil-tubes called vittae (Apiaceae), or in lysigenous or schizogenous passages (Pinaceae, Rutaceae). They may be formed directly by the protoplasm, by decomposition of the resinogenous layer of the cell wall, or by the hydrolysis of certain glycosides. In the conifers, volatile oils may occur in all tissues; in the rose, they appear in appreciable quantities only in the petals; in cinnamon, only in the bark and the leaves; in the apiaceous fruits, only in the pericarp; in the mints, only in the glandular hairs of the stems and leaves; and in the orange, one kind of oil occurs only in the flower petals and another kind only in the rind. The individual spices would be the particular plant organ that contains the volatile oil such as the bark, buds, bulbs, flowers, fruit, leaves, rhizomes, roots, seeds, or in some cases the entire plant tops.

Chemical constituents of volatile oils and spices may be divided into two broad classes, based on their biosynthetic origin; (1) terpenoid derivatives formed via the acetate-mevalonic acid pathway, and (2) aromatic compounds formed via the shikimic acid-phenylpropanoid route.

Although volatile oils differ greatly in their chemical constitution, they have a number of physical properties in common. They possess characteristic odors, they are characterized by high refractive indices, most of them are optically active, and their specific rotation is often a valuable diagnostic property. As a rule, volatile oils are immiscible with water; however, they are soluble in ether, alcohol, and most organic solvents.

Several points of differentiation exist between volatile oils and fixed oils. Volatile oils can be distilled from their natural sources; they do not consist of glyceryl esters of fatty acids. Hence, they do not leave a permanent grease spot on paper and cannot be saponified with alkalies. Volatile oils do not become rancid as do the fixed oils, but instead, on exposure to light and air, they oxidize and resinify.

Practically all volatile oils consist of chemical mixtures that are often quite complex; they vary widely in chemical composition. Almost any type of organic compound may be found in volatile oils (hydrocarbons, alcohols, ketones, aldehydes, ethers, oxides, esters, and others), and only a few possess a single component in a high percentage (clove oil contains not less than 85% of phenolic substances, chiefly eugenol). However, it is not uncommon for a volatile oil to contain over 200 components, and often the trace constituents are essential to the odor and flavor. The absence of even one component may change the aroma. Plants of the same species grown in different parts of the world usually have the same components, but the percentages that are present may differ.

Methods of Obtaining Volatile Oils

Volatile oils are usually obtained by steam distillation of the plant parts containing the oil. The method of distillation depends on the condition of the plant material.

In the method of **direct steam distillation,** applicable to fresh plant drugs (peppermint, spearmint), the crop is cut and placed directly into a metal distilling tank on a truck bed. The truck is driven to a distilling shed where steam lines are attached to the bottom of the distilling tank. The plant material is still green and contains considerable natural moisture; therefore, maceration is unnecessary. Steam is forced through the fresh herb and carries the oil droplets through a vapor pipe attached at the top of the tank to the condensing chamber.

During steam distillation, certain components of a volatile oil tend to hydrolyze, whereas other constituents are decomposed by the high temperatures. Ideal distillation methods utilizing steam should provide for the highest possible diffusion rate of steam and water through plant membranes and should thus keep the hydrolysis and decomposition at a minimum.

Some volatile oils cannot be distilled without decomposition and are usually obtained by **expression** (lemon oil, orange oil) or possibly by other mechanical means. In the United States, the general method for obtaining citrus oils involves puncturing the oil glands by rolling the fruit over a trough lined with sharp projections that are long enough to penetrate the epidermis and pierce the oil glands located in the outer portion of the peel (**ecuelle** method). A pressing action on the fruit removes the oil from the glands, and a fine spray of water washes the oil from the mashed peel while the juice is extracted

Table 6–1
Representative Volatile Oils and Spices

Name	Part Used	Botanical Origin	Production Areas	Important Constituents	Use
Anise (aniseed)	the dried, ripe fruit	the annual herb, *Pimpinella anisum* (Apiaceae)	Spain, France, Egypt	1–3% volatile oil containing 80–90% (*E*)-anethole, 10–15% chavicol	flavor
Caraway	the dried, ripe fruit	the biennial herb, *Carum carvi* (Apiaceae)	Netherlands, Poland, Russia, northern Africa, India, Pakistan	3–6% volatile oil containing 50–85% (+)-carvone, 40–50% (+)-limonene	flavor
Citronella oil	volatile oil distilled with steam from freshly cut or partially dried leaves	the grass, *Cymbopogon winterianus* and *C. nardus* (Poaceae)	Sri Lanka, Indonesia, China, Taiwan, Argentina, Brazil, India	5–55% (+)-citronellol, 25–40% geraniol, 11–15% (+)-citronellol	perfume, insect repellant
Eucalyptus oil	the dried, scythe-shaped leaf	the tree *Eucalyptus globulus* and other species of *Eucalyptus* (Myrtaceae)	Australia, Brazil, Spain, Portugal, Angola, South Africa, China, India	70–85% cineole, 5–15% α-pinene	antiseptic, mild anesthetic, stimulating expectorant
Fennel	the dried, ripe fruit	the perennial herb *Foeniculum vulgare* (Apiaceae)	Spain, Russia, Bulgaria, Italy	volatile oil containing 65–70% (*E*)-anethole, 10–15% limonene, 6–7% fenchone, 4% methyl chavicol	flavor, carminative
Lavender oil	volatile oil distilled with steam from the fresh flowering tops	the dwarf shrub, *Lavandula angustifolia* (Lamiaceae)	France, Bulgaria, Russia, Australia	30–60% (−)-linalyl acetate, (−)-linalool, cineole, terpinen-4-o1	perfume
Lemon oil	volatile oil obtained by expression, without the aid of heat, from the fresh peel	the small evergreen tree *Citrus limon* (Rutaceae)	Spain, Italy, California, Florida, Argentina, Cyprus, Brazil, Israel, Australia, Ivory Coast, Greece	70–80% (+)-limonene, 8–10% β-pinene, 8–10% γ-terpinene, 2–4% citral	flavor, perfume
Orange oil	volatile oil obtained by expression from the fresh peel of the ripe fruit	the tree, *Citrus sinensis* (Rutaceae)	California, Florida, Brazil, Italy, Israel	1–2% decanal, more than 90% limonene	flavor
Pine oil	volatile oil obtained by extraction and fractionation or by steam distillation of the wood	the tree, *Pinus palustris* and other species of *Pinus* (Pinaceae)	southeastern United States	65% α-terpineol, 10% methyl chavicol and related phenol ethers, 9% borneol, 8% fenchol, 4% menthols	disinfectant, deodorant
Rose oil (otto of rose)	volatile oil distilled with steam from the fresh flowers	perennial herbs or shrubs, *Rosa gallica, R. damascena, R. alba, R. centifolia,* and varieties of these species (Rosaceae)	Bulgaria, southern France, Turkey, Morocco, Russia	geraniol, (−)-citronellol, nerol, 2-phenylethanol	perfume

Table 6–1
Representative Volatile Oils and Spices—*(Continued)*

Name	Part Used	Botanical Origin	Production Areas	Important Constituents	Use
Spearmint oil	volatile oil distilled with steam from the fresh, overground parts of the flowering plant	the perennial herb *Mentha spicata* or of *M. cardiaca* (Lamiaceae)	Washington, Idaho, Wisconsin, Michigan, Indiana, China	45–60% (−)-carvone, (−)-limonene, cineole	flavor, carminative
Thyme	the dried leaves and flowering tops	an evergreen herbaceous shrub, *Thymus vulgaris, T. zygis,* and its variety *gracilis* (Lamiaceae)	Spain, Italy, France, Greece	volatile oil containing thymol, carvacrol, p-cymene, α-terpinene, γ-terpinene	flavor
Turpentine oil	volatile oil distilled from the oleoresin	the tree *Pinus palustris* and other species of *Pinus* (Pinaceae)	southeastern United States	65% α-pinene, 30% β-pinene	counterirritant
Wintergreen oil (gautheria oil, betula oil, sweet birch oil)	volatile oil distilled with steam from the dried plant material	the leaves of the shrublike perennial *Gautheria procumbens* (Ericaceae) or the bark of the tree *Betula lenta* (Betulaceae)	eastern United States and Canada	98% methyl salicylate	flavor, counterirritant, antiinflammatory

through a center tube that cores the fruit. The resulting oil-water emulsion is separated by centrifugation. A variation in this process is to remove the peel from the fruit before the oil is extracted.

Often the volatile oil content of fresh plant parts (flower petals) is so small that oil removal is not commercially feasible by the aforementioned methods. In such instances, an odorless, bland, fixed oil or fat is spread in a thin layer on glass plates. The flower petals are placed on the fat for a few hours; then, repeatedly, the old petals are removed, and a new layer of petals is introduced. After the fat has absorbed as much fragrance as possible, the oil may be removed by extraction with alcohol. This process is known as **enfleurage** and was formerly used extensively in the production of perfumes and pomades.

In the perfume industry, most of the modern essential oil production is accomplished by **extraction**, using solvent systems based on such volatile solvents as petroleum ether or benzene. The chief advantage of extraction over distillation is that uniform temperature (usually 50°C) can be maintained during most of the process. As a result, extracted oils have a more natural odor that is unmatched by distilled oils, which may have undergone altered chemical constitu-

tion by the high temperatures. This feature is of considerable importance to the perfume industry; however, the established distillation method is a low-cost operation compared to the cost of the extraction process.

Medicinal and Commercial Uses

Many crude drugs are used medicinally because of their volatile oil content; however, in numerous cases, the volatile oils separated from the drugs are used as drugs themselves. Similarly, various crude drugs are powdered and are employed as spices and condiments (anise, clove, nutmeg). The volatile oil drugs and the separated oils are most commonly used for flavoring purposes. They may possess a carminative action, but a few (eucalyptus oil, wintergreen oil) possess additional therapeutic properties. In addition to their pharmaceutic uses, the volatile oils are employed widely as flavors for foods and confections and in the spice, perfume, and cosmetic trades.

The fabrication of **perfumes** is a multimillion dollar industry. Perfumery materials such as volatile oils are used directly not only for perfumes and cosmetics but also are essential for the manufacture of soaps, toiletries, and deodorizers and for masking or providing odor to household cleaners, polishes, and insecticides.

Chemistry of Volatile Oils and Spices

In recent years, advances in analytic instrumentation, particularly in the area of chemical separation techniques based on capillary-column gas chromatography and high-pressure liquid chromatography, coupled with computerized instruments that combine gas chromatography with mass spectrometry, have led to the precise identification of the components of volatile oils, including trace constituents.

Many volatile oils and spices consist largely of **monoterpenoids** (Fig. 6–3); however, another major group of constituents are the **phenylpropanoids.** These compounds contain the C_6 phenyl ring with an attached C_3 propane side chain. Figure 6–6 illustrates examples of these natural products. Many of the phenylpropanoids found in volatile oils and spices are phenols or phenol ethers. In some cases, the propane side chain has been abridged to give a C_6-C_1 structure, such as in methyl salicylate and vanillin.

Because the various constituents of volatile oils and spices are responsible for their charac-

teristic odors, flavors, and therapeutic properties, a chemical classification of these agents should be based on their principal chemical constituents. However, because the types of constituents are so diverse and so numerous, the assignment of the oil or the oil-bearing drug to a definitive place in such a classification is often difficult.

In addition to the molecular structure, the **stereochemistry** of the constituents of volatile oils markedly determines the type of olfactory response evoked by the compounds. Geometric isomers, whether *ortho/meta/para* or *cis/trans*, are in most cases readily distinguished both as to quality and strength of odor. An interesting stereochemical feature of many terpenes is the fact that both **enantiomers** (optically active isomers) exist in nature. In some cases, a plant species produces only one of the enantiomers, whereas a different species may produce both. Among the monoterpenes that occur as the (+) form in certain species and as the (−) enantiomeric form in others are limonene, α-fenchol,

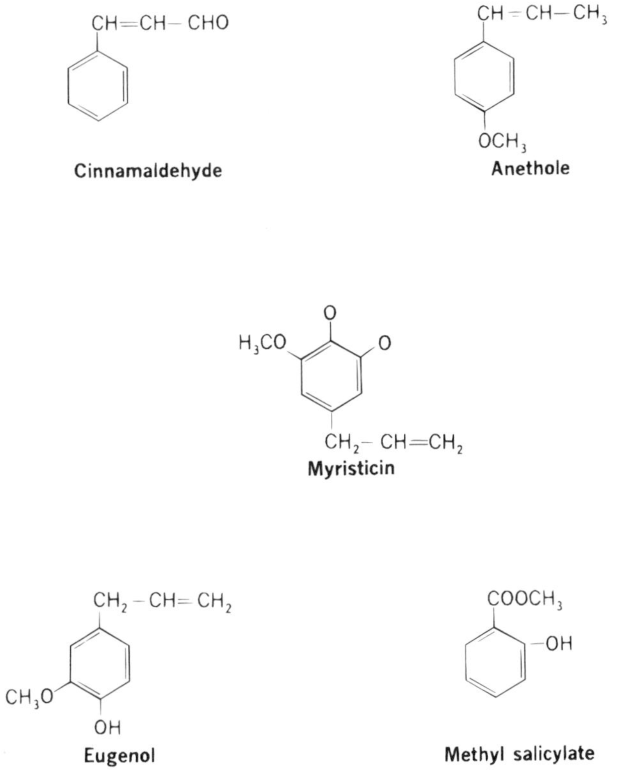

Cinnamaldehyde

Anethole

Myristicin

Eugenol

Methyl salicylate

Fig. 6–6. Representative phenylpropanoids and abridged phenylpropanoids found as constituents of volatile oils and spices.

borneol, menthone, carvone, and linalool. In addition, limonene, α-terpinol, α-fenchol, carvone, and camphor, as well as many others, can be found in plants as the racemic mixture.

As with many other natural product compounds that exist in enantiomeric forms, such as alkaloids and amino acids, the physiologic responses elicited by each isomer can differ. For example, (+)-carvone has an odor and flavor of caraway, whereas (−)-carvone produces a spearmint odor and flavor. These observations lend support to the stereochemical theory of olfaction which proposes that different kinds of olfactory receptor sites are in the nose. Odorant molecules could lodge on these sites and would have shapes and sizes (varying stereochemistry) that were complementary to the shape and size of the particular receptor. A proper fit at the receptor would be required to initiate a nerve impulse that would register in the brain the perception of the odor.

Cinnamon

Cinnamon or Saigon cinnamon is the dried bark of *Cinnamomum loureirii* Nees (Fam. Lauraceae).

An important cinnamon in U.S. commerce is **Ceylon cinnamon**, the dried inner bark of shoots of coppiced trees of *C. zeylanicum* Nees (Fam. Lauraceae).

Cassia cinnamon is the dried bark of *C. cassia* (Nees) Nees.

Cinnamomum may be from the Arabic, *kinnamon;* the Malay, *kaju manis*, sweet wood; or the Hebrew, *ginnamon*; *Loureirii* is in honor of the French botanist Loureiro; *zeylanicum* signifies Ceylon; *Cassia* is from the Greek *kassia*, meaning to strip off the bark.

Cinnamon is named as a spice in the biblical books of Moses, by the ancient Greek and Latin historians, and in Chinese herbals as early as 2700 B.C. Its cultivation in Ceylon probably dates from 1200 A.D.

The wild cinnamon trees seldom exceed 9 meters in height. The leaves are coriaceous, green, and glossy; the flowers are in terminal panicles; and the fruit is fleshy and ovoid.

Practically all commercial cinnamon is now obtained from cultivated trees in Sri Lanka (Ceylon), southwestern China, Vietnam, Laos, Indonesia, the West Indies, the Seychelles, Madagascar, and many other localities. However, cinnamon from southeastern Asia and adjacent islands is superior in quality.

The bark is gathered from young trees usually less than 6 years old and, in Sri Lanka, mostly from coppice shoots 18 to 36 months old. The leaves, branches, and stem tips are distilled with steam for the volatile oil. The bark is cut transversely and longitudinally and peeled. In Sri Lanka and Indonesia, the bark is scraped while fresh to remove epidermis and cork; in China, it is planed to remove partially the cork. In Sri Lanka, many layers of the thin inner bark are rolled into one quill; in Indonesia, several layers may be quilled together; and in China and Vietnam, each layer is quilled separately or only 2 or 3 layers are quilled together. Saigon cinnamon yields from 2 to 6% of volatile oil; cassia cinnamon, 0.5 to 1.5%; and Ceylon cinnamon, 0.5 to 1%. Other constituents are mannitol, which causes the sweetness of the bark, and tannin, which is abundant in cassia cinnamon. Saigon, Ceylon, and cassia cinnamon are carminatives and flavors.

The powdered cinnamon found in the grocery trade is frequently a blend of several kinds of cinnamon. The blending is done either to improve the aromatic quality or to cheapen the product.

Cinnamon oil is the volatile oil distilled with steam from the leaves and twigs of *Cinnamomum cassia* (Nees) Nees ex Blume (Fam. Lauraceae) and rectified by distillation. It is also known as **cassia oil.**

Cinnamon oil is a yellowish to brownish liquid that becomes darker and thicker by age or by exposure to air; it possesses the characteristic odor and taste of cassia cinnamon.

The principal constituent of the oil is cinnamic aldehyde, 80 to 95%; the remainder consists of terpenes, such as limonene, *p*-cymene, (−)-linalool, and β-caryophyllene, and other compounds such as eugenol.

Cinnamon oil is used as a flavoring agent; it is also a carminative and pungent aromatic. It has antiseptic properties.

Clove

Clove or cloves is the dried flower bud of *Eugenia caryophyllus* (Sprengel) Bullock et Harrison (*E. caryophyllata* Thunberg) (Fam Myrtaceae). *Eugenia*, which is Latin, and *caryophyllus*, which is Greek, mean "nut-leaf" and refer to the nutlike flower buds; "clove" is from the Latin *clavus*, meaning a nail, and refers to the shape of the whole spice.

The plant is a tree that grows to 15 meters in

height and is indigenous to the Molucca Islands but cultivated on the islands of Panang, Ambon, Pemba, Zanzibar, Sumatra, Madagascar, and Mauritius as well as in the Seychelles and the West Indies. The buds are gathered when they change from green to crimson and are carefully dried in the sun.

The best cloves come from Tanzania which provides four fifths of the world's supply. Clove was known to the Chinese before 266 B.C. The Dutch, who won possession of the Spice Islands in 1605, endeavored to create a monopoly and destroyed all the trees except those on the islands of Ambon and Ternate. In 1770, however, the French succeeded in introducing the tree into Mauritius and Réunion. From there, its cultivation spread to other clove-growing areas. Almost 65% of the world's supply of cloves is ground and mixed with tobacco in cigarettes and consequently smoked. The largest consumer is Indonesia, which imports more than half of Tanzania's cloves each year.

Clove contains a volatile oil, 14 to 20%; gallotannic acid, 10 to 13%; oleanolic acid; vanillin; and the chromone, eugenin.

Clove is a carminative and a flavor.

Clove oil is the volatile oil distilled with steam from the dried flower buds of *Syzgium aromaticum* (L.) Merr. et L.M. Perry . It contains not less than 85%, by volume, of total phenolic substances, chiefly eugenol.

The oil contains free eugenol (70 to 95%), eugenol acetate, and 5 to 8% β-caryophyllene. Together these constituents constitute about 99% of the oil, but they do not account for the characteristic, fresh, fruity note of clove oil. This is produced by several minor constituents, especially methyl-*n*-amyl ketone.

Clove oil is classed as a flavor. It is commonly employed as a toothache remedy that is applied topically to dental cavities as required. Clove oil also possesses antiseptic, counterirritant, and carminative properties. Oils with a particularly high content of eugenol are used in the commercial production of vanillin.

Eugenol or 4-allyl-2-methoxyphenol is a phenol obtained from clove oil and from other sources. It is usually prepared from clove oil by shaking with a 10% solution of sodium hydroxide to form sodium eugenolate. The mixture is washed with ether, and the sodium eugenolate is then decomposed with sulfuric acid. The eugenol is separated by steam distillation. It is a colorless or pale yellow, thin liquid that has a strongly aromatic odor of clove and a pungent spicy taste.

Eugenol is classed as a dental analgesic. It is applied topically to dental cavities and often mixed with zinc oxide as a temporary dental filling.

Nutmeg

Nutmeg or myristica is the dried, ripe seed of *Myristica fragrans* Houttuyn (Fam. Myristicaceae) deprived of its seed coat and arillode and with or without a thin coating of lime. The tree is indigenous to the Molucca and neighboring islands and is now extensively cultivated in other tropical regions, including the West Indies. The botanical name, *Myristica fragrans*, refers to the fragrance of the nutmeg. The commercial supply is largely derived from the Malay Archipelago. The trees bear continuously. Two or three crops are collected yearly. First the fleshy pericarp is removed and then the arillode, which constitutes **mace** when dried, is removed. The seeds are dried, requiring from 3 to 6 weeks, and then the brittle testa is cracked off.

With the exception of those from Penang, nutmegs are partially coated with lime to protect them from attack by insects.

Nutmegs were introduced into Europe by the Arabs about the middle of the 12th century but were not a prevailing article of commerce until the sea routes to the Indies were opened in the 16th century. They played an important part in the Dutch spice monopoly until the tree began to be cultivated in other parts of the world in 1800.

Nutmeg contains fixed oil, 25 to 40%, that is solid at ordinary temperatures, sometimes occurs in prismatic crystals, and is known as ''nutmeg butter''; volatile oil, 8 to 15%, that contains myristicin and safrole; proteins in considerable amounts; and starch. Myristica is a flavor and a condiment.

In recent years, nutmeg has gained a reputation, especially among prison inmates, as a hallucinogenic agent. However, the relatively large amount (up to 15 g) that must be ingested to cause the desired intoxication also produces flushing of the skin, tachycardia, absence of salivation, and other undesirable side effects. The active principal(s) responsible for the effects on the central nervous system have not been identified with certainty, but elemicin and myristicin are believed to be involved. Some theories involve the *in vivo* biotransformation of these nutmeg constituents into amphetaminelike, nitrogen-containing metabolites.

Dihydromethysticin

Nutmeg oil or myristica oil is the volatile oil distilled with steam from the dried kernels of the ripe seeds of *Myristica fragrans*.

The oil contains 10 to 30% α-pinene, 10 to 20% β-pinene, 15 to 30% sabinene, 5 to 12% myristicin, 2 to 7% (±)-limonene, 3 to 6% γ-terpinene, and 1 to 2% safrole.

Nutmeg oil is a flavoring agent. It possesses carminative properties.

Peppermint

Peppermint consists of the dried leaf and flowering top of *Mentha piperita* Linné (Fam. Lamiaceae). *Mentha* is from the Greek *Mintha*, the name of a mythical nymph metamorphosed into this plant; *piperita* is from the Latin *piper*, meaning pepper, and alludes to the aromatic and pungent taste of peppermint.

The plant is a perennial herb indigenous to Europe and naturalized in the northern United States and Canada. It is extensively cultivated in areas where the fertile soil has high water-holding capacity. If rainfall is not sufficient, an irrigation system is essential. Peppermint requires a daytime length of 15 to 16 hours and as much sunlight as possible. The plants are propagated by rhizome cuttings. When in flower, they are cut with a mowing machine, raked into windrows, dried for a few hours in the sun, and hauled to the still house. If the plant is to be used as a drug, it is carefully dried and preserved. Several varieties of peppermint are cultivated in the United States; but, whereas the American peppermint oil is all derived from *M. piperita*, the Japanese peppermint oil is obtained from *M. arvensis* Linné var. *piperascens*. Peppermint contains volatile oil (about 1%), resin, and tannin.

Commercial dried peppermint usually consists of the dried herb, though it should contain not more than 2% of stems over 3 mm in diameter. It loses some volatile oil during drying and more during storage; the usual commercial sample has suffered 95% deterioration and yields no volatile oil upon steam distillation. However, the distillate water may be aromatic.

Peppermint oil is the volatile oil distilled with steam from the fresh overground parts of the flowering plant of *Mentha piperita*, rectified by distillation and neither partially nor wholly dementholized. It yields not less than 5% of esters, calculated as menthyl acetate, and not less than 50% of total menthol, free and as esters.

About 90% of the American production of the oil is obtained from Washington, Oregon, and Idaho, principally from the Willamette river valley and Madras areas of Oregon, the Columbia river basin of Washington, and portions of the Snake river valley in Idaho. The remainder of the oil is produced in Wisconsin and Indiana. A few years ago, southern Michigan was the major area of mint cultivation in the United States, but a fungus blight (*Verticillium* wilt) infected crops and caused abandonment of thousands of acres of formerly productive land. In recent years, wilt-resistant strains of peppermint have been developed by using the technique of irradiation mutations, thereby eliminating the threat to the industry of fungal blight.

Peppermint oil is a colorless or pale yellow liquid that has a strong, penetrating odor of peppermint and a pungent taste that is followed by a sensation of cold when air is drawn into the mouth.

American peppermint oil contains from 50 to 78% of free (−)-menthol and from 5 to 20% combined in various esters such as the acetate. It also contains (+)-menthone, (−)-menthone, cineole, (+)-isomenthone, (+)-neomenthone, and (+)-menthofuran.

Because of the commercial importance of mint oils, the interconversions of the various terpene constituents of the oils have been studied more extensively than those of other volatile oil plants.

The availability of substantial amounts of both biochemical and genetic data provided an opportunity to understand the genetic control of the production of monoterpenoids in the genus *Mentha* of which there are approximately 25 species, an equal number of hybrids, and a larger number of intraspecific chemical races or chemotypes. Using both *in vivo* and *in vitro* experimental systems, the sequence of intermediates has been established (Fig. 6–7), and the relevant enzymes have been isolated and characterized. Recently, a gene encoding a key enzyme (4S-limonene synthase) of the pathway has been iso-

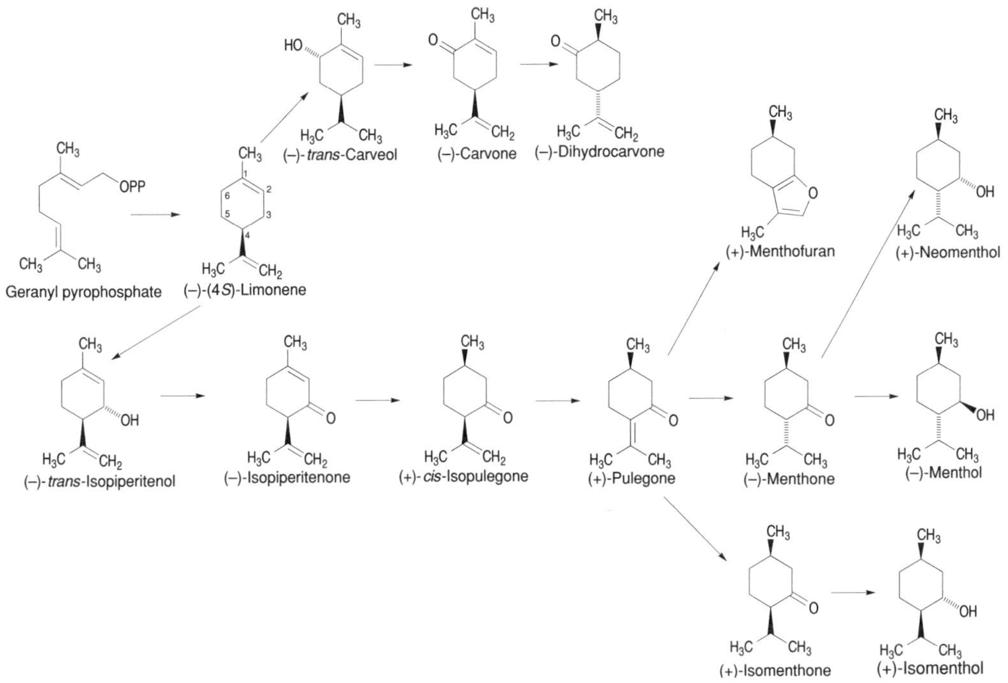

Fig. 6–7. Pathways of monoterpenoid biosynthesis in *Mentha* species.

lated, sequenced, and functionally expressed in a bacterial host.

The regiospecificity of oxygenation is programmed very early in the monoterpenoid biosynthetic sequence where (−)-(4*S*)-limonene, the first cyclic monoterpenoid to arise from the common intermediate geranyl pyrophosphate, is hydroxylated at C-3 to yield (−)-*trans*-isopiperitenol (in peppermint-type species) or at C-6 to afford (−)-*trans*-carveol (in spearmint-type species).

The influence of environmental factors on essential oil composition has been apparent to commercial producers for many years. Plants of the same species and genotype may produce oils of different quality when grown in different areas. The long days of northern latitudes favor the production of a peppermint oil that contains relatively small amounts of menthone and menthofuran and large amounts of menthol, whereas plants subjected to short-day illumination produce an oil that contains small amounts of menthol and relatively large amounts of menthofuran. High concentrations (up to 30% in some cases) of menthofuran in such oils impart a disagreeable cloying odor to products in which they may be incorporated.

Peppermint oil is a pharmaceutic aid (flavor). It has been used as a carminative, a stimulant, and a counterirritant. Its chief commercial importance is as a flavor for confections, especially for chewing gum.

RESINS AND RESIN COMBINATIONS

Resins are amorphous products with a complex chemical nature. They are usually formed in schizogenous or in schizolysigenous ducts or cavities and are end products of metabolism. Physically, resins are usually hard, transparent, or translucent and, when heated, they are complex mixtures of resin acids, resin alcohols, resinotannols, esters, and resenes. They are insoluble in water, and some investigators believe resins are oxidation products of the terpenes. Several resins are used in pharmacy and in the arts, among which rosin, guaiac, and mastic are typical examples.

Resins often occur in more or less homogeneous mixtures with volatile oils; the mixtures are known as **oleoresins.** Natural oleoresins are exemplified by turpentine. Oleoresins also occur in mixtures with gums; these mixtures are called

oleo-gum-resins. Because gums are water-soluble carbohydrate derivatives, they can be separated from oleoresins rather easily. Oleo-gum-resins include myrrh. The nomenclature of these resinous combinations is, at best, artificial because small amounts of volatile oil are often present in resins, and small amounts of gum are often present in oleoresins.

Balsams are resinous mixtures that contain cinnamic acid, benzoic acid, or both, or esters of these acids. Benzoin, Peru balsam, Tolu balsam, and storax are typical balsams. The term ''balsam'' has been erroneously applied to some oleoresins, e.g., balsam of copaiba. This error has occasionally led to some confusion.

When resins are separated and purified, they are usually brittle, amorphous solids that fuse readily when heated, after passing through a preliminary stage of softening. They are insoluble in water but dissolve in alcohol or other organic solvents. On evaporation these solutions deposit the resin as a varnishlike film. Resins burn with a characteristic, smoky flame.

Resins may be the final products in destructive metabolism. Many are believed to be oxidation products of the terpenes. They are usually more or less complex mixtures, and their principal constituents may be classified as follows.

Resin acids contain a large proportion of diterpenoid oxyacids, usually combining the properties of carboxylic acids and phenols. They occur both in the free state and as esters. They are soluble in aqueous solutions of the alkalies, usually forming soaplike solutions or colloidal suspensions. Their metallic salts are known as resinates, and some of these resinates are used extensively in the manufacture of cheap soaps and varnishes. Examples of resin acids are abietic acid in rosin or colophony and commiphoric acid in myrrh.

Complex alcohols of high molecular weight, known as **resinotannols,** give a tannin reaction with iron salts. **Resinols** do not give such a reaction. The resin alcohols occur in the free state and as esters in combination with simple aromatic acids (benzoic, salicylic, cinnamic, and umbellic). The following resinotannols have been isolated: peruresinotannol from balsam of Peru, siaresinotannol and sumaresinotannol from benzoin, and toluresinotannol from balsam of Tolu. The following are examples of resinols: benzoresinol from benzoin and storesinol from storax.

Complex neutral substances devoid of characteristic chemical properties are called **resenes.**

They do not form salts or esters and are insoluble in and resist hydrolysis by alkalies.

Pharmaceutic resins are usually obtained (1) by extracting the drug with alcohol and precipitating the resin in water; (2) by separating the oil from oleoresin by distillation, as with rosin from turpentine; or (3) by collecting the natural product that has exuded as oleoresin from the plant through natural or artificial punctures and from which the natural oil has partially evaporated into the atmosphere, as with mastic.

Rosin

Rosin or colophony is a solid resin obtained from *Pinus palustris* Miller and other spices of *Pinus* Linné (Fam. Pinaceae).

The commercial grades of rosin vary in color from light amber (the finest or ''water-white'' grade) to almost black (and very dirty). Rosin has a great variety of technical uses. Only the light-colored transparent rosins are used medicinally.

Rosin usually occurs as shiny, angular fragments that are translucent, amber-colored, and often covered with a yellowish dust. Rosin is hard, brittle, and easily pulverized.

Rosin contains from 80 to 90% of the anhydrides of abietic acid (which, on treatment with alcohol, are changed into crystalline abietic acid); sylvic acid, which is probably a decomposition product of abietic acid; sapinic acid; pimaric acid and other acids; and resene, a hydrocarbon.

Rosin is used as a stiffening agent in cerates, plasters, and ointments. Commercially, rosin is used in the manufacture of varnishes, varnish and paint dryers, printing inks, soap, sealing wax, floor coverings, and numerous other products. Rosin is frequently used as an adulterant of other resinous products.

Eriodictyon

Eriodictyon or yerba santa is the dried leaf of *Eriodictyon californicum* (Hooker et Arnott) Torrey (Fam. Hydrophyllaceae). *Eriodictyon* is Greek and means woolly, referring to the hairy leaves. The plant is an evergreen shrub indigenous to the mountains of California and northern Mexico. The drug has been employed by the Indians of California for many years.

Eriodictyon contains a resin, eriodictyol (the aglycone of eriodictin), xanthoeriodictyol, chrysoeriodictyol, homoeriodictyol, eriodictyonic acid, formic acid, butyric acid, volatile oil, and tannin.

Eriodictyon is a flavor used to disguise the bitterness of certain preparations, such as those containing quinine. It has also been used as a stimulating expectorant.

Mastic

Mastic, mastiche, or mastich is the concrete resinous exudate from *Pistacia lentiscus* Linné (Fam. Anacardiaceae). The plant is a shrub or small tree indigenous to the Mediterranean region and cultivated in the Grecian archipelago, especially on the island of Chios. The resinous juice collects in cavities in the inner bark. Long incisions are made in the trunk and in larger branches, through which the resin exudes. The resin finally collects in small tears on the outside. The origin of the use of mastic is lost in antiquity; it is mentioned by both Theophrastus and Pliny. Mastic has long been chewed by Oriental women as a breath sweetener and is a common article in Oriental bazaars. Its employment in medicine dates back to about the 13th century.

Mastic contains about 90% of a resin, consisting of α-resin (mastichic acid), which is soluble in alcohol, and β-resin (masticin), which is insoluble in alcohol, and a volatile oil, 1 to 2.5%, which has the balsamic odor of the drug and consists chiefly of (+)-pinene. A bitter principal is also present. Mastic is used in the form of a dental varnish to seal cavities.

Kava

Kava or kava-kava is the dried rhizome and roots of *Piper methysticum* Forster (Fam. Piperaceae). The plant is a large shrub widely cultivated in Oceania; its underground parts have been extensively used by the natives of these islands in the preparation of an intoxicating beverage.

In addition to large quantities of starch, the drug contains about 5 to 10% of a resin from which six different, closely related styrylpyrones have been isolated in pure form: yangonin, desmethoxyyangonin, kawain, dihydrokawain, methysticin, and dihydromethysticin. Pharmacologic studies have shown that all of the kava pyrones are more or less potent, centrally acting skeletal muscle relaxants. In addition to inducing changes in motor function and reflex irritability, they possess antipyretic and local anesthetic properties. Differences in action are largely quantitative. The central nervous and peripheral activities of the kava pyrones are sufficient to account for the native use of the drug.

Cannabis

Cannabis, Indian hemp, marihuana, or pot consists of the dried flowering tops of the pistillate plants of *Cannabis sativa* Linné (Fam. Moraceae).

The plant is an annual, dioecious herb indigenous to central and western Asia and is cultivated in India and other tropical and temperate regions for the fiber and seed. *Cannabis* is the ancient Greek name of hemp.

Cannabis was used in China and India, spread slowly through Persia to Arabia where the resin was known as **hashish,** and probably was introduced into European and American materia medica about the time of Napoleon.

Through many years of selective cultivation, two genetic types of cannabis have evolved. One, designated the drug type, is rich (up to 15%) in the psychoactive constituent $(-)$-Δ^9-*trans*-tetrahydrocannabinol (Δ^9-THC). The other, referred to as the hemp type, contains little active principal (cannabidiol is the predominant cannabinoid) but has the elongated bast fibers desired in the manufacture of rope.

The Δ^9-THC is concentrated into a resin which is secreted into trichomes found on the small leaves (bracts) and bracteoles (leaf-like structure that encloses the ovary) of the flowering tops of the female plant. Consequently, for drug purposes either the resin (hashish) is used or the flowering tops of the female plant (marihuana). The male plant produces an equivalent amount of active constituents; however, it is not concentrated into a resin but found throughout the plant.

The amount of resin found in the pistillate flowering tops of *C. sativa* markedly decreases when the plants are grown in the more temperate climates. Thus, Indian cannabis yields 20% or more of resin; Wisconsin hemp, 6% or less.

The unusual sensations induced in humans by the uncontrolled use of cannabis are obtained more promptly and with less drug by inhaling the smoke of burning cannabis than by oral dosage. By smoking marihuana, the drug effects are noticeable almost immediately and reach a peak in 30 minutes. Users experience euphoria and relaxation. Intoxicated persons also develop an altered time sense with an enhanced awareness of their environment. Thought processes are slowed, short-term memory impaired, and one has difficulty concentrating. In most users driving performance is impaired. The importation into the United States of rather crude **Mexican cannabis (marihuana)** cigarettes began several decades ago. As the demand for these cigarettes **(reefers)** increased and the habit of smoking them spread to school children, federal and state narcotic agents started a campaign to stamp out their sale. The importation of Indian cannabis was prohibited, and even large areas of naturally growing American hemp were destroyed. This campaign continues and has resulted in discontinued medicinal use of cannabis in the United States.

Δ⁹-THC

In addition to Δ^9-THC, other constituents isolated from cannabis resin include cannabinol, cannabidiol, cannabidiolic acid, cannabichromene, cannabigerol, and Δ^8-*trans*-tetrahydrocannabinol. Tetrahydrocannabinols (Δ^8- and Δ^9-THC) possess euphoric activity, cannabinol is weakly active, and cannabichromene and cannabidiolic acid are sedative principals. Δ^9-THC has been synthesized and the pure compound utilized for physiologic studies in human beings.

Cannabis is cultivated to a considerable extent for its bast fibers, **hemp**, and for its fruits, **hempseed;** the latter contain about 20% of a fixed oil that is expressed and used in the manufacture of paints and soap; the cake meal is used as cattle food.

(−)-Δ⁹-*trans*-Tetrahydrocannabinol

Δ⁹-Tetrahydrocannabinol or dronabinol is a meroterpenoid prepared from the plant *Cannabis sativa* or through chemical synthesis. It has as antiemetic effect and is used orally in the treatment of the nausea and vomiting associated with cytotoxic drugs that are used in cancer chemotherapy. Its mechanism of action is possibly through binding to opiate receptors in the forebrain and indirectly inhibiting the emetic center in the medulla oblongata. A secondary, mild anxiolytic activity may contribute to its overall efficacy.

In addition, because marihuana and Δ^9-THC stimulate the appetite, Δ^9-THC is used in the treatment of anorexia associated with weight loss in patients with AIDS.

OLEORESINS

Oleoresins are homogenous mixtures of resins and volatile oils.

There is no sharp line of demarcation between these various types of resinous substances, and classification is sometimes difficult. Small proportions of volatile oils are present in many resins. Depending on the relative amount of volatile oil in the mixture, oleoresins may be liquid, semisolid, or solid. Usually there is a small amount of ''natural'' exudate from oleoresin-containing trees owing to insect damage, broken branches, and other injuries, but the commercial supplies are generally obtained by artificial incision through the bark and even into the wood.

Turpentine

Turpentine, gum turpentine, gum thus is the concrete oleoresin obtained from *Pinus palustris* Miller and from other species of *Pinus* (Fam. Pinaceae).

''Gum'' turpentine or ''gum'' is a common name among the collectors and dealers of turpentine but is a misnomer from the scientific standpoint. Turpentine is not related to the true gums and mucilages of carbohydrate origin.

Turpentine is collected from the longleaf pine (*P. palustris* Miller) and from the slash pine (*P. elliottii* Engelmann var. *elliottii*) that grow in North and South Carolina, Georgia, and northern Florida. The trees form vast forests and present a characteristic appearance owing to the ''face'' of the cut surface. Turpentine yields depend on the treatment and the size of the tree. If skillfully worked, trees yield for 15 to 20 years.

The oleoresin is secreted in ducts located directly beneath the cambium in the sapwood. During the spring of the year, bark is chipped from the tree by using a ''bark hack,'' a long-handled cutting blade. Following removal of the rounded chip, a spray of 50% solution of sulfuric acid is applied to the freshly cut surface. As the sap (oleoresin) flows, it is guided by metal gutters into containers attached directly to the tree trunk; the thick liquid that collects is removed periodically and taken to the turpentine still.

The acid treatment collapses the thin-walled parenchymal cells that line the resin ducts. This allows the duct channels to become larger, providing a more rapid flow of oleoresin and reducing the chances of hardened secretions blocking the outlets. The acid does not stimulate greater production of oleoresin by the tree, but it enables more oleoresin from the ducts to escape, thus prolonging the flow. If applied properly, acid treatment does not injure the tree.

The usual turpentining season lasts about 32 weeks. The product of the first year's cutting is superior and is known as "virgin" turpentine. On steam distillation, it yields from 15 to 30% of volatile oil (turpentine oil). The hot filtered residue left after distillation constitutes rosin.

The United States is the world's largest producer of rosin and turpentine, accounting for about 70% of the supply. This industry is often referred to as "naval stores" trade because the wooden sailing vessels of the 17th century used enormous quantities of tar and pitch obtained from the coniferous forests of Europe. Since then, the trade has followed the location of the pine forests, moving from New England southward as the trees were depleted or became inaccessible.

Turpentine occurs as yellowish, opaque masses that are lighter internally, more or less glossy, sticky when warm, and brittle in the cold.

The drug constituents are volatile oil and resin. It is employed externally as a counterirritant.

Ginger

Ginger or zingiber is the dried rhizome of *Zingiber officinale* Roscoe (Fam. Zingiberaceae), known in commerce as Jamaica ginger, African ginger, and Cochin ginger. The outer cortical layers are often either partially or completely removed. *Zingiber* is from the Arabic *Zindschebil*, meaning root of Zindschi (India). The specific name refers to its use as an ingredient of preparations made in drug shops.

The ginger plant is propagated in Jamaica by rhizome cuttings that are planted in March and April. The rhizomes are dug and peeled in December and January. As soon as they are peeled, the rhizomes are washed in water for hours, then dried in the sun for 5 to 6 days. They are covered at night and during rainy weather.

Ginger was known in China as early as the 14th century B.C.

It was used as a spice by the Greeks and Romans. From the 11th to the 13th centuries, ginger was a common import from the East. Marco Polo observed it in China and India from 1280 to 1290. Ginger was introduced into Jamaica and other islands of the West Indies by the Spaniards, and drug exports from the West Indies to Spain were made in considerable quantities as early as 1547.

Ginger owes its characteristic aroma to about 1 to 3% of a volatile oil, the principal constituents of which are three sesquiterpenoids: bisabolene, zingiberene, and zingiberol. The characteristic pungency of the drug is attributed to ginger oleoresin, from which two aromatic ketones, zingerone and shogaol, have been isolated. In addition, ginger contains more than 50% of starch.

Ginger is classed as a flavor; it is used as a condiment, an aromatic stimulant, and a carminative. Much of the ginger consumed in the present-day market is used in the manufacture of ginger ale.

OLEO-GUM-RESINS

Oleo-gum-resins are mixtures of resin, gum, volatile oil, and, frequently, small quantities of other substances. A principal oleo-gum-resin is myrrh.

Myrrh

Myrrh or gum myrrh is an oleo-gum-resin obtained from *Commiphora molmol* Engler, from *C. abyssinica* (Berg) Engler, or from other species of *Commiphora* Jacquin (Fam. Burseraceae). The name myrrh is from the Arabic *murr*, meaning bitter; *Commiphora* is Greek and means gum bearing; *molmol* is the native Somali name; and *abyssinica* refers to the habitat of the plant. The plants are small trees that sometimes attain a height of 10 meters and are found growing on the Arabian peninsula and in Ethiopia and Somalia.

The oleo-gum-resin exudes naturally or from incisions made in the bark; it is at first a yellowish color, but soon hardens in the intense heat of these countries, becomes darker, and is then collected. Practically all of the commercial supply comes from Somalia.

There are numerous references to myrrh in the Old Testament, but it is highly possible that the product thus designated was bdellium. Myrrh was an ingredient of the embalming material of the Egyptians. Its use in incense and perfumes in ceremonial religious life since the days of remote antiquity is well known. Theophrastus, Pliny, and other early writers mention myrrh, and from early times it has been valued in domestic medicine for its aromatic qualities.

Myrrh contains a volatile oil, 2.5 to 8%, that has the characteristic odor of myrrh; resin, 25 to 40%, composed of several constituents, among which are resin acids (α-, β- and γ-commiphoric acids), resenes, and phenolic compounds, namely protocatechuic acid and pyrocatechin; gum, about 60%, consisting of soluble and insoluble portions and forming a mucilage that does not readily ferment (being of the acacia type) and yielding arabinose; and a bitter principle, sparingly soluble in water but soluble in alcohol.

Myrrh is a protective; it has also been employed as a stimulant and a stomachic. It is used in mouthwashes as an astringent.

BALSAMS

Balsams are resinous mixtures that contain large proportions of benzoic acid, cinnamic acid, or both, or esters of these acids. Benzoin is sometimes referred to as a balsamic resin. The medicinal balsams include Tolu balsam, Peru balsam, storax, and benzoin.

Storax

Storax is a balsam obtained from the trunk of *Liquidambar orientalis* Miller, known in commerce as Levant storax, or of *L. styraciflua* Linné, known in commerce as American storax (Fam. Hamamelidaceae). Storax is also known as **liquid storax** or **styrax.**

The term *styrax* is from the Arabian *assitirax*, meaning a sweet-smelling exudation; *liquidambar* is from the Latin *liquidus*, meaning fluid, and from the Arabian *ambar*, meaning amber; *orientalis* means pertaining to the Orient; and *styraciflua* means to flow storax.

L. orientalis is a tree that attains a height of about 15 meters and grows in Asia Minor. *L. styraciflua* is a tree that attains a height of up to 40 meters and grows in southern North America, Central America, and South America. Levant storax is a pathologic product; its formation is induced by bruising or puncturing the bark of the tree in early summer, thereby causing the cambium to produce new wood with balsam-secreting ducts. In autumn, the bark, which is more or less saturated with balsam, is peeled off and the balsam is recovered by pressing.

Most of the American storax is produced in Central America where large forests of *L. styraciflua* are found. The balsam exudes into natural pockets between the bark and the wood and may be located by excrescences on the outside of the bark. These pockets, which contain up to 4 kg of the balsam, are tapped with gutters, and the balsam is led into containers. A large quantity is also produced in the United States but is used mostly in the tobacco industry for flavoring cigarettes.

The early Arabian physicians were acquainted with storax, and it is mentioned as early as the 12th century. Most of the styrax used in the pharmacy comes from Turkey and Honduras.

Levant storax occurs as a viscid, grayish to grayish brown, more or less opaque, semiliquid mass that deposits a heavier, dark brown, oleoresinous stratum on standing. American storax is a nearly clear, yellowish brown semiliquid that becomes hard, opaque, and darker colored. Storax is insoluble in water but almost completely soluble in warm alcohol.

Levant storax consists of about 50% of two resin alcohols, α-storesin and β-storesin, which are partly free and partly in combination with cinnamic acid. α-Storesin is amorphous but forms a crystalline compound with potassium. β-Storesin occurs as white flakes that do not form a crystalline compound with potassium. Storax also contains storesin cinnamate, 10 to 20%; styracin or cinnamyl cinnamate, 5 to 10%, in needle-crystals that are colorless, odorless, and tasteless; phenylpropyl cinnamate, 10%, a liquid with the odor and taste of styrax; volatile oil, 0.5 to 1%; a trace of vanillin; free cinnamic acid, from 2 to 5%; and small amounts of several other substances. Free cinnamic acid may be obtained from storax by microsublimation with a yield of up to 20%.

American storax contains related storesins and other principals of Levant storax: it yields 7% of volatile oil by steam distillation and contains about 28% of cinnamic acid, 23% of cinnamein, 35% of resin esters, and 2% of resin acids.

Storax is a pharmaceutic aid for compound benzoin tincture. It has been used as a stimulant, an expectorant, and an antiseptic.

Peruvian Balsam

Peruvian balsam, Peru balsam, or balsam of Peru is obtained from *Myroxylon pereirae* (Royle) Klostzsch (Fam. Fabaceae)

The balsam trees attain a height of about 25

meters and are especially abundant along the coast of El Salvador in Central America. The tree has been naturalized in Florida and in Sri Lanka. It was frequently referred to by writers who described the conquest of Guatemala in 1524. In the 17th century, the drug appeared in a German pharmacy, after which its use became universal.

The balsam is a pathologic product and is formed by injury to the trees. Most of the commercial supply comes from El Salvador, although some is produced in Honduras.

Peruvian balsam occurs as a dark brown, viscid liquid that appears reddish brown and transparent in thin layers. It is free from stringiness or stickiness and has an empyreumatic, aromatic, vanilla-like odor and a bitter, acrid, persistent taste.

The drug contains cinnamein, about 60%, which is a volatile oil consisting chiefly of benzyl cinnamate and a lesser amount of benzyl benzoate; resin esters, 30 to 38%, which are composed mostly of peruresinotannol cinnamate and benzoate; vanillin; free cinnamic acid; peruviol; and other substances in small amounts.

Peru balsam is a local protectant and rubefacient; it also is a parasiticide in certain skin diseases. It is an antiseptic and vulnerary and is applied externally either alone, in alcoholic solution, or in the form of an ointment. The drug is employed for its astringent properties in various preparations used to treat hemorrhoids.

Tolu Balsam

Tolu balsam is a balsam obtained from *Myroxylon balsamum* (Linné) Harms (Fam. Fabaceae). Tolu balsam is sometimes called balsam of Tolu.

The balsam trees grow abundantly along the lower Magdalena River in Colombia. Tolu is a district near Cartagena, where the balsam was once extensively produced.

Balsam of Tolu is usually considered to be a pathologic product similar to balsam of Peru or coniferous oleoresins.

Tolu balsam occurs as a plastic solid that gradually hardens, becoming brown or yellowish brown. It is transparent in thin layers, brittle when old, dried, or exposed to cold, and shows numerous crystals of cinnamic acid. Its odor is agreeably aromatic, resembling that of vanilla, and its taste is aromatic and slightly pungent.

The drug contains resin esters, 75 to 80%, chiefly toluresinotannol cinnamate with a small

quantity of the benzoate; volatile oil, 7 to 8%, chiefly benzyl benzoate; free cinnamic acid, 12 to 15%; free benzoic acid, 2 to 8%; vanillin; and other constituents in small quantities.

Tolu balsam is a pharmaceutic aid for compound benzoin tincture. It is sometimes used as an expectorant and is extensively used as a pleasant flavoring in medicinal syrups, confectionery, chewing gum, and perfumery.

Benzoin

Benzoin is the balsamic resin obtained from *Styrax benzoin* Dryander, *S. paralleloneurus* Perkins, known in commerce as Sumatra benzoin, *S. tonkinensis* (Pierre) Craib ex Hartwich, or other species of the Section Anthostyrax of the genus *Styrax*, known in commerce as Siam benzoin (Fam. Styraceae). *Styrax* is the ancient Greek name of storax applied to a sweet-scented gum and to the tree producing it; *benzoin* is from the Arabic *ben*, meaning fragrant, or the Hebrew *ben*, meaning branch, and *zoa*, an exudation, meaning the juice of the branch; *tonkinensis* is named after Tonkin, the northern region of Vietnam.

The plants are trees of medium height that grow in southeastern Asia and the East Indies. *S. benzoin* is cultivated throughout Sumatra; *S. tonkinensis* in Thailand, Vietnam, and Laos. Benzoin is a pathologic product developed by incising the bark. After about 2 months, the exuding balsamic resin becomes less sticky and firm enough to collect.

The first tapping of *S. benzoin* yields the so-called almond tears. The second tapping yields a more fluid substance. The almond tears and the fluid substance are imported into Singapore and are admixed (possibly with adulterants) to produce block benzoin.

Benzoin was unknown to the Greeks and Romans. It was first mentioned by Ibn Batuta, who visited Sumatra in the 14th century. In the 15th century, it still appeared as a precious balsam, but in the 16th century it was an article of Venetian commerce.

The use of Siam benzoin is confined almost entirely to perfumery. The tears of Siam benzoin are graded according to size and color; the smaller tears and siftings are darker in color. In pharmacy, only the Sumatra benzoin is used. Before World War II, Sumatra benzoin was obtained directly from Sumatra; today almost all Sumatra benzoin is imported from Singapore.

Sumatra benzoin occurs as blocks or irregular

masses composed of tears of variable size imbedded in a translucent or opaque matrix. It is brittle, and internally the tears are milky white, becoming soft when warmed and gritty when chewed. The matrix is reddish or grayish brown; the odor is agreeable, balsamic, and resembles that of storax; the taste is aromatic and resinous.

Siam benzoin occurs mostly in separate concavo-convex tears that are yellowish brown to rusty brown externally and milky white on the freshly broken surface. The tears are brittle but become soft when warmed and plastic when chewed. Siam benzoin has a vanillalike odor.

Siam benzoin consists principally of coniferyl benzoate (60 to 70%), plus smaller amounts of free benzoic acid (10%), the triterpene siaresinol, (6%), and a trace of vanillin.

Sumatra benzoin contains free balsamic acids, chiefly cinnamic (10%) and benzoic (6%), as well as esters derived from them. Triterpene acids, especially 19-hydroxyoleanolic and 6-hydroxyoleanolic, and traces of vanillin, phenylpropyl cinnamate, cinnamyl cinnamate, and phenylethylene are also present.

Sumatra benzoin yields not less than 75% of alcohol-soluble extractive; Siam benzoin yields not less than 90% of alcohol-soluble extractive. Benzoin possesses antiseptic, stimulant, expectorant, and diuretic properties.

Compound benzoin tincture is employed as a topical protectant and is applied as required. It contains benzoin, aloe, storax, and Tolu balsam and is valuable as an expectorant when vaporized.

Benzoic acid is now a synthetic product but was first obtained by sublimation from Sumatra benzoin. It occurs as white crystals, usually in the form of scales or needles. It has a slight odor of benzoin and is volatile at moderate temperatures, freely so in steam.

Benzoic acid and its sodium salt are extensively used as preservatives of foods, drinks, fats, pharmaceutic preparations, and other substances. Medicinally, benzoic acid is used primarily as an antifungal agent.

SUGGESTED READINGS

Agurell, S., Dewey, W.L., Willette, R.E., eds.: *The Cannabinoids: Chemical, Pharmacologic, and Therapeutic Aspects.* Orlando, Florida, Academic Press, Inc., 1984.

Charalambous, G., ed.: *Spices, Herbs and Edible Fungi.* Amsterdam, Elsevier Science B.V., 1994.

Connolly, J.D., Hill, R.A.: *Dictionary of Terpenoids,* Vols. 1-3. London, Chapman & Hall, 1991.

Cragg,G.M., Schepartz, S.A., Suffness, M., Grever, M.R.: The Taxol Supply Crisis. New NCI Policies for Handling the Large-scale Production of Novel Natural Product Anticancer and Anti-HIV Agents. J. Nat. Prod., 56 (10): 1657, 1993.

Croteau, R., Gershenzon, J.: Genetic Control of Monoterpene Biosynthesis in Mints (*Mentha:*Lamiaceae). In *Recent Advances in Phytochemistry,* Vol. 28: *Genetic Engineering of Plant Secondary Metabolites.* Ellis, B.E., Kuroki, G.W., Stafford, H.A.,eds. New York, Plenum Press, 1994.

Dev, S.,ed.: *Handbook of Terpenoids: Monoterpenoids,* Vols. I-II. Boca Raton, Florida, CRC Press, Inc., 1982.

Dev, S.,ed.: *Handbook of Terpenoids: Diterpenoids,* Vols. 1-4. Boca Raton, Florida, CRC Press, Inc., 1985-1986.

Dey, P.M., Harborne, J.B.,eds.: *Methods in Plant Biochemistry,* Vol. 7: *Terpenoids.* San Diego, Academic Press, Inc., 1991.

Erman, W.F.: *Chemistry of the Monoterpenes,* Parts A and B. New York, Marcel Dekker, Inc., 1985.

Farrell, K.T.: *Spices, Condiments, and Seasonings.* Westport, Connecticut, the AVI Publishing Company, Inc., 1985.

Harborne, J.B.,Tomas-Barberan, F.A., eds.: *Ecological Chemistry and Biochemistry of Plant Terpenoids.* Oxford, Clarendon Press, 1991.

Nahas, G.G.: *Keep off the Grass.* Middlebury, Vermont, Paul S. Eriksson, Publisher, 1990.

Nes, W.D., Parish, E.J., Trzaskos, J.M., eds.: *Regulation of Isopentenoid Metabolism.* Washington, DC, American Chemical Society, 1992.

Purseglove, J.W., Brown, E.G., Green, C.L., Robbins, S.R.J.: *Spices,* Vols. 1-2. Burnt Mill, United Kingdom, Longman Group Limited, 1981.

Rogers, J.A., Jr.: Essentials Oils, Kirk-Othmer Encyclopedia of Chemical Technology, 3rd ed., *16*:307, 1981.

Souza, N.J., Shah, V.: Forskolin-An Adenylate Cyclase Activating Drug from an Indian Herb. In *Economic and Medicinal Plant Research,* Vol. 2. Wagner, H., Hikino, H., Farnsworth, N.R., eds., London, Academic Press Limited, 1988.

Starks, M.: *Marijuana Chemistry: Genetics, Processing and Potency.* Berkeley, California, Ronin Publishing, 1990.

Taylor, W.I., Chant, B., van Loveren, G.: Perfumes, Kirk-Othmer Encyclopedia of Chemical Technology, 3rd ed., *16*:947, 1981.

Teranishi, R., Buttery, R.G., Sugisawa, H., eds.: *Bioactive Volatile Compounds from Plants.* Washington, DC, American Chemical Society, 1993.

Towers, G.H.N., Stafford, H.A., eds.: *Recent Advances in Phytochemistry,* Vol. 24: *Biochemistry of the Mevalonic Acid Pathway to Terpenoids.* New York, Plenum Press, 1990.

Trigg, P.I.: Qinghaosu (Artemisinin) as an Antimalarial Drug. In *Economic and Medicinal Plant Research,* Vol. 3. Wagner, H., Hikino, H., Farnsworth, N.R., eds., London, Academic Press Limited, 1989.

Weaver, J.C.: Natural resins, Kirk-Othmer Encyclopedia of Chemical Technology, 3rd ed., *20*: 197, 1982.

Wolff, I.A.: *Handbook of Processing and Utilization in Argriculture,* Vol. II, Part 2. Boca Raton, Florida, CRC Press, Inc., 1983.

7

Steroids

Steroids constitute a natural product class of compounds that is widely distributed throughout nature. The diversity of biologic activities of steroids includes the development and control of the reproductive tract in humans (estradiol, progesterone, testosterone), the molting of insects (ecdysone), and the induction of sexual reproduction in aquatic fungi (antheridiol). In addition, steroids contribute to a wide range of therapeutic applications, such as cardiotonics (digitoxin), vitamin D precursors (ergosterol), oral contraceptive agents (semisynthetic estrogens and progestins), anti-inflammatory agents (corticosteroids), and anabolic agents (androgens).

NOMENCLATURE

A steroid is any compound that contains a cyclopentanoperhydrophenanthrene nucleus. The chemical nomenclature of steroids is based on this fundamental carbocycle with adjacent side-chain carbon atoms. Each parent tetracyclic hydrocarbon bears a specific stem name, and some of the principal stereoparent hydrocarbons are shown in Figure 7–1. Steroids are numbered and rings are lettered as indicated in the structural formula for cholesterol. If one or more of the carbon atoms shown in the structure of cholesterol is not present, the numbering of the remainder is undisturbed.

Cholesterol

When the rings of a steroid are denoted as projections onto the plane of the paper, an atom or group attached to a ring is termed α (alpha) if it lies below the plane of the paper or β (beta) if it lies above the plane of the paper. In formulas, bonds to atoms or groups attached in an α configuration are shown as broken lines, and bonds to atoms or groups attached in a β configuration are shown as solid lines and may be thickened. Bonds to atoms or groups whose configuration is not known are denoted by wavy lines and designated ξ (xi) in the chemical name.

The use of a steroid stem name implies that atoms or groups attached at the ring-junction positions 8, 9, 10, 13, and 14 are oriented as shown in Figure 7–2 (8β, 9α, 10β, 13β, 14α,), and a carbon chain (R) attached to position 17 is assumed to be β-oriented. The backbone of the side chain at position 17 is denoted as in the plane of the paper (lines of ordinary thickness). Stereochemistry due to substituents on the chain is then indicated by the customary thick or broken lines denoting bonds that project, respectively, above and below the plane of the paper. The configuration of hydrogen or a substituent at the ring-junction position 5 is always designated by adding α or β after the numeral 5. This numeral and letter are placed immediately before the stem name. The implication of these conventions of nomenclature is that, in most steroids, rings B and C and rings C and D are fused *trans*, whereas rings A and B may be fused either *cis* or *trans*. For example, the bile acid, cholic acid, has a *cis*-fused A/B ring junction. The chemical name of cholic acid is 3α, 7α, 12α-trihydroxy-5β-cholan-24-oic acid. The sex hormone androsterone, chemical name 3α-hydroxy-5α-androstan-17-one, has a *trans*-fused A/B ring junction. An exception to these guidelines on ring fusion is made for the cardiac steroids with either cardanolide or bufa-

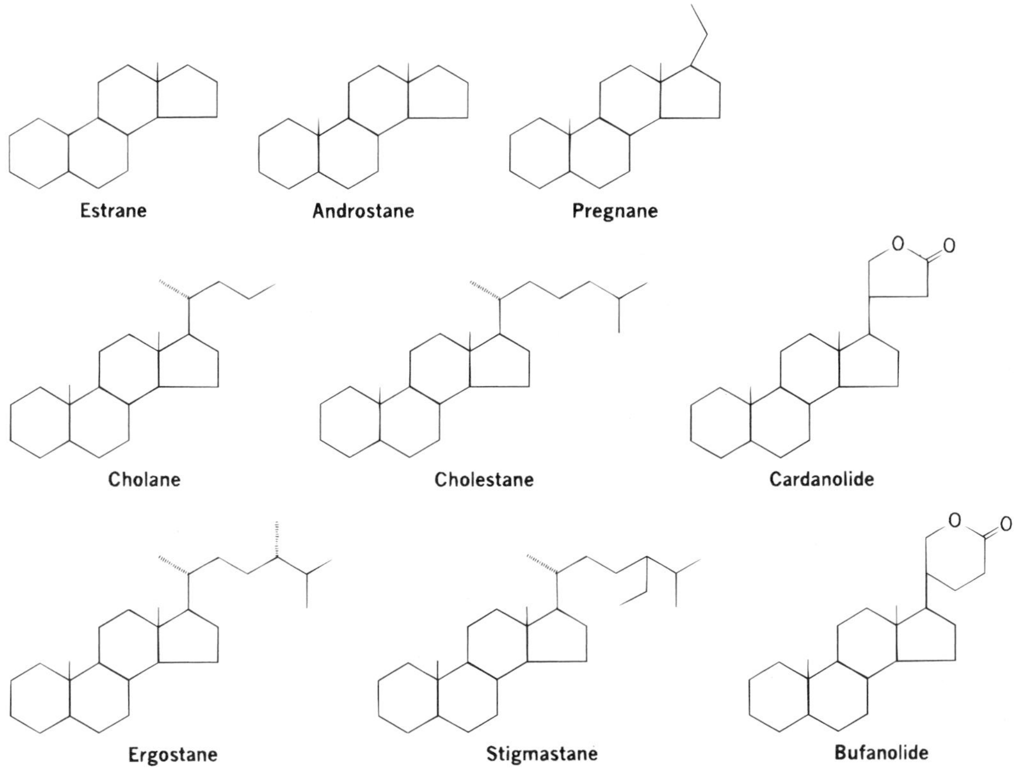

Fig. 7-1. Principal steroid stereoparent hydrocarbons.

nolide as the stereoparent. The 14β-configuration as well as the 20R-configuration are implied in the name; therefore, the former recommendation that the configuration at C-14 must always be stated as an affix has been abandoned.

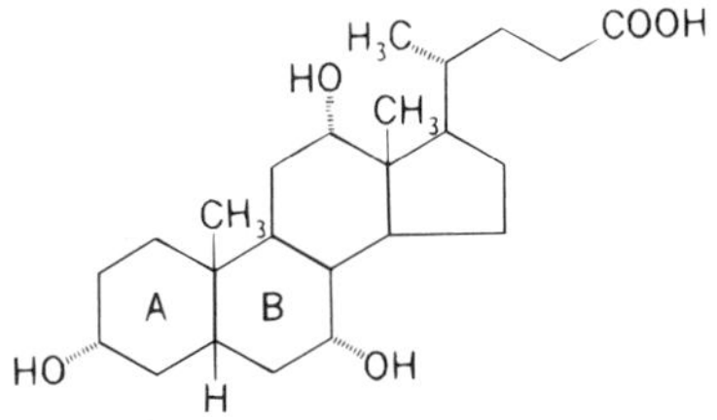

Cholic acid

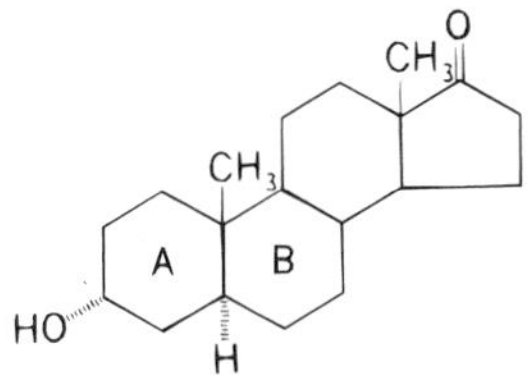

Androsterone

BIOSYNTHESIS

Steroids are formed biosynthetically from isopentenyl pyrophosphate (active isoprene) and involve the same sequence of reactions as does terpenoid biosynthesis. In fact, the triterpenoid squalene is an intermediate in steroid biosynthesis. Most knowledge of the biosynthesis of steroids has been derived from studies of cholesterol production. Although this compound is not necessarily a direct precursor of all other steroids, its formation may be considered as a general mechanism of steroid biosynthesis. The familiar acetate $\longrightarrow$ mevalonate $\longrightarrow$ isopentenyl

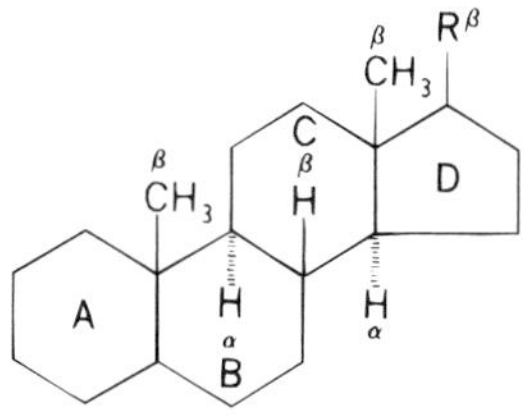

Fig. 7-2. Orientation of steroid substituents.

pyrophosphate →→ squalene →→ cholesterol pathway is outlined in Figure 7–3.

The first step in the pathway by which squalene is transformed into sterols is its stereospecific conversion into (3S)-2,3-oxidosqualene by squalene epoxidase. In the next step, the key enzyme involved in the cyclization of 2,3-oxidosqualene to the first cyclic sterol precursor in animals and fungi is 2,3-oxidosqualene:lanosterol cyclase. Lanosterol is replaced in photosynthetic organisms by its isomer cycloartenol, and the enzyme involved is 2,3-oxido-squalene:cycloartenol cyclase. The cyclization reaction has been called one of the most complicated in all of biochemistry. For example, squalene is an acyclic molecule with six double bonds, and the lanosterol molecule has four rings and seven asymmetric centers, all properly oriented. As shown in Figure 7–3, a proton initiates the cyclization by attacking the epoxide bond. Each of the rings form successively, involving attack by a π bond on a specific carbon. The reactions are fast enough and the intermediates rigid enough that stereochemistry is preserved as the rings form. Each π-bond attack leaves behind a carbonium ion, which is the target of the next attack.

After the rings are formed, the resulting carbonium ion intermediate, which has a positive charge at C-20, is stabilized by rearrangements involving two hydride shifts (17→20, 13→17) and two methyl shifts (14→13, 8→14). These shifts result in the migration of the positive charge to C-8 and, with the loss of a proton from C-9, either the 9,10,19-cyclopropane ring of cycloartenol or the 8,9-double bond of lanosterol may be formed. The conversion of the C_{30} compound, lanosterol, to the C_{27} steroid, cholesterol, involves the loss of three methyl groups, the shift of a double bond, and a reduction of a double bond. The sequence in which these reactions take place may vary, depending on the organism. Consequently, numerous intermediates, including zymosterol, have been isolated that represent various stages in this transformation.

Cholesterol Biosynthesis Inhibitors

An important class of therapeutic agents has evolved from early studies on the antibiotic mevastatin, also known as compactin, which is a potent inhibitor of (3S)-3-hydroxyl-3-methylglytaryl-CoA (HMG-CoA) reductase, the rate-limiting enzyme in endogenous cholesterol biosynthesis. Mevastatin effectively lowers LDL cholesterol levels in patients with hypercholesterolemia, a major risk factor in the development of cardiovascular diseases such as coronary heart disease and stroke.

Mevastatin was isolated from the fungi *Penicillium citrinum* and *P. brevicompactum* and the closely related compound lovastatin has been isolated from cultures of *Aspergillus terreus* and *Monascus ruber*. These compounds can be distinguished by a functionalized hexahydronaphthalene ring system and a β-hydroxy-δ-lactone portion linked by an ethylene bridge. Compounds with this structure are referred to as mevinic acids and are formed in fungi by the head-to-tail coupling of two polyketide chains, each derived from acetate units.

Lovastatin. **Lovastatin or mevinolin** is produced by fermentation of *Aspergillus terreus* Thom (Fam. Aspergillaceae). Lovastatin differs from mevastatin (not commercially available) by the presence of a methyl group at the 6α position of the hexahydronaphthalene ring system. This structural modification enhances the *in vitro* HMG-CoA reductase-inhibiting activity by a factor of 2 to 3 compared with that of mevastatin. Lovastatin is a prodrug and is hydrolyzed *in vivo* to mevinolinic acid which is the lactone ring-opened 3′,5′-dihydroxyheptanoic acid derivative. This portion of the molecule resembles the 3-hydroxy-3-methylglutaryl portion of HMG-CoA. It has been postulated that the tight binding of mevinolinic acid to HMG-CoA reductase is the result of the ability of the 3′,5′-dihydroxyheptanoic acid chain to interact with the HMG binding domain, and the hexahydronaphthalene portion of the molecule interacts with an adjacent hydrophobic pocket on the enzyme which is not utilized in substrate binding.

Inhibition of HMG-CoA reductase blocks endogenous cholesterol biosynthesis. In the liver, which requires cholesterol as a substrate for bile acid synthesis, hepatocytes are stimulated to form a greater number of LDL receptors which promotes an increased influx of LDL cholesterol from plasma with a resulting decrease in plasma LDL cholesterol levels.

Structure-activity relationship studies have shown that the introduction of an additional aliphatic group at the 2″ position of lovastatin increases potency. This observation led to the synthesis of **simvastatin** which has a methyl group introduced at the 2″ position. This modification increases the intrinsic inhibitory activity by about 2.5 times of that exhibited by lovastatin. **Pravastatin** is prepared by microbial transformation using *Streptomyces carbophilus*. It differs from lovastatin in that it contains a hydroxyl

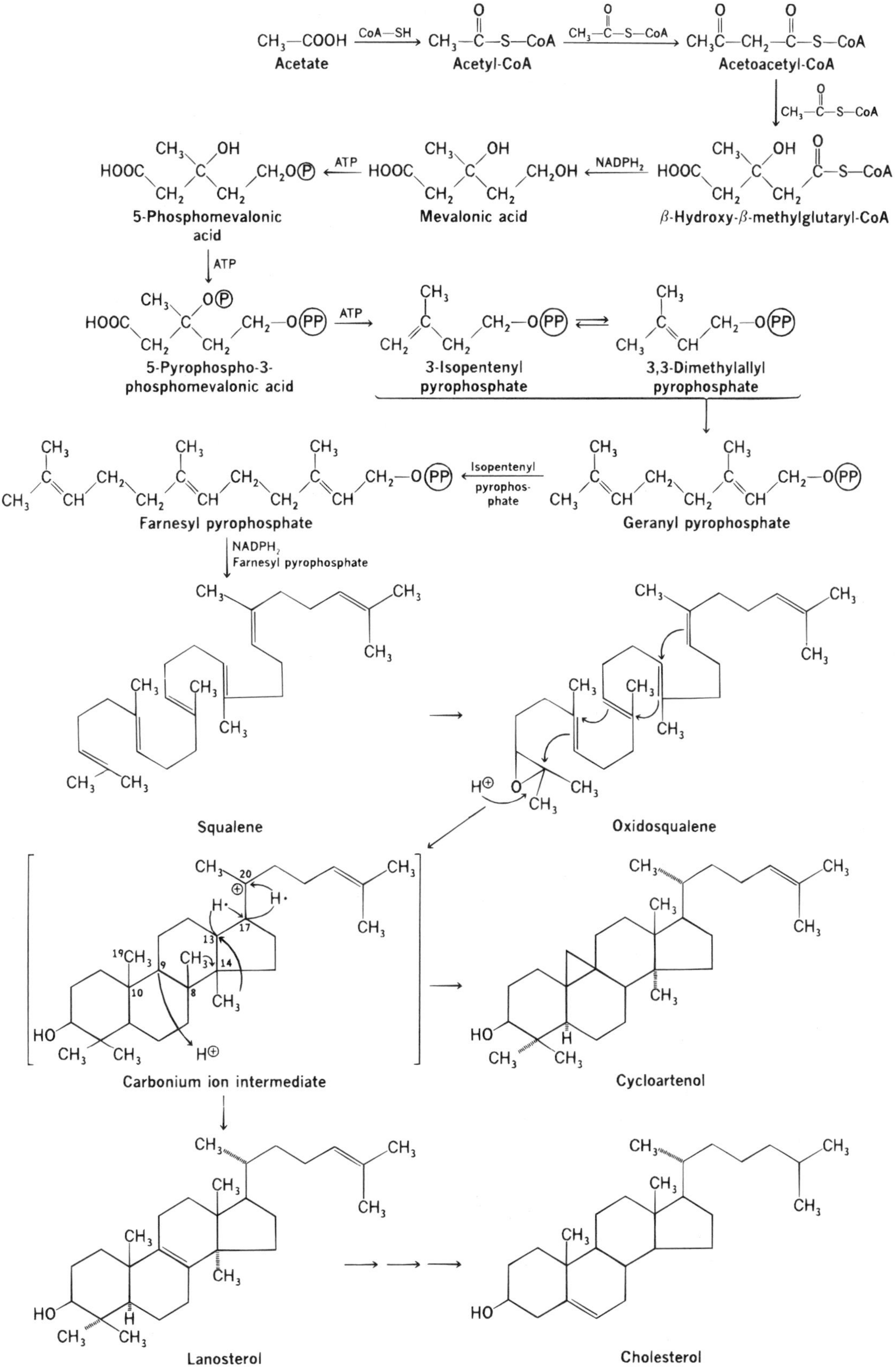

Fig. 7–3. Biosynthesis of cholesterol.

group at the 6β position of the hexahydronaphthalene portion, making it more hydrophilic than
lovastatin. In addition, the lactone ring has been
opened to give the 3′,5′-dihydroheptanoic acid
active form. Lovastatin, simvastatin, and pravastatin are all widely used in the treatment of hypercholesterolemia.

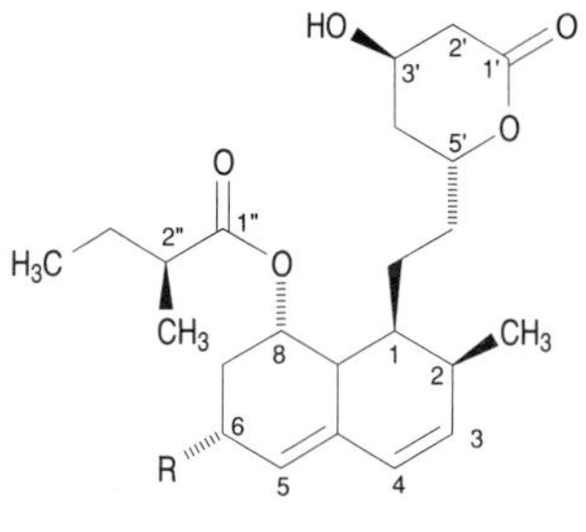

R=H   Mevastatin (Compactin)
R=Me Lovastatin

STEROLS

The first steroids isolated from nature were a
series of C_{27}-C_{29} alcohols that were found in the
lipid fractions of many tissues. These compounds were solids and therefore named **sterols**
from the Greek *stereos*, meaning solid (Fig.
7–4). The most widely occurring sterol is cholesterol. It was first isolated from human gallstones and, because it is a constituent of animal
cell membranes, it has been found in all animal
tissue. It is one of the chief constituents of lanolin and therefore is found in many drug products.

Much has been written about cholesterol and
human health. Cholesterol is present in athero-
sclerotic plaques, and feeding of cholesterol to
susceptible animals has induced atherosclerosis.
In humans, atherosclerosis and coronary heart
disease are frequently associated with conditions
in which the blood cholesterol is elevated. Recently, the results of numerous clinical studies
have indicated that the lowering of serum cholesterol levels lowers the risk of coronary heart
disease and may produce a regression of athero-
sclerotic lesions.

The principal sterol in fungi is ergosterol. This
C_{28} sterol arises biosynthetically through a transmethylation reaction of the cholestane side chain
involving *S*-adenosyl methionine. Ergosterol is
also known as provitamin D_2 because, upon ultraviolet irradiation, a series of isomerizations
with the subsequent opening of ring B results in
the formation of vitamin D_2. Vitamin D_2 is
formed in the same manner from 7-dehydro-

cholesterol. This compound occurs in small
amounts with cholesterol in animal tissue, including human skin, where irradiation from the
sun catalyzes the formation of vitamin D_3.

The most common sterol in plants is β-sitosterol (stigmast-5-en-3β-ol), a C_{29} compound. It
has been shown that a second transmethylation
from methionine accounts for the C-29 atom. In
general, sitosterols are widely distributed
throughout the plant kingdom, and may be obtained from wheat germ oil, rye germ oil, corn
oil, cottonseed oil, and other seed oils.

Closely related to β-sitosterol is the sterol,
stigmasterol, which was first isolated from calabar beans but is also found in soybean oil. The
double bond at position 22 of stigmasterol allows it to be more readily converted into the
pregnane-type steroid hormones than is β-sitosterol; consequently, the extraction of stigmasterol from soybean oil is an important commercial process.

VITAMIN D

Vitamin D is a term that is used for several
related steroids and their metabolites that are essential for the absorption and utilization of calcium. Cholecalciferol, vitamin D_3, or 9,10-seco-
cholesta-5,7,10(19)-trien-3β-ol is the primary
form of the vitamin encountered in zoologic species; it is stored in a number of tissues, including
the liver and skin. Fish liver oils are a rich natural source of this material. Ergocalciferol, vitamin D_2, or 9,10-secoergosta-5,7,9(10),-22-tet-
raen-3β-ol is derived from ergosterol, a plant
steroid. It is the form of this vitamin normally
used to fortify such foods as milk, bread, and
cereals.

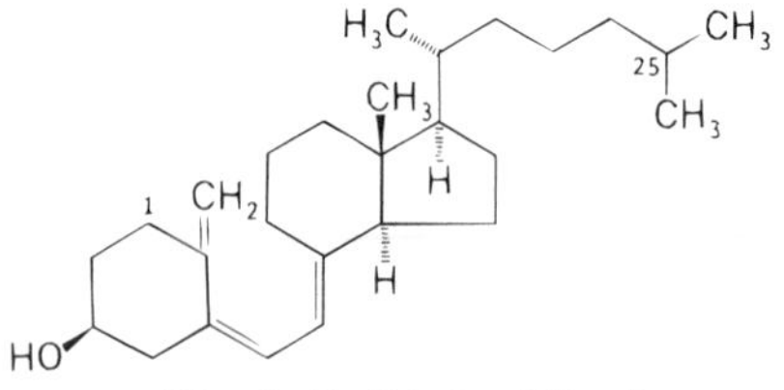

Vitamin D₃ (Cholecalciferol)

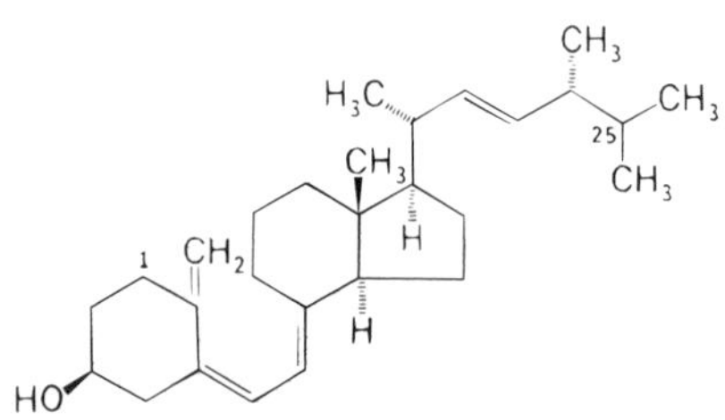

Vitamin D₂ (Ergocalciferol)

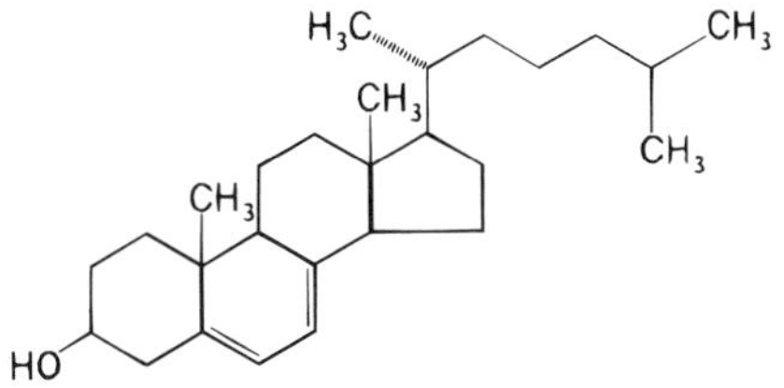

7-Dehydrocholesterol
(Provitamin D_3)
Cholesta-5,7-dien-3β-ol

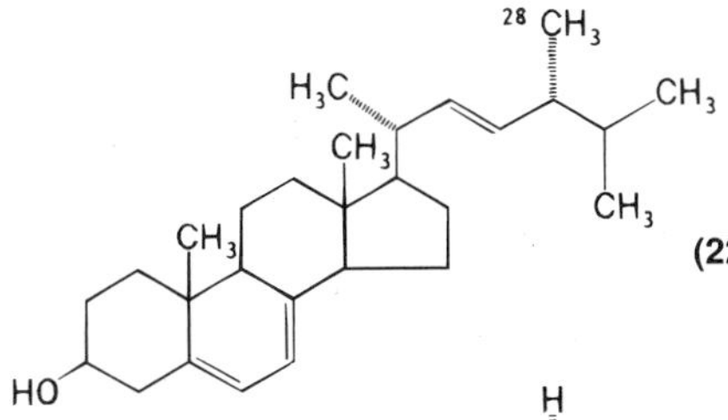

Ergosterol
(Provitamin D_2)
(22*E*)- Ergosta-5,7,22-trien-3β-ol

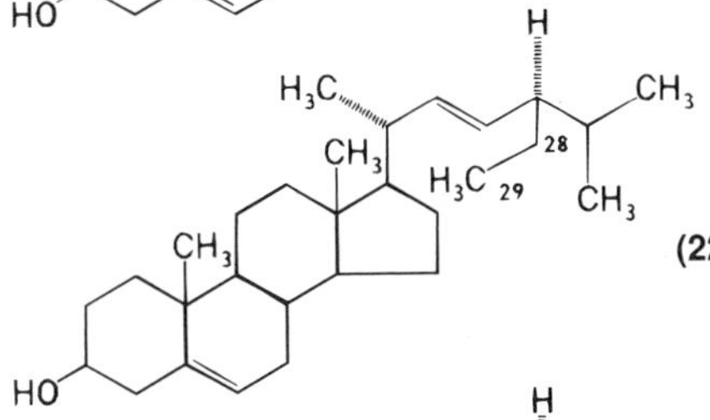

Stigmasterol
(22*E*)- Stigmasta-5,22-dien-3β-ol

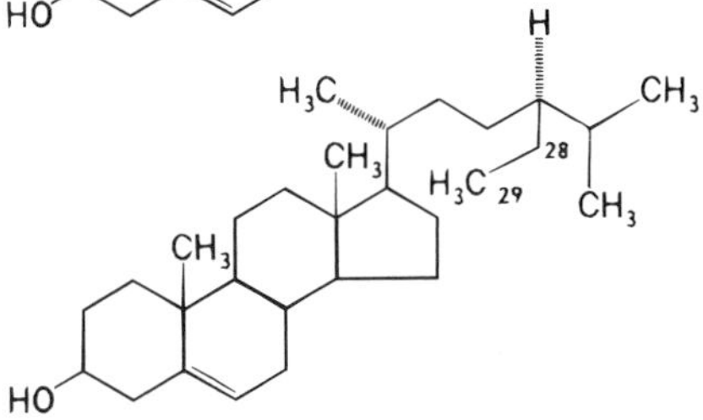

β-Sitosterol
Stigmast-5-en-3β-ol

Fig. 7–4. Sterols.

Vitamin D has been called the sunshine vitamin since ultraviolet light is involved in the conversion of provitamin substances to vitamins D_2 and D_3. 7-Dehydrocholesterol is converted to cholecalciferol in the skin upon exposure to the ultraviolet rays in sunlight, and ergosterol is converted to ergocalciferol *in vitro* by controlled exposure to ultraviolet irradiation. If the irradiation process is not adequately controlled, ergocalciferol becomes contaminated with undesirable reaction products, including lumisterol, tachysterol, toxisterol, and suprasterols.

Cholecalciferol and ergocalciferol undergo metabolic hydroxylations in the body to yield molecular forms with greater physiologic activity. The initial activation reaction occurs in the liver and involves formation of 25-hydroxyl derivatives (calcifediol and 25-hydroxyergocalciferol, respectively). The second hydroxylation reaction occurs in the kidney and involves the 1-position; the resulting calcitriol and 1,25-dihydroxyergocalciferol are considered to be the most active molecular forms of this vitamin.

Dihydrotachysterol, a substance prepared by synthetic reduction of a tachysterol, is closely related to ergocalciferol and possesses useful vitamin D activity. This compound undergoes hydroxylation in the liver to give an active 25- hydroxyl metabolite; no kidney metabolism occurs or is required for full activity.

Vitamin D is absorbed readily from the small intestine of normal individuals, but deficiencies caused by malabsorption are known. Cholecalciferol is absorbed with somewhat greater efficiency than ergocalciferol. Bile salts are required for absorption of the latter material.

The body's requirements for vitamin D are normally satisfied by dietary sources and by the activating action of sunlight (ultraviolet component) on the skin. Butter, cream, and liver are good natural sources of vitamin D, and milk and cereals are usually fortified with this vitamin.

Vitamin D aids in the utilization of calcium and phosphate and is essential to the development and maintenance of strong teeth and bones. Deficiency states lead to rickets in children and osteomalacia in adults. Calcitonin and parathyroid hormone are also involved in calcium homeostasis. Vitamin D increases serum calcium and phosphate concentrations by stimulating absorption of these ions from the small intestine and by mobilizing calcium resorption from bone. The enhanced serum levels of calcium and phosphate normally promote bone mineralization, and the vitamin effect on bone resorption of calcium becomes significant only in hypocalcemic conditions, in which it helps prevent muscular tetany.

Vitamin D, the antiarchitic vitamin, is indicated specifically for the prevention and treatment of deficiency states. Such conditions are rarely encountered in persons receiving a balanced diet and some exposure to sunlight. However, deficiencies are sometimes encountered in patients with intestinal malabsorption of various etiologies, in those on strict vegetarian diets (no dairy products), in which cholesterol and vitamin intake is inadequate, and in those with renal impairment, in which activation of the vitamin is precluded. Vitamin D is also used to treat familial hypophosphatemia and hypoparathyroidism and to supplement the diet in therapeutic regimens involving long-term use of cholestyramine or anticonvulsant drugs. Calcitriol has special utility in patients with kidney failure.

Individuals vary in their sensitivity to vitamin D, and some infants may show hyperactivity even with low doses. However, most toxicities are associated with prolonged ingestion of high doses and can be serious. Chronic vitamin D-induced hypercalcemia may result in soft-tissue calcification, including lethal vascular calcification and nephrocalcinosis. Common symptoms may include gastrointestinal disturbances and hypertension. The serum calcium levels of patients receiving 50,000 units of ergocalciferol per day should be monitored closely; serum calcium concentrations should be maintained at 8 to 9 mg per 100 ml.

BILE ACIDS

In the liver of humans and other animals, the side chain of cholesterol is degraded to C_{24} steroids, which possess a C-24 carboxyl. These steroids are collected in the bile; therefore, they are referred to as the bile acids (Fig. 7–5). The primary bile acids formed in the human liver are cholic acid and chenodeoxycholic acid. Deoxycholic acid and lithocholic acid are also found in substantial amounts in mammalian bile; however, they are not formed in the liver. They are produced in the intestinal tract by the action of microorganisms on cholic acid to form deoxycholic acid and on chenodeoxycholic acid to form lithocholic acid. Their presence in the bile is attributed to enterohepatic circulation. Generally, the bile acids do not exist in the free state but are conjugated through a peptide bond to either glycine or taurine. The conjugated bile acids are discharged into the duodenum where they act as emulsifying agents to aid in the intestinal absorption of fat. Chenodeoxycholic acid and ursodeoxycholic acid are bile acids that are used as cholelitholytic agents. In addition, ursodeoxycholic acid is used in chronic liver disease such as primary biliary cirrhosis.

Chenodiol (chenodeoxycholic acid), when administered in therapeutic doses, increases the proportion of chenodiol in the bile acid pool, biliary cholesterol saturation is reduced, and uncalcified cholesterol gallstones undergo gradual dissolution (cholelitholytic effect). Chenodiol may reduce biliary cholesterol saturation by suppressing hepatic synthesis of cholesterol and decreasing biliary cholesterol secretion. Chenodiol has no effect on radiopaque (calcified) gallstones or on bile pigment gallstones.

The duration of treatment may be 2 years or more. In addition, stones may recur when therapy is discontinued. Because there is a high incidence of adverse effects, such as elevated liver enzyme levels and a dose-related diarrhea, this agent is recommended only in patients who are poor surgical risks for a cholecystectomy. Dose-related hepatotoxicity has been observed in many animal species and has been attributed to the formation of lithocholic acid from chenodiol by the intestinal microbial flora. However, there is some evidence that hepatotoxicity may result directly from chenodiol.

Ursodiol (ursodeoxycholic acid) is found in small quantities in normal human bile and in large quantities in the bile of certain species of bears. It is an epimer of chenodiol having a 7β-hydroxyl rather than a 7α-hydroxyl as in chenodiol. This difference in chemistry results in decreased formation of lithocholic acid because the 7-dehydroxylation reaction by the intestinal microbial flora appears to be alpha-specific; there-

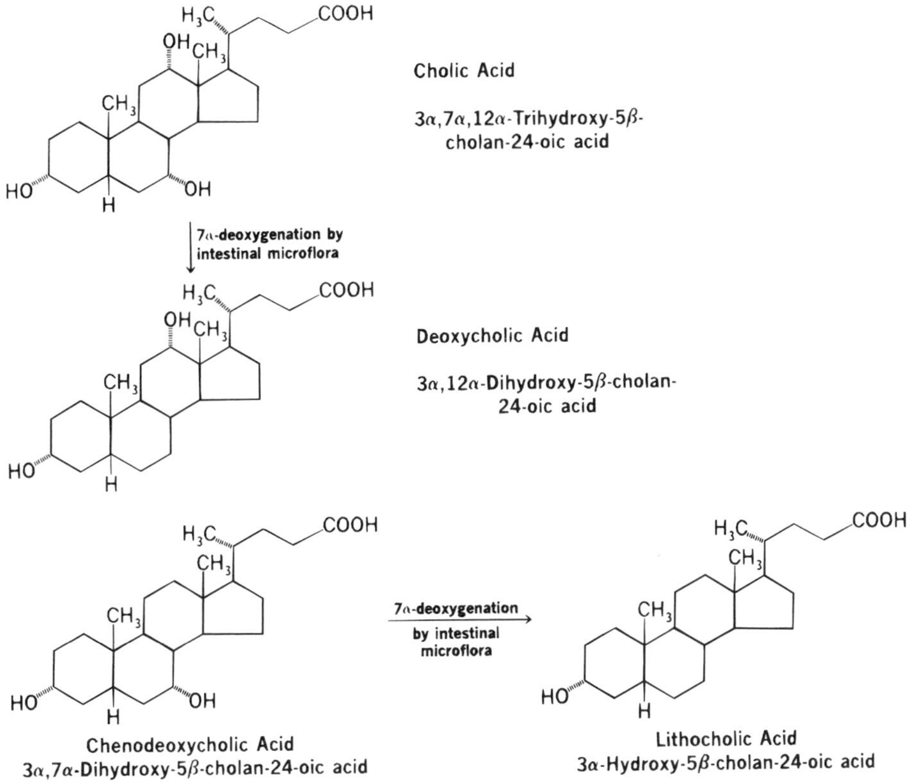

Fig. 7–5. Bile acids.

fore, ursodiol presents a decreased risk of hepatotoxicity.

CARDIAC GLYCOSIDES

Some steroids present in nature are characterized by the highly specific and powerful action that they exert on the cardiac muscle. These steroids occur as glycosides with sugars attached at the 3-position of the steroid nucleus. Because of their action on the heart muscle, they are named cardiac glycosides (Fig. 7–6). The steroid aglycones or genins are of two types: a cardenolide or a bufadienolide. The more prevalent in nature are the cardenolides, which are C_{23} steroids that have as a 17β side chain an α,β-unsaturated 5-membered lactone ring. The bufadienolides are C_{24} homologs of the cardenolides and carry a doubly unsaturated 6-membered lactone ring at the 17-position. The bufadienolides derive their name from the generic name for the toad, *Bufo*. (The prototype compound bufalin was isolated from the skin of toads.) An unusual aspect of the chemistry of both cardenolides and bufadienolides is that the C/D ring junction has the *cis*-configuration. To obtain optimum cardiac activity, the aglycone should possess an α,β unsaturated lactone ring that is attached β at the 17-position of the steroid nucleus and the A/B and C/D ring junctions should have the *cis*-configuration. Metabolic reduction of the double bond in the lactone ring of digoxin to form dihydrodigoxin may explain why certain individuals are refractory to digoxin therapy. If the glycoside is cleaved, the aglycone retains cardiac activity; however, the sugar portion of the glycoside confers on the molecule solubility properties important in its absorption and distribution in the body, and the stereochemistry and conformation of the sugar moiety influence the binding affinity to a sugar-binding site on the receptor protein. Oxygen substitution on the steroid nucleus also influences the distribution and metabolism of glycosides. In general, the more hydroxy groups on the molecule, the more rapid the onset of action and the subsequent dissipation from the body.

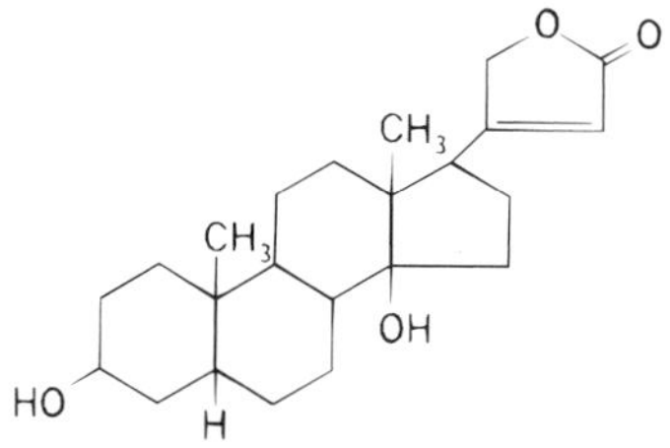

Digitoxigenin
3β,14-dihydroxy-5β-card-20(22)-enolide

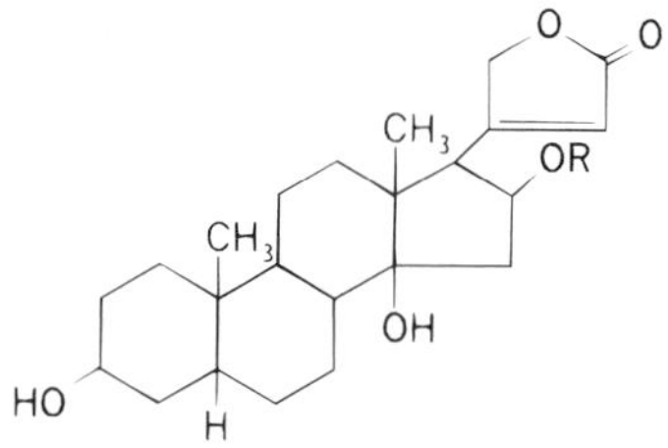

Gitoxigenin   R = H
3β,14,16β-trihydroxy-5β-card-20(22)-enolide

Gitaloxigenin   R = CHO
16β-formyloxy-3β,14-dihydroxy-5β-card-20(22)-enolide

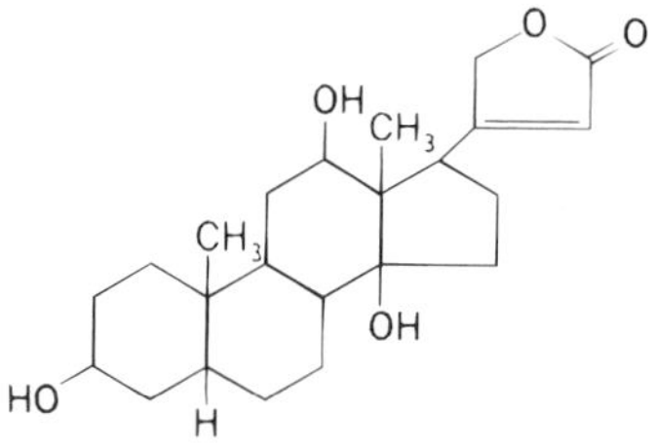

Digoxigenin
3β,12β,14-trihydroxy-5β-card-20(22)-enolide

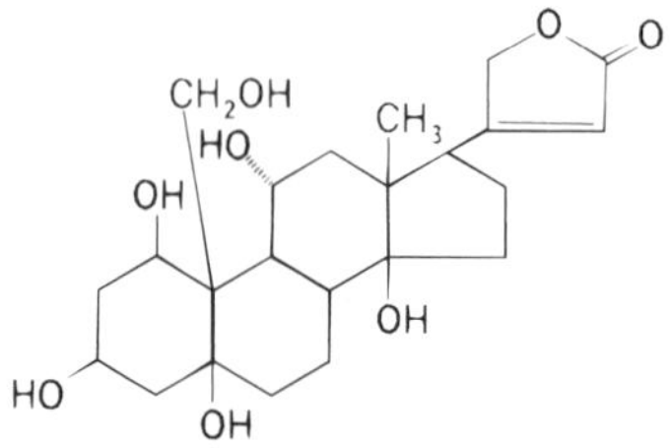

Ouabagenin
1β,3β,5,11α,14,19-hexahydroxy-5β-card-20(22)-enolide

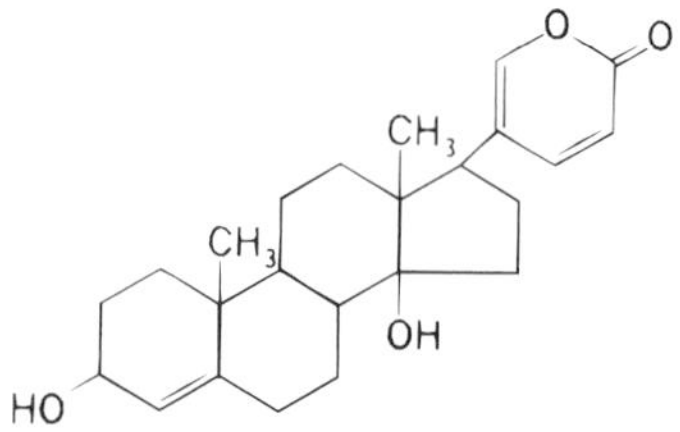

Scillarenin
3β,14-dihydroxy-bufa-4,20,22-trienolide

Fig. 7–6. Structural formulas of several aglycones of cardiac glycosides.

The use of the cardiac glycosides in therapeutics stems from the ability of these compounds to increase the force of systolic contraction (positive inotropic action). An increase in contractility in the failing heart results in a more complete emptying of the ventricle and a shortening in the length of systole. Thus, the heart has more time to rest between contractions. As the myocardium recovers as a result of increased cardiac output and circulation, the heart rate is deceased through a reflex vagal effect. In addition, the improved circulation tends to improve renal secretion, which relieves the edema often associated with heart failure. Cardiac glycosides are also drugs of choice for controlling rapid ventricular rate in patients with atrial fibrillation or atrial flutter.

In the use of cardiac glycosides to treat congestive heart failure, the patient is usually given an initial loading dose of the drug to bring the heart under the influence of the drug. Because the amount required varies with the patient and the drug used, the preparation is given in divided doses while titrating the dose against signs of improvement. The patient is usually continued indefinitely after the loading dose by administering a daily maintenance dose that replaces the amount of drug that is metabolized and excreted. In toxic concentrations, the glycosides may increase cardiac automaticity and lead to ectopic tachyarrhythmia. Ventricular extrasystoles are the most frequent effect. With all the glycosides, the therapeutic level appears to be approximately 50 to 60% of the toxic dose. This finding explains why dosage must be carefully determined experimentally for each patient.

Despite numerous experimental investigations, the mechanism of action of the cardiac glycosides is still not completely known; however, observations have implicated Na^+, K^+-ATPase as the receptor enzyme. This enzyme catalyzes the active transport of Na^+ out of the cell and the subsequent transport of K^+ into the cell.

Na^+, K^+-ATPase operates in all cell membranes to maintain the unequal distribution of Na^+ and K^+ ions across the membrane. However, in the myocardium the ion exchange is rapid because it is required after each heartbeat; therefore, an inhibition of Na^+, K^+-ATPase has a greater effect on heart tissue than on other cells of the body. When the heart beats, a wave of depolarization passes through it, changing the permeability of the cell membranes. Na^+ moves into the cell by passive diffusion and K^+ moves out. Na^+, K^+-ATPase supplies the energy from ATP to reverse this process and to pump the Na^+ out of the cell and the K^+ into the cell against a concentration gradient.

Inhibition of Na^+, K^+-ATPase by the cardiac glycoside results in an increase in Na^+ and a decrease in K^+ within the cell which, in turn, stimulates a secondary Na^+ Ca^{++} exchange mechanism that functions to remove intracellular Na^+ with a subsequent increase in intracellular Ca^{++}. The small amount of Ca^{++} that enters the cell promotes the release of a much larger amount of Ca^{++} from the intracellular storage sites. The positive inotropic action or muscle contraction enhancement of cardiac glycosides is mediated through the increase in Ca^{++}. Ca^{++} interacts with troponin C which then, through its action on tropomyosin, unmasks the binding sites on actin that bind myosin, allowing for the formation of the contractile protein actomyosin (Fig. 7–7).

Drug Interactions

This postulated mechanism implicating intracellular cation levels explains the development of toxicity symptoms in patients with certain plasma-electrolyte imbalances who receive cardiac glycoside therapy. Potassium depletion increases the susceptibility to cardiac glycoside toxicity; therefore, patients on concomitant therapy with such potassium-depleting drugs as thiazide diuretics and corticosteroids with mineralocorticoid activity may require potassium supplementation or a reduced dosage of cardiac glycosides. Conversely, patients treated with cardiac glycosides should not commence the ex-

cessive ingestion of any product containing absorbable calcium, e.g., milk, calcium gluconate, and dibasic and tribasic calcium phosphate. Also, such patients should not be given parenteral calcium because hypercalcemia can potentiate the cardiac effect.

Digitalis

Digitalis or foxglove is the dried leaf of *Digitalis purpurea* Linné (Fam. Scrophulariaceae). *Digitalis* is from the Latin *digitus,* meaning finger, and refers to the finger-shaped corolla, so named by Tragus in 1539; *purpurea* is Latin and refers to the purple color of the flower. The plant is a biennial herb, probably indigenous to central and southern Europe and naturalized in various parts of Europe and in the northern and western United States and Canada.

Digitalis seems to have been used externally by the Welsh. Parkinson recommended it in 1640, but its internal use was not in vogue until its recommendation by Withering in 1776. It is an important drug and has been official in most pharmacopeias of the world since the 18th century.

The leaves of other *Digitalis* species, *D. dubia, D. ferruginea, D. grandiflora, D. lanata, D. lutea, D. mertonensis, D. nervosa, D. subalpina,* and *D. thapsi,* also show the presence of cardiac glycosides. Digitalis and the digitalis glycosides used in the U.S. are obtained principally from England and Germany. The drug contains a large number of glycosides, of which the most important from a medicinal viewpoint are digitoxin, gitoxin, and gitaloxin. The total concentration of these three glycosides varies appreciably with the plant source and the conditions of growth. Also, because all are secondary glycosides derived by hydrolysis of some of the sugars from the primary or parent glycosides occurring in the leaf, their concentration depends on the manner of treatment of the plant material following harvesting.

Nearly 30 other glycosides have been identified in the drug. The major glycosides, in terms of concentration, include purpurea glycoside A, purpurea glycoside B, glucogitaloxin, glucodigitoxigenin-bis-digitoxiside, glucogitaloxigenin-bis-digitoxiside, glucoevatromonoside, glucogitoroside, glucolanadoxin, digitalinum verum, glucoverodoxin, stropeside, and verodoxin.

In monitoring patient therapy with digitoxin and digoxin, radioimmune assay techniques have been developed that allow for the measure-

Relaxed Muscle   Activated Muscle

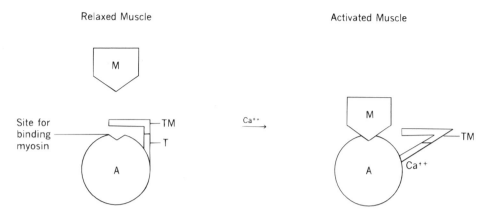

Fig. 7–7. Schematic diagram showing the interaction of contractile protein during muscle contraction. A = actin, M = myosin, TM = tropomyosin, T = troponin C. In the relaxed muscle, tropomyosin masks the sites on actin to which myosin binds through steric blockage. In the activated muscle, Ca^{++} interacts with troponin C, which brings about a conformational change in tropomyosin, unmasking the actin-to-myosin binding sites and allowing for the formation of actomyosin.

ment of nanogram quantities of these glycosides in the blood serum. The underlying principle is that nonradioactive glycoside (in known standard solution or in patients' sera) will compete with radioactively labeled glycoside for combining sites on antidigitalis antibody. If one mixes varying quantities of unlabeled glycoside with a standard amount of radiolabeled glycoside, the amount of radioactivity bound by a standard amount of antibody will decrease as increasing amounts of unlabeled glycoside are added. A standard curve can then be constructed from which the concentration of glycoside in a patient's blood serum can be determined on the basis of the decrease it causes in the binding of radioactive glycoside by specific antibody. Radiolabeled glycosides and antisera are commercially available. If stored properly, antibodies are stable for many years, and 1 ml of antiserum may be employed in more than 100,000 determinations.

Digitoxin

Digitoxin is a cardiotonic glycoside obtained from *D. purpurea, D. lanata,* and other suitable species of *Digitalis.* The chemical name of digitoxin is 3β-[(*O*-2,6- dideoxy-β-D-*ribo*-hexopyranosyl-(1 → 4)-*O*-2,6-dideoxy-β-D-*ribo*-hexopyranosyl-(1→4)-*O*-2,6-dideoxy-β-D-*ribo*-hexopyranosyl)oxy] -14 -hydroxy -5β- card - 20(22)-enolide. 2,6-Dideoxy-β-D-*ribo*-hexo-pyranoseis the chemical name for the rare sugar digitoxose. On hydrolysis, digitoxin yields one molecule of

digitoxigenin and three of digitoxose. It is a highly potent drug and should be handled with exceptional care. Digitoxin occurs as a white or pale buff, odorless, microcrystalline powder. It is a bitter substance that is practically insoluble in water and slightly soluble in alcohol. It is the most lipid-soluble of the cardiac glycosides used in therapeutics.

Digitoxin

The major pharmacokinetic parameters for digitoxin include complete oral absorption, which distinguishes it from other cardiac glycosides. Upon oral administration, the onset of action is 1 to 4 hours with a peak at 8 to 14 hours. Approximately 50 to 70% of the glycoside is converted by the liver to inactive genins, which are excreted in the kidneys. Because of a long plasma half-life (168 to 192 hours), it may take from 3 to 5 weeks for complete dissipation of the drug from the body following discontinuation of therapy. It is estimated that a drug-serum level of 14 to 26 ng/ml is required for full therapeutic effect, and levels exceeding 35 ng/ml may produce symptoms of toxicity.

Digitalis Lanata

Digitalis lanata or Grecian foxglove is the dried leaves of *Digitalis lanata* Ehrhart, a plant indigenous to southern and central Europe. It is the source of digoxin; however, nearly 70 different glycosides have been detected in the leaves of *D. lanata*. All are derivatives of five different aglycones, three of which (digitoxigenin, gitoxigenin, and gitaloxigenin) also occur in *D. purpurea*. The other two types of glycosides derived from digoxigenin and diginatigenin occur in *D. lanata* but not in *D. purpurea*. The five types of primary glycosides are designated lanatosides A through E, according to the identity of the aglycone. The lanatosides are sometimes referred to as digilanids, especially in the older literature.

None of the primary glycosides of *D. lanata* is identical to those found in *D. purpurea*. Even those that have the same aglycone differ by the presence of an acetyl group attached to the third digitoxose residue. Removal of the acetyl group and sugar residues by selective hydrolysis results in secondary glycosides, some of which, e.g., digitoxin, occur in both species. Glycosides derived from aglycones of the C and D series may be obtained only from *D. lanata*.

Digoxin

Digoxin (Lanoxin) is the most widely used of the cardiotonic glycosides, and it is obtained from the leaves of *D. lanata*. On hydrolysis digoxin yields one molecule of digoxigenin and three of digitoxose. It is a highly potent drug and should be handled with exceptional care. Digoxin occurs as a white, crystalline powder.

Digoxin tablets are 60 to 80% absorbed, and variable bioequivalence among different brands of digoxin tablets has been demonstrated. Because of the low therapeutic index of the drug, it is recommended that, in the absence of good comparative bioavailability data, a patient should not be changed from one brand of tablet to another after a reasonable therapeutic effect has been achieved with one preparation. Otherwise, either a toxic or nontherapeutic effect may result owing to a change in the bioavailability of the drug. In addition, in approximately 10%

of patients up to 40% of orally administered digoxin is converted by the intestinal microflora to the inactive dihydrodigoxin.

A solution-filled capsule is available that provides a 90–100% absorption, and with enhanced bioavailability bacterial inactivation is decreased.

Upon oral administration, the onset of action is 30 minutes to 2 hours, with a peak at 2 to 6 hours. Digoxin is also administered parenterally for a more rapid effect. The major route of elimination is the kidneys, and with a plasma half-life of 30 to 40 hours, complete dissipation of effects following discontinuation of therapy takes from 6 to 8 days. It is estimated that a drug-serum level of 0.5 to 2 ng/ml is required for full therapeutic effect, and levels exceeding 2.5 ng/ml may produce symptoms of toxicity.

Digoxin has the same uses and precautions as digitoxin and is indicated when the risk of digitalis intoxication is great, since it is relatively short-acting and rapidly eliminated when compared with digitoxin. However, digitoxin may be indicated in patients with impaired renal function.

Other Cardioactive Drugs

A number of plants contain cardioactive glycosides, and some of them have been employed for many years as cardiac stimulants and diuretics. Several are more potent than digitalis, but they are less reliable because their dosage cannot be controlled properly. Although most of these drugs were recognized officially for years and were considered efficacious, they have been superseded by the digitalis glycosides. A few are currently under reinvestigation.

Convallaria or lily-of-the-valley root is the dried rhizome and roots of *Convallaria majalis* Linné (Fam. Liliaceae). More than 40 cardioactive glycosides have been isolated from this drug. Principal among these is convallatoxin, a monoglycoside composed of the genin of K-strophanthin (strophanthidin) and the sugar of G-strophanthin (rhamnose). Other minor glycosides include convallatoxol and convalloside.

Apocynum, black Indian hemp, dog bane, or Canadian hemp consists of the dried rhizome and roots of *Apocynum cannabinum* Linné (Fam. Apocynaceae). The chief constituent is cymarin, although apocannoside and cyanocannoside have also been isolated from *A. cannabinum*.

Adonis or pheasant's eye is the dried overground portion of *Adonis vernalis* Linné (Fam. Ranunculaceae). Cardioactive glycosides identified in the drug include adonitoxin, cymarin, and K-strophanthin.

Black hellebore or Christmas rose is the dried rhizome and roots of *Helleborus niger* Linné (Fam. Ranunculaceae). The chief constituent is hellebrin. Black hellebore possesses cardiac stimulant properties in contrast to green hellebore (see veratrum viride), which is a cardiac depressant.

Oleander is another plant that contains cardiac glycosides. The leaves of *Nerium oleander* Linné (Fam. Apocynaceae) have been used to treat cardiac insufficiency. The chief constituent is oleandrin, a 3-glycosido-16-acetyl derivative of gitoxigenin.

Strophanthus is the dried, ripe seed of *Strophanthus kombe* Oliver, or of *S. hispidus* DeCandolle (Fam. Apocynaceae), that is deprived of the awn. Strophanthus seeds have long been used by native Africans in the preparation of arrow poisons. These poisons were first observed in western Africa by Hendelot and in East Africa by Livingstone. Early specimens sent to Europe established the powerful cardiac properties of the seeds.

K-stophanthoside, also known as stroposide, is the principal primary glycoside in both *S. kombe* and *S. hispidus*. It is composed of the genin, strophanthidin, coupled to a trisaccharide consisting of cymarose, β-glucose, and α-glucose. α-Glucosidase removes the terminal α-glucose to yield K-strophanthin-β, and the enzyme, strophanthobiase, contained in the seed converts this to cymarin plus glucose. A mixture of these glycosides, existing in the seed in concentrations of up to 5%, was formerly designated strophanthin or K-strophanthin. Recent studies have revealed additional glycosides as minor constituents.

Ouabain is a glycoside of ouabagenin and rhamnose. It may be obtained from the seeds of *Strophanthus gratus* (Wall et Hook.) Baillon or from the wood of *Acokanthera ouabáïo* Poiss. (Fam. Apocynaceae). It is extremely poisonous. Ouabain is also known as G-strophanthin.

Squill or squill bulb consists of the cut and dried, fleshy, inner scales of the bulb of the white variety of *Urginea maritima* (Linné) Baker, known in commerce as white or Mediterranean squill; or of *U. indica* Kunth, known in commerce as Indian squill (Fam. Liliaceae). The central portion of the bulb is excluded during its processing.

Squill contains about a dozen cardioactive glycosides. The principal one, scillaren A, comprises about two thirds of the total glycoside fraction. On hydrolysis, it yields the aglycone scillarenin, a bufadienolide, plus rhamnose and glucose. Other minor glycosides includes glucoscillaren A (scillarenin + rhamnose + glucose) and proscillaridin A (scillarenin + rhamnose).

Squill is an expectorant, but it also possesses emetic, cardiotonic, and diuretic properties.

Red squill consists of the bulb or bulb scales of the red variety of *U. maritima,* which is imported for use as a rat poison. It should not be present in the medicinal squill and may be detected by the presence of red, pink, or purple epidermal or parenchymal tissues.

Most of the squill imported into the United States is of the red variety. Each year, a considerable tonnage is used as a rodenticide. Rodents lack the vomiting reflex, which makes red squill particularly lethal to these animals. The inadvertent ingestion by humans of plant materials that contain cardiac glycosides induces the vomiting reflex and reduces the life-threatening aspects of the toxic manifestations.

STEROID HORMONES

The steroid hormones can be divided into two classes, the **sex hormones** and the **adrenocortical hormones**. The former are produced primarily in the gonads and mediate the growth, development, maintenance, and the function of the reproductive tract and the accessory sex organs. These hormones fall into three chemically and physiologically distinct categories: the **estrogens** and **progestins**, which regulate various functions of the female reproductive tract, and the **androgens**, which stimulate the development of the male reproductive organs. The adrenocortical hormones are produced by the outer cortical portion of the adrenal glands, and they are divided into two classes, depending on their biologic activity. The hormones that principally affect the excretion of fluid and electrolytes, with a subsequent sodium retention, are called **mineralocorticoids**; those that affect intermediary metabolism are termed **glucocorticoids**.

The production of steroid hormones in the body is initiated by the releasing factors of the hypothalamus, which travel to the anterior lobe of the pituitary gland where they induce the release of tropic hormones into the blood. When stimulated by the appropriate tropic hormone, steroids are synthesized at the target site, either

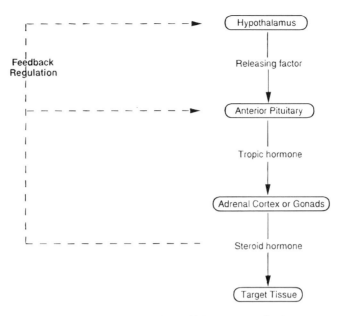

Fig. 7–8. Regulation of steroid hormone production.

the adrenal cortex or the gonads. Steroid level in the blood is held in balance by a mechanism of negative feedback regulation that is medicated through the hypothalamus and the anterior pituitary gland. When excess active steroid is in the blood that reaches the hypothalamus, the production of the hypothalamic releasing factors is stopped (Fig 7-8).

This phenomenon of negative feedback regulation can cause problems in drug therapy with steroid hormones. For example, prolonged therapy with corticosteroids may cause irreversible atrophy of the adrenal cortex. A high corticosteroid level in the body suppresses the hypothalamus from secreting the corticotropin-releasing factor (CRF) which, in turn, suppresses release of corticotropin (ACTH). The amount of ACTH secreted at anytime is influenced by the integration of CRF stimulation on the anterior pituitary and negative feedback from circulating corticosteroids. The lack of stimulatory impact of ACTH results in atrophy of the adrenal cortex.

Biosynthesis of Steroid Hormones

Biosynthesis of the numerous steroid hormones of the adrenal cortex, gonads, and placenta is an extremely complex specialty field. Only the briefest essentials can be presented here. When one realizes that more than 70 different steroids have been isolated from the adrenal

gland alone, one can easily understand why the biosynthetic relationships are complex.

Like other steroids of biologic origin, these hormones are derived from the well-known acetate-mevalonic acid pathway which, in this case, leads first to cholesterol (see Fig. 7–3 for details). Partial side-chain degradation of cholesterol leads to pregnenolone and then to progesterone, both of which serve as precursors of the other steroid hormones.

The conversion of cholesterol to pregnenolone is catalyzed by a mixed-function oxidase enzyme complex that involves a desmolase and requires O_2 and NADPH. This conversion appears to be the rate-limiting step in steroid hormone biosynthesis and is under the influence of the tropic hormones of the anterior pituitary. In the case of ACTH stimulation of steroidogenesis, ACTH activates adrenal cortical adenyl cyclase, which causes a rise in cyclic AMP and a subsequent activation of glycogen phosphorylase. This enzyme breaks down glycogen to produce glucose-6-phosphate, which then is oxidized via the hexose monophosphate shunt pathway, yielding NADPH. An increase in the availability of this coenzyme increases the activity of the desmolase and the hydroxylase reactions.

Enzymes in the adrenals and the gonads remove the side chain and hydroxylate the steroid nucleus in the 17 α-position to form the andro-

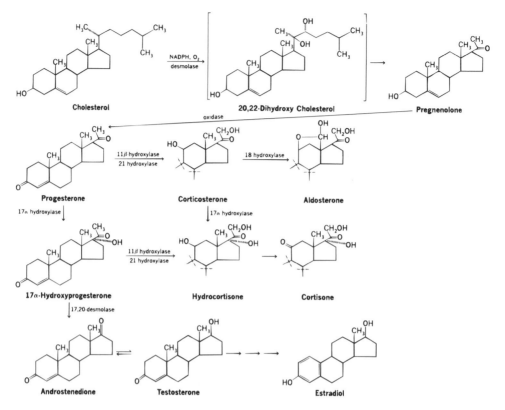

Fig. 7–9. Biosynthesis and bioconversion of steroid hormones.

gens. After loss of the angular 19-methyl group, androgens are aromatized to estrogens. The adrenals also hydroxylate progesterone in positions 21, 11, and/or 17 to produce the classic adrenocortical hormones. Production of aldosterone involves 18-hydroxylation and dehydrogenation reactions.

Some of the principal conversions are illustrated in the simplified scheme shown in Figure 7–9.

The steroid hormones are bound to proteins, primarily albumins, for transport in the blood. These steroid-protein complexes per se are physiologically inert and protect the steroid from metabolic inactivation. The strength of binding varies and can be generalized by classification as follows: the corticosteroids tend to be weakly bound, the estrogens are more strongly bound, and progesterone and testosterone are intermediate between the two extremes.

Reductive processes are normally involved in the metabolism of steroid hormones. The di-, tetra-, and hexahydric metabolites may be formed and usually entail progressive reduction

of the 4-ene, 3-keto, and 20-keto functions. The reduced forms are usually excreted as the more soluble uronides or sulfate esters involving the 3-oxygen function. In case of the metabolism of estradiol and testosterone, the initial metabolic reaction is oxidative , involving the 17-hydroxyl function, but subsequent metabolic steps are reductive, with eventual conjugation.

Mechanism of Action

The steroid hormones have diverse actions, and several specific receptor proteins, varying with the particular target tissue, have been isolated for each action. The primary structure of a large number of steroid receptors has been deduced from the sequences of cloned cDNAs. The protein structures show great similarity, and it is not surprising that it is difficult to separate different hormonal activities of a parent hormone through chemical structural modification. For example, changes in the chemical structure of testosterone does not allow for the complete separation of the androgenic activity from the anabolic activity of this hormone. The same applies when attempting to separate the glucocorticoid/mineralocorticoid activity of corticosteroids. Steroid hormones act through a stimulation of protein synthesis. The lipophilic steroids enter the cells of the target tissue by diffusion and bind the specific protein receptors located in the cytoplasm (corticosteroids) or the nucleus (androgens, estrogens, progestins) of the cell. This binding results in a series of conformational changes in the receptor, leading to an increase in affinity for specific DNA regulatory sites for target genes. After binding, transcription of target genes is enhanced which results in the increased production of a particular enzyme protein. For example, mineralocorticoids produce an increase in the synthesis of enzymes that are necessary for active transport of Na^+, which leads directly to increased Na^+ reabsorption in the renal tubules.

Commercial Production of Steroids

The steroid hormones and their semisynthetic analogs represent a multimillion-dollar annual business for the American drug industry. When one considers the social, political, and economical implications associated with the use of oral contraceptive drugs, the importance of steroids to humankind cannot be questioned. At the present time, the principal source of the steroid chemical nucleus used in the drug industry is the plant kingdom; however, in the not-too-distant past, the source of steroid hormones was from the gonads and adrenal glands of animals that were used as food by humans. The amount of hormone present in these glands was extremely small, and large quantities of glands were required to isolate milligram quantities of hormone; consequently, it was not practical to use the pure hormone in therapy. For example, in 1934, Schering Laboratories, Berlin, needed 625 kg of ovaries from 50,000 sows in order to obtain 20 mg of pure crystalline progesterone.

Today, the steroid industry represents the culmination of efforts by many scientists; however, a few can be singled out for their pioneering work in steroid chemistry. One of these men is Russell E. Marker. Marker is responsible for the discovery of a commercially feasible conversion of steroidal sapogenins to progesterone. His early work involved the search for plant species that were rich in steroidal sapogenins. When he found that Mexican yams, various species of *Dioscorea*, were rich in these compounds, he

moved to Mexico City in 1943, where he isolated diosgenin from *D. macrostachya (D. mexicana)*, known in Mexico as *cabeza de negro*. From diosgenin, employing the chemical degradation illustrated in Figure 7–10, he managed to prepare more than 3 kg of progesterone (at the time valued at $80 a gram). This hormone and the process used to prepare it were the foundation stones for the Syntex Company.

During the 1930s, several scientists, including E. C. Kendal, a chemist at the Mayo Clinic, and T. Reichstein, a chemist at the Federal Institute of Technology, Zurich, Switzerland, almost simultaneously and independently isolated steroids from the adrenal cortex of cattle. Stimulated by the potential therapeutic importance of these compounds, the Merck Company in 1944 successfully produced 15 mg of cortisone from 1 kg of deoxycholic acid, utilizing 36 separate chemical steps. However, in 1949, when P.S. Hench of the Mayo Clinic announced cortisone's dramatic effectiveness in treating rheumatoid arthritis, the increased demand for cortisone required a more readily available and inexpensive source. The problem was solved in 1952 when scientists at the Upjohn Company found a microorganism, *Rhizopus arrhizus*, that could convert progesterone, a readily available starting material because of the Marker degradation, to 11α-hydroxyprogesterone in an 80 to 90% yield. The extremely difficult problem of introducing an oxygen function in the 11-position of the steroid nucleus by using chemical methods was therefore solved (Fig. 7–11).

A vast amount of research resulted in extension and improvement of this basic procedure with other precursors and numerous microorganisms. Relatively inexpensive starting materials, such as stigmasterol from soybeans, hecogenin from the sisal industry, or diosgenin from *Dioscorea* species, are now employed.

Stigmasterol may be converted chemically to progesterone, which is, in turn, incubated in large fermenters with suitable microorganisms under specified conditions to yield 11α-hydroxyprogesterone, which may then be converted chemically to cortisone. Similarly, cortexolone (Reichstein's substance S) is prepared chemically from diosgenin and is then converted by *Streptomyces fradiae* or *Cunninghamella blakesleeana* to cortisol (hydrocortisone).

Cortisone or cortisol is dehydrogenated in the Δ^1-position by *Corynebacterium simplex* or by *Fusarium* species to yield prednisone or prednisolone, respectively.

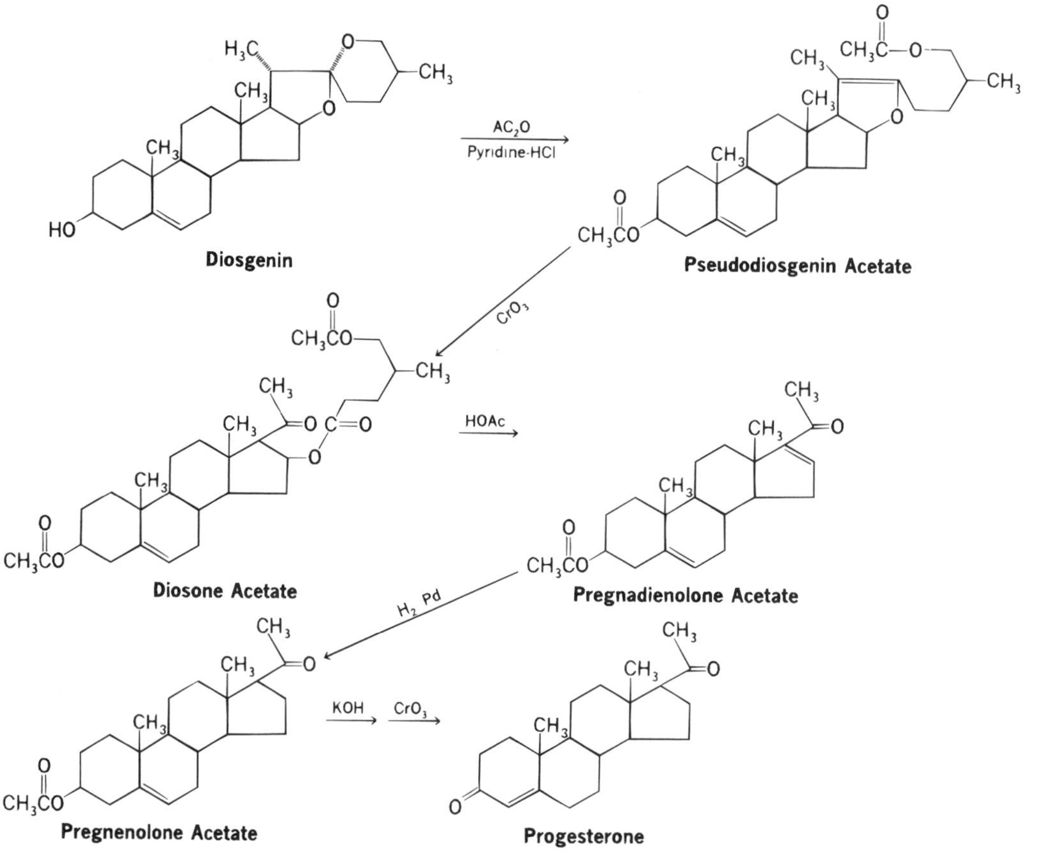

Fig. 7–10. The Marker degradation.

Certain microorganisms also can hydroxylate synthetically prepared fluorosteroids in the 16α-position to produce triamcinolone (Fig. 7–12).

Adrenal Cortex

The adrenal cortex is essential to life. Removal of about 85% of cortical tissue is lethal in a few days. In animals so treated, life may be maintained by the administration of extracts of hormones of the adrenal cortex.

Cortical deficiency in animals is marked by a loss of appetite and weight, vomiting and diarrhea, weakness, and a fall in temperature, metabolism, and blood pressure. There is a loss of blood fluid, with resulting concentration of

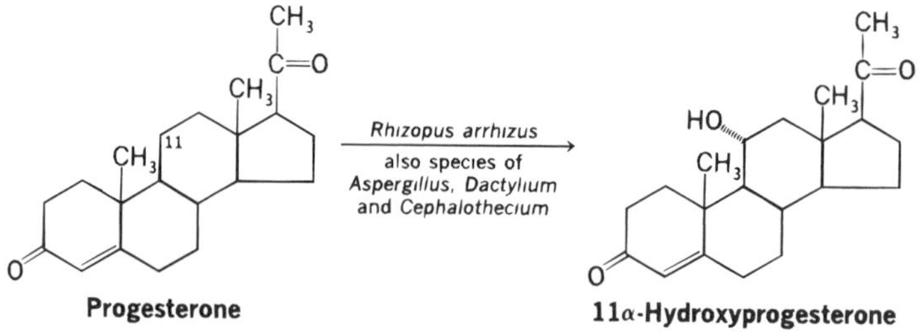

Fig. 7–11. Introduction of an oxygen function into the 11-position of the steroid nucleus.

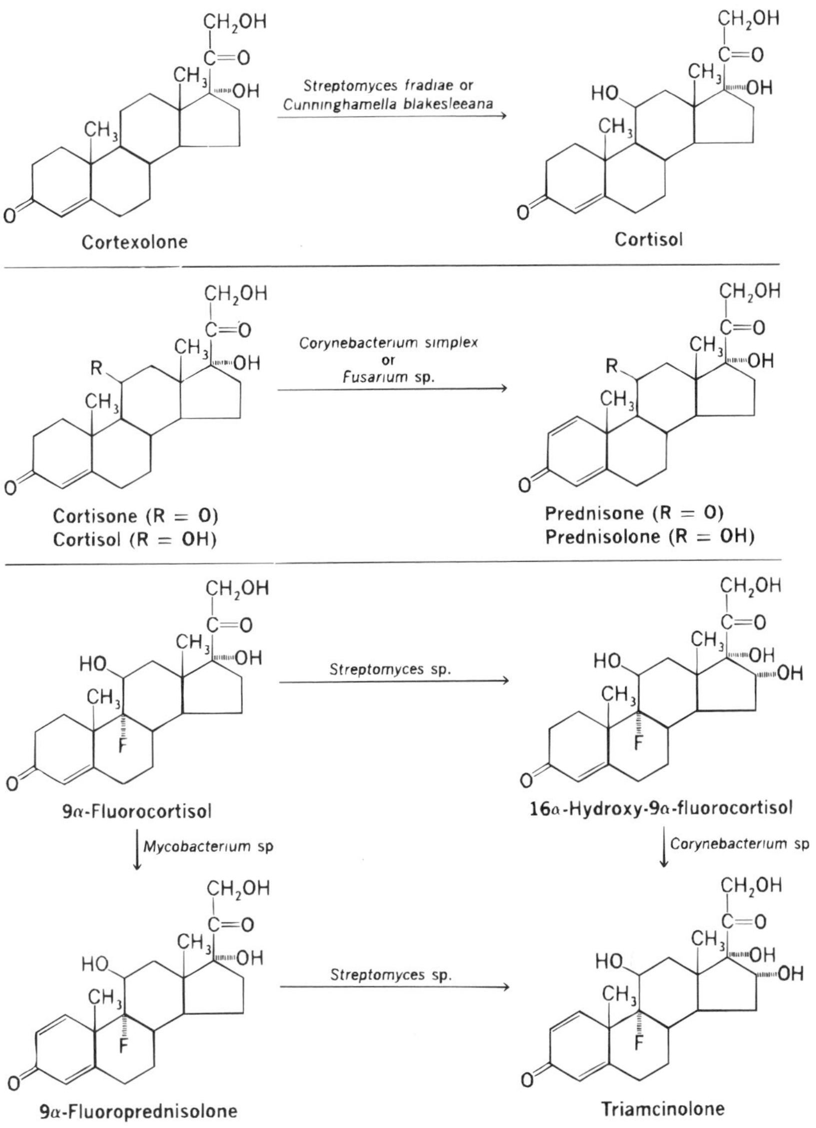

Fig. 7–12. Microbiologic transformation in production of glucocorticoids.

blood, and a fall in serum sodium, with a rise in serum glucose and potassium. Kidney damage is frequently present. These developments can be prevented or restored to normal by the administration of cortical extracts and frequently by the simple use of a high sodium, low potassium intake.

The human counterpart of this deficiency picture is seen in the clinical development of Addison's disease (chronic adrenocortical insufficiency), usually owing to tuberculosis or tumor of the adrenal cortex. Associated with this disease are degeneration of the gonads, a marked

increase in capillary permeability, and an increased sensitivity to insulin. Sodium loss with potassium retention may be the outstanding condition of the disease. If untreated, Addison's disease terminates fatally in 1 to 3 years, usually owing to hypoglycemia, dehydration, nutritional disturbances, or secondary infection.

Excessive adrenal cortical activity, as in tumors or because of the presence of accessory cortical tissue, results in profound growth abnormalities, especially seen in the genitalia and in the secondary sex characteristics. In young children, there is precocious sexual development and desire and obesity or unusual muscular development. In adult females, virilism usually develops, associated with a masculine appearance, often with homosexuality. The bearded lady of the circus frequently falls into this category. Treatment of cortical hyperactivity is principally surgical.

Some 70 or more steroids have been isolated from cortical extracts. These exhibit in some degree the action of adrenal cortex. Some, in addition, manifest estrogenic, androgenic, and progesterone-like activity, further indicating the close relationship between the adrenal cortex and the gonads.

Adrenocortical steroids include cortisone, hydrocortisone, desoxycorticosterone, and aldosterone. Cortisone and hydrocortisone constitute the majority of the hormones that regulate protein and carbohydrate metabolism. They have been referred to as the glucocorticoids. Aldosterone and desoxycorticosterone have been referred to as mineralocorticoids. Aldosterone is the principal adrenal steroid that regulates sodium, potassium, and water balance in the organism; however, it is not available for therapeutic use. Also, many agents that are considered primarily glucocorticoids possess variable mineralocorticoid activity as well.

Adrenocortical steroids are used most effectively in replacement therapy for such conditions as Addison's disease or surgically caused adrenal cortex deficiency.

The glucocorticoids are also used for their anti-inflammatory activity; therapy based on this pharmacologic response is an effective palliative approach in rheumatoid arthritis and a number of other conditions involving the inflammatory response. However, caution must be used in balancing the advantages and disadvantages of prolonged administration of corticosteroid therapy, such as may be involved in arthritic conditions. Exogenous sources of corticosteroids may cause a disruption in the physiologic balance among the biosynthetically related steroid hormones; toxic manifestations in such situations often involve changes that are normally considered to be dominated by gonadal hormones. As was discussed earlier, another potential problem of serious consequence is irreversible atrophy of the adrenal cortex.

Glucocorticoid therapy provides palliative treatment of symptoms in many allergic disorders, such as bronchial asthma, and is lifesaving for patients in anaphylactic shock. These compounds are used as immunosuppressive agents in organ transplants and autoimmune disorders and as antitumor agents in the treatment of malignancies, especially in certain leukemias and lymphomas.

Cortisone or 17,21-dihydroxypregn-4-ene-3,11,20-trione is one of the glucocorticoid substances of the adrenal cortex. The acetate ester of this hormone is used intramuscularly, orally, and topically to treat a wide variety of situations, such as rheumatoid arthritis, other collagen diseases, Addison's disease, and certain allergic and asthmatic conditions. An appreciable sodium-retaining property can be a major problem with the systemic use of cortisone.

Cortisone Acetate

Hydrocortisone or cortisol is $11\beta,17,21$-trihydroxypregn-4-ene-3,20-dione. It is considered the principal glucocorticoid substance of the adrenal cortex. This hormone and its acetate ester are used intramuscularly, orally, and topically for the same purposes as cortisone acetate. Intra-articular, intralesional, or soft tissue injection of cortisol always involves the acetate ester. Hydrocortisone sodium phosphate and hydrocortisone sodium succinate are water-soluble and are used in parenteral formulations when intravenous administration is indicated.

There are indications that cortisol is slightly more potent in some patients than cortisone and gives slightly better overall effects. However, it may exhibit the same disadvantages of sodium retention that were noted with cortisone.

The potential therapeutic utility of the glucocorticoids has promoted intensive efforts to discover modifications of the naturally occurring hormones that will be more potent and more specific in their activity. The best success has been achieved with desired increases in potency. Prednisone and prednisolone represent early achievements in these efforts. Elimination of any mineralocorticoid activity has been a major objective; a degree of success has been attained with such compounds as betamethasone, dexamethasone, methylprednisolone, and triamcinolone, but the ideal of total separation of mineralocorticoid activity from glucocorticoid substances has not yet been achieved. It is interesting to note that successful modifications in the basic steroid molecule fall into four categories:

1. Δ^1-dehydrogenation
2. 16α-hydroxylation
3. 6α- or 9α-fluorination
4. 6α-, 16α-, or 16β-methylation.

Gonads

The ovaries and testes are exocrine (ova, sperm) as well as endocrine (hormonal) in function. They develop under the influence of anterior pituitary hormones, particularly:

1. The follicle-stimulating hormone (FSH) leads to the development of the ovarian follicles, to their formation of ova and of estrogen, and to the development of the testes and the maturation of the spermatozoa.
2. The luteinizing hormone (LH) is necessary to the development of the corpora lutea in the ovarian follicles after ovulation, to the formation of progesterone by the corpora lutea, and to the production of androgen in the matured testis.

Androgens (male hormones) and estrogens (female follicular hormones) act to:

1. Develop and maintain the secondary characters of sex.
2. Depress anterior pituitary function, leading in turn to the depression of the testis or the ovary.

Progesterone (corpus luteum hormone) similarly depresses anterior pituitary function and presents a mixed antagonism-synergism with estrogenic activity, as will be indicated later.

Gonadal hyperactivity or excessive therapy may thus result in a picture of precocious or excessive sexual development, with the generalized effects of anterior pituitary depression. Gonadal hypoactivity, as occurs in the natural menopause or following surgical removal of the gonads, results in a mixed picture of sexual regression and enhanced anterior pituitary activity, with psychic disturbance and the involvement of other endocrine glands, particularly the thyroid.

Testes

Following castration in the male, the sex organs atrophy, and sexual desire and activity are diminished. These functions are restored by the administration of testis hormone. Hypogonadism (eunuchoidism) is inadequate development of the testes owing to pituitary disorder, infection, or other disease.

Hypergonadism is most frequently seen in young males, owing to testis tumors; this results in precocious development of sex organs and male characteristics. Therapy is usually surgical.

Testosterone is believed to be the true testis hormone, although it has been identified only in the bull's testis. It was synthesized by Ruzicka from cholesterol in 1936. Androsterone and dehydroandrosterone are urinary excretion products, relatively inactive in humans.

Androgen preparations have been valuable in the replacement therapy of male hypogonadism and in the treatment of impotence and male climacteric symptoms. In females they are used to treat metastatic breast cancer and postpartum breast pain and engorgement. Testosterone is not an aphrodisiac, and its use may produce the general effects of anterior pituitary depression. It may produce virilism in the female, and skin reactions similar to acne vulgaris may frequently develop.

Anabolic effects, especially with regard to protein synthesis and nitrogen retention in the body, have been noted with androgens. This action is potentially useful as supportive therapy in a number of debilitating conditions. Attempts have been made to prepare steroid compounds that separate anabolic effects from other androgenic activities, and the ultimate limitations on this therapeutic approach are keyed to the success of these efforts. The ideal separation has not been achieved with such compounds as oxandrolone, nandrolone, and other anabolic substances that are currently available.

Testosterone or 17β-hydroxyandrost-4-en-3-one is the active male hormone. The quantities used for drug purposes are prepared synthetically. The 17-hydroxyl function of testosterone is readily oxidized and metabolized to the much less physiologically active keto compound. Thus, testosterone is not administered orally. The hormone may be used buccally, implanted subcutaneously, applied transdermally, or injected intramuscularly. However, many formulations for these purposes utilize derivatives of the hormone, such as the cypionate, ethanthate, and propionate esters of the 17-hydroxyl group, which are characterized by delayed absorption and destruction.

The introduction of a methyl substituent at C-17 is another manipulation that has been used to circumvent the chemical and metabolic instability of testosterone. Preparations of methyltestosterone are used buccally and orally for androgenic purposes.

Testosterone

Ovary

The human ovaries are paired organs. One is situated on each lateral pelvic wall in the posterior layer of the broad ligament, behind and below the lateral extremity of each fallopian tube (oviduct). Each is about the size and shape of an unshelled almond and weighs 4 to 8 g.

Ova develop within primitive ovarian follicles (graafian follicles) under the influence of the follicle-stimulating hormone of the anterior pituitary. Ovulation with the extrusion of one ovum from a ripened follicle normally occurs each month during the childbearing period. The ruptured follicle undergoes cellular change to become the corpus luteum under the influence of the luteinizing hormone of the anterior pituitary. The ovary elaborates two types of hormones: the **estrogens,** elaborated in the developing graafian follicle and probably also in the placenta during pregnancy; and the progestins, normally elaborated by the corpus luteum and, in the latter half of pregnancy, by the placenta.

Deficiency in estrogenic activity is most frequently experienced in the normal menopause or following surgical removal of the ovaries. Local changes in the tissues of the vagina and vulva may result from estrogenic deficiency of any cause. The estrogens are necessary to:

1. Develop and maintain secondary female sex characteristics.
2. Develop and maintain the uterus and the vagina.
3. Aid in the presecretory development of the mammary glands.
4. Act as a growth hormone for uterine smooth muscle cells during pregnancy.

Estrogens act further to excite or sensitize the uterine muscle and to depress the anterior pituitary function. Preparations of estrogenic substances are employed in the management of:

1. Symptoms of the natural or surgical menopause.
2. Osteoporosis in postmenopausal women.
3. Local atrophic and degenerative changes in the adult vagina and vulva, resulting from estrogen deficiency.
4. Suppression of lactation in engorged, painful mammary glands, presumably by a direct action in the breast.
5. Prostatic cancer in the male, presumably by balancing an excessive persistence of androgen—the principle of ''biochemical castration.''
6. Palliative treatment of breast cancer in selected women and men or those with metastatic disease.

The natural ovarian hormones are steroids. The three major estrogenic hormones are estradiol and its oxidation products, estriol, and estrone. These hormones can be isolated from urine during pregnancy and can be prepared synthetically. Other estrogenic substances occur naturally, and amorphous mixtures of some of these steroids obtained from pregnant mare's urine are used in therapy under the designations of conjugated and esterified estrogens.

Estrogens may be administered orally, parenterally, transdermally, by implantation, or by inunction for systemic activity. Orally administered natural estrogens are destroyed in greater part. Estriol is the best of the pure, naturally occurring estrogens for oral use; oral efficiency of estriol is about one-fifth that achieved by parenteral administrations. Conjugated and esterified estrogens are also used orally, and the introduction of an ethinyl substituent at C-17 of estradiol gives a potent, orally effective compound.

As much as 90% of parenterally administered natural estrogens may be destroyed. This factor, in addition to rapid absorption, tends to diminish their efficiency and the effective period of therapy. Pharmaceutic manipulations, which have proved useful in achieving a prolonged action, include the use of esters, such as cypionate or valerate, and of formulations involving sterile vegetable oils. These manipulations slow absorption and destruction of the hormones; they also lessen the side effects of nausea and vomiting.

Implantation of the estrogens or their esters provides an even longer duration of action than do preparations administered intramuscularly. Transdermal administration is efficient, and because it avoids first pass hepatic metabolism, lower doses of estrogen can be used to prevent undesirable side effects. Suppositories containing estrogenic substances provide local treatment of changes in the vagina or vulva, or treatment of gonorrheal vaginitis in female children, with a minimum of systemic effect.

The natural estrogens exhibit carcinogenic properties upon prolonged administration to animal strains having hereditary susceptibility to mammary cancer. On this basis, the use of estrogens is contraindicated in women who have a personal or family history of mammary or genital cancer.

Estradiol or estra-1,3,5(10)-triene-3,17β-diol is used orally, injected intramuscularly, applied transdermally, and implanted subcutaneously.

Estradiol

Estrone or estra-1,3,5(10)-trien-3-ol-17-one is used intramuscularly.

The designation **conjugated estrogens** (Premarin) refers to a mixture of the sodium salts of the sulfate esters of the estrogenic substances that are of the type excreted by pregnant mares. This mixture of estrogenic substances must contain not less than 50% and not more than 65% of sodium estrone sulfate and not less than 20% and not more than 35% of sodium equilin sulfate. Equilin is estra-1,3,5(10),7-tetraen-3-ol-17-one and is one of the estrogens that appears in pregnant mare's urine in increasing quantities as the stage of pregnancy advances; equilin is only slightly less potent than estradiol. Conjugated estrogens may be administered orally or paren-

terally, and a progestin may be added concurrently or sequentially.

The designation **esterified estrogens** also refers to a mixture of the sodium salts of the sulfate esters of the estrogenic substances that are of the type excreted by pregnant mares. This mixture differs from conjugated estrogens because it has more estrone and less equilin metabolites. It must contain not less than 75% and not more than 85% of sodium estrone sulfate and not less than 6.5% and not more than 15% of sodium equilin sulfate. It is used orally for the same purposes as are preparations of conjugated estrogens.

A number of stilbene derivatives, as well as various other compounds, have estrogenic activity. These synthetic substances are active orally and have been used in some instances as therapeutic substitutes for the estrogenic steroids. These stilbene derivatives are absorbed rapidly, destroyed slowly, and active for a prolonged period. However, the side effects of nausea and vomiting also tend to be enhanced. Diethylstilbestrol is probably the best known of these substances, but other useful derivatives include chlorotrianisene.

Corpus Luteum

The corpus luteum is essential to the maintenance of human pregnancy during the first half of the term. Its principal hormonal functions are:

1. Preparation of the uterine mucosa to receive the fertilized ovum.
2. Development of the maternal placenta.
3. Continuation of the development of the mammary glands in preparation for lactogenic action of anterior pituitary.
4. Suppression of ovulation for the duration of pregnancy.
5. Antagonism of the stimulating effect of estrogens on the uterine muscle to produce a relaxation of the uterus.

The active hormone of the corpus luteum is progesterone. It can be prepared synthetically from a number of steroidal substances. Progesterone is relatively inactive on oral administration, and it is given intramuscularly. This hormone is used in the treatment of amenorrhea, dysmenorrhea, endometriosis, functional uterine bleeding, and threatened or habitual abortion.

Progesterone is pregn-4-ene-3,20-dione. A number of synthetic progestins have been developed that have such advantages over progesterone as fewer side effects when administrated over prolonged periods, oral efficacy, and greater potency. Such compounds as hydroxy-progesterone caproate in oil, medroxyprogesterone acetate (Provera), and norethindrone (Norlutin) may be used as therapeutic substitutes for the natural hormone.

One of the normal physiologic functions of progesterone is to suppress ovulation during pregnancy. This hormone is not formed during the first half of a normal menstrual cycle, but administration of it or of some other progestational agent during this part of the menstrual period offers an effective means of birth control. When progestins are used as oral contraceptives, some estrogenic substance is frequently added, either by combined formulation or sequential administration, to the therapeutic approach to reduce side effects.

Progesterone

Progesterone is also available in an intrauterine device (IUD). The hormone is dissolved in silicone oil, and the flexible polymer of the IUD acts as a membrane to allow for the slow release of progesterone (65 μg daily) into the uterine cavity. The IUD contains enough progesterone to last 1 year, and the failure rate is about 2%. The failure rate of the same device without progesterone is approximately 18%. The product is called Progestasert.

SUGGESTED READINGS

Danielsson, H., Sjövall, J., eds.: *New Comprehensive Biochemistry: Sterols and Bile Acids,* Vol 12. Amsterdam, Elsevier Science Publishers B.V., 1985.

Duax, W.L., Griffin, J.F.: The Structure and Receptor Binding of Steroid Hormones, In *Advances in Drug Research,* Vol 18. Testa, B.,ed., London, Academic Press Limited, 1989.

Endo, A., Hasumi, K.: HMG-CoA Reductase Inhibitors, Nat. Prod. Rep., *10* (6): 541, 1993.

Goodwin, T.W.: Biosynthesis of Plant Sterols and Other Triterpenoids. In *Biosynthesis of Isoprenoid Compounds,* Vol. 1. Porter, J.W., Spurgeon, S.L., eds. New York, John Wiley & Sons, Inc., 1981.

Makin, H.L.J., ed.: *Biochemistry of Steroid Hormones,* 2nd ed. Oxford, Blackwell Scientific Publications, 1984.

Moss, G.P.: IUPAC-IUB Nomenclature of Steroids. Pure Appl. Chem., *61*: 1783, 1989.

Nes, W. D., Parish E. J., Trzaskos, J. M., eds.: *Regulation of Isopentenoid Metabolism.* Washington, DC, American Chemical Society, 1992.

Repke, K. R. H., Weiland, J., Megges, R., Schön, R.: Approach to the Chemotopography of the Digitalis Recognition Matrix in Na$^+$/K$^+$-transporting ATPase as a Step in the Rational Design of New Inotropic Steroids. In *Progress in Medicinal Chemistry,* Vol 30. Ellis, G. P., Luscombe, D. K., eds., Amsterdam, Elsevier Science Publishers B. V., 1993.

Thomas, R., Gray, P., Andrews, J.: Digitalis: Its Mode of Action, Receptor, and Structure-Activity Relationships. In *Advances in Drug Research,* Vol 19. Testa, B., ed., London Academic Press Limited, 1990.

Wilkerson, R. D.: *Cardiac Pharmacology.* New York, Academic Press, Inc., 1981.

Witzmann, R. F.: *Steroids. Keys to Life.* New York, Van Nostrand Reinhold Co., 1981.

Zeelen, F. J.: *Medicinal Chemistry of Steroids.* Amsterdam, Elsevier Science Publishers B. V., 1990.

Zeelen, F. J.: Medicinal Chemistry of Steroids: Recent Developments. In *Advances in Drug Research,* Vol 22. London, Academic Press Limited, 1992.

8

Phenylpropanoids

Phenylpropanoids represent a large group of natural products derived from the aromatic amino acids phenylalanine and tyrosine or in some special cases the intermediates of the shikimic acid biosynthetic pathway. As their name suggests, most of these compounds contain in their structure a phenyl ring attached to a three-carbon propane side chain, and in contradistinction to the alkaloids, cyanogenic glycosides, and glucosinolates, they are devoid of nitrogen. Because most of the phenylpropanoids are phenolic in nature with one or more hydroxyl groups on the aromatic ring, they are often collectively referred to as **plant phenolics.**

Various categories of phenylpropanoids include the **hydroxycinnamic acids** such as *p*-coumaric acid and caffeic acid, **phenylpropenes** which arise from dehydration of cinnamyl alcohols that are produced by the reduction of cinnamic acids, **coumarins** which are lactones derived from *o*-hydroxycinnamic acids, and **chromones** which are isomeric with coumarins. In addition, some compounds are considered **abridged phenylpropanoids** with either no side chain such as with catechol, or a side chain with one carbon atom as with gallic acid, benzoic acid, salicin, methyl salicylate, and vanillin, or with two carbon atoms as with 2-phenylethanol. In some cases, the side chains from two phenylpropanoids react with each other to form bisphenylpropanoid derivatives called **lignans** or **neolignans**. With the **flavonoids** one aromatic ring and its C_3 side chain have a phenylpropanoid origin from *p*-coumaroyl CoA derived from phenylalanine, and another aromatic ring in the molecule is the result of a condensation with three molecules of malonyl CoA via polyketide biosynthesis. Phenylpropanoids also serve as building units in the formation of high-molecular-weight polymers in plants. The two major types of these polymers are the **lignins** and the **tan-** nins. Lignins are sequestered in the secondary layer of the cell wall in association with the cellulose matrix where the phenolic hydroxyl groups of the lignins may be hydrogen bonded or covalently linked to hemicellulose. Lignin contributes to the strength of the cell wall, and the ability to synthesize it is thought to have been a decisive factor in the adaptation of plants to a terrestrial habitat in evolution because only with lignified cell walls did it become possible to construct the rigid stems of woody plants and trees.

Plant tannins are a diverse group of phenolic compounds that are related primarily in their ability to complex with proteins. They are generally subdivided into two groups, **condensed tannins**, often referred to as **proanthocyanidins**, and **hydrolyzable tannins**.

BIOSYNTHESIS OF PHENYLPROPANOIDS

The principal precursors for **phenylpropanoid** compounds are cinnamic acid and *p*-hydroxycinnamic acid, also known as *p*-coumaric acid. In plants, these compounds arise from the aromatic amino acids phenylalanine and tyrosine, respectively, which in turn are synthesized via the shikimic acid pathway (Fig. 8–1). This biosynthetic pathway has been elucidated in microorganisms by using auxotrophic mutants of *Escherichia coli* and *Enterobacter aerogenes* that require the aromatic amino acids for growth. In the biosynthesis, two glucose metabolites, erythrose 4-phosphate and phosphoenolpyruvate, react to yield a phosphorylated 7-carbon keto sugar, DAHP. This compound cyclizes to 3-dehydroquinic acid, which is then converted to shikimic acid. Shikimic acid, through a series of phosphorylated intermediates, yields choris-

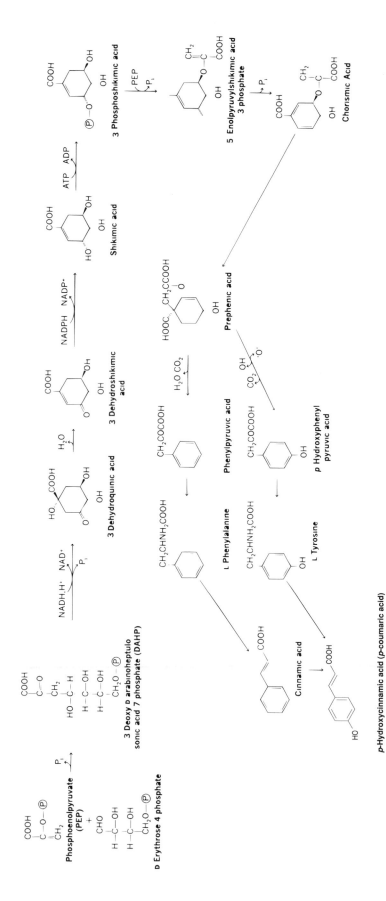

Fig. 8–1. The shikimic acid pathway in phenylpropanoid biosynthesis.

132

mic acid, which is an important branch-point intermediate. One branch leads to anthranilic acid and then to tryptophan. The other leads to prephenic acid, the last nonaromatic compound in the sequence. Prephenic acid can be aromatized in two ways. The first proceeds by dehydration and simultaneous decarboxylation to yield phenylpyruvic acid, the direct precursor of phenylalanine. The second occurs by dehydrogenation and decarboxylation to yield *p*-hydroxyphenylpyruvic acid, the precursor of tyrosine.

The phenylpropanoid precursor, cinnamic acid, is formed by the direct enzymatic deamination of phenylalanine, and *p*-coumaric acid can originate in an analogous way from tyrosine or by hydroxylation of cinnamic acid at the para position. *p*-Coumaric acid, also known as *p*-hydroxycinnamic acid, is a central intermediate in the biosynthesis of many of the phenylpropanoids, including the simpler compounds such as other hydroxycinnamic acids and alcohols and the phenylpropenes, for example anethole and eugenol, as well as more chemically complex compounds such as flavonoids, lignans, neolignans, and lignin (Fig 8–2). Flavonoids arise

from *p*-coumaroyl CoA and three molecules of malonyl CoA. Lignans and neolignans are formed via oxidative dimerization of coniferyl alcohol units. Two of these units are joined through a variety of possible covalent linkages of the carbon and oxygen atoms present in the C$_3$ side chain. Subsequent reactions lead to substitution of the aromatic rings and production of polycyclic compounds. Lignins are polymers that are thought to be derived by phenolic oxidative coupling of different types of hydroxycinnamoyl alcohol units, the most important being *p*-coumaryl alcohol, coniferyl alcohol, and sinapyl alcohol that arise from hydroxycinnamic acid precursors via the corresponding CoA esters and aldehydes.

SIMPLE PHENYLPROPANOIDS

The **simple phenylpropanoids** are categorized on the basis of their relatively low molecular weight and minor structural modifications from the phenylpropanoid biosynthetic interme-

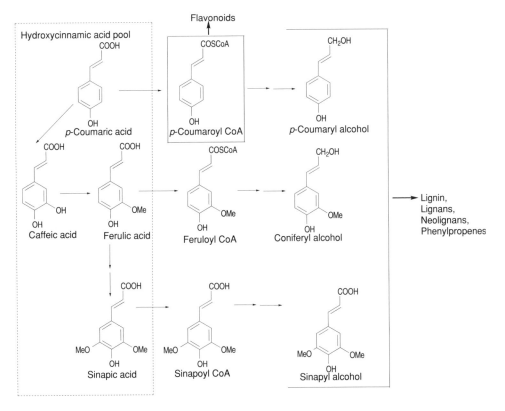

Fig. 8–2. The reactions of general phenylpropanoid metabolism.

diates. Included in this category are the **phenyl-propenes** which are volatile, lipid-soluble compounds usually isolated along with terpenes from volatile oils; consequently, they contribute to the odors and flavors of plants. Anethole, eugenol, and myristicin are compounds in this group and are discussed in chapter 6. The phenylpropenes are formed from hydroxycinnamoyl alcohols; for example, coniferyl alcohol is the immediate precursor of eugenol and methyleugenol with methyleugenol subsequently serving as the precursor to myristicin.

Abridged phenylpropanoids are usually phenols and acids, rarely aldehydes and alcohols, that arise from the β-oxidation of the C_3 side chain of either p-cinnamoyl CoA or p-coumaroyl CoA with subsequent oxidative decarboxylation. Compounds with additional phenolic hydroxyl groups in the meta position are not formed by hydroxylation of these resulting intermediates but by a pathway which branches from the main shikimate pathway at 3-dehydroshikimic acid. Abridged phenylpropanoids include benzoic acid, capsaicin, gallic acid, methyl salicylate, salicin, and vanillin.

***p*-Hydroxycinnamic acids** such as p-coumaric acid and caffeic acid and their methylated derivatives such as ferulic acid and sinapic acid are widely distributed in plants and occur free and in a large number of different esterified forms. The hydroxycinnamic acids (and their esters) can exist in both Z and E forms, but usually occur naturally as the E form which undergoes isomerization during isolation to yield an equilibrium mixture of both isomers.

Coumarins are lactones which are derived from p-hydroxycinnamic acids which undergo ortho hydroxylation then ring closure between the ortho hydroxyl group and the carboxylic group of the side chain, after a *trans* to *cis* isomerization of the side-chain double bond. More than 700 different plant coumarins have been isolated, and coumarin itself is widely distributed and has the characteristic odor of new mown hay.

The **chromones** represent a small group of plant phenolics that are isomeric with coumarins; however, technically they are not phenylpropanoids because their biosynthetic origin is probably from acetate via the polyketide biosynthetic pathway. The best known chromone is the furochromone khellin, which is a potent coronary vasodialator.

Capsicum

Capsicum or cayenne pepper is the dried, ripe fruit of *Capsicum frutescens* Linné, known in commerce as African chillies, of *C. annuum* Linné var. *conoides* Irish, known in commerce as Tabasco pepper, or *C. annuum* var. *longum* Sendt, known in commerce as Louisiana long pepper, or of a hybrid between the Honka variety of Japanese capsicum and the old Louisiana short capsicum, known in commerce as Louisiana short pepper (Fam. Solanaceae). Capsicum must be labeled to indicate which variety is contained in the package.

Capsicum is from the Latin *capsa*, meaning a box, and refers to the partially hollow, boxlike fruit; *frutescens* is Latin and refers to the shrubby character of the plant; and *annuum* is Latin and refers to the annual character of the plant.

C. frutescens is a small spreading shrub reaching 1 meter in height and is indigenous to tropical America and cultivated in tropical localities in Africa, India, America, and Japan. Apparently, the more tropical the climate, the more pungent the fruit. *C. annuum* is an herbaceous, annual form cultivated in mildly temperate to semitropical localities in central and southern Europe, Mexico, the United States, and other countries. It is cultivated under the names of garden pepper, paprika, pimento, Mexican chillies, Tabasco pepper, and others. All of these are desirable as condiments. The medicinal value of capsicum as a counterirritant depends on its pungency.

African cayenne comes chiefly from Kenya and Tanzania in East Africa and Sierra Leone in West Africa and is usually designated in the trade by the port from which it is shipped. Japanese chillies, usually exported from Kobe, are somewhat less pungent than African capsicum but more pungent than Madras or Bombay chillies from India.

Capsicum was first mentioned in 1494 by Chauca, a physician who accompanied Columbus on his second voyage to the West Indies. Plants were introduced into India by the Portuguese at an early date and later into Africa.

Tabasco peppers are about twice the size and Louisiana peppers up to 10 times the size of African capsicum. The outer epidermis of the pericarp of these peppers consists of irregular (not quadrangular) cells with thickened and strongly beaded, lignified, radial walls. They also possess a hypodermis of elongated cells with thickened, strongly beaded radial walls of cellulose or cuticularized cellulose. These features readily distinguish these peppers, in whole or powdered form, from genuine African capsicum.

Capsicum contains capsaicin (about 0.02%), an extremely pungent principal, in the dissepiments of the fruit. Capsaicin is the vanillyl amide of isodecenoic acid, and the vanillyl group is an abridged phenylpropanoid arising from phenylalanine.

Capsaicin

It imparts a distinctly pungent taste to water, even when diluted to 1 part in 11 million parts of water. Capsicum also contains about 1.5% of a volatile oil, a fixed oil, carotenoids, and up to 0.2% of ascorbic acid (vitamin C).

Topical preparations of capsaicin in concentrations of 0.025 to 0.075% have been found effective in the treatment of pain of rheumatoid arthritis and osteoarthritis, postherpetic neuralgia, diabetic neuropathy, and postmastectomy and postamputation neuroma (phantom pain syndrome). Capsaicin causes a depletion of the neuropeptide substance P from local sensory C-type nerve fibers. Substance P mediates the transmission of pain impulses from the peripheral nerves to the spinal cord. So even if the condition causing the pain continues to be present, no perception of the pain reaches the brain. Depletion of substance P does not occur immediately, and effective use of a topical preparation requires application 4 or 5 times daily for a period of at least 4 weeks. Users must be cautioned to wash their hands thoroughly after each application and to avoid touching the eyes or mucous membranes after applications.

Coumarin

Coumarin is the lactone of *o*-hydroxycinnamic acid. The name coumarin originates from a Caribbean name *coumarou* for the tonka tree. It occurs as colorless, prismatic crystals and has a characteristic fragrant odor and a bitter, aromatic, burning taste. It is soluble in alcohol. Coumarin can be synthesized readily.

Coumarin

Coumarin is rather widely distributed in nature. It occurs in **tonka beans**, coumarin-containing seeds of *Dipteryx odorata* (Aublet) Willdenow and *D. oppositifolia* (Aublet) Willdenow, (Fam. Lamiaceae), formerly used pharmaceutically as flavoring agents. Coumarin has been isolated from sweet vernal grass (*Anthoxanthum odoratum* Linné, Fam. Poaceae), sweet clover [*Melilotus albus* Medicus and *M. officinalis* (Linné) Lamarck, Fam. Lamiaceae], sweet-scented bedstraw (*Galium triflorum* Michaux, Fam. Rubiaceae), and red clover (*Trifolium pratense* Linné, Fam. Lamiaceae).

Coumarin and extracts of tonka beans were formerly used as flavoring agents. However, coumarin-drug interactions occur with a number of therapeutic substances, and the FDA has banned the use of coumarin and coumarin-containing materials for flavoring purposes. Some coumarin derivatives still find application for their anticoagulant properties. The antispasmodic activity of the barks of *Viburnum prunifolium* Linné (blackhaw) and *V. opulus* Linné (true cramp bark) (Fam. Caprifoliaceae) has been attributed to scopoletin (6-methoxy-7-hydroxycoumarin) and other coumarins.

Bishydroxycoumarin or dicumarol is a drug related to coumarin. It was obtained originally from improperly cured leaves and flowering tops of *Melilotus officinalis* (Linné) Pall. (Fam. Lamiaceae), but it is now prepared synthetically. Dicumarol is an anticoagulant.

Dicumarol

A number of synthetic analogs of bishydroxycoumarin also are used in anticoagulant therapy; these include warfarin salts. Coumarin derivatives are indirect-acting anticoagulants and used for the prophylaxis and treatment of venous thrombosis and pulmonary embolism. They act in the liver by interfering with the action of vitamin K which is necessary for the gamma-carboxylation of glutamic acid residues in the precursor proteins of coagulation factors II, VII, IX, and X. Because the effects of coumarin derivatives are delayed, they are generally used for follow-up therapy after the effects of heparin therapy have been established.

Psoralens

Psoralens are photosensitizing furocoumarins that occur in a number of plant families, including the Apiaceae and Rutaceae, where they are a common cause of phototoxicity. In addition, they are produced as phytoalexins by celery plants, *Apium graveolens,* after infection with the fungus *Sclerotina sclerotiorum.* **Methoxsalen, 8-methoxypsoralen, or xanthotoxin,** a constituent of the cremocarps of *Ammi majus* Linné (Fam. Apiaceae), is used to facilitate repigmentation in idiopathic vitiligo (leukoderma) and for symptomatic control of severe, disabling psoriasis. Methoxsalen may be applied topically or taken orally. Therapeutic regimens require cautious patient exposure to ultraviolet radiation (sunlight); repigmentation therapy usually involves extended periods of time. Risks inherent in therapy with methoxsalen, including carcinogenesis, cataract development, and actinic degeneration of the skin, restrict its use to specialists.

Trioxsalen or 4,5′,8-trimethoxypsoralen, a synthetic furocoumarin, is also available for use in the treatment of vitiligo.

OMe

Methoxsalen

Echinacea

As used in the United States, the terms **echinacea, cone flower,** and **purple cone flower** refer to the dried rhizome and roots of *Echinacea angustifolia* De Candolle or *E. pallida* (Nutt.) Nutt. These plants are perennial herbs of the family Asteraceae and are native to the midwestern states. In Europe, the entire fresh, flowering plant is employed medicinally, as is another species, *E. purpurea* (Linné) Moench. Both species are said to have the same properties.

Echinacea was introduced into American medicine in 1885 by Dr. H.C.F. Meyer, who recommended it as a ''blood purifier.'' He probably gained his knowledge of the plant from the early settlers and the Indians. Both groups valued it

highly as a remedy against various types of infections, in treating bites of poisonous reptiles and insects, as a palliative agent in malignant conditions, and for its wound-healing properties. The drug continues to be used in this country as a folk medicine in the treatment of these same conditions, but particularly to increase resistance to infections. The drug is consumed orally in the United States, for preventing and treating the common cold and its associated conditions, such as sore throat. Echinacea is taken either in powdered form, as an infusion or decoction, or as an alcoholic tincture or extract. In Europe, it is used primarily in lotions and cosmetics for its wound-healing action, and, in injectable forms, to stimulate the body's immune system.

Echinacea has no direct bactericidal or bacteriostatic properties. It acts as an immunostimulant and increases phagocytosis and promotes the activity of the lymphocytes, resulting in the increased release of tumor necrosis factor. There are indications that it also induces the production of properdin and interferon.

The exact identity of the principles in echinacea responsible for these effects is still undergoing intensive study. High-molecular-weight polysaccharides, including a heteroxylan that activates the phagocytes and an arabinogalactan that promotes the release of tumor necrosis factor, play a significant role. Stimulation of phagocytosis is apparently also enhanced by various alkamides and the phenylpropanoid chicoric acid.

Chicoric acid

Khellin

Khellin is a furochromone found in the fruit of *Ammi visnaga* Lam. (Fam. Apiaceae). The plant grows in Mediterranean countries and has been used for urethral spasm and renal colic. Khellin is available outside the United States in tablets and injection and is a potent coronary vasodilator and bronchodilator in the treatment of coronary insufficiency, angina pectoris, and bronchial asthma. Khellin is the prototype for the synthetic mast-cell stabilizing drug cromolyn sodium. It is an antiasthmatic and antiallergic agent that acts locally on the lung to which it is applied by inhalation.

Khellin

LIGNANS AND NEOLIGNANS

Lignans and **neolignans** are typically found as dimeric phenylpropanoid derivatives chemically related to the polymeric lignins of the plant cell and are found in woody tissues. Reduction of ferulic acid to coniferyl alcohol is a primary step in the production of lignans which are formed via oxidative dimerization of coniferyl alcohol units and linked through the β-carbon atom of the C_3 side chains. Typically they are found as single enantiomeric forms, but racemic products are also encountered. They vary substantially in oxidation levels, degree of substitutions, and structural complexity. Neolignans are formed by unsymmetrical carbon-carbon links in the side chains. Lignans and neolignans play an important role in the plant defense as antimicrobial, antifungal, and antifeedant agents. Because they have antitumor and antiviral activity, lignans are of considerable pharmacological interest.

Podophyllum

Podophyllum consists of the dried rhizome and roots of *Podophyllum peltatum* Linné (Fam. Berberidaceae). It is also known as **mayapple** or **American mandrake**.

Podophyllotoxin

The generic name is Greek and means footlike leaf; *peltatum* means shieldlike. The plant is a perennial herb that has a long, jointed, and branching rhizome. The rhizomes are dug either early in the spring or in the autumn after the aerial parts have died down. Most of the commercial supplies come from the central United States and from Virginia and North Carolina. The drug was known to the Indians, who introduced it to the early settlers. The drug should not be confused with mandragora, referred to as mandrake by the ancient Greeks and Asiatics.

Mayapple is an important American botanical drug; the annual production is several hundred tons and supplies both domestic and export demands.

Podophyllum contains 3.5 to 6% of a resin whose active principles are lignans. These include podophyllotoxin (20%), α-peltatin (10%), and β-peltatin (5%). A number of lignan glycosides are in the plant, but because of their water solubility, they are lost during the normal preparation of the resin.

The antimitotic and purgative properties of these compounds depend on a lactone ring in the *trans* configuration. Treatment with mild alkali produces epimerization with formation of the stable *cis* isomers, which are physiologically inactive. Picropodophyllin is an inactive *cis* isomer produced in this way from the active *trans* podophyllotoxin. Podophyllum yields not less than 5% of podophyllum resin. Podophyllum possesses drastic purgative properties. Its resin is also employed as an antimitotic and caustic.

Indian podophyllum, the rhizome of *Podophyllum emodi* Wallich, a plant growing on the lower slopes of the Himalayas, is larger and yields 11.4 to 12% of resin that contains about twice as much podophyllotoxin as the resin obtained from *P. peltatum*.

Podophyllum resin is also known as **podophyllin** and is the powdered mixture of resins removed from podophyllum by percolation with alcohol and by subsequent precipitation from the concentrated percolate when added to acidified water.

The precipitated resin is washed twice with water and is dried and powdered. It is an amorphous powder that varies in color from light brown to greenish yellow and turns darker when subjected to temperatures exceeding 25°C or when exposed to light. It has a slight, peculiar, bitter taste and is highly irritating to the eye and to mucous membranes in general.

Podophyllum resin is a caustic for certain papillomas. It is applied topically as a 25% dispersion in compound benzoin tincture or in a 70 to 96% solution of alcohol. Podophyllum resin has also been used as a drastic purgative and as a hydragogue cathartic.

A number of lignans with lactone rings in the *trans* configuration are the tumor-inhibiting constituents of podophyllum resin. Such compounds include podophyllotoxin, several podophyllotoxin derivatives, and α- and β-peltatin. The peltatins are responsible for most of the purgative effects of the drug.

Etoposide

Etoposide is a semisynthetic podophyllotoxin derivative used as an antineoplastic agent. It differs structurally from podophyllotoxin by having an ethylidene glucoside attached at the C-1 position; it has an epimeric configuration at the C-4 position of ring C, and there is a hydroxyl group at the C-4′ position rather than a methoxy group. This hydroxyl group is associated with etoposide's ability to induce single-stranded DNA breaks, and the ethylidene glucoside moiety is associated with the drug's inability to inhibit microtubule assembly, a property which may decrease the toxic effects associated with podophyllotoxin.

Etoposide is used in combination with other chemotherapeutic agents for refractory testicular tumors and as a first line treatment in small cell lung cancer. It has also been used in the treatment of acute nonlymphocytic leukemias, Hodgkin's disease, non-Hodgkin's lymphomas, Kaposi's sarcoma, and neuroblastoma.

The exact mechanism of action of etoposide is not known, but it appears to damage DNA, thereby inhibiting or altering DNA synthesis. Etoposide appears to be cell-cycle dependent and cycle-phase specific, inducing G_2-phase arrest and preferentially killing cells in the G_2 and late S phases. It may induce single-stranded DNA breaks indirectly through endonuclease activation, inhibition of intranuclear type II topoisomerase, or formation of a free radical metabolite via an enzymatic reaction involving the 4′-hydroxyl group of the E ring.

Teniposide is a semisynthetic derivative of podophyllotoxin which is used as a component of multiple-drug antineoplastic regimens for induction therapy in childhood acute lymphoblastic leukemia that is refractory to induction with other therapy. Teniposide differs structurally from etoposide by the addition of a thenylidene ring on the glucopyranoside ring. Its mechanism of action is postulated to be similar to that of etoposide.

Etoposide

FLAVONOIDS

Flavonoids are among the most widely distributed natural product compounds in plants with over 2,000 different compounds reported occurring both in the free state and as glycosides. Their chemical structures are based upon a C_6-C_3-C_6 carbon skeleton with a chroman ring bearing a second aromatic ring in position 2,3, or 4. The major general structural categories are flavones, flavanones, flavonols, anthocyanidins, and isoflavones. In some cases, the six-membered heterocyclic ring is replaced by a five-membered ring (aurones) or exists in an open-chain isomeric form (chalcones). In addition to glycosylated derivatives, methylated, acylated, prenylated, or sulfated derivatives also occur. A variety of flavonoids have been assigned different roles in nature as antimicrobial compounds, stress metabolites, or signaling molecules.

The general biosynthesis of flavonoids involves the central intermediate *p*-coumaroyl CoA and three malonyl CoA units to elongate the side chain of the original phenylpropanoid unit. Closure of the A ring produces the chalcone structure and subsequent reaction closes the B ring (Fig. 8–3).

Rutin

Rutin, the rhamnoglucoside of the flavonoid quercetin, is found in many plants, and it and the citrus bioflavonoid hesperidin have been called vitamin P or the permeability factor. They have a history of use in the treatment of various conditions characterized by capillary bleeding and increased capillary fragility. Claims have also been advanced for the value of citrus bioflavonoids in treating symptoms of the common cold. Evidence for the therapeutic efficacy of rutin and citrus bioflavonoids is not conclusive, and prod-

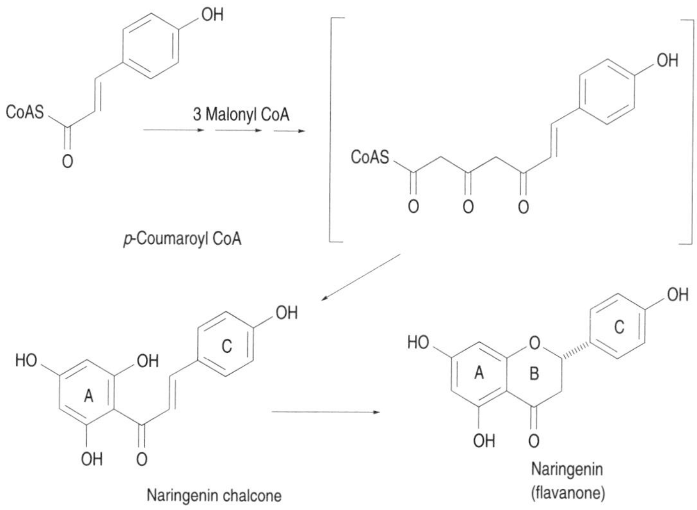

Fig. 8–3. General flavonoid biosynthetic pathway.

ucts containing them are no longer marketed for medicinal purposes in the United States. They are included in some preparations as dietary supplements.

Milk Thistle

Milk thistle consists of the ripe fruits, freed from their pappus (tuft of silky hairs), of *Silybum marianum* (Linné) Gaertn. (Fam. Asteraceae). This herb has been widely used and extensively investigated as a cure or preventive for a wide range of liver problems. A crude mixture of antihepatotoxic principles was first isolated from the plant and designated silymarin. Subsequently, silymarin was shown to consist of several flavonolignans, including principally **silybin** accompanied by isosilybin, dehydrosilybin, silydianin, and silychristin.

Silymarin has considerable therapeutic potential in protecting intact liver cells or cells not yet irreversibly damaged by acting on the cell membranes to prevent the entry of toxic substances. Protein synthesis is also stimulated, thereby accelerating the regeneration process and the production of hepatocytes. It has been demonstrated that silybin binds to a regulative subunit of the DNA-dependent RNA polymerase I at a specific site by imitating a natural steroid effector and thus activates this enzyme. As a consequence, the synthetic rate of ribosomal RNAs is enhanced, leading to an increased formation of intact ribosomes which results in increased protein synthesis.

The herb can be used as a supportive treatment for chronic inflammatory liver conditions and cirrhosis. It is marketed in the form of capsules containing a concentrated extract representing 140 mg of silymarin.

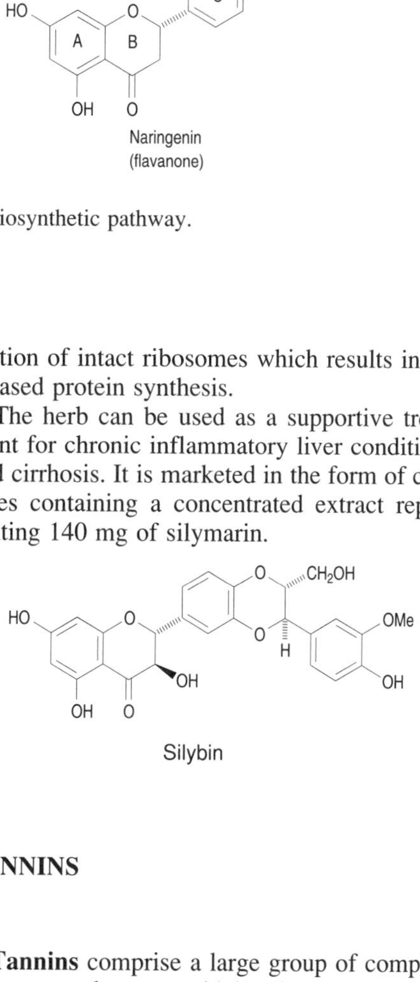

Silybin

TANNINS

Tannins comprise a large group of complex substances that are widely distributed in the plant kingdom; almost every plant family embodies species that contain tannins. When tannins occur in appreciable quantities, they are usually localized in specific plant parts, such as leaves, fruits, barks, or stems.

Chemically, tannins are complex substances; they usually occur as mixtures of polyphenols that are difficult to separate because they do not crystallize. Some authors prefer to use the term "tannin extracts" rather than "tannins." Recently, the use of chromatographic methods has enabled research workers not only to confirm the complicated nature of tannin extracts but also to identify the simple polyphenols present in small amounts in such mixtures. Determination of the latter is important because complex tannins are generally considered to have arisen from simple polyphenols by polymerization. Many condensed tannins have never been isolated or characterized; thus, their biogenetic development is not positively known.

Tannins are customarily divided into two chemical classes, based on the identity of the phenolic nuclei involved and on the way they are joined. Members of the first class consist of gallic acid and hexahydroxydiphenic acid and their derivatives esterified with glucose. Because such esters are readily hydrolyzed to yield the phenolic acids and the sugar, they are referred to as **hydrolyzable tannins**.

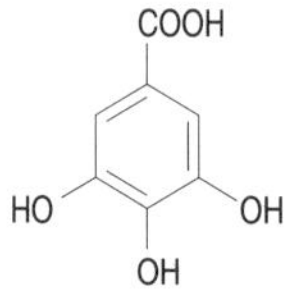

Gallic acid

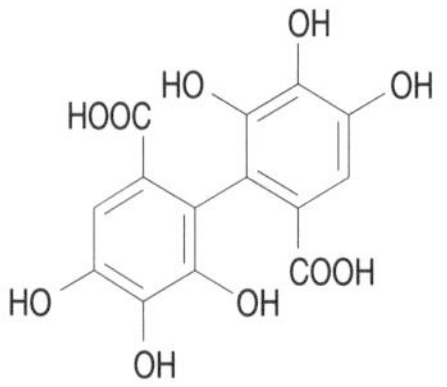

Hexahydroxydiphenic acid

Nonhydrolyzable or condensed tannins compose the second class. The term **proanthocyanidin** is used alternatively for condensed tannins because on treatment with hot acid some of the carbon-carbon bonds are broken, yielding anthocyanidin monomers. Basically, these tannins contain only phenolic nuclei but frequently are linked to carbohydrates or proteins. Most such tannins result from the condensation of two or more flavan-3-ols, such as catechin, or of flavan-3,4-diols, such as leucocyanidin. When treated with hydrolytic agents, these tannins tend to polymerize, yielding insoluble, usually red-colored products known as phlobaphenes.

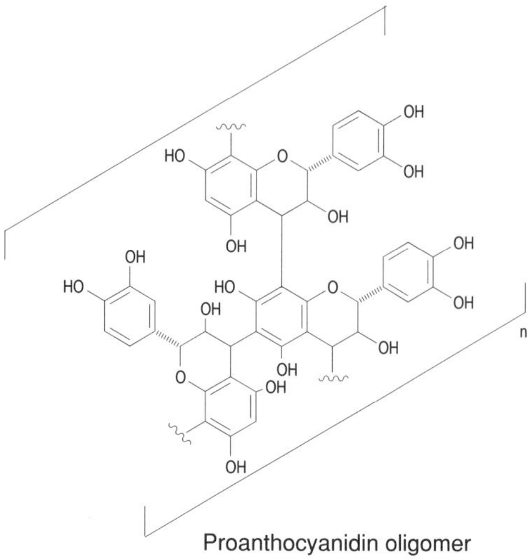

Proanthocyanidin oligomer

Both classes of tannins are widely distributed in nature. It must be emphasized that, in many species, both types are present, although one type generally tends to predominate in any particular plant part.

Tannins are noncrystallizable compounds that, with water, form colloidal solutions possessing an acid reaction and a sharp "puckering" taste. They cause precipitation of solutions of gelatin as well as of alkaloids; they form dark blue or greenish black soluble compounds with ferric salts; they produce a deep red color with potassium ferricyanide and ammonia; and they are precipitated by salts of copper, lead, and tin and by strong aqueous potassium dichromate (or 1% chromic acid) solutions. In alkaline solutions, many of their derivatives readily absorb oxygen.

Tannins precipitate proteins from solution and can combine with proteins, rendering them resistant to proteolytic enzymes. When applied to living tissues, this action is known as an "astringent" action and forms the basis for therapeutic application of tannins. Tannin-bearing drugs, such as hamamelis and nutgall, as well as partially purified tannins (tannic acid) and their derivatives (acetyltannic acid), are used in medicine as astringents in the gastrointestinal tract and on skin abrasions. In the treatment of burns, the proteins of the exposed tissues are precipitated and form a mildly antiseptic, protective coat under which the regeneration of new tissues may take place.

Reports on the utility and safety of the long-term ingestion of quantities of plant materials rich in condensed tannins are contradictory and somewhat difficult to reconcile based on present knowledge. Some epidemiologic and experimental evidence has suggested they may be hazardous owing to their carcinogenic potential. The habitual chewing of betel nut (*Areca catechu* Linné), an alkaloid-containing drug that is also rich in condensed catechin tannin, has been linked to high rates of oral and esophageal cancer in India and South Africa. Even the drinking of ordinary tea [leaves of *Camellia sinensis* (Linné) O. Kuntze] has been implicated. It has been reported that the British, who add milk to their tea, thereby binding the tannin, have a much lower incidence of esophageal "obstruction" than do the Dutch, who formerly drank large quantities of tea without milk. Experimentally, the subcutaneous injection into rats of aqueous extracts of tannin-rich *Areca catechu* and *Rhus copallina* Linné produced a significant number of malignant mesenchymal tumors.

On the other hand, recent research conducted with condensed tannins—also commonly referred to as leucoanthocyanidins, oligomeric proanthocyanidins, or pycnogenols—has shown these compounds are very effective antioxidants and serve as active free-radical scavengers. Such compounds extracted from the seeds of grapes (*Vitis vinifera* Linné) or from the needles or bark of certain pine trees (*Pinus pinaster* Soland.) are now commonly marketed as dietary supplements. They are thought to be effective in improving such conditions as peripheral arterio-venous circulation, capillary fragility, retinopathies, inflammatory collagen disease, and the like. Green tea (*Camellia sinensis*), which contains up to 30% of these polyphenolic compounds is also being recommended for its antioxidative properties. The leucoanthocyanins (condensed tannins) from the above-named sources have apparently been shown to be devoid of toxicity in both short-term and long-term tests in small animals. Obviously, additional clinical trials in human beings are needed to resolve questions concerning the safety and efficacy of the condensed tannins as therapeutic agents.

The ability of tannins to precipitate proteins is also utilized in the process of vegetable tanning, which converts animal hides to leather. The tannin not only affects the pliancy and toughness of the leather but also acts as a preservative because of its antiseptic qualities. Various types of tannins produce a variety of leathers; thus, certain hydrolyzable types form a "bloom," whereas the nonhydrolyzable types produce the

"tanner's red." The deeply colored compounds obtained with iron salts have been used on a commercial scale in the manufacture of inks. Because of their precipitating qualities, solutions of tannins are utilized in the laboratory as reagents for the detection of gelatin, proteins, and alkaloids. In the antidotal treatment of alkaloidal poisoning, tannin solutions are extremely valuable for inactivating the alkaloid by the formation of insoluble tannate.

Hamamelis Leaf

Hamamelis leaf or witch hazel leaves is the dried leaf of *Hamamelis virginiana* Linné (Fam. Hamamelidaceae).

Hamamelis is from the Greek *hama*, meaning at the same time, and *melis*, meaning a fruit; *virginiana* indicates that the plant is found in Virginia, although the actual habitat ranges from New Brunswick to Minnesota and extends southward to Florida and Texas. The plant is a shrub or small tree that attains a height of 8 meters and is found particularly in low, damp woods. The flowers appear in the fall as the fruits of the previous year ripen. The leaves are collected throughout the summer and are dried in the open air, preferably under shade to preserve the green color. The commercial supply comes from the Blue Ridge Mountain region, chiefly from Virginia, North Carolina, and Tennessee. The decoction or infusion of witch hazel leaves has been commonly used since the days of the early colonists who learned of the drug from the American Indians.

Hamamelis leaf contains hamamelitannin and a second tannin that appears to be derived from gallic acid; a hexose sugar, a volatile oil, a bitter principal, gallic acid, and calcium oxalate. Hamamelis leaf possesses astringent and hemostatic properties.

Hamamelis Water or Distilled Witch Hazel Extract is prepared by steam distillation of the recently cut and partially dried dormant twigs of *Hamamelis virginiana*. Essentially, it is a hydroalcoholic solution of the volatile oil of that plant.

Analyses of the volatile oil reveal that it contains 2-hexen-1-al (9.7%), acetaldehyde (3.2%), α-ionone (3.5%), β-ionone (1.0%), and safrole (0.2%).

Although tannins are not carried over in the distillation process, hamamelis water is nevertheless widely utilized for its astringent properties resulting from the 14 to 15% alcohol to which the final product is adjusted. It is incorporated in hemorrhoidal products, preparations for treating insect bites and stings, and even teething preparations. The contained volatile oil does confer a pleasant fragrance to such products.

Nutgall

Nutgall is the excrescence obtained from the young twigs of *Quercus infectoria* Olivier and allied species of *Quercus* (Fam. Fagaceae). The oak galls are obtained principally from Aleppo in Asiatic Turkey.

The excrescence (gall) is caused by the puncture of a hymenopterous insect, *Cynips tinctoria*, and the presence of the deposited ovum. Several stages in the development of the gall correspond to the development of the insect:

1. When the larva begins to develop and the gall begins to enlarge, the cells of the outer and central zones contain numerous small starch grains.
2. When the chrysalis stage is reached, the starch near the middle of the gall is replaced in part by gallic acid, but the peripheral and central cells contain masses of tannic acid.
3. As the winged insect develops, nearly all of the cells contain masses of tannic acid with a slight amount of adhering gallic acid.
4. When the insect emerges from the gall, a hole to the central cavity is formed. Thus, the tannic acid, owing to the presence of moisture and air, may be oxidized in part into an insoluble product, and the gall becomes more porous, thereby constituting the so-called **white gall** of commerce.

The technical and medicinal use of galls was known to the ancient Greeks (450 B.C.). Since the Crusades, great quantities of galls have been exported from Asia Minor.

The principal constituent is tannic acid, which is found to the extent of 50 to 70%; the drug also contains gallic acid, 2 to 4%; ellagic acid; starch; and resin.

Nutgall, the chief source of tannic acid, is used in the tanning and dyeing industry and, formerly, in the manufacture of ink. Medicinally, it has astringent properties.

Japanese and Chinese galls are formed on *Rhus chinensis* Mill. (Fam. Anacardiaceae) as a result of the stings of certain plant lice (*Aphis*).

These galls are rich in tannin and, as they contain less coloring matter than the oak galls, are used in the manufacture of gallic acid.

Tannic Acid

Tannic acid, gallotannic acid, or tannin is a tannin usually obtained from nutgall. The powdered galls are extracted with a mixture of ether, alcohol, and water, and the liquid separates into two layers. The aqueous layer contains gallotannin, and the ethereal layer contains the free gallic acid present in the gall. After separation, the solution of gallotannin is evaporated, and the tannin is purified in various ways.

Tannic acid is not a single homogeneous compound but is a mixture of esters of gallic acid with glucose, whose exact composition varies according to its source. The tannin from Chinese galls analyzes entirely as octa- or nonagalloylglucose and yields, on hydrolysis, methyl gallate and 1,2,3,4,5-pentagalloylglucose. Turkish tannin, which is a mixture of hexa- or heptagalloylglucoses, hydrolyzes to form methyl gallate and a mixture of 1,2,3,6- and 1,3,4,6-tetragalloylglucose. On milder treatment, both types of tannic acid yield methyl *m*-digallate, indicating the presence of a *m*-trigalloyl group in each.

Tannic acid occurs as an amorphous powder, glistening scales, or spongy masses that are light brown to yellowish white. The odor is faint, and the taste is strongly astringent. Tannic acid is soluble in water, alcohol, and acetone and insoluble in ether, chloroform, and benzin.

Tannic acid is an astringent. It was formerly used in the treatment of burns, but this application has been discontinued. Its topical use is now restricted to the treatment of bed sores, minor ulcerations, and the like. As an alkaloidal precipitant, it has been employed in cases of alkaloidal poisoning.

Gallic acid is 3,4,5-trihydroxybenzoic acid that crystallizes with one molecule of water. It occurs in nutgall and can be prepared from tannic acid by hydrolysis with dilute acids. Bismuth subgallate is used by ostomates to help control odors.

SUGGESTED READINGS

Britton, G.: *The Biochemistry of Natural Pigments.* Cambridge, Cambridge University Press, 1983.

Cheeke, P. R., ed.: *Toxicants of Plant Origin*, Vol. IV. *Phenolics.* Boca Raton, Florida, CRC Press, Inc., 1989.

Hahlbrock, K., Scheel, D.: Physiology and Molecular Biology of Phenylpropanoid Metabolism, *Annu. Rev. Plant Physiol. Plant Mol. Biol., 40*: 347,1989.

Harborne, J. B., Mabry, T. J., eds.: *The Flavonoids.* London, Chapman and Hall, Ltd., 1982.

Harborne, J. B., Mabry, T. J. eds.: *The Flavonoids: Advances in Research Since 1980.* London, Chapman and Hall, Ltd., 1988.

Haslam, E.: *Plant Polyphenols: Vegetable Tannins Revisited.* Cambridge, Great Britain, Cambridge University Press, 1989.

Haslam, E.: *Shikimic Aced: Metabolism and Metabolites.* Chichester, England, John Wiley & Sons Ltd., 1993.

Hemingway, R. W., Laks, P. E., eds.: *Plant Polyphenols: Synthesis, Properties, Significance.* New York, Plenum Press, 1992.

Hikino, H., Kiso, Y.: Natural Products for Liver Diseases. In *Economic and Medicinal Plant Research,* Vol. 2. Wagner, H., Hikino, H., Farnsworth, N.R., eds. London, Academic Press Limited, 1988.

Lewis, N. G., Davin, L. B.: Evolution of Lignan and Neolignan Biochemical Pathways. In *Isopentenoids and Other Natural Products: Evolution and Function.* Nes, W. D., ed., Washington, DC, American Chemical Society, 1994.

Murray, R. D. H., Mendez, J., Brown, S. A.: *The Natural Coumarins.* Chichester, England, John Wiley & Sons Ltd., 1982.

Pathak, M. A., Drinnick, J. K., eds.: *National Cancer Institute Monograph 66: Photobiology, Toxicology, and Pharmacalogic Aspects of Psoralens.* Bethesda, Maryland, U. S. Department of Health and Human Services, 1984.

Stafford, H. A.: *Flavonoid Metabolism.* Boca Raton, Florida, CRC Press, Inc., 1990.

Stafford, H. A., Ibrahin, R. K., eds.: *Recent Advances in Phytochemistry,* Vol. 26, *Phenolic Metabolism in Plants.* New York, Plenum, Press, 1992.

9

Alkaloids

The **alkaloids** represent a group of natural products that has had a major impact throughout history on the economic, medical, political, and social affairs of humans. Many of these agents have potent physiological effects on mammalian systems as well as other organisms, and as a consequence, some constitute important therapeutic agents. Atropine, morphine, quinine, and vincristine are representative of a host of agents used to treat a gamut of disease conditions that range from malaria to cancer. In addition, some alkaloids are extremely poisonous. The alkaloids of the ergot fungus, for example, have been responsible for epidemics of mass poisonings with thousands of deaths among the populace of Europe all through the Middle Ages because of the ingestion of rye bread, a staple in the diet, that was contaminated with the fungus. The poisonous nature of alkaloids has also been used beneficially for such things as arrow poisons in hunting and warfare. The dried plant extract known as curare that contains tubocurarine is used by the Indians of the Amazon basin for dipping their blow darts and arrows. Some alkaloid-containing plants have been employed for executions, as in ancient Greece with the death of Socrates who consumed a draught of poison hemlock which contains the alkaloid coniine. At the time of the Roman empire, the wicked Livia, the wife of Emperor Augustus, eliminated enemies and political rivals by murdering them at dinner parties through the surreptitious use of belladonna (the source of atropine) in the food.

Other alkaloids have potent psychotropic effects and have been widely used for these purposes. Compounds in this category include arecoline found in betel nut, which is chewed by millions of people in the Far East for its stimulant effect; caffeine, which may be the most widely used CNS stimulant around the world; cocaine, which is used illicitly in the United States; and nicotine, the constituent responsible for the psychological and physical dependence associated with the chronic use of tobacco.

Alkaloids are difficult to define because they do not represent a homogeneous group of compounds from either the chemical, biochemical, or physiologic viewpoint. Consequently, except for the fact that they are all organic nitrogenous compounds with a limited distribution in nature, reservations must be appended to any general definition. Plants have been a rich source of alkaloids, but some are found in animals, fungi, and bacteria; practically all have been reproduced in the laboratory by chemical synthesis. Most, but not all, possess basic properties, owing to the presence of an amino nitrogen, and many, especially those pertinent to pharmacy and medicine, possess marked physiologic activity. In spite of the difficulties attending a precise definition, the term alkaloid is extremely useful and is commonly applied to basic nitrogenous compounds of plant origin that are physiologically active.

In the plant kingdom, the alkaloids appear to have a restricted distribution in certain families and genera. Among the angiosperms, the Apocynaceae, Papaveraceae, Ranunculaceae, Rubiaceae, Solanaceae, and Berberidaceae are outstanding for alkaloid-yielding plants. Although it has been claimed that the monocotyledons do not produce alkaloids, investigations indicate that the Amaryllidaceae and Liliaceae are two of the most promising families in which to search for alkaloid-yielding plants.

Specific alkaloids are ordinarily confined to specific plant families (hyoscyamine in Solanaceae, colchicine in Liliaceae). Nicotine, which is found in a number of widely scattered plant families, is an exception to this rule. The occurrence of ergot alkaloids in the fungus *Claviceps purpurea* and certain *Ipomoea* species (Convolvulaceae) is also an exception and may be attributed to either parallel or convergent evolution of certain complex biochemical pathways. Alkaloids may occur in various parts of the plant: in seeds (physostigma, areca), in underground stems (sanguinaria), in roots (belladonna root), in rhizomes and roots (ipecac, hydrastis), and in barks (cinchona). They are also found in fungi (ergot).

The names of the alkaloids are obtained in various ways: (1) from the generic name of the plant yielding them (hydrastine, atropine), (2) from the specific name of the plant yielding them (cocaine, belladonnine), (3) from the common name of the drug yielding them (ergotamine), (4) from their physiologic activity (emetine, morphine), and (5) occasionally from the discoverer (pelletierine).

Sometimes a prefix or suffix is added to the name of a principal alkaloid to designate another alkaloid from the same source (quinine, quinidine, hydroquinine). By agreement, chemical rules designate that the names of all alkaloids should end in "ine."

Alkaloids usually contain one nitrogen atom although some such as ergotamine, may contain up to five. The nitrogen may exist as a primary amine (RNH_2), as a secondary amine (R_2NH), or as a tertiary amine (R_3N).

Because the nitrogen atom bears an unshared pair of electrons, such compounds are basic and resemble ammonia's chemical properties. The degree of basicity varies greatly, depending on the structure of the molecule and the presence and location of other functional groups. Like ammonia, the alkaloids are converted into their salts by aqueous mineral acids, and when the salt of an alkaloid is treated with hydroxide ion, nitrogen gives up a hydrogen ion and the free amine is liberated. Quaternary ammonium compounds [$R_4N^+X^-$], such as tubocurarine chloride or berberine chloride, have four organic groups covalently bonded to nitrogen, and the positive charge of this ion is balanced by some negative ion. The quaternary ammonium ion, having no proton to give up, is not affected by hydroxide ion; consequently, quaternary ammonium compounds have chemical properties quite different from those of the amines.

Despite the difficulty in precisely characterizing alkaloids by definition, they do have in common a surprising number of physical and chemical properties. For the most part, the alkaloids are insoluble or sparingly so in water, but the salts formed on reaction with acids are usually freely soluble. The free alkaloids are usually soluble in ether, chloroform, or other relatively nonpolar, immiscible solvents in which, however, the alkaloidal salts are insoluble. This permits a ready means for the isolation and purification of the alkaloids as well as for their quantitative estimation. Most of the alkaloids are crystalline solids, although a few are amorphous. An additional few, coniine, nicotine, and sparteine, which lack oxygen in their molecules, are liquids. Alkaloidal salts are crystalline, and their crystal form and habit are often a useful means of rapid microscopic identification.

Alkaloids are usually classified according to the nature of the basic chemical structures from which they derive. A number of these structures are shown in Figure 9-1. Arecoline, lobeline, and nicotine are derivatives of **pyridine** and **piperidine;** atropine, hyoscyamine, and hyoscine are derived from **tropane,** a condensation product of pyrrolidine and piperidine; the cinchona alkaloids, quinine, quinidine, cinchonine, and cinchonidine, contain **quinoline** as the principal nucleus; hydrastine, (+)-tubocurarine, emetine, and the opium alkaloids are characterized by the **isoquinoline** nucleus. Other types include ergonovine, reserpine, and strychnine, which derive from the **indole** ring; pilocarpine, which has the **imidazole** ring; caffeine and theobromine, which are **purine** bases, and protoveratrine, which contains a **steroidal** structure.

The alkaloids, like other amines, form double salts with compounds of mercury, gold, platinum, and other heavy metals. These double salts are usually obtained as precipitates, and many of them are microcrystallographically characteristic. The common alkaloidal reagents include Wagner's (iodine in potassium iodide), Mayer's (potassium mercuric iodide), Dragendorff's (potassium bismuth iodide), and many others. The alkaloids usually possess a bitter taste.

Much has been written about the possible function of alkaloids in plants and about the reasons why they occur there. Some of the possibilities that have been discussed include their functions as (1) poisonous agents protecting the plant against insects and herbivores, (2) end products of detoxification reactions representing a metabolic locking-up of compounds otherwise harmful to the plant, (3) regulatory growth factors, or (4) reserve substances capable of supplying nitrogen or other elements necessary to the plant's economy.

Although certain exceptions exist because of the diverse nature of alkaloids, the evidence for

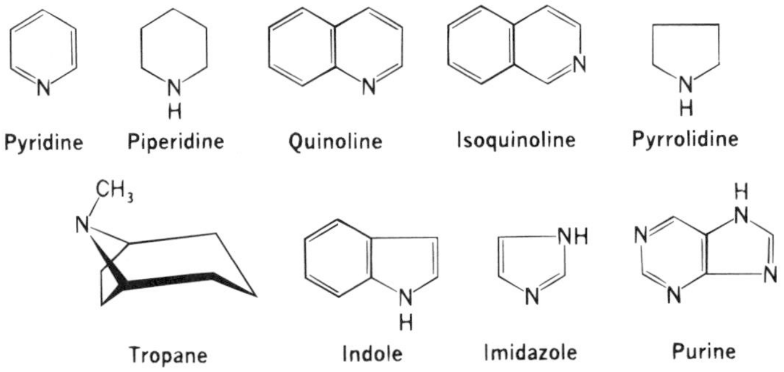

Fig. 9–1. Important nitrogen-containing ring structures present in alkaloidal drugs.

any result of alkaloid formation useful to the existence of the plant is slight. Perhaps the best example of such a result is found in the wild plants of certain arid regions, where overgrazing by domestic animals has taken place for centuries. An extremely high percentage of such plants contains alkaloids that, because of their bitter taste or toxic properties, apparently confer survival value on the species producing them. Plants lacking such distasteful substances were long ago exterminated. However, to avoid being teleologic, we must emphasize that protection, like the other postulated functions, is a consequence of, not a reason for, alkaloid formation.

Perhaps alkaloids should be viewed as products of metabolic experimentation that reflect the intermediary evolutionary stages now attained by plants. Alkaloid formation is probably best regarded as a metabolic act involving longer or shorter reaction sequences that begin with substances normal and essential in plant metabolism and end with compounds not necessarily serving such a purpose. Because the process is genetically controlled, an alkaloid-producing plant is merely a plant in which this additional metabolic reaction has evolved through mutation of one or more genes. Proof that such changes occur irrespective of the utility of ultimate products is given by the thousands of terpenoids, polysaccharides, glycosides, phenylpropanoids, and steroids to which no essential role in plant metabolism can be ascribed.

Like many of these other secondary constituents, the alkaloids may be thought of as resulting from a "metabolic error," which will probably be eliminated when plants approach a stage of ultimate adaptation and eliminate all redundant features and processes. They are thus a kind of waste product retained within the organism that produces them. It must be emphasized that, un-

like many such substances with which we are familiar, the alkaloids are structurally complex end products of energy-requiring reaction sequences.

The pharmacologic action of alkaloids varies widely: some (morphine, codeine) are analgesics and narcotics whereas others (strychnine, brucine) are central stimulants. Some (atropine) are mydriatics whereas others (physostigmine, pilocarpine) are miotics. Some (ephedrine) cause a rise in blood pressure, but others (reserpine) produce a decrease in essential hypertension. In fact, the alkaloids are capable of extensive physiologic activity.

The biosynthesis of many alkaloidal structures can be rationalized through simple chemical reactions that involve amino acids. The amino acids that most often serve as alkaloidal precursors include phenylalanine, tyrosine, tryptophan, histidine, anthranilic acid, lysine, and ornithine. Some of the general reactions that are of particular importance include the decarboxylation and transamination of the amino acids to yield a corresponding amine or aldehyde. These can react to form a Schiff base which, in turn, can react with a carbanion in a Mannich-type condensation. These general reactions are illustrated in Figure 9-2. Specific examples of alkaloid biosynthesis are discussed under the various structural groups of alkaloids.

PYRIDINE-PIPERIDINE ALKALOIDS

On reduction, the tertiary base, pyridine, is converted into the secondary base, piperidine. These two nuclei form the basis of this group, which is sometimes divided into three subgroups: (1) derivatives of piperidine, including lobeline from lobelia; (2) derivatives of nico-

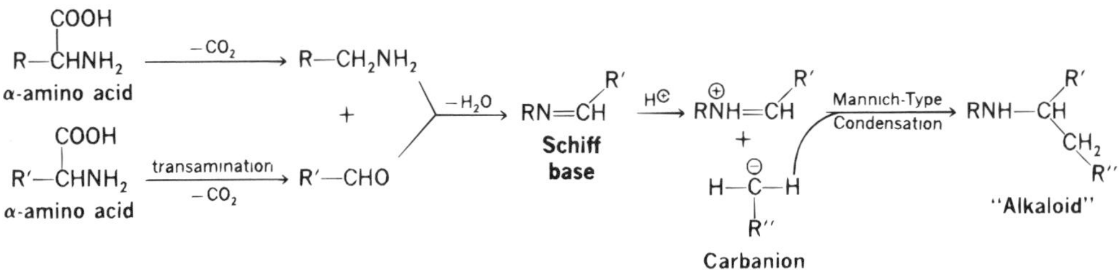

Fig. 9–2. General reactions in alkaloid biosynthesis.

tinic acid, including arecoline from areca; and (3) derivatives of both pyridine and pyrrolidine, including nicotine from tobacco. The important alkaloidal drugs and their alkaloids that are classified in this group are areca, arecoline hydrobromide, lobelia, lobeline, and nicotine.

Biosynthesis of Pyridine-Piperidine Alkaloids

More than 80 years ago, the Swiss chemist Trier proposed that **nicotine** was biosynthesized from nicotinic acid and proline. If proline is considered a representative of the ornithine-proline-glutamic acid group, this remarkable hypothesis may be considered correct. The biosynthetic pathways leading to nicotine are summarized in Figure 9-3.

Tracer studies have shown that ornithine is incorporated into nicotine by tobacco plants. This incorporation results in a symmetric labeling pattern of nicotine. Putrescine, *N*-methylputrescine, and *N*-methylaminobutanal are all incorporated, and the key intermediate is thought to be the *N*-methylpyrrolinium ion which, through electrophilic aromatic substitution, attaches to C-3 of the pyridine ring of nicotinic acid. Nicotinic acid is formed in higher plants and certain microorganisms via quinolinic acid by the condensation of glyceraldehyde-3-phosphate and aspartic acid.

Nicotine is primarily a product of root metabolism, but the formation of small amounts, as well as subsequent reactions such as the demethylation of nicotine, can occur in the leaves of plants.

Areca

Areca, areca nut, or betel nut is the dried, ripe seed of *Areca catechu* Linné (Fam. Arecaceae). *Areca* is the Spanish and Portuguese term for the betel nut. *Catechu* is the East Indian

name for an astringent extract or juice. *Areca catechu* is a beautiful tall palm extensively cultivated in India, southeastern Asia, the East Indies, and to some extent East Africa. The fruit is a nut that contains a single seed with a thin seed coat and a large ruminate endosperm. The seeds are removed from the fruits, boiled in water containing lime, and dried. India is a major producer of areca, but its production is mostly consumed domestically.

Areca is mixed with lime, the leaves of *Piper betel* Linné, and occasionally gambir. The mixture is used as a stimulant masticatory in India and the East Indies. In India, the mixture is known as "punsupari." Betel chewing has been practiced since early times. The natives chew fresh betel nuts; dried betel nuts are used for pharmaceutical purposes. The value of areca as a taeniacide apparently has been known in the East for a long time but was not known to western civilization until 1863.

Areca contains several alkaloids that are reduced pyridine derivatives. Among them are arecoline (arecaidine methyl ester), arecaidine (*N*-methyl guvacine), guvacine (tetrahydronicotinic acid), and guvacoline (guvacine methyl ester). The total alkaloid content can reach 0.45%. Arecoline, the most abundant and physiologically most active alkaloid, is a liquid occurring to the extent of about 0.2%. Areca also contains tannin (about 15%), lipids, volatile oils, and gum.

Areca is classified as an anthelmintic in veterinary practice and is employed as a vermicide and taeniafuge.

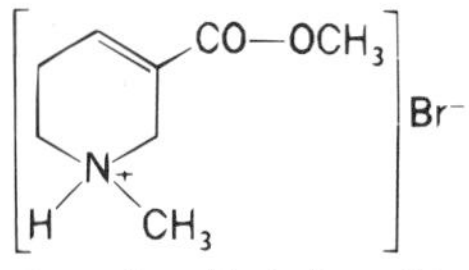

Arecoline Hydrobromide

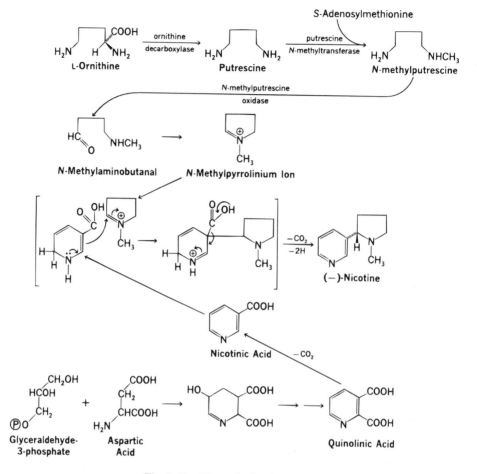

Fig. 9–3. Biosynthesis of nicotine.

Lobelia

Lobelia or Indian tobacco consists of the dried leaves and tops of *Lobelia inflata* Linné (Fam. Lobeliaceae). *Lobelia* was named in honor of Matthias de L'Obel, a Flemish botanist (1538 to 1616); *inflata* refers to the fruit, which is hollow and distended. The plant is an annual herb indigenous to the eastern and central United States and to Canada.

Commercial supplies come from collecting stations in North Carolina, Virginia, and Tennessee. It should be collected after a portion of the capsules has become inflated; then it should be carefully dried and preserved. Lobelia was employed by the Indians, when necessity required, as a substitute for tobacco. Its emetic properties were first observed in 1785, and the drug was introduced into medicine in 1807.

The drug contains 14 alkaloids, of which lobe-line is the major and most important, a pungent volatile oil, resin, lipids, and gum.

Lobeline, (−)-lobeline, or alpha lobeline (to distinguish it from a mixture of the lobelia alkaloids formerly designated as lobeline) occurs as colorless crystals that are slightly soluble in water but readily soluble in hot alcohol.

(−)-Lobeline

Lobeline produces similar, but weaker, pharmacologic effects to those of nicotine on the peripheral circulation, neuromuscular junctions, and the central nervous system. For this reason, lobeline sulfate was formerly incorporated in tablets or lozenges that were intended to aid in breaking the tobacco habit (smoking deterrents). The majority of controlled studies showed that lobeline had only a placebo effect on decreasing the physical craving for cigarettes, so these products were removed from the market.

Nicotine

Nicotine is a pyridine alkaloid obtained from the dried leaves of the tobacco plant *Nicotiana tabacum* Linné (Fam. Solanaceae). *Nicotiana* was named after Jean Nicot, a French diplomat, who probably introduced tobacco into Europe; *tabacum* refers to the Indian name for the pipe or tube used for smoking it. The plant is a tall annual herb indigenous to tropical America, and the leaves contain from 0.6 to 9.0 percent nicotine and a lesser amount of nornicotine.

Nicotine is colorless to pale yellow, very hygroscopic, oily, volatile liquid with an unpleasant, pungent odor and a sharp, burning, persistent taste.

Nicotine is a ganglionic (nicotinic) cholinergic-receptor agonist with complex pharmacologic actions that include effects mediated by binding to receptors in autonomic ganglia, the adrenal medulla, the neuromuscular junction, and the brain. Chronic use of nicotine may result in psychologic and physical dependence. As a temporary aid for the cessation of cigarette smoking, the drug is available in transdermal systems, and it is also available bound to an ion exchange resin in a chewing gum base. These alternative sources of nicotine help reduce the withdrawal symptoms associated with nicotine addiction.

TROPANE ALKALOIDS

Tropane is a dicyclic compound formed by the condensation of a pyrrolidine precursor (ornithine) with three acetate-derived carbon atoms. Both pyrrolidine and piperidine ring systems can be discerned in the molecule.

The 3-hydroxy derivative of tropane is known as tropine. Its esterification with (−)-tropic acid yields hyoscyamine (tropine tropate), which may be racemized to form atropine.

Biosynthesis of Tropane Alkaloids

Because of the commercial importance of hyoscyamine and scopolamine, investigation of their biosynthesis has been extensive, especially in *Datura* species. Feeding studies with labeled ornithine have revealed that this amino acid is incorporated stereospecifically to form the pyrrolidine ring of tropine. The remaining three carbon atoms are derived from acetate and thus complete the piperidine moiety. Methylation results via transmethylation from *S*-adenosylmethionine to complete the tropine nucleus.

Phenylalanine is the precursor of tropic acid. Tracer studies have shown that the side chain of the amino acid undergoes a novel type of intramolecular rearrangement during the conversion. Esterification of tropic acid with tropine produces hyoscyamine. These reactions are summarized in Figure 9-4.

The important drugs and alkaloids in this group are belladonna leaf, hyoscyamus, stramonium, atropine, hyoscyamine, scopolamine, coca, and cocaine.

Belladonna

Belladonna leaf, belladonna herb, or deadly nightshade leaf consists of the dried leaf and flowering or fruiting top of *Atropa belladonna* Linné or of its variety *acuminata* Royle ex Lindley (Fam. Solanaceae). Belladonna leaf yields not less than 0.35% of alkaloids.

Atropa is from *Atropos*, meaning inflexible, the name of the Greek Fate who cuts the thread of life, and probably alludes to the poisonous character of the drug. Belladonna is from the Italian *bella*, meaning beautiful, and *donna*, meaning lady. (The juice of the berry, when placed in the eyes, causes dilation of the pupils, thus giving a striking appearance.)

The plant is a perennial herb that grows to a meter in height. It is indigenous to central and southern Europe and to Asia Minor and is cultivated in sunny locations in England, Germany, India, and the United States. At present, the chief source of supply is the Balkans.

The poisonous character of the plant has been known for many years, particularly in its indigenous localities. It was the subject of many treatises during the 18th century. Its mydriatic properties were first recorded in 1802, but its analgesic properties were not recognized until 1860. The leaves were used earlier than the root, whose use did not occur until about 1860.

The leaf yields alkaloids in concentrations ranging up to more than 1%. About three fourths of the isolated alkaloid mixture is (−)-hyoscyamine; the remainder is atropine. The latter compound exists, at most, only in traces in fresh plant material. Atropine is formed by racemization during the extraction process. Small but

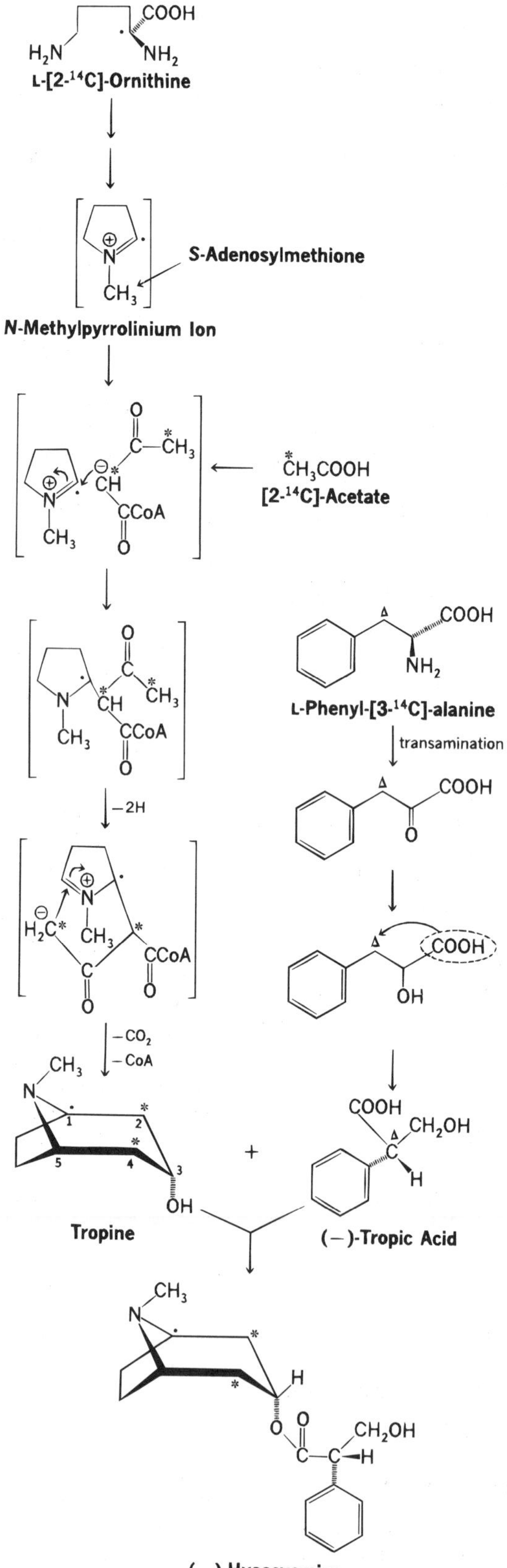

Fig. 9–4. Biosynthesis of hyoscyamine.

varying amounts of other bases are found in the root but not in the leaf. These include apoatropine, belladonnine, cuscohygrine, and scopolamine.

The yield of alkaloids averages as follows: roots, 0.6%; stems, 0.05%; leaves, 0.4%; unripe berries, 0.19%; ripe berries, 0.21%; seeds, 0.33%.

Belladonna acts as an antimuscarinic agent, which accounts for its use as a spasmolytic drug. It is used as adjunctive therapy in the treatment of peptic ulcer; functional digestive disorders, including spastic, mucous, and ulcerative colitis; and diarrhea, diverticulitis, and pancreatitis. It possesses anticholinergic properties and is used to control excess motor activity of the gastrointestinal tract and spasm of the urinary tract.

Belladonna leaf is commonly administered in the form of the tincture (30 mg alkaloids/100 ml) or the extract (1.25 g alkaloids/100 g).

Solanaceous Alkaloids

The principal alkaloids of this group are (−) hyoscyamine, atropine [(±)-hyoscyamine], and scopolamine (also known as hyoscine). These are tropine derivatives and esters and may be prepared synthetically but are usually obtained by extraction from plants of the Solanaceae. These include *Atropa belladonna, Datura stramonium, Hyoscyamus niger,* and *Hyoscyamus muticus* also known as Egyptian henbane which is cultivated in Egypt and southern California. Another important source is the dried leaves of *Duboisia* plants of Australia. These are large shrubs and include *D. myoporoides* R. Brown and *D. leichardtii* F. von Mueller.

Atropine and scopolamine are competitive with acetylcholine at the postganglionic synapse (muscarinic site) of the parasympathetic nervous system. Clinically useful effects obtained from blocking the muscarinic activity of acetylcholine are an antispasmodic effect used principally to relieve spasms of the bowel in the treatment of spastic colitis, gastroenteritis, and peptic ulcer; an antisecretory effect used to reduce respiratory secretions in anesthesia (antisialogogue), gastric secretions in peptic ulcer therapy, and nasal and sinus secretions in common cold and allergy medications; and a mydriatic and cycloplegic effect used to prevent adhesions between the iris and lens of the eye in cases of iritis.

Atropine is an antidote in cases of poisoning caused by cholinesterase inhibitors such as physostigmine and organophosphate insecticides.

Scopolamine has a depressant activity on the central nervous system and is used to treat motion sickness. It is also employed for preanesthetic sedation and for obstetric amnesia in conjunction with analgesics, and to calm delirium.

Toxicity symptoms that can occur during the therapeutic use of atropine, scopolamine, and belladonna tincture are skin rash, skin flushing, mouth dryness, difficulty in urination, eye pain, blurred vision, and light sensitivity. The patient should also be advised that such antacids as alumina gels may interfere with absorption of these drugs when taken simultaneously.

Hyoscyamine, the tropine ester of (−)-tropic acid, is asymmetric and accounts for the natural occurrence of the optical isomer. When (−)-hyoscyamine is extracted from the plants in which it occurs, it usually is racemized during the process and thus converted into the (±)-compound, which is atropine. The piperidine ring system of tropine can exist in two principal conformations. The chair form has the lowest energy requirement. In addition, two stereoisomeric forms can exist because of the rigidity imparted to the molecule through the ethane chain across positions 1 and 5. Pharmacologically, the most active isomer results when the esteratic group is substituted axial at position 3, as in the case of (−)-hyoscyamine and atropine.

Hyoscyamine sulfate is extremely poisonous and occurs as white, odorless crystals or as a crystalline powder; it is deliquescent and is affected by light.

Hyoscyamine sulfate is an anticholinergic. It is used to aid in the control of gastric secretion, visceral spasm, hypermotility in spastic colitis, pylorospasm and associated abdominal cramps. In parkinsonism it is used to reduce rigidity and tremors and to control associated sialorrhea and hyperhidrosis.

Atropine sulfate occurs as colorless crystals or as a white, crystalline powder. It is extremely poisonous. It effloresces in dry air and is slowly affected by light.

Atropine sulfate is an anticholinergic. Used in surgery as an antisialogogue to control bronchial, nasal, pharyngeal, and salivary secretions, it is usually injected intramuscularly prior to induction of anesthesia. During surgery, the drug is given intravenously when reduction in pulse range and cessation of cardiac action are attributable to increased vagal activity. It is also useful in pylorospasm and other spastic conditions of the gastrointestinal tract and for ureteral and biliary colic when administered concomitantly with morphine.

Scopolamine or hyoscine is an alkaloid that is particularly abundant in *Datura fastuosa* var. *alba* and in *D. metel*. It is an ester that, upon hydrolysis, yields tropic acid and scopoline, a base resembling tropine.

It occurs as an almost colorless, syrupy liquid from its chloroformic solution and as colorless crystals from its ether solution. It is levorotatory.

Scopolamine hydrobromide or hyoscine hydrobromide occurs as colorless or white crystals or as a white, granular powder that is odorless and slightly efflorescent in dry air. It is extremely poisonous. Scopolamine hydrobromide is classified as an anticholinergic.

At usual therapeutic doses, scopolamine is a central nervous depressant, whereas atropine is a stimulant. For this reason, scopolamine hydrobromide is used for preanesthetic sedation and for obstetric amnesia in conjunction with analgesics; it is also employed for calming delirium. It is administered subcutaneously or intramuscularly in a single dose.

In addition to its systemic anticholinergic effects, scopolamine is effective in the prevention of nausea and vomiting associated with motion sickness. It is applied as the free base in a transdermal system behind the ear at least 4 hours before the antiemetic effect is required. The scopolamine is gradually released from an adhesive matrix of mineral oil and polyisobutylene. A continuous controlled release of scopolamine flows from the drug reservoir through a rate-controlling membrane to maintain a constant plasma level for 3 days.

(−)-Scopolamine

Hyoscyamus

Hyoscyamus or henbane is the dried leaf, with or without the stem and flowering or fruiting top, of *Hyoscyamus niger* Linné (Fam. Solanaceae) and contains not less than 0.04% of the alkaloids of hyoscyamus. *Hyoscyamus* is the ancient Greek and Latin name formed from two Greek words, meaning hog and bean. The plant is poisonous to swine.

The plant is an annual or biennial herb indigenous to Europe, western Asia, and northern Africa and is cultivated in the former Soviet Union, the Balkans, Belgium, England, Germany, and, to some extent, the United States and Canada. The biennial form is most generally cultivated in England; the annual form is cultivated on the Continent. Dioscorides mentioned the plant, and under the name of henbane, it has been employed in European domestic medicine from the remotest times. It is mentioned in Anglo-Saxon works on medicine written in the 11th century and in the *Arabian Nights*. After the Middle Ages the drug fell into disuse but was reintroduced into European medicine about 1760, largely through the efforts of Störck.

The alkaloids, hyoscyamine and scopolamine, 0.05 to 0.15%, of which three fourths is hyoscyamine, are the active principles.

Stramonium

Stramonium, jimson weed, or Jamestown weed consists of the dried leaf and flowering or fruiting tops with branches of *Datura stramonium* Linné or of its variety *tatula* (Linné) Torrey (Fam. Solanaceae). It yields not less than 0.25% of alkaloids. The name *Datura* is derived from the Sanskrit, *dhattura* and from the Arabic *tatura* or *tatula*, the native name; *stramonium* is from the French *stramoine*, meaning stinkweed. The plant is an annual herb that attains a height of about 2 meters.

Over the years there has been considerable disagreement as to the indigenous habitat of *Datura stramonium*. Linnaeus gave it as America; others have attributed it to South America, Europe, or Asia. Modern authorities apparently favor North America. *D. stramonium* var. *tatula* has purple flowers and stem. This difference is caused by a single pair of genes and is not taxonomically significant. The active constituents in both plants are the same.

Stramonium was grown in England in about the 16th century from seeds obtained from Constantinople. The early settlers near Jamestown, Virginia, used it as a ''pot herb'' with fatal results, thus establishing its common name of Jamestown weed, which was subsequently modified in some areas to jimson weed. It can serve as a source of atropine. The drug contains hyoscyamine and scopolamine, the former being more abundant.

Stramonium seed is the ripe seed of *D. stramonium*. The ripening capsules are gathered and dried until the seeds shake out. The seeds are reniform, flattened, 3 to 4 mm in length, bluish black, and minutely reticulate.

Stramonium seed contains about 0.4% of alkaloids, principally hyoscyamine with a small proportion of scopolamine and traces of atropine.

Stramonium is generally regarded as a noxious weed and has frequently caused poisoning in children when seeds were ingested. The chief toxic symptoms are those of atropine poisoning: dilated pupils, impaired vision, dryness of the skin, secretions, extreme thirst, hallucinations, and loss of consciousness. Because of the potential for psychotropic effects, stramonium seeds have also been agents of abuse among the teenage population in the United States. Sometimes this abuse has led to death from overdose due to central nervous system depression, circulatory collapse, and hypotension. Although newspaper items often describe the circumstances, such cases are also reported in the medical literature. Because the plant is rather widespread, pharmacists may be asked to help in identifying the plant and in applying emergency measures pending arrival of a physician.

Cocaine

Coca or coca leaves have been described as the dried leaves of *Erythroxylum coca* Lamarck, known commercially as Huanuco coca, or of *E. truxillense* Rusby, known commercially as Truxillo coca (Fam. Erythroxylaceae). The plants are shrubs or small trees that attain a height of about 2 meters and are indigenous to certain areas of South America. They have been cultivated there for centuries. *Erythroxylum* is from two Greek words meaning red and wood, alluding to the color of the plants; *coca* is the Spanish name for the tree; and *truxillense* is from Truxillo, a coastal city in Peru.

Peru and Bolivia are the only two countries currently authorized under international agreements to grow coca legally for the pharmaceutical market. These two countries are also the source of most of the illicit coca leaves used as a source for cocaine. The plants are cultivated at an altitude of 500 to 2000 meters in Peru and Bolivia; about 25% of the harvest is consumed by the indigenous population who chew the coca leaves. Approximately 2% is exported in legitimate commerce for the manufacture of pharma-

ceutic cocaine. The remainder of the crop is available for the production of illicit substances.

In the processing of the leaves to cocaine, the farmers themselves often engage in the first steps by turning the leaves into **coca paste** which is easier to transport to a cocaine processing laboratory. Processing of coca paste into cocaine occurs mostly in Columbia, and clandestine laboratories for this purpose are commonplace throughout the country. Between 100 and 200 kg of dried leaves is needed to make a single kilogram of paste, and 2.5 kg of coca paste will yield 1 kg of cocaine. The leaves are collected from twigs that are cut off in the spring, pruned again in June, and pruned for a third time in the fall. The dried, crushed leaves are mixed with water and calcium carbonate or lime to produce an alkaline reaction. The mixture is crushed, kerosene or gasoline is added, and the mixture is stirred. After the leaf pulp is discarded, the kerosene is mixed with acidified water, and the aqueous layer is separated and made alkaline with ammonia or baking soda, which precipitates a thick, aromatic paste containing not only cocaine but also several other alkaloids. The smoking of coca paste has become a drug abuse problem in Peru, Bolivia, Colombia, and Ecuador.

Cocaine was first isolated in 1860, but until 1884, coca was considered only as an inferior substitute for tea. In that year, Koller discovered its local anesthetic properties.

Coca leaves contain three basic types of alkaloids: derivatives of ecgonine (cocaine, cinnamylcocaine, α- and β-truxilline), tropine (tropacocaine, valerine), and hygrine (hygroline, cuscohygrine). Only the ecgonine derivatives are commercially important. The composition of the alkaloid mixture in the leaf varies qualitatively and quantitatively according to the variety of the plant and, to some extent, to the stage of development of the leaves when collected.

Huanuco coca contains 0.5 to 1% of ester alkaloids, derivatives of tropine and ecgonine, of which cocaine constitutes the major part. Cuscohygrine is the principal nonester alkaloid in the leaf.

Truxillo coca has a somewhat lower content of ester alkaloids, but a much higher percentage (up to 75%) of this quantity is cocaine.

Coca leaves were highly valued by the natives long before the Spanish conquest; the shrub was known as "The Divine Plant of the Incas." Monardes published an extensive article on the drug in 1569. The natives chew the leaf mixed with lime and are thus able to travel great distances without experiencing fatigue and without any but the most meager food rations.

At present, coca chewing is an integral part of the native culture pattern in many isolated highland areas of Colombia and in most of the mountainous sections of Peru, Bolivia, and the northwestern part of Argentina. Its use has spread from these areas to the lowlands and is prevalent in most parts of the northwestern Amazon valley in Colombia and Peru.

Much has been written about the effect this habit has on its practitioners. Dr. R.E. Schultes, the well-known ethnobotanist at Harvard University, expressed the following opinion:

''What is very commonly overlooked or even purposely ignored in many governmental and sociologic circles is the fact that coca as chewed by the native is not of necessity physically, socially, and morally dangerous. It has nothing in common with cocaine addiction, and coca chewing does not lead to addiction . . . . Unwise legal prohibitions in certain Andean areas aimed at extirpation of the coca custom have invariably driven the Indian, deprived in his inhospitable cold altitudes of the euphoric coca, to the dangerously poisonous local distilled drinks with an attendant rapid rise in crime.''

Cocaine is an alkaloid obtained from the leaves of *Erythroxylum coca* and *E. truxillense* and their varieties. As explained subsequently, much of the alkaloid is actually prepared by semisynthesis from plant-derived ecgonine.

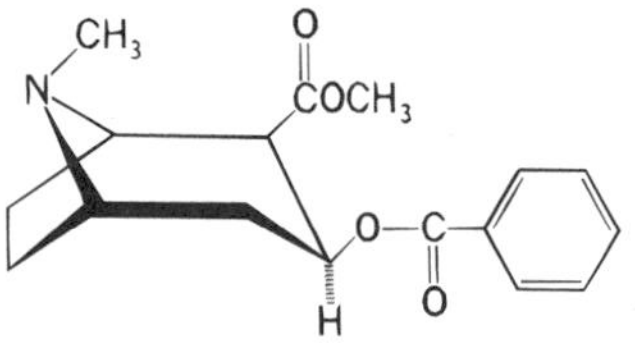

(−)-Cocaine

Cocaine is the methyl ester of benzoylecgonine. When hydrolyzed, it splits into ecgonine, benzoic acid, and methyl alcohol. Cinnamylcocaine splits into ecgonine, methyl alcohol, and cinnamic acid, whereas α- and β-truxilline split into ecgonine, methyl alcohol, and α- and β-truxillic acids. (The truxillic acids are isomeric dicinnamic acids.)

The production of cocaine is ordinarily conducted on a large scale by a number of methods that are similar but not identical. Many of the important steps are protected by patents. Ordinarily, the total bases are extracted, the ester alkaloids are converted to (−)-ecgonine by acid hydrolysis, and cocaine is synthesized from it by esterification first with methanol and then with benzoic acid. When this procedure is utilized, only the total content of ecgonine derivatives in the leaf is commercially significant.

Cocaine has multiple central and peripheral nervous system actions. Over most of its effective dose range, it is a psychomotor stimulant with a strong abuse potential. The action responsible for the rewarding property, and hence the abuse liability, is through a prolongation of dopamine in the synapse by blocking the dopamine reuptake mechanism. When drug access is unlimited, cocaine has the ability to dominate behavior, reducing other behaviors such as eating and sleeping. It has one of the highest reinforcing potentials of any drug as measured by breaking point studies and is the drug which animals with unlimited access are most likely to select repeatedly in preference to food and water, to the point of death.

Cocaine hydrochloride is the hydrochloride of the alkaloid cocaine. It occurs as colorless crystals or as a white, crystalline powder.

Cocaine hydrochloride is an ingredient in Brompton's cocktail, which is widely used to control severe pain associated with terminal cancer. Because of its CNS stimulant properties, cocaine counteracts the narcotic-induced sedation and respiratory depression associated with the narcotic analgesic ingredient (morphine or methadone) used in the cocktail. It also potentiates the analgesic effect.

The United States, in the 1990s, is in the middle of a cocaine abuse epidemic in many major urban areas. Government officials estimated that in 1991, 6.4 million people in the United States had used cocaine during the year. Cocaine and cocaine hydrochloride, as agents of abuse, are generally inhaled or sniffed and are rapidly absorbed across the pharyngeal mucosa, resulting in cerebral stimulation and euphoria. In addition, they are injected intravenously and subcutaneously, and cocaine free-base is smoked. Inhalation of the vapors of alkaloidal cocaine, known as ''free-basing,'' has become a popular practice because of the rapidity of onset and the intensity of the euphoric experience. The reason for converting cocaine hydrochloride to the free amine is that the latter substance volatilizes at about 98°C whereas the salt volatilizes at 195°C, a temperature at which some of the cocaine is decomposed.

Crack is an extremely addictive smokable form of cocaine processed from cocaine hydrochloride by adding ammonia or sodium bicarbonate and water, and heating the mixture to produce the free base. When cooled, the resulting pebble-sized crystalline form of cocaine base can be sold in small quantities making crack more affordable and thus contributing to its popularity. The name crack refers to the sound made when the ''rocks'' of cocaine are smoked. When smoked, the cocaine is absorbed by pulmonary capillaries and moves from the lungs to the left side of the heart and then directly to the brain; the effects are perceptible in 7 to 10 seconds. Repeated use results in psychic dependence and tolerance; therefore, cocaine is classified as a Schedule II drug under the Controlled Substances Act.

Cocaine served as the model for a large number of synthetic local anesthetics that have been produced to increase the stability and reduce the toxicity of the natural product. Some of them are vasodilators and are often employed in conjunction with epinephrine. Such compounds are considered in detail in the standard textbooks of medicinal chemistry.

QUINOLINE ALKALOIDS

Alkaloids containing quinoline as their basic nucleus include those obtained from cinchona (quinine, quinidine, cinchonine, and cinchonidine).

Cinchona and its alkaloids are the only members of this group that are therapeutically important at present. Cinchonine, which is isomeric with cinchonidine, is the parent alkaloid of the quinine series. Quinine and its isomer, quinidine, represent 6-methoxycinchonine.

Biosynthesis of Quinoline Alkaloids

Studies with labeled geraniol and tryptophan - 2-^{14}C indicate that quinine is metabolically derived from the monoterpenoid-tryptophan pathway that leads to the corynane-type indole alkaloids. The most distinctive feature of quinine biosynthesis appears to be cleavage of the benzopyrrole ring of the tryptophan moiety and rearrangement to form the quinuclidine ring system and then the quinoline moiety. Details of the biosynthetic processes are lacking, but a presumed biogenetic origin involving strictosidine and corynantheal as intermediates is illustrated

in Figure 9-5. Both of these compounds are precursors.

Cinchona

Cinchona, cinchona bark, or Peruvian bark is the dried bark of the stem or of the root of *Cinchona succirubra* Pavon et Klotzsch, or its hybrids, known in commerce as red cinchona; or of *C. ledgeriana* (Howard) Moens et Trimen, *C. calisaya* Weddell, or hybrids of these with other species of *Cinchona*, known in commerce as calisaya bark or yellow cinchona (Fam. Rubiaceae).

Cinchona was named in honor of the Countess of Chinchon, wife of the Viceroy of Peru; *succirubra* is Latin and means red juice; *calisaya* is the Spanish and Indian name in Peru for the bark of a tree; *ledgeriana* is named in honor of Charles Ledger who introduced *Cinchona* into the East Indies. The plants are trees indigenous to the Andes of Ecuador and Peru, and are cultivated in Indonesia and India. They grow optimally at an elevation of 1000 to 3000 meters. There are over 36 known species and hybrids of *Cinchona*.

Just before World War II, Java (Indonesia) supplied over 90% of the world consumption of this important drug. When the Japanese cut off this supply from the world, several synthetic antimalarials (chloroquine, quinacrine, and primacrine) were developed to replace cinchona. Cultivation of cinchona trees was also undertaken in several countries in Central and South America (where it originally occurred). Alkaloid production from these trees during the early months of World War II was a deciding factor in preventing further advances by the Japanese in the Pacific area. Extraction techniques were improved in such a manner as to utilize all of the important alkaloids in any type of cinchona bark that could be obtained from any source.

The Dutch have now resumed the manufacture of cinchona alkaloids using bark obtained from Indonesia. A certain amount of alkaloids is produced in Germany; owing to economic factors, practically none is produced in the United States.

Cultivation gives the opportunity to select seeds from plants producing high-quality bark and to hybridize one choice strain with another. Thus, hybrids of *Cinchona ledgeriana-Cinchona calisaya* produce a higher yield of alkaloids than do either of the parent species. Selected seeds planted in seed beds develop into

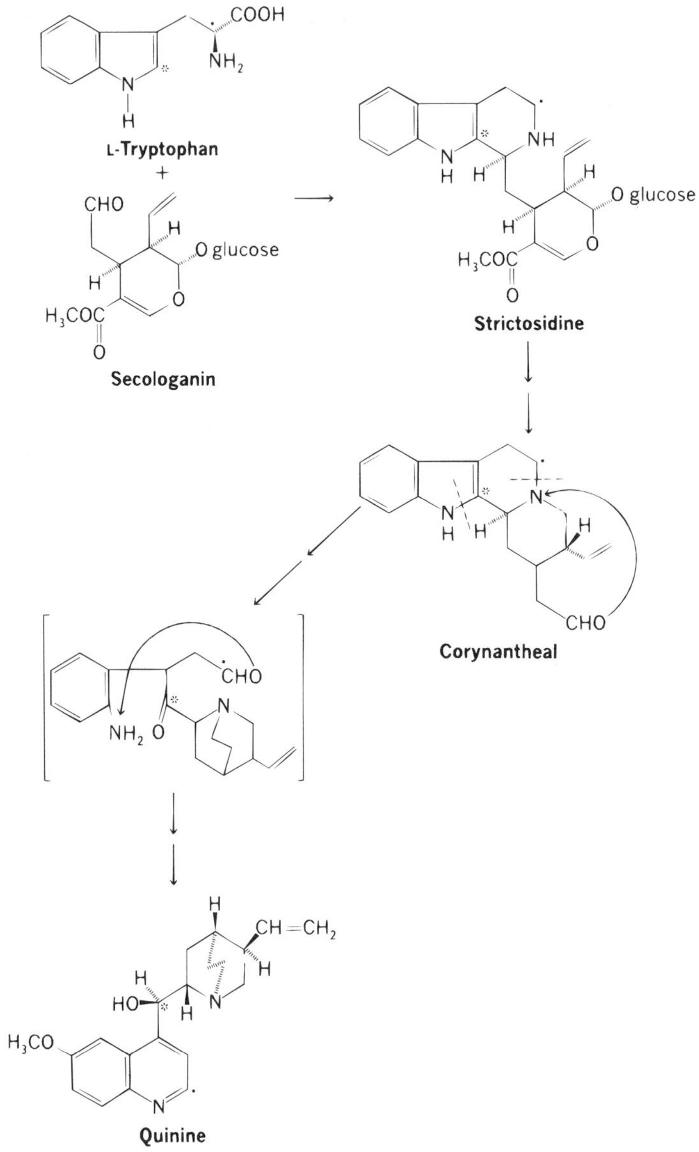

Fig. 9–5.   Probable biosynthetic origin of quinine.

young plants that can be transplanted within 2 years. The stems tend to grow tall, the lower branches tend to die and drop off, and the tree crowns grow closely, thus shading the trunks. Shade is favorable to the production of quinine. Trees that are 6 to 9 years old possess the maximum amount of alkaloids in the bark. They can easily be uprooted with tractors, and the fresh bark of both trunk and roots can then be removed by hand. When young bark is dried, it may have an alkaloidal content three times as great as that

in bark from an old tree. A considerable amount of cinchona bark enters into the manufacture of vermouth and certain bitter liqueurs.

A number of fantastic tales have been told about the origin of the medicinal use of cinchona. One of these states that an Indian in Peru was overcome with fever and was forced to drink stagnant water from a pond into which several cinchona trees had fallen. Enough alkaloids had been extracted by the prolonged maceration that, within hours of drinking the solution, the Indian's fever had abated and he eventually recovered.

A Jesuit missionary learned of the use of the drug from the Indians. He taught others, among them Canizares, the corregidor of Loxa. Canizares sent the bark to Juan de Vega, who at that time was treating the Countess Ana de Osorio, wife of the Count of Chinchon and Viceroy of Peru, for tertian fever. The Countess recovered and shortly thereafter introduced the bark into Europe. The use of cinchona was further spread through the efforts of the Jesuit Order. For the next half century or more, Europe seethed with a controversy over cinchona. The drug was both widely condemned and widely praised. Early names for the drug were Countess bark, Jesuit's bark, and Peruvian bark. It is interesting to note that Linnaeus, when naming the genus, desired to honor the Countess but omitted the second letter in the name Chinchon. This error has continued to the present day. The tree yielding cinchona bark was unknown until 1737. In 1854, the Dutch began its introduction into Java, and in 1860, the English introduced it into India.

The alkaloids are chiefly formed in the parenchymal cells of the middle layers of the bark. Cinchona contains some 25 closely related alkaloids, the most important of which are quinine, quinidine, cinchonine, and cinchonidine, and the average yield is 6 to 7%, of which from one half to two thirds is quinine in the yellow barks. In the red barks, cinchonidine exists in greater proportion; specimen pieces have yielded as high as 18% of total alkaloids. Another constituent of cinchona is cinchotannic acid, from 2 to 4%, which decomposes into the nearly insoluble cinchona red, occurring in red barks to the extent of 10%.

Cinchona and its alkaloids have been used in the treatment of malaria fever for many years. Quinine continues to be used for malaria in many parts of the world, but in the United States this alkaloid is utilized primarily in the preparation of effervescent tonic water. Quinidine is now the principal cinchona alkaloid employed therapeutically.

Overdoses of cinchona products result in temporary loss of hearing and in impaired sight. Ringing in the ears is a symptom of toxicity. When these symptoms are produced as the result of continuous use of cinchona or of quinine, the condition has been called **cinchonism**.

Cuprea bark is obtained from *Remijia purdieana* Triana and *R. pedunculata* Flückiger (Fam. Rubiaceae), of central and southern Col-

ombia. It has a copper-red color, is hard, compact, and heavy, and contains 2 to 6% of alkaloids, of which one third may be quinine. Cuprea bark is a commercial source of quinidine.

Cinchona Alkaloids

Quinidine is a stereoisomer of quinine and is present in cinchona barks to the extent of 0.25 to 1.25%.

Quinidine sulfate is the sulfate of an alkaloid obtained from various species of *Cinchona* and their hybrids and from *Remijia pedunculata*, or prepared from quinine. It is odorless, has a bitter taste, and darkens when exposed to light. It is readily soluble in water, alcohol, methanol, and chloroform.

Quinidine is used to treat various cardiac arrhythmias such as premature atrial, AV junctional, and ventricular contractions; atrial and ventricular tachycardia; atrial flutter; and atrial fibrillation. Its antiarrhythmic mechanism is through membrane stabilization (Class I). By combining with fast sodium channels in the inactive state, quinidine inhibits recovery after repolarization. There is a depression of phase 0, and the action potential duration is prolonged. When administered orally, the peak serum levels are slightly lower with the gluconate and polygalacturonate salt than with the sulfate salt. Toxic reactions occur at blood serum levels above 8 μg/ml. The patient should be instructed to notify the physician if skin rash, fever, unusual bleeding or bruising, ringing in the ears, or visual disturbance occurs.

Quinidine Sulfate

Quinidine gluconate is available in sustained release tablets.

Intravenous quinidine gluconate is an agent of choice in the treatment of severe, life-threatening malaria caused by *Plasmodium falciparum*.

Quinidine polygalacturonate affords controlled and more uniform absorption through the intestinal mucosa than does quinidine sulfate. In addition, it produces a lower incidence of gastrointestinal irritation.

Quinine is the diastereoisomer of quinidine. It occurs as white, odorless, bulky, bitter crystals or as a crystalline powder. It darkens when exposed to light and effloresces in dry air. It is freely soluble in alcohol, ether, and chloroform but slightly soluble in water.

Quinine

Quinine sulfate is the sulfate of an alkaloid obtained from the bark of *Cinchona* species. It occurs as white, odorless, bitter, fine, needlelike crystals that are usually lusterless. It becomes brownish when exposed to light. It is not readily soluble in water, alcohol, chloroform, or ether.

The drug is an antimalarial and once was the only agent available to treat this disease, which afflicts millions of people worldwide. The exact mechanism of the antimalarial activity of quinine is not known; however, it is believed to act by intercalation of the quinoline moiety into the DNA of the *Plasmodium* parasite, thereby reducing the effectiveness of DNA to act as a template. Intercalating agents such as quinine are rigid planar polycyclic molecules that insert between the adjacent stacked base pairs of the double helix of DNA. This results in DNA that has increased length, and because of a greater electrostatic interaction between the intercalated molecule and the two DNA strands, there is an inhibition of the strand separation that is required for replication and transcription of the genetic code. Quinine sulfate has been used for suppression or chemoprophylaxis of malaria caused by *Plasmodium falciparum, P. malariae, P. ovale,* and *P. vivax;* however, other antimalarial agents are currently preferred for prophylaxis. Recently, it has regained considerable importance in the treatment of chloroquine-resistant falciparum malaria in combination with pyrimethamine and sulfadoxine or tetracycline or clindamycin. The patient should be instructed to notify the physician if ringing in the ears or visual disturbance occurs.

Quinine has a skeletal muscle relaxant effect, increasing the refractory period by direct action on the muscle fiber, decreasing the excitability of the motor end-plate by a curariform action, and affecting the distribution of calcium within the muscle fiber. Therefore, it was widely used for the prevention and treatment of nocturnal recumbency leg cramps. However, the FDA has now prohibited the OTC sale of quinine for this purpose because suitable clinical trials proving its efficacy were never conducted.

ISOQUINOLINE ALKALOIDS

The isoquinoline structure occurs in a considerable number of alkaloids in widely separated plant families. They represent the largest single group of plant alkaloids, and there is great variation in their chemical structures. Some of the important isoquinoline subgroups are the **benzylisoquinolines** represented by papaverine and tubocurarine, the **benzophenanthridines** represented by sanguinarine, the **pthalideisoquinolines** that contain a γ-lactone ring and are represented by hydrastine, the **morphinans** represented by the opium alkaloids (codeine, morphine, thebaine), the **protoberberines** represented by berberine, and those with the **emetine** skeleton. In addition, with the isoquinoline group of alkaloids frequently the nitrogen is in the quaternary form as in the case of berberine, sanguinarine, and tubocurarine which greatly influences their solubility properties.

Biosynthesis of Isoquinoline Alkaloids

Although the isoquinoline alkaloids possess relatively complex structures, the basic biosynthetic reactions that account for their formation in plants are quite simple. These compounds result from the condensation of a phenylethylamine derivative with a phenylacetaldehyde derivative. Both of these moieties are derived from phenylalanine or tyrosine. The biosynthesis of morphine and related alkaloids has been studied extensively, and these experiments provide some of the most complete and detailed observations available for any secondary plant constituent. The biosynthetic pathway leading to morphine is shown in Figure 9-6. Morphine is a modified benzylisoquinoline. The key intermediate in its formation is the benzylisoquinoline alkaloid (*S*)-norcoclaurine which is formed by a Mannich-type condensation of dopamine with *p*-hydroxyphenylacetaldehyde (formed directly

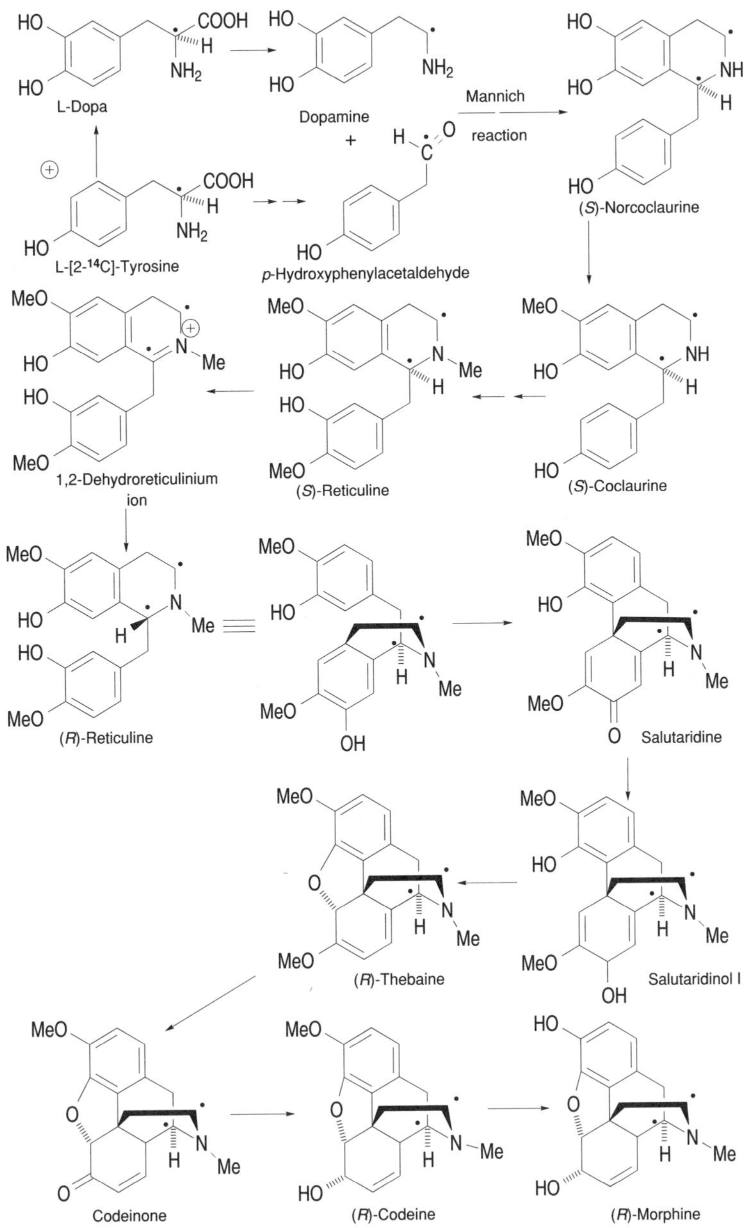

Fig. 9–6. Biosynthesis of morphine.

from tyrosine). (*S*)-Norcoclaurine is methylated to (*S*)-coclaurine, and hydroxylation followed by a second methylation yields (*S*)-reticuline. (*R*)-Reticuline, however, is the isomer with the same relevant configuration as thebaine, codeine, and morphine. Therefore, (*S*)-reticuline must be racemized to (*R*)-reticuline. This racemization is enzymatic, is substrate specific, and proceeds through a reversible oxidation-reduction mechanism via the 1,2-dehydroreticulinium ion. In addition, in order to obtain the morphinan ring system of morphine, the benzylisoquinoline skeleton of (*R*)-reticuline must be twisted to allow for an oxidative phenolic coupling that gives rise to salutaridine. Another interesting aspect of this pathway is the biosynthetic relationship of thebaine, codeine, and morphine; stepwise demethylation of the therapeutically unimportant thebaine leads first to the relatively mild analgesic codeine and then to the potent narcotic morphine.

P. somniferum has a highly evolved and useful secondary metabolism that culminates, at least from the therapeutic viewpoint, in morphine. *P. bracteatum* Lindley, a thebaine-producing poppy, appears to lack any significant demethylation capability; this feature is not only useful for biosynthetic studies but has recently become commercially significant. Because thebaine can be converted to codeine semisynthetically, a source of the latter alkaloid is assured without concomitant production of morphine, which is more subject to abuse by drug addicts. These two species emphasize the subtle metabolic difference that frequently separates useful plants from those of only scientific interest.

Presumably, morphine and other opium alkaloids are formed primarily in various cells of the poppy plant and are excreted into the lactiferous ducts. However, isolated latex is capable of alkaloid biosynthesis in the presence of suitable precursors and cofactors. The latex is also capable of metabolic destruction of morphine, and diurnal variations in alkaloid composition of the latex have been recorded. These observations, which establish a metabolic function for the latex, are fundamentally significant and undoubtedly contribute to the normal variability in alkaloid composition of crude opium samples.

Ipecac

Ipecac consists of the dried rhizome and roots of *Cephaelis ipecacuanha* (Brotero) A. Richard, known in commerce as Rio or Brazilian ipecac, or of *Cephaelis acuminata* Karsten, known in commerce as Cartagena, Nicaragua, or Panama ipecac (Fam. Rubiaceae). Ipecac yields not less than 2% of the ether-soluble alkaloids of ipecac.

Cephaelis is from two Greek words, meaning head and to collect or roll up, and refers to the inflorescence; *ipecacuanha* is Portuguese from the Brazilian Indian *ipekaaguene*, meaning a

creeping plant that causes vomiting; *acuminata* refers to the acute apex of the leaf.

The plants are low, straggling shrubs, with slender rhizomes bearing annulated wiry roots. *C. ipecacuanha* is indigenous to Brazil, which furnishes most of the present supply. It has been cultivated to a limited extent in Malaysia and in India. *C. acuminata* is indigenous to the northern portions of Colombia and extends into Panama and Nicaragua. Apparently, ipecac was used as an insect repellant and amebicide by the South American Indians. The drug was first mentioned by a Jesuit friar in 1601. It was introduced into Europe by Le Gras in 1672 and by 1690 was well-known in medicine.

In Rio (Brazilian) ipecac, the total alkaloid content reaches slightly over 2%, about one-third cephaeline and two-thirds emetine. At the present time, the plants are becoming rather scarce despite the laws of most South American countries that require a portion of the root to be planted when collections are made. Roots that are collected are usually immature, and the total alkaloid content barely reaches the minimum percentage.

In Cartagena (Colombia) ipecac and in Panama ipecac, the total alkaloid content reaches 2.2%. The rhizomes and roots from Nicaragua and Costa Rica yield more than 2.5% of total alkaloids. In these varieties, the ratio of emetine to cephaeline is somewhat constant and is composed of about one-third emetine to two-thirds cephaeline.

Ipecac, in the form of a syrup, is used in the treatment of drug overdose and in certain poisonings. It produces emesis through a local irritant effect on the gastrointestinal mucosa and a central medullary effect by stimulation of the chemoreceptor trigger zone. The usual dose in adults and children older than one year of age is 15 ml, followed by one to two glasses of water and may be repeated once in 20 minutes if emesis does not occur. The syrup should be recovered by gastric lavage if emesis does not occur after the second dose. Ipecac syrup should not be confused with ipecac fluid extract, which is 14 times stronger. Ipecac mixed with opium (as Dover's powder) acts as a diaphoretic. Ipecac syrup is included in poison antidote kits because of its emetic properties.

Emetine or methylcephaeline is an alkaloid obtained from ipecac or prepared synthetically by methylation of cephaeline. It was discovered by Pelletier and Magendie in 1817.

Emetine hydrochloride is a hydrated hydrochloride of emetine. It occurs as a white, odorless, crystalline powder that becomes yellowish when exposed to light. It is freely soluble in water and alcohol.

Emetine hydrochloride is an antiamebic and acts primarily in the intestinal wall and the liver. It inhibits polypeptide chain elongation, thereby blocking protein synthesis. The drug is not administered orally because it produces nausea and vomiting. Emetine hydrochloride has been used extensively as an antiprotozoan, particularly in the treatment of amebic dysentery, pyorrhea alveolaris, and other amebic diseases; however, it is no longer approved for these uses in the United States because it can accumulate in the body, producing potentially lethal toxic effects. It possesses expectorant and emetic properties.

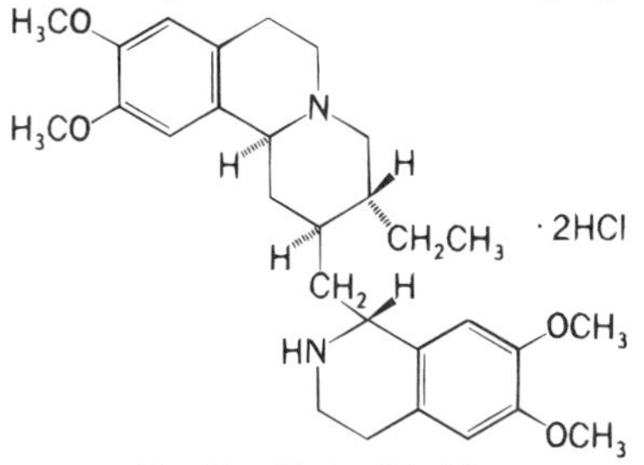

Emetine Hydrochloride

Hydrastis

Hydrastis or goldenseal consists of the dried rhizome and roots of *Hydrastis canadensis* Linné (Fam. Ranunculaceae).

Hydrastis is Greek and means to accomplish or act with water; the species name refers to the habitat. The plant is a perennial herb with a short horizontal rhizome that bears numerous long, slender roots. Internally, the rhizome and roots show a golden yellow color. Goldenseal was plentiful in the forests of the eastern United States and Canada; in recent years, it has become almost extinct because of ruthless over collection. Goldenseal has been cultivated in Oregon, Washington, North Carolina, Tennessee, Michigan, Wisconsin, and other localities; most of the commercial supply now comes from Arkansas and from the Blue Ridge Mountain area. The plants, propagated from rhizome buds, require 3 to 4 years to produce a marketable drug. It is gathered in autumn, the terminal buds are replanted, and the drug is carefully dried. Hydrastis was known to the Cherokee Indians, who used it as a dye and an internal remedy. These Indians introduced its use to the early American settlers.

Three alkaloids have been isolated from hydrastis: hydrastine, berberine, and canadine. Of these, hydrastine (1.5 to 4%) is the most important. Hydrastis yields not less than 2.5% of anhydrous ether-soluble alkaloids.

The hydrastis alkaloids, hydrastine and berberine, are used as astringents in inflammation of the mucous membranes.

Hydrastine is a phthalideisoquinoline and is readily soluble in chloroform, alcohol, and ether but almost insoluble in water.

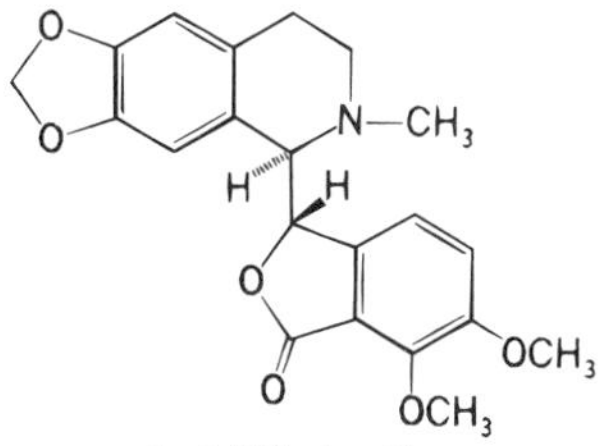

(−)-β-**Hydrastine**

Berberine is readily soluble in water but almost insoluble in ether. The salts of berberine form yellow crystals.

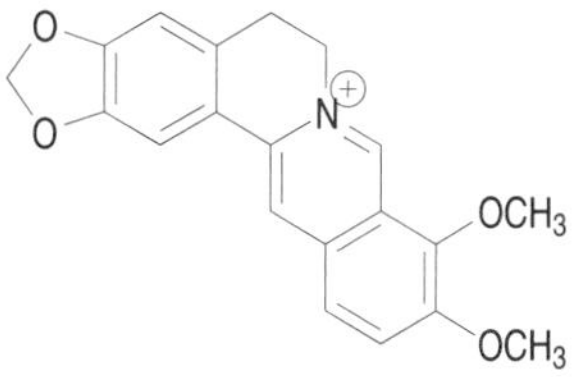

Berberine

Sanguinaria

Sanguinaria or bloodroot is the dried rhizome of *Sanguinaria canadensis* Linné (Fam. Papaveraceae). The generic name is from *sanguinarius*, meaning bloody, and refers to the color of the latex; *canadensis* refers to the plant habitat in Canada. The plant is a low perennial herb with a horizontal branching rhizome that bears slender roots and contains an orange-red latex. The plant grows in the rich open woodland in North America east of the Mississippi. Most of the collection takes place in the eastern states. Bloodroot was used by the Indians to stain their faces and was also used as an acrid emetic. Its use in homemade cough remedies seems to have been adopted by the early settlers.

Sanguinaria contains alkaloids, including sanguinarine (about 1%), chelerythrine, protopine, and allocryptopine. These alkaloids are colorless but tend to form colored salts. Sanguinarine yields reddish salts with nitric or sulfuric acids; yellowish salts are formed with chelerythrine. Sanguinarine is a benzophenanthradine type of isoquinoline alkaloid.

Sanguinarine

All alkaloids of sanguinaria are found in other members of the Papaveraceae.

Sanguinaria has stimulating expectorant and emetic properties. In addition, sanguinaria extract, representing a mixture of the total alkaloids, has been incorporated into toothpaste and mouthwash for the prevention of the development of dental plaque and subsequent periodontal disease.

Tubocurarine Chloride

Curare or South American arrow poison is a crude dried extract from the bark and stems of *Strychnos castelnaei* Weddell, *S. toxifera* Bentham, *S. crevauxii* G. Planchon (Fam. Loganiaceae) and from *Chondodendron tomentosum* Ruiz et Pavon (Fam. Menispermaceae). The term ''curare'' is derived from *woorari* or *urari*, Indian words for poison. Curare varies in composition among the Indian tribes. Each tribe modifies the formula in accordance with tribal custom.

The young bark is scraped off the plants, mixed with other substances, and boiled in water and strained or extracted by crude percolation with water. It is evaporated to a paste over a fire or in the sun. The earliest available preparations were named according to the containers in which the drug was packaged: **calabash** (gourd), **tube** (bamboo), or **pot** (clay pot) **curare.** Curare is obtained from the Orinoco basin, the upper Amazon regions, and the eastern Ecuadorian plateau. It is a brownish or black, shiny, resinoid mass with a bitter taste, that is readily soluble in cold water and in dilute alcohol.

Any given sample of the drug contains at least several of a large possible number of alkaloids and quaternary compounds, but the specific composition varies according to the identity of the plant material from which it was prepared.

(+)-Tubocurarine, the most important constituent, is a quaternary compound that contains a bis-benzylisoquinoline structure. The crude extract exhibits a paralyzing effect on voluntary muscle (curariform effect) by blocking nerve impulses to skeletal muscles at the myoneural junction. It also produces a toxic action on blood vessels as well as a histaminelike effect.

Curare was brought to England by Sir Walter Raleigh in 1595, but it has only recently come into prominence in medical circles. Bernard, Kolliker, Langley, and other investigators studied the effect of curare on mechanisms of neuromuscular activity; however, its heterogeneous nature, its variability, and its uncertain supply limited its use in therapeutics.

Tubocurarine chloride or (+)-tubocurarine chloride is a white or yellowish white to grayish white, odorless, crystalline powder. It is derived from tube curare and was first isolated by Boehm in 1898 and later by King in 1947. King obtained it from *Chondodendron tomentosum* and confirmed the structure as a quaternary ammonium compound. It is soluble in water and in alcohol but is insoluble in acetone, chloroform, and ether.

(+)-Tubocurarine chloride

Tubocurarine chloride is standardized by the ''head-drop'' crossover test in rabbits in which groups of animals for testing and for control are used on alternate days (crossover). The standard ''head-drop'' dose is the least amount of the drug capable of producing muscle relaxation so that the head of the animal drops in a characteristic manner.

Tubocurarine chloride is a nondepolarizing neuromuscular blocking agent and is employed intramuscularly or intravenously as a skeletal muscle relaxant to secure muscle relaxation in surgical procedures without deep anesthesia. It is also used to control convulsions of strychnine poisoning and of tetanus; it is an adjunct to shock therapy in neuropsychiatry and a diagnostic aid in myasthenia gravis.

Opium

Opium or gum opium is the air-dried milky exudate obtained by incising the unripe capsules of *Papaver somniferum* Linné or its variety *album* DeCandolle (Fam. Papaveraceae). The term *opium* is from the Greek *opion*, meaning poppy juice; *Papaver* is the Latin name for the poppy; *somniferum* is Latin and means to produce sleep.

The opium poppy is an annual herb with large, showy, solitary flowers that vary in color from white to pink or purple. The color of its seeds is also variable, ranging from blue-black or gray to yellow-white or rose-brown. Plants that produce the lighter-colored seeds have been classified as variety *album*, but this designation is not employed in modern taxonomic writings. Because of its long history as a cultivated plant, numerous varieties of *P. somniferum* exist, and their taxonomy is extremely complicated.

The plant was first cultivated somewhere in the northeastern corner of the Mediterranean region, where opium was first produced. Opium was then introduced into India (the date is uncertain). Some scholars credit the introduction to Alexander the Great (327 B.C.), others to the Arabs who invaded the Province of Sind in the 8th century. The first recorded cultivation of the opium poppy in India dates from the 15th century, and cultivation began in Macedonia and Persia (Iran) about the middle of the 19th century. The opium poppy is grown commercially now in many countries throughout the world, but production is concentrated in a zone that extends from the Turkish Anatolian Plain to the northern border of Laos. The discovery of the medicinal qualities of opium is lost in antiquity. Theophrastus (3rd century B.C.) mentioned it, and Dioscorides (77 A.D.) distinguished between the juice of the poppy and an extract of the entire plant. In 1805-6, Sertürner first published his studies dealing with the isolation of the alkaloid morphine from opium.

Cultivation, Collection, and Commerce The cultivation of the opium poppy is controlled internationally by the International Narcotics Control Board of the United Nations. At the present time, the only country with a major involvement in the licit production of opium to meet world requirements is India. In addition, opium is produced in China and the Democratic People's Republic of Korea exclusively to meet domestic medical needs.

The opium poppy, however, is widely cultivated for the purpose of harvesting poppy seed, the straw being obtained as a by-product and used as a raw material in the production of morphine. The morphine is extracted from poppy straw, prepared by cutting and drying the entire overground plant at a suitable stage of development. The major producers of poppy straw are Turkey, Australia, France, and Spain. Turkey, formerly a major producer of both licit and illicit opium, has made it illegal to produce opium and permits poppy cultivation exclusively for the production of poppy straw and seeds. Most of the opium destined for the illicit trade originates in remote border areas of Myanmar, Thailand, and Laos, commonly referred to as the "Golden Triangle," and in India, Pakistan, Afghanistan, and Mexico.

For the production of opium in northern India, the poppy seeds are sown in winter in well-cultivated soil. In the spring, when the plants have attained a height of 15 cm, the fields are cultivated, and the plants are thinned to stand about 60 cm apart. The poppy blossoms in April or May, and the capsules mature in May or June. Each plant bears from 5 to 8 capsules (see Fig. 9-7).

The ripening capsules, about 4 cm in diameter, change from bluish green to yellowish in color. This time is critical for latex collection. The capsules are incised with a knife, which is usually 3-bladed, and the incision is made around the circumference of the capsule. The latex tubes open into one another; therefore, it is not necessary to incise them all. Great skill, however, is required so that the endocarp is not cut. When the endocarp is broken, the latex flows into the interior of the capsule and is lost. The latex, which is at first white, rapidly coagulates and turns brown to blackish. In Rajasthan, each capsule is incised four or five separate times, and it is claimed that the third lancing produces the highest yield of latex. The morning after each lancing, the congealed opium is scraped off the capsules with an iron scoop or knife before the heat makes it stick too tightly. Thus each capsule may be handled ten times. When sufficient latex is collected, it is kneaded into balls that are wrapped in poppy leaves and dried in the shade. Additional processing of the

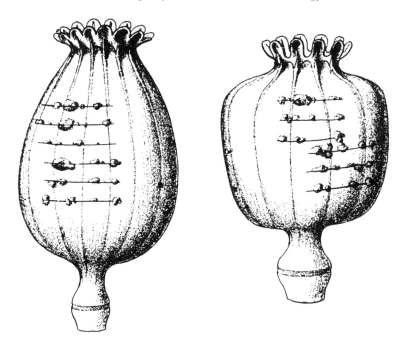

Fig. 9–7. Poppy capsules showing the milky juice exuding from transverse incisions and forming irregular globular masses on the surface. The hardened milky juice forms opium.

raw opium takes place at government collection centers. Rectangular pans containing about 35 kg of opium sit in the sun, and every 30 minutes or so each pan is stirred with wooden paddles. Eight to 20 days of stirring, depending on the sun, reduces the moisture content from 30% to 10%. When sufficiently dry, it is formed into 5-kg cakes. Externally, opium is pale olive-brown or olive-gray. It is more or less plastic when fresh and becomes hard and brittle or tough when kept. Internally, it is coarsely granular or nearly smooth, reddish brown, frequently interspersed with lighter areas, and somewhat lustrous. Its odor is characteristic, and its taste is bitter and characteristic.

Indian opium is produced in the states of Madhya Pradesh, Rajasthan, and Uttar Pradesh. At present it is the only licit source of opium. The 5-kg cakes are shipped in polyethylene bags. Indian opium yields about 10% of anhydrous morphine.

More than 30 different alkaloids have been obtained from opium and its extracts, some of which are alteration products of the alkaloids occurring naturally in the drug. The most impor-

tant of these are **morphine,** which exists to the extent of 4 to 21%; **codeine,** 0.8 to 2.5%; **noscapine** (formerly **narcotine**), 4 to 8%; **papaverine,** 0.5 to 2.5%; and **thebaine,** 0.5 to 2%. Other alkaloids include narceine, protopine, laudanine, codamine, cryptopine, lanthopine, and meconidine.

Opium also contains from 3 to 5% of meconic acid, which exists free or in combination with morphine, codeine, and other alkaloids. It forms rhombic prisms that are soluble in water and alcohol and give a red color in solutions of ferric chloride. The color is not altered when diluted hydrochloric acid is added. Because meconic acid is found only in opium, this test may be used for the detection of opium. Opium in its normal, air-dried condition yields not less than 9.5% of anhydrous morphine.

Opium is a pharmaceutic necessity for the production of powdered opium. It acts chiefly on the central nervous system; its action first stimulates and then depresses nerve response. It serves as an analgesic, a hypnotic, and a narcotic; it checks excessive peristalsis and contracts the pupil of the eye.

Paregoric or camphorated opium tincture is classed as an antiperistaltic. It may be mixed before taking with a small amount of water to form a milky solution. Relatively small doses of opium are effective in controlling diarrhea and do not produce substantial analgesia.

Laudanum, opium tincture, or deodorized opium tincture is used similarly to paregoric.

Poppy seed or maw seed is the dried seed of *Papaver somniferum* variety *nigrum* DeCandolle. The seeds are bluish black or yellowish white, reniform, from 0.5 to 1 mm in diameter, and reticulate. They have a yellowish hilum scar, a white oily endosperm, and a curved embryo. Their taste is slight and oily. Poppy seeds are used in baking (poppy seed rolls). They contain about 50% of a fixed oil **(poppy seed oil),** which is used in some parenteral formulations, by artists as a drying oil, and also for food and salad dressings. **Poppy seed oil cake** is used as a cattle food. Poppy seed contains no significant quantity of alkaloids.

Alkaloids of Opium

Morphine is the most important of the opium alkaloids. Morphine and the related alkaloids are morphinan isoquinoline derivatives. The molecule contains a phenolic and an alcoholic hydroxyl group.

The alkaloid and its salts occur as white silky crystals, sometimes in cubic masses, or as a fine crystalline powder. It is stable in air, odorless, and bitter-tasting.

Morphine

Morphine is the prototype of opiate analgesic drugs which act at several sites in the central nervous system to produce analgesia. Morphine has agonist activity at the mu (μ) and kappa (κ) opiate receptor subtypes. Analgesia at the supraspinal level as well as euphoria, respiratory depression, and physical dependence results from agonist activity at the μ receptor. Agonist activity at the κ receptor is responsible for analgesia at the spinal level, miosis, and sedation.

Morphine and its salts are classed as narcotic analgesics; they are strongly hypnotic and nar-

cotic. Their use tends to induce nausea, vomiting, constipation, and habit formation.

Centrally acting analgesics, in most cases, have certain structural features in common. They are: (1) a central carbon atom with no hydrogen substitution (quaternary), (2) a phenyl group or isostere attached to this carbon atom, (3) a tertiary nitrogen atom, and (4) a two-carbon bridge separating the tertiary nitrogen atom and the central carbon atom.

Morphine and the related opium alkaloids that have analgesic activity possess these structural features. In the case of morphine, the central carbon atom is C-13; the phenyl ring attached to C-13 is composed of carbon atoms 1 to 4 and 11 and 12; and the tertiary nitrogen atom is linked via a two-carbon bridge (C-15, C-16) to the central carbon atom.

Codeine is the most widely used opium alkaloid. It may be either obtained from opium (0.2 to 0.7%) or prepared from morphine by methylation or from thebaine by appropriate reduction and demethylation. Codeine is methylmorphine in which the methyl group replaces the hydrogen of the phenolic hydroxyl group. Codeine and its salts occur as fine needles or as white crystalline powders that effloresce in air.

Codeine

Codeine and its salts are narcotic analgesics and antitussives; they are used as sedatives, especially in allaying coughs. Although its action is similar to that of morphine, codeine is considerably less toxic and involves much less danger of habit formation.

Diacetylmorphine or heroin is formed by the acetylation of morphine; the hydrogen atoms of both the phenolic and alcoholic hydroxyl groups are replaced by acetyl groups. Heroin's action is similar but more pronounced than that of morphine. Because of its potency and the danger of habit formation, its manufacture in the United States is forbidden by law, and its use in medicine has been discontinued.

Papaverine occurs naturally in opium to the extent of about 1%, but it may also be produced synthetically. **Papaverine hydrochloride** occurs as white crystals or as a white crystalline powder. It is odorless but has a slightly bitter taste.

Papaverine hydrochloride is a smooth muscle relaxant. It is used principally for the relief of cerebral and peripheral ischemia associated with arterial spasm and myocardial ischemia complicated by arrhythmias.

Hydromorphone hydrochloride or dihydromorphinone hydrochloride differs from morphine hydrochloride because one of the hydroxyl groups of morphine is replaced by a ketone group, and the adjacent double bond is removed. It is prepared by reducing morphine in hydrochloric acid solution with hydrogen in the presence of a catalyst.

Hydromorphone

The drug is a powerful narcotic analgesic and tends to strongly depress the respiratory mechanism. Its dosage is smaller than that of morphine; it causes nausea and constipation less frequently than does morphine, and perhaps it is less habit-forming. It is well known by the tradename Dilaudid.

Hydrocodone bitartrate or dihydrocodeinone bitartrate bears the same relation to codeine as dihydromorphinone does to morphine—a ketone group replaces one of the hydroxyl groups and the adjacent double bond is saturated. It is classed as an antitussive and is an aid in treating a troublesome cough.

A long-standing prescription product composed of the hydrochlorides of the alkaloids of opium in the same proportion in which they occur in the natural product is Pantopon. This drug has been freed from inert or irritating gums, waxes, and resins, and it may be administered parenterally, either subcutaneously or intramuscularly.

The term **"opioid"** has been devised to refer to the synthetic morphinelike compounds. Many of these substances offer the same narcotic and pain-relieving properties as morphine, but may not be as habit-forming. Others possess the cough-relieving activity of codeine but are not addictive.

INDOLE ALKALOIDS

A number of important alkaloids possess an indole ring as part of their structure. Strychnine and brucine (dimethoxystrychnine) from nux vomica and physostigmine from physostigma belong to this group. However, strychnine and brucine also contain a quinoline nucleus, and some authors classify them in the quinoline group.

The important drugs and their alkaloids of the indole group are rauwolfia, reserpine, catharanthus (vinca), vinblastine, vincristine, nux vomica, strychnine, brucine, physostigma, physostigmine, ergot, ergotamine, ergonovine, and yohimbine.

Biosynthesis of Indole Alkaloids

Many of the therapeutically useful indole alkaloids are rather complex multicyclic molecules. Incorporation of a tryptamine moiety into this type of alkaloid was established at a fairly early stage in the study of alkaloid biosynthesis. The origin of the balance of the molecules proved more elusive. However, it is now established that the nontryptophan portions of the molecules are derived from monoterpenoid precursors. Three general monoterpenoid skeletons give rise to most of the complex indole alkaloids; these skeletons are designated as the aspidospermane, corynane, and ibogane types, taking the names from the genera of plants that are rich in alkaloids with the respective monoterpenoid nucleus (Fig. 9-8).

The reactive form of the terpenoid presumably involves an aldehyde group, and the loss of one carbon atom during the biosynthetic process to give a C_9 unit appears to be fairly common. Many of the details on the sequence of biosynthetic reactions and various rearrangements remain to be clarified. It is suspected that the corynane type of monoterpenoid moiety is metabolically the most primitive. Studies on the formation of therapeutically unimportant monomeric alkaloids in *Catharanthus roseus* have demonstrated that the glucoside, secologanin, provides the terpenoid unit. Evidence suggests that secologanin reacts initially with tryptamine to form strictosidine (Fig. 9-5) and that the glycosidic linkage is cleaved during subsequent metabolic steps.

The *Rauvolfia* alkaloids, ajmaline, reserpine, and serpentine, are derived from a corynane-type monoterpenoid precursor. They can be used

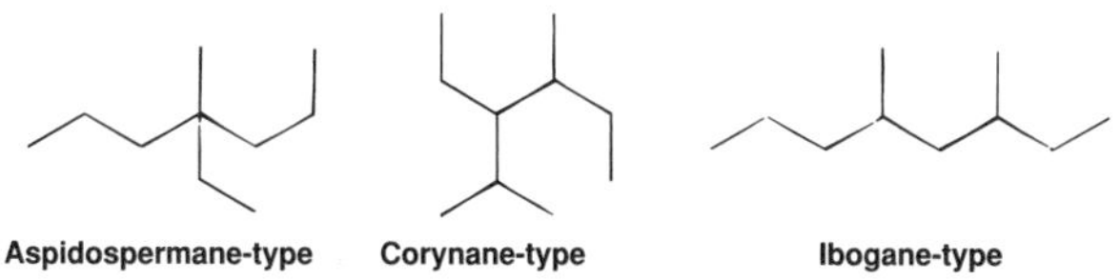

Fig. 9–8. Carbon skeletons of the general types of monoterpenoid precursors of indole alkaloids.

to illustrate some of the multicyclic structures that arise during tertiary cyclization and rearrangement steps in biosynthesis (Fig. 9-9).

Rauwolfia Serpentina

Rauwolfia serpentina is the dried root of *Rauvolfia serpentina* (Linné) Bentham (Fam. Apocynaceae). Sometimes fragments of rhizome and aerial stem bases are attached. When assayed as directed, it contains not less than 0.15% of the reserpine-rescinnamine group of alkaloids, calculated as reserpine. The genus name was selected in honor of Dr. Leonhard Rauwolf, a noted 16th century German botanist, physician, and explorer; *serpentina* refers to the long, tapering, snakelike roots of the plant. It must be emphasized that the name of the drug and the name of the genus of plants from which it derives are spelled differently. For technical reasons, the genus must be spelled with a *v* instead of a *w*. The plant *Rauvolfia serpentina* is thus the correct botanic origin of the drug rauwolfia serpentina (rauwolfia).

For centuries *Rauvolfia serpentina* was used by the medicine men of India to treat a variety of maladies, ranging from snake-bite to insanity.

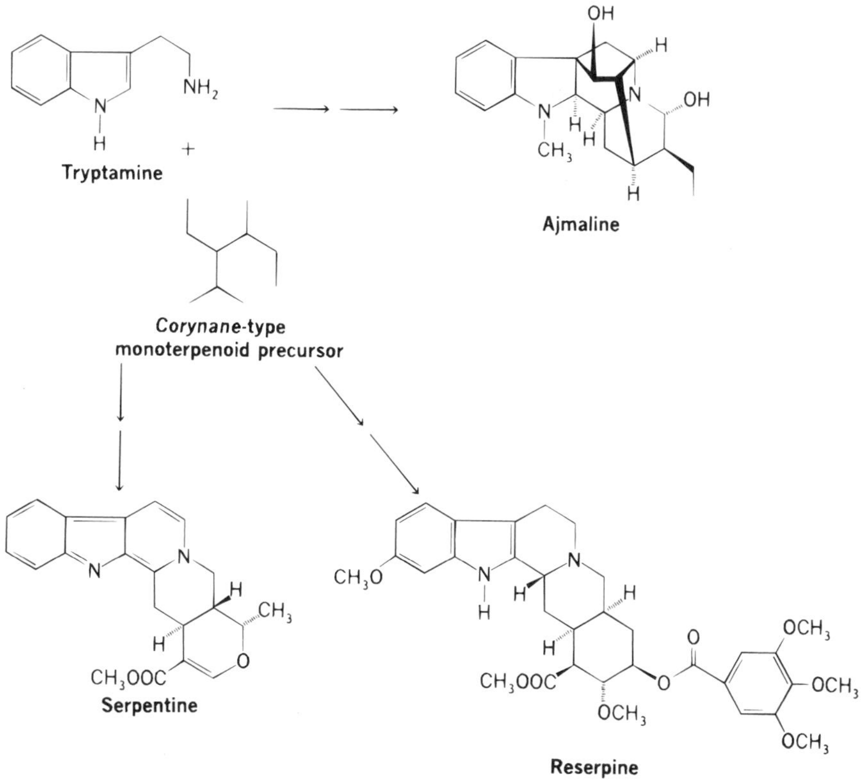

Fig. 9–9. Biosynthesis of *Rauvolfia* alkaloids.

In 1563, Garcia de Orta mentioned the plant and its uses in his book on the drugs of India, but European physicians were skeptical of its properties. Consequently, it was not until 1952, when Müller and colleagues succeeded in isolating the alkaloid reserpine that this plant was conceded to be valuable. In the form of the powdered root, the alkaloidal extract, and purified alkaloids, rauwolfia serpentina has become an exceedingly important therapeutic aid in the treatment and control of hypertension.

The plant is referred to as *sarpagandha* in Sanskrit, *chota-chand* or *chandrika* in Hindi, *pagla-ka-dawa* (insanity cure) in the dialect of Bihar, and also by such other names as *patalagandhi, dhanburua*, and *covanamilpori*. A native plant of India, Myanmar, Sri Lanka, Vietnam, Malaysia, Indonesia, and the Philippines, rauwolfia occurs in hot, moist regions. Practically all commercial supplies at the present time come from India and Thailand. Three varieties of *R. serpentina* roots have been sold on the Indian markets: Bihar, Dehra Dun, and Assam.

R. serpentina is an erect shrub that reaches 1 meter in height and has cylindric stems. These stems bear pale bark and exhibit a light-colored viscous latex when ruptured. It has leaves that may be simple and opposite or, more commonly, arranged in whorls of three to five. The white or pale rose flowers are arranged in terminal and axillary cymes. The fruit is a single, two-lobed drupe that turns purplish black when mature.

Three series of alkaloids have been reported: (1) weakly basic indole alkaloids, (2) indoline alkaloids of intermediate basicity, and (3) strong anhydronium bases. The principal alkaloids, reserpine, rescinnamine, and deserpidine, are tertiary indole alkaloids that have a carbocyclic structure in ring E and are of the corynane type. Other tertiary indole alkaloids exhibit a heterocyclic structure in ring E: δ-yohimbine (identical with ajmalicine, tetrahydroserpentine, and raubasine) and reserpiline. Ajmaline, isoajmaline, rauwolfinine, and others are listed as tertiary indoline alkaloids; however, these bases do not have a tranquilizing action. Serpentine, serpentinine, and alstonine are classed as strongly basic anhydronium alkaloids. The latter type is not considered of practical therapeutic importance. From the 25 or more species of *Rauvolfia* investigated, at least 50 alkaloids have been reported.

Rauwolfia alkaloids probably exert their hypotensive effects by depletion of catecholamine and serotonin stores in many organs, including the brain and adrenal medulla, and by reduction of uptake of catecholamines by adrenergic neurons. Their sedative and tranquilizing properties are thought to be related to depletion of amines in the central nervous system.

Powdered rauwolfia serpentina is *R. serpentina* root reduced to a fine or very fine powder that is adjusted, if necessary, to conform to the official requirements for reserpine-rescinnamine group alkaloids by admixture with lactose or starch or with a powdered rauwolfia serpentina containing a higher or lower content of these alkaloids. It contains not less than 0.15% and not more than 0.20% of reserpine-rescinnamine group alkaloids, calculated as reserpine.

Rauwolfia serpentina is a hypotensive. (Reserpine is the chief alkaloid and has strong hypotensive and sedative activity.) A total alkaloidal determination is not indicative of activity unless the proportion of alkaloids is known.

Because at least 50 alkaloids have been isolated, it is easy to understand the claim that the whole root exhibits a medicinal action that is different from that of reserpine. A definite lowering of blood pressure in hypertensive states, a slowing of the pulse, and a general sense of euphoria follow administration. It is used in mild essential hypertension and also as adjunctive therapy with other agents in more severe forms of hypertension. It is also indicated to relieve the symptoms in agitated psychotic states such as schizophrenia in patients unable to tolerate other antipsychotic agents.

Reserpine is a white or pale buff to slightly yellow, odorless, crystalline powder that darkens slowly when exposed to light and rapidly when in solution. The structural formula is shown in Figure 9-9.

Reserpine is an antihypertensive and antipsychotic agent.

Reserpine has been obtained in commercial quantities from four different species of *Rauvolfia; R. serpentina, R. micrantha* Hooker filius, *R. tetraphylla* Linné, and *R. vomitoria* Afzelius. Several of these present problems in the separation of the alkaloids. In *R. serpentine*, reserpine and rescinnamine both respond to the extraction procedures, and the end result of the assay procedure is a mixture of both. In *R. tetraphylla*, reserpine and deserpidine (raunormine) are extracted together; in *R. vomitoria*, reserpine must be separated from the resins.

Laboratory investigators in France have developed a method of synthesizing reserpine on a commercial scale. However, the natural alkaloid is much less expensive than the synthetic, and, with large quantities of *R. vomitoria* available from tropical Africa, the commercial supplies appear to be sufficient to provide adequate amounts of reserpine and related alkaloids for many years to come. In addition, other species of plants are being studied to ascertain their alkaloidal composition. Because the family Apocy-

about 6 % of a mixture of alkaloids, the principal one of which is yohimbine. Yohimbine has successfully treated impotence in patients with vascular or diabetic problems. Its peripheral autonomic nervous system effect is to increase cholinergic and decrease adrenergic activity. In male sexual performance, erection is linked to increased cholinergic activity which results in

Rescinnamine

naceae consists of many additional species, it is probable that untapped sources of reserpine and other valuable alkaloids may be discovered by pharmacognosists and plant chemists.

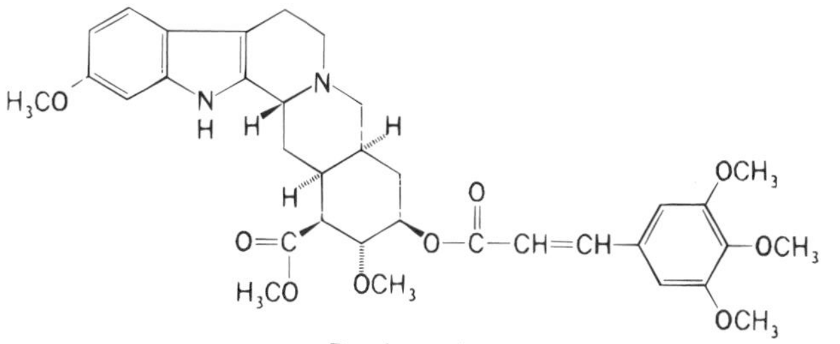

Rescinnamine is an alkaloid that occurs in several species of *Rauvolfia*. Its appearance, properties, and solubility are somewhat similar to those of reserpine. Chemically, it is the methyl reserpate ester of 3,4,5-trimethoxycinnamic acid. It is used to treat mild essential hypertension.

Deserpidine (canescine, recanescine) is an alkaloid obtained from the root of *Rauvolfia canescens* L. Chemically, it is 11-desmethoxyreserpine. It has the same uses as Rauwolfia serpentina and reserpine and is claimed to have fewer side effects.

In mild or moderate hypertension, rauwolfia or its derivatives may be the sole therapy, but in more severe hypertension, rauwolfia acts synergistically with more potent hypotensive agents. Products are available that utilize combinations of rauwolfia, deserpidine, or reserpine with thiazide diuretics and/or other antihypertensive agents.

Yohimbine

Yohimbine is an indole alkaloid of the corynane type obtained from the bark of the West African tree *Pausinystalia yohimbe* (K. Schum.) Pierre (Fam. Rubiaceae). The bark contains

increased penile blood inflow, decreased penile blood outflow, or both, causing erectile stimulation.

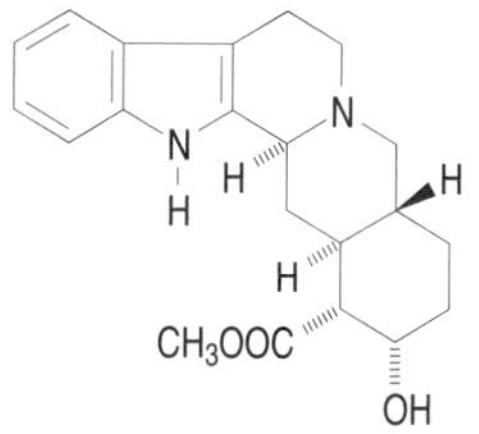

Yohimbine

Catharanthus

Catharanthus or vinca is the dried whole plant of *Catharanthus roseus* G. Don (Fam. Apocynaceae), formerly designated *Vinca rosea* Linné. The plant is an erect, ever-blooming pubescent herb or subshrub that is woody at the base and stands 40 to 80 cm high. It probably originated in Madagascar but is now cosmopolitan in the tropics and is widely cultivated as an ornamental. The flowers are normally violet, rose, or white; ocellate forms are found in cultivated varieties. Botanically, it is closely related to *Vinca minor* Linné, the common periwinkle.

During the course of a modern scientific investigation prompted by the folklore reputation of this plant as an oral hypoglycemic agent, the ability of certain fractions to produce peripheral granulocytopenia and bone marrow depression in rats was observed by the Canadian group of Noble, Beer, and Cutts. Continued study led to the isolation of an alkaloid, vinblastine, which produced severe leukopenia in rats.

Recognizing the anticancer potential of this plant, G.H. Svoboda and coworkers at Eli Lilly and Company isolated an extremely large number of alkaloids from the plant. Of these, four bisindole compounds, vinblastine, vinleurosine, vinrosidine, and vincristine, possess demonstrable oncolytic activity.

Because the active alkaloids exist in the crude drug in relatively small amounts, enormous quantities of the latter are required for commercial production. Nearly 500 kg of catharanthus are utilized to produce 1 g of vincristine. To satisfy the demand, the plant is collected from both natural and cultivated sources in Madagascar, Australia, South Africa, South America, the West Indies, Europe, India, and the southern United States.

Catharanthus Alkaloids

More than 90 different alkaloids have been isolated from catharanthus. They are generally indole and dihydroindole derivatives, some of which occur in other members of the Apocynaceae. These include ajmalicine, tetrahydroalstonine, serpentine, and lochnerine. The alkaloids with antineoplastic activity belong to a new class of bisindole derivatives. These alkaloids are composed of an indole and a dihydroindole unit, catharanthine and vindoline, respectively. The former belongs to the ibogane type and the latter to the aspidospermane type of monoterpenoid indole alkaloids.

The most characteristic effect of these drugs is the arrest of cell division at metaphase, in a manner resembling the effect of colchicine. Both vinblastine and vincristine bind tightly to tubulin and interfere with the functioning of the microtubule system, which is a component of the mitotic spindle. Recent findings indicate that the alkaloids actually inhibit the polymerization of tubulin into microtubules.

Vinblastine sulfate, vincaleukoblastine sulfate, or VLB, tradename Velban, is the salt of an alkaloid extracted from catharanthus. It is unstable and is available in sealed ampules, which should be stored in a refrigerator to ensure extended stability. The alkaloid is used for the treatment of a wide variety of neoplasms and is recommended for generalized Hodgkin's disease, lymphocytic lymphoma, histiocytic lym-

R=CH$_3$ Vinblastine Sulfate
R=CHO Vincristine Sulfate

phoma, mycosis fungoides, advanced testicular carcinoma, Kaposi's sarcoma, and choriocarcinoma and breast cancer unresponsive to other therapies. Vinblastine is effective as a single agent but is usually administered with other antineoplastic agents in combination therapy for an enhanced therapeutic effect without additive toxicity. It is administered intravenously in doses regulated by the patient's age, body surface, and white-blood-cell count.

Vincristine sulfate, leurocristine sulfate, VCR, or LCR, tradename Vincristine, is also obtained from catharanthus. The structure of this alkaloid is quite similar to that of vinblastine, differing only in the substitution of an *N*-formyl group for the *N*-methyl group of vinblastine. Despite the structural similarities, there are differences in the antitumor spectra of the two compounds, and no cross-resistance has been observed. Because vincristine sulfate is unstable, refrigerated storage in sealed ampules is essential. It is recommended for the treatment of acute lymphocytic leukemia and in combination therapy in Hodgkin's disease, lymphosarcoma, reticulum cell sarcoma, rhabdomyosarcoma, neuroblastoma, and Wilms' tumor.

The dose must be calculated and administered cautiously since overdose may be fatal. It is administered intravenously.

Vindesine is a semisynthetic derivative of vinblastine where the acetyl group at position 4 of the vindoline moiety has been removed. Even though it is derived from vinblastine, it has anti-neoplastic activity more closely resembling that of vincristine. Clinical trials indicate that it has good activity in difficult-to-treat or refractory cancer types, and there appears to be a lack of cross resistance with vincristine and vinblastine. **Vinorelbine tartrate** is a semisynthetic derivative of vinblastine which is prepared by removing the ethyl side chain at position 4′ of the catharanthine moiety, and the 4′-hydroxyl is removed as water to introduce an unsaturation at 3′,4′. The derivative is a 3′-noranhydrovinblastine. It is indicated as a single agent or in combination with cisplatin for the first line treatment of non-small cell lung cancer.

Nux Vomica

Nux vomica is the dried, ripe seed of *Strychnos nux-vomica* Linné (Fam. Loganiaceae). *Strychnos* is the Greek name for a number of poisonous plants; *nux-vomica* is from two Latin words and means a nut that causes vomiting.

The plant is a small tree, about 12 meters tall, that is native to the East Indies and is also found in the forests of Sri Lanka, on the Malabar Coast, and in northern Australia. The fruit is a berry with from three to five seeds that are freed from the bitter pulp by washing before exportation. Most of the commercial supply comes from Cambodia and Sri Lanka. The drug was introduced into Europe about the 16th century, although it was used mainly for poisoning animals. Its use in medicine began about 1640. The natives of India apparently had no knowledge of its medicinal value.

Nux vomica contains alkaloids, 1.5 to 5%, consisting chiefly of **strychnine** and **brucine**, the former comprising from one third to one half of the total amount.

Nux vomica and the seeds of the closely related *Strychnos ignatii* Bergius (**ignatia** or **St. Ignatius bean**) serve as a commercial source of strychnine and brucine. The former alkaloid is commonly marketed as strychnine sulfate or strychnine phosphate.

Strychnine and brucine (dimethoxystrychnine) are modified corynane-type monoterpenoid indole alkaloids and are obtained from nux vomica or ignatia by extraction with dilute sulfuric acid. The solution is concentrated. The alkaloids are precipitated with lime, separated by means of solvent, and purified by recrystallization.

Strychnine is interesting pharmacologically and is a valuable tool in physiologic and neuroanatomic research. It is extremely toxic, functioning as a central stimulant. The alkaloid produces excitation of all parts of the central nervous system and blocks inhibitory spinal impulses at the postsynaptic level. This leads to an exaggeration in reflexes, with resulting tonic convulsions. Fatal poisoning in humans ordinarily results from doses of 60 to 90 mg. The drug is seldom employed in modern medical practice but is utilized as a vermin killer. Brucine, which is less toxic than strychnine, has been used commercially as an alcohol denaturant because it is extremely bitter.

Strychnine

Physostigmine

Physostigma, Calabar bean, or ordeal bean is the dried, ripe seed of *Physostigma venenosum* Balfour (Fam. Fabaceae) yielding not less than 0.15% of the alkaloids of physostigma.

The name *Physostigma* is Greek and means an inflated or bladderlike stigma; *venenosum* is Latin and means full of poison. The plant is a perennial, woody climber that grows on the banks of streams in West Africa, particularly in the vicinity of the Gulf of Guinea. In 1846, Daniell described the use of the seed, known as *esere* by the natives of old Calabar, to prove the innocence or guilt of persons accused of crime.

Calabar bean contains several alkaloids—physostigmine (eserine), eseramine, geneserine, and physovenine. Physostigmine is the major alkaloid and is present in the cotyledons to the extent of 0.04 to 0.3%.

Physostigmine or eserine is an alkaloid usually obtained from the dried, ripe seed of *P. venenosum*. It occurs as a white, odorless, microcrystalline powder that may acquire a red tint when exposed to heat, light, air, or contact with traces of metal. This color change indicates hydrolysis to eseroline and oxidation to rubreserine. These degradation products are irritating to the eye and lack substantial pharmacologic activity. Therefore, physostigmine should be preserved in tight, light-resistant containers in quantities not exceeding 1 g.

Physostigmine is a reversible inhibitor of the cholinesterases and thus enhances the effects of endogenous acetylcholine. In the eye, increase in cholinergic activity leads to miosis, contraction of the ciliary muscle, and a decrease in intraocular pressure caused by an increased out-flow of the aqueous humor. Physostigmine is employed in ophthalmology to treat glaucoma.

Physostigmine salicylate or eserine salicylate is the salicylate of the alkaloid physostigmine. It is a white powder that also acquires a red tint when exposed to the conditions described under physostigmine. It also should be preserved in tight, light-resistant containers in quantities not exceeding 1 g.

Physostigmine Salicylate

Physostigmine salicylate is a cholinergic (ophthalmic) and is administered topically, 0.1 ml of a 0.25 to 0.5% solution, to the conjunctiva. Because it prolongs and exaggerates the effect of acetylcholine, physostigmine salicylate is given by injection as an antidote in poisonings caused by anticholinergic agents.

Physostigmine sulfate or eserine sulfate is the sulfate of the alkaloid physostigmine. This white, microcrystalline powder is deliquescent in moist air and acquires the red tint previously described. Storage requirements are the same as for physostigmine and physostigmine salicylate. It is a cholinergic (ophthalmic) used in the form of a 0.25% ointment that is applied topically to the conjunctiva.

Ergot

Ergot, rye ergot, or secale cornutum was formerly defined in the official compendia as the dried sclerotium of *Claviceps purpurea* (Fries) Tulasne (Fam. Clavicipitaceae) developed on plants of rye, *Secale cereale* Linné (Fam. Gramineae). Ergot was required to yield not less than 0.15% of the total alkaloids of ergot calculated as ergotoxine and water-soluble alkaloids equivalent to not less than 0.01% of ergonovine.

The generic name, *Claviceps*, refers to the clublike character of the sclerotium; *purpurea* refers to its purple color. Because these sclerotia are long and somewhat pointed, the common name of **spurred rye** has been applied to the drug.

At present, ergot alkaloids are obtained on a commercial scale from both parasitic and saprophytic sources. The former is the dried sclerotium of *C. purpurea* developed on rye plants. Some alkaloids are also obtained from the fermentation broth in which the mycelium of selected strains of *Claviceps paspali* Stevens & Hall has been grown saprophytically in submerged culture.

The qualitative and quantitative composition of the alkaloids obtained from either source is influenced by a number of factors, but especially by the identity of the strain (chemical race) of organism involved. At present, both peptide alkaloids and nonpeptide (water-soluble) alkaloids are obtained from parasitically developed ergot sclerotia. Only the latter type is produced commercially in saprophytic culture. However, lysergic acid produced by fermentation is converted on a commercial scale to the peptide alkaloid ergotamine by chemical semisynthesis.

Some knowledge of the rather complex life cycle of the ergot fungus is required to understand the different methods of production of the alkaloids. In nature, the organism is parasitic. In the spring, one of its spores comes into contact with the ovary of a grass, frequently rye, where it germinates, forming hyphal strands that penetrate into the host tissue. The hyphae eventually form a mass of tissue known as a **mycelium**, which supplants the ovary. Some of the hyphal strands produce asexual spores, known as conidiospores, which become suspended in a viscous, sugary liquid known as honeydew. Honeydew is secreted by the mycelium. Insects are attracted to this honeydew and carry it and the spores to other host plants, where the process is repeated. This stage of development of the organism is termed the asexual or **sphacelial stage**.

In the second stage of development, the mycelium eventually replaces the entire ovary, then gradually hardens, becomes dark purple, and forms a resting body, known as a **sclerotium**. The sclerotium, in turn, normally falls to the ground, overwinters, and in the spring, produces sexual spores (ascospores) that repeat the entire cycle. This second phase of development of the organism is referred to as the sexual or **ascigerous stage**.

When ergot spores are germinated in a suitable nutrient medium in the laboratory (saprophytic growth), hyphae are formed. The hyphae produce mycelium and conidiospores, but no further development occurs. Because the medicinally useful alkaloids are normally produced only during the latter stages of parasitic sclerotial development, the difficulties in producing them in saprophytic mycelial culture are apparent.

Before the introduction of modern agricultural practices, the fungus periodically invaded rye fields in Russia and in other European countries, and the ergot sclerotia were harvested with the rye grains. Rye flour made from the contaminated rye grains was subsequently made into rye bread and ingested. Thus, the fungus was responsible for severe outbreaks of a poisoning, both in humans and in cattle, which is today known as ergotism. One form of ergotism, common in parts of France, was characterized by the appearance of gangrene in the extremities. The gangrene was caused by the restricted blood flow resulting from the vasoconstrictor action of the ergot alkaloids. The second type, which frequently occurred east of the Rhine in Germany, was characterized by convulsions. Although the factors responsible for the different types of ergotism have not been completely clarified, it is believed that the convulsive variety is associated with a dietary deficiency of vitamin A. Before the causative agent was known, gangrenous ergotism was often referred to as "St. Anthony's fire." As early as 1582, the drug was known to promote uterine contractions.

Currently, ergot is cultivated in Germany, Switzerland, and eastern Europe. Entire fields of rye are utilized for this purpose. Prior to fertilization, the flowers of the plants are artificially inoculated with conidiospores of *Claviceps purpurea*. Different types of inoculative apparatus are employed. A small hand-operated puncture board studded with eyed or grooved needles that are dipped into a spore suspension before application to the rye inflorescence is the simplest device but requires an adequate supply of inexpensive labor. The same principle is utilized in motor-driven machines with needle-studded inoculating rollers that are mounted on the front of tractors and are capable of inoculating 5 to 7 acres of rye per day.

Cultured conidiospores are utilized for the inoculum. Much effort has been devoted to the isolation, development, and selection of the best strains of *C. purpurea* for field cultivation. Strains capable of producing about 0.35% of selected alkaloids, principally ergotamine, are now employed.

Approximately 6 weeks after inoculation, the mature sclerotia are harvested. They may be picked by hand or collected by machines developed especially for this purpose in Hungary and Germany. Sclerotia not collected in these ways can be harvested with the grain and separated after threshing by sieving, by specific gravity, or by electrostatic attraction processes. Ergot must be dried immediately after collection and stored properly to prevent deterioration.

Large-scale production of lysergic acid derivatives in submerged culture was achieved in 1960. An artificially virulented strain of *C. paspali* Stevens & Hall, which produced several simple lysergic acid derivatives, especially (+)-lysergic acid methylcarbinolamide, in stirred fermenters containing a suitable medium, was utilized. The alkaloids obtained can be converted to lysergic acid, which is utilized for the semisynthesis of ergonovine and ergotamine. Ergot alkaloids are derived biosynthetically from a combination of tryptophan and acetate metabolism. Studies with various physiologic strains of *Claviceps* species, including some significant stereospecific experiments, have clarified many of the key steps leading to the biosynthesis of the lysergic acid nucleus. Dimethylallyl pyrophosphate condenses at the 4-position of tryptophan as an initial step in the pathway (Fig. 9-10). The next intermediate arises from the N-methylation of dimethylallyltryptophan to give N_α-methyldimethylallyltryptophan. The next anticipated step would be decarboxylation, with a subsequent formation of chanoclavine I. The number of intermediates and enzymatic conversions in these events is still unknown. Concerning the biosynthetic mechanism of alkaloid formation, these is evidence that two *cis-trans* isomerizations in the isoprenoid moiety take place in the course of forming the tetracyclic ring system. If the *trans* methyl group of dimethylallylpyrophosphate is radioactively labeled, the *cis* methyl group of chanoclavine I will be labeled indicating one *cis-trans* isomerization, and the *trans* methyl group of the isoprenoid moiety of agroclavine will be labeled indicating a second isomerization. Agroclavine undergoes stepwise oxidation to elymoclavine and eventually to lysergic acid. The carboxyl group of lysergic acid forms a peptide linkage with an amino group of a variety of amino acids or peptide residues to yield the therapeutically useful ergot alkaloids.

Synthesis of lysergic acid derivatives and clavine alkaloids in higher plants *(Ipomoea* spe-

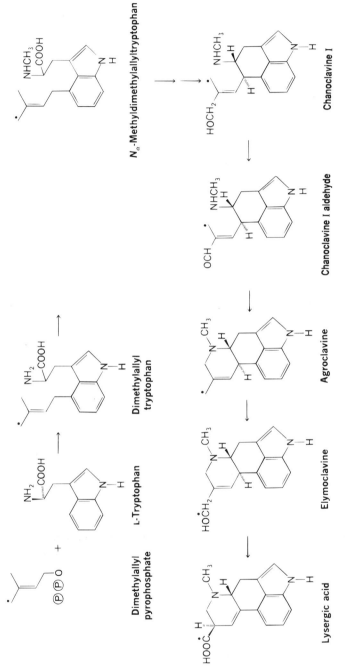

Fig. 9–10. Biosynthesis of lysergic acid.

cies) apparently takes place from the same precursors.

Ergot contains or produces a large number of alkaloids, the most important of which are ergonovine, ergotamine, and a mixture of ergocristine, ergokryptine, and ergocornine that has been marketed for many years under the name, ergotoxine. The alkaloids are often separated into two groups based on their solubility in water. Ergonovine is the principal component of the water-soluble fraction. Ergotamine and the ergotoxine group are water-insoluble and are often referred to as peptide alkaloids. Significant semisynthetic alkaloids include methylergonovine, dihydroergotamine, ergoloid mesylates, methysergide, and LSD.

The medicinally useful alkaloids, either natural or semisynthetic, are all derivatives of (+)-lysergic acid. Because that compound is readily converted to its isomer, (+)-isolysergic acid, the corresponding isolysergic acid derivatives often accompany the (+)-lysergic acid alkaloids in the plant material or are produced during the course of extraction. Isolysergic acid derivatives are practically physiologically inert. They are named by inserting an additional syllable, -in, in the name of the corresponding lysergic acid derivatives, e.g., ergotamine-ergotaminine.

Ergot Alkaloids

Ergonovine maleate or ergometrine maleate occurs as a white or faintly yellow, odorless, microcrystalline powder. It is affected by light and is readily soluble in water but less soluble in alcohol.

The alkaloid was discovered almost simultaneously in 1935 by five independent research groups, and it was assigned four different names. To resolve the conflict, a fifth name, ergonovine, was officially adopted in the United States. That title has not been accepted elsewhere. Ergometrine is used in practically all other countries, except Switzerland, where ergobasine is preferred. Establishment of a clear-cut priority is difficult, but based on the first isolation of a pure compound, it probably should be awarded to ergobasine. Even in the United States, the accepted chemical name of the isolysergic acid isomer of ergonovine is ergometrinine.

Because of its ready solubility in water, this alkaloid has marked advantages over the other ergot alkaloids (Fig 9-11). The oxytocic effect of the drug, either orally, subcutaneously, or intramuscularly, is sometimes noted within 5 minutes after giving the dose, and its effect is more marked than that of either ergotoxine or ergotamine. However, the vasoconstrictor action is much less marked.

Ergonovine maleate (Ergotrate maleate) is an oxytocic and produces much faster stimulation of the uterine muscles than do other ergot alkaloids. The gravid uterus is very sensitive to this effect, and small doses of alkaloid can be given immediately postpartum to increase the frequency and amplitude of uterine contractions as well as to increase the basal tone of the uterine smooth muscle, resulting in a decrease in blood loss from the postpartum uterus.

Methylergonovine maleate is a semisynthetic homolog of ergonovine prepared from lysergic acid and 2-aminobutanol. It occurs as a white to pinkish tan microcrystalline powder.

Methylergonovine maleate is an oxytocic reputed to be slightly more active and longer acting than ergonovine.

Ergotamine tartrate occurs as colorless crystals or as a white, crystalline powder, sparingly soluble in water or in alcohol. Ergotamine possesses oxytocic properties, but it is not employed for that effect. It is used to prevent or abort vascular headaches, including migraine and cluster headaches. The mechanism of action is probably direct vasoconstriction of the dilated carotid artery bed with a concomitant decrease in the amplitude of pulsations. It may inhibit receptor uptake of norepinephrine at sympathetic nerve endings, increasing the vasoconstrictive action, and the drug is also an antagonist of serotonin activity.

Ergotamine tartrate is used with caffeine for the treatment of migraine headache. Both act as cerebral vasoconstrictors; caffeine is believed to enhance the action of ergotamine.

Dihydroergotamine mesylate is the salt of a semisynthetic alkaloid prepared from ergotamine by hydrogenation of the Δ^9 double bond in the lysergic acid nucleus. Dihydroergotamine is employed in the treatment of migraine because it is more effective and better tolerated than the parent alkaloid.

Ergotoxine was formerly employed as a reference standard in the form of ergotoxine ethanesulfonate, which was discontinued because it was a variable mixture of three closely related alkaloids, ergocristine, ergokryptine, and ergocornine. A mixture of equal parts of these

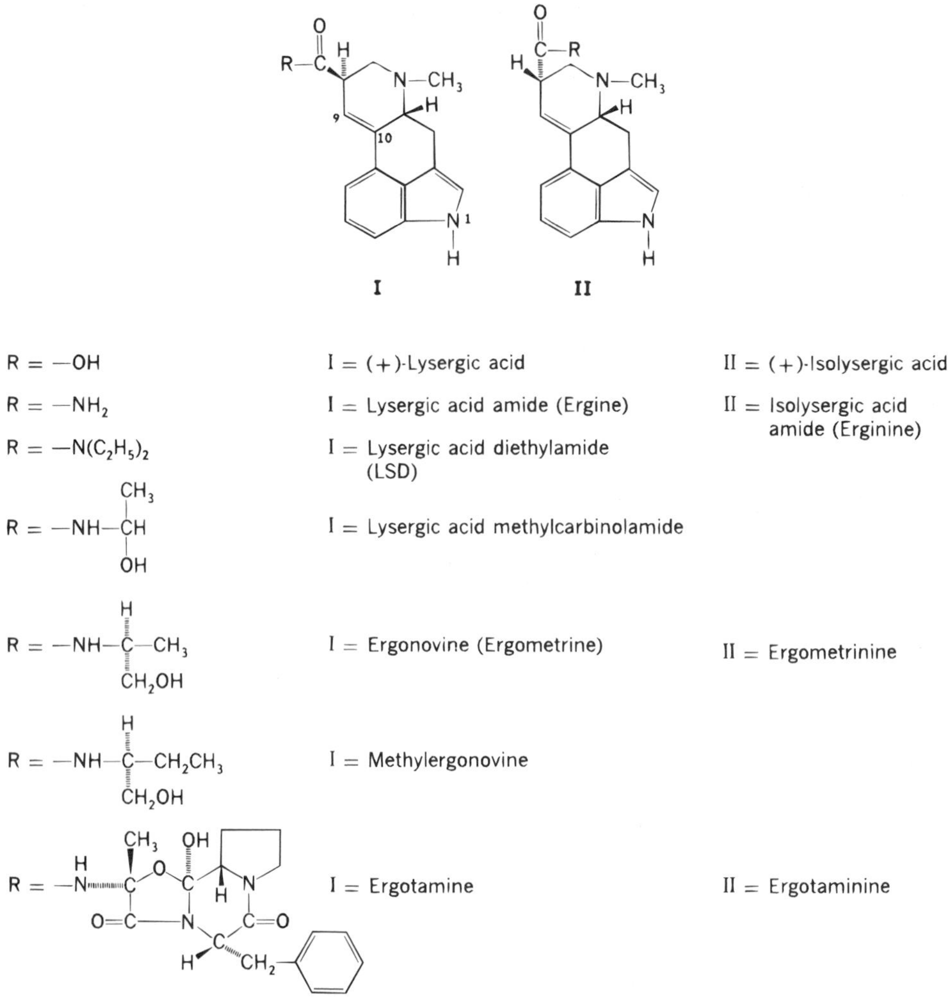

R = —OH   I = (+)-Lysergic acid   II = (+)-Isolysergic acid

R = —NH$_2$ I = Lysergic acid amide (Ergine)   II = Isolysergic acid amide (Erginine)

R = —N(C$_2$H$_5$)$_2$ I = Lysergic acid diethylamide (LSD)

R = —NH—CH(CH$_3$)OH   I = Lysergic acid methylcarbinolamide

R = —NH—C(H)(CH$_3$)CH$_2$OH   I = Ergonovine (Ergometrine)   II = Ergometrinine

R = —NH—C(H)(CH$_2$CH$_3$)CH$_2$OH   I = Methylergonovine

R = (cyclic peptide structure)   I = Ergotamine   II = Ergotaminine

Fig. 9–11. Structural relationships of ergot alkaloids.

component alkaloids is hydrogenated to eliminate the Δ^9 double bond of the lysergic acid nucleus and to yield an equivalent mixture of dihydroergocristine, dihydroergokryptine, and dihydroergocornine. The methanesulfonates of this mixture, known as **ergoloid mesylates**, are marketed for the relief of symptoms of idiopathic decline in mental capacity in geriatric individuals. They produce vasorelaxation, increased cerebral blood flow, lowering of systemic blood pressure, and bradycardia.

Methysergide maleate is the salt of methylergonovine that has an additional methyl group attached to the nitrogen at position 1 of the lysergic acid nucleus. It is prepared by semisynthesis from lysergic acid. Methysergide is a serotonin antagonist employed in the prophylaxis of vascular headache.

The patient should be advised to take medication with meals and to notify the physician if cold, numb, or painful hands, leg cramps, abdominal or chest pain, or change in skin color occurs.

Lysergic acid diethylamide or LSD does not occur in nature but is prepared by semisynthesis. The compound has a two-fold action, producing a predominant central sympathetic stimulation that parallels a slight depression. Discovered by A. Hofmann in 1943 during the course of experiments directed toward the synthesis of analeptics, it is the most active and most specific psychotomimetic agent known. The effective oral dose in humans is 30 to 50 μg. LSD is of considerable interest and value in experimental psychiatry. Because of widespread misuse, the drug is available, at this writing, only to qualified scientific investigators.

Drugs Related to Ergot. The active principals of **ololiuqui**, an ancient Aztec hallucinogenic drug still used in Mexico for magicoreligious purposes, have been identified as ergot alkaloids. Seeds of ololiuqui, *Rivea corymbosa* (Linné) Hallier filius (Fam. Convolvulaceae), as well as certain closely related *Ipomoea* species (commonly known as morning glories) and *Argyreia* species, contain up to about 0.05% of total alkaloids. (+)-Lysergic acid amide (ergine), the principal psychotomimetic compound in these species, is accompanied by (+)-isolysergic acid (erginine), ergonovine, (+)-lysergic acid methylcarbinolamide, and certain clavine alkaloids.

Many of these morning glories are widely cultivated ornamentals. The ready availability of their seeds has led to misuse by individuals who ingest the seeds to experience hallucinations. Needless to say, the practice is dangerous because of the extreme potency of the active principals.

Occurrence of the biosynthetically complex ergot alkaloids in both fungi and higher plants is unusual and of considerable chemotaxonomic interest. Aside from *Claviceps* species and the members of the Convolvulaceae, ergot alkaloids have been reported only in a few other fungi—*Aspergillus fumigatus, Balansia cyperi, B. obtecta, Penicillium chermesinum, P. gorlenkoanum, P. kapuscinskii, P. roquefortii, Rhizopus arrhizus,* and *Sphacelia typhina.* Only clavine alkaloids were detected in many of these species.

IMIDAZOLE ALKALOIDS

The imidazole (glyoxaline) ring is the principal nucleus in pilocarpine from pilocarpus. Pilocarpine is a monoacidic tertiary base containing a lactone group as well as the imidazole nucleus. Obvious structural similarities suggest that this alkaloid probably is formed from histidine or a metabolic equivalent, but experimental confirmation of such a biosynthetic origin is lacking.

Pilocarpus and pilocarpine are the important drugs of this group.

Pilocarpine

Pilocarpus or jaborandi consists of the leaflets of *Pilocarpus jaborandi* Holmes (Pernam-

buco jaborandi), or of *P. pinnatifolius* Lamaire (Paraguay jaborandi) (Fam. Rutaceae). The plants are shrubs indigenous to Brazil.

All of the commercial kinds of pilocarpus, when freshly dried, yield from 0.5 to 1% of the alkaloid pilocarpine. Isopilocarpine, pilocarpidine, and pilosine are also present in some of the species. Even under ideal storage conditions, the leaves lose at least half of their alkaloidal content in 1 year through deterioration. Leaves that are 2 years old are practically worthless.

Pilocarpine

Pilocarpine is the lactone of pilocarpic acid, an acid with a glyoxaline nucleus. It is an oily, syrupy liquid, though its salts crystallize easily. It may be obtained by treating the powdered leaves with sodium carbonate, extracting with benzene, and then shaking the benzene extract with dilute hydrochloric or nitric acid. The aqueous solution is then made alkaline and shaken with chloroform; the chloroform solution is then shaken with acid, and the alkaloidal salt is allowed to crystallize.

Pilocarpine directly stimulates the muscarinic receptors in the eye, causing constriction of the pupil and contraction of the ciliary muscle. In narrow-angle glaucoma, miosis opens the anterior chamber angle to improve the outflow of aqueous humor. In chronic open-angle glaucoma, the increase in outflow is independent of the miotic effect. Contraction of the ciliary muscle enhances the outflow of aqueous humor via indirect effects on the trabecular system.

Pilocarpine hydrochloride is the hydrochloride of an alkaloid obtained from the dried leaflets of *Pilocarpus jaborandi* or of *P. microphyllus.* It is hygroscopic.

Pilocarpine nitrate is the nitrate of the alkaloid. It is stable in air but is affected by light.

Pilocarpine hydrochloride occurs as colorless, translucent, odorless, faintly bitter crystals; pilocarpine nitrate occurs as shiny, white crystals.

Both pilocarpine hydrochloride and pilocarpine nitrate are cholinergic (ophthalmic) drugs used in the treatment of glaucoma. They are applied topically, as a 0.25 to 10% solution of pilocarpine hydrochloride or as a 0.5 to 6% solution of pilocarpine nitrate to the conjunctiva. The patient should be advised to wash hands immediately after application. Pilocarpine is also available in an ocular therapeutic system that provides continuous release over one week following placement in the conjunctival cul-de-sac.

STEROIDAL ALKALOIDS

The steroidal alkaloids are derived biosynthetically from six isoprene units and could be classified as triterpenoids or steroids; however, they also contain nitrogen giving them basic properties. The nitrogen may be part of a ring system, usually incorporated at a late stage in biosynthesis, or it may be as an *N*-methyl substituted amino group. Steroidal alkaloids have been found in the plant families Apocynaceae, Buxaceae, Liliaceae, and Solanaceae.

The important drugs of this group are veratrum viride and veratrum album.

Veratrum Viride

Veratrum viride, American or green hellebore, consists of the dried rhizome and roots of *Veratrum viride* Aiton (Fam. Liliaceae).

Veratrum is from the Latin *vere,* meaning truly, and *ater,* meaning black. *Viride* is Latin and means green. The drug was known to the Indians, who probably introduced its use to the early settlers. The plant grows in wet meadows in the mountainous sections of New England and the eastern United States, North Carolina, Tennessee, and northern Georgia. Most of the commercial drug is collected in New York State and eastern Canada. The rhizomes are dug, cleaned, cut longitudinally, and dried.

Veratrum viride contains a large number of alkaloids customarily classified in three groups on the basis of their chemical constitution. Group I, consisting of esters of the steroidal bases (alkamines) with organic acids, includes cevadine, germidine, germitrine, neogermitrine, neoprotoveratrine, protoveratrine, and veratridine. Group II includes pseudojervine and veratrosine, which are glucosides of the alkamines. The alkamines themselves—germine, jervine, rubijervine, and veratramine—compose group III. The ester alkaloids, germidine and germitrine, are probably the most important therapeutically. The complexity and relative instability of these constituents account for the problems encountered in the biologic standardization of this drug.

Veratrum viride possesses hypotensive, cardiac-depressant, and sedative properties. It has been used in the treatment of hypertension. Small doses principally affect blood pressure without notably changing respiratory or cardiac rate. The drug has its most uniform effects in small doses.

White hellebore or European hellebore is the dried rhizome of *Veratrum album*, Linné (Fam. Liliaceae). It is similar to *V. viride* but is indigenous to central and southern Europe. White hellebore is similar in appearance and structure to green hellebore, but the external color is much lighter.

The drug contains a complex mixture of ester alkaloids, glycoalkaloids, and alkamines similar, and in some cases identical, to those occurring in veratrum viride. Two ester alkaloids, protoveratrine A and protoveratrine B, are the most active. On hydrolysis, both yield protoverine, acetic acid, methylbutyric acid, and methylhydroxybutyric acid (in protoveratrine A) or methyldihydroxybutyric acid (in protoveratrine B).

White hellebore possesses hypotensive properties, but the crude drug is not used therapeutically. Both white and green hellebores are also employed as insecticides.

ALKALOIDAL AMINES

The alkaloids in this group do not contain heterocyclic nitrogen atoms. Many are simple derivatives of phenylethylamine and, as such, are derived from the common amino acids, phenylalanine or tyrosine. Some of the alkaloids in this category whose biosynthesis has been studied utilizing labeled precursors include mescaline in the peyote cactus (*Lophophora williamsii*), ephedrine in *Ephedra distachya,* cathinone in the khat plant (*Catha edulis*), and colchicine in the autumn crocus (*Colchicum autumnale*).

In the biosynthesis of colchicine, ring A and five carbon atoms of the seven-membered ring B of colchicine derive from phenylalanine (Fig. 9-12). Tyrosine cannot replace phenylalanine as a precursor for this part of the molecule. Radioactivity from tyrosine-3-^{14}C is incorporated into the C-12 position of the tropolone ring C. Many of the details of the biosynthetic pathway are unknown; a phenethylisoquinoline intermediate is suspected, and androcymbine

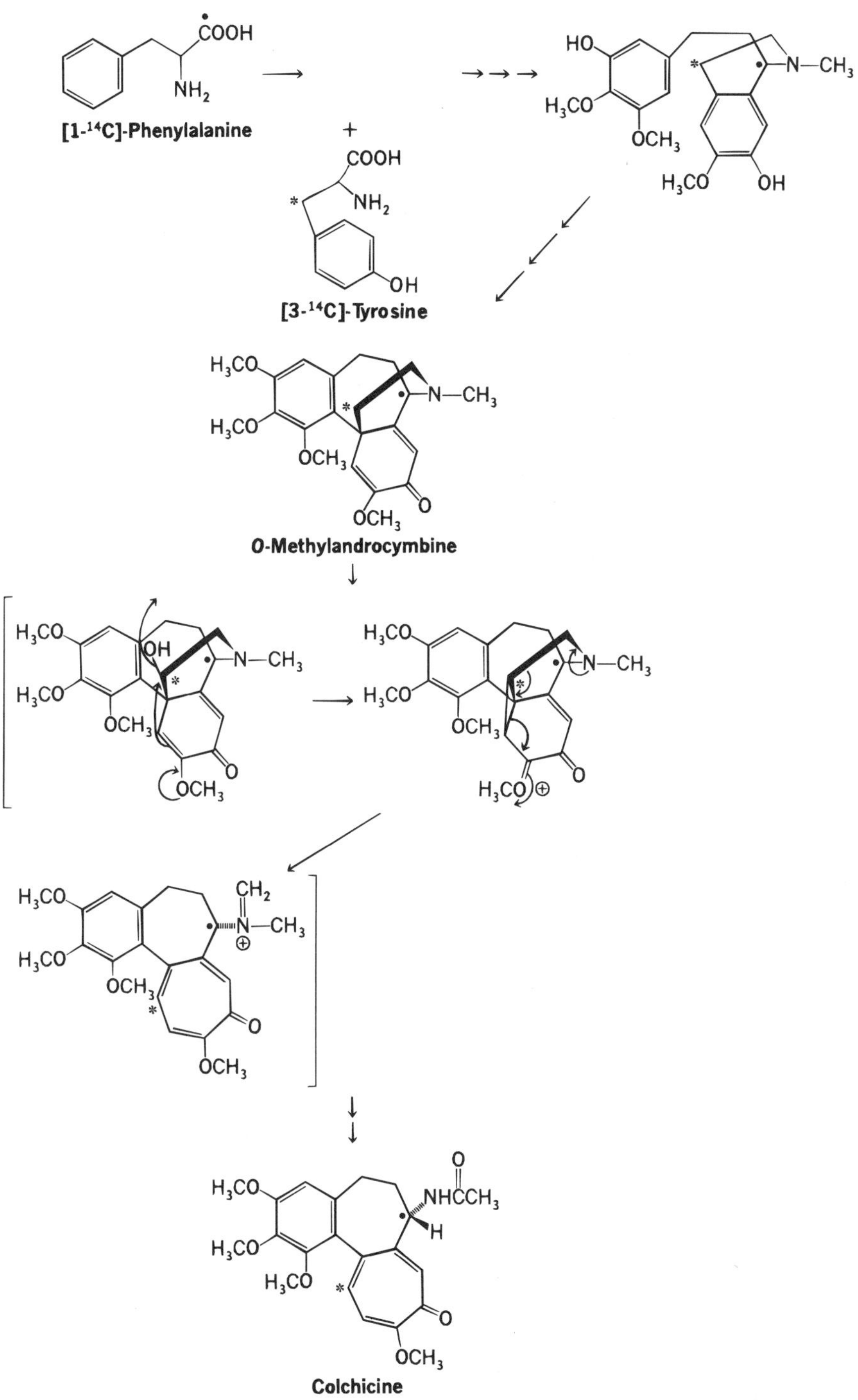

Fig. 9–12. Biosynthetic incorporation of phenylalanine and tyrosine into colchicine.

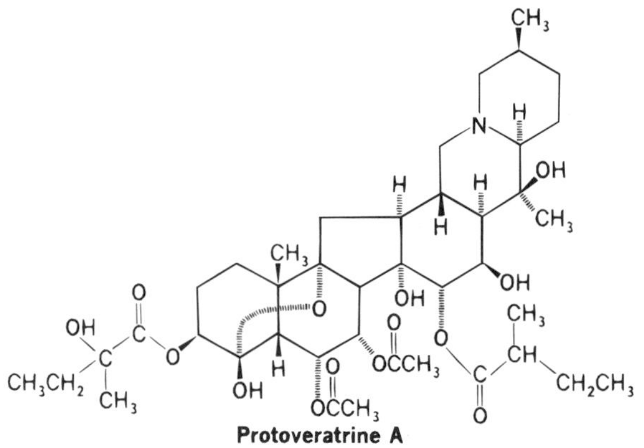

Protoveratrine A

also occurs in *Colchicum*. Labeled acetate is readily incorporated into the acetyl group of the molecule, presumably during a terminal phase of biosynthesis.

Other alkaloidal amines are tryptamine derivatives and, as such, are biosynthesized from tryptophan. Examples include gramine in *Hordeum vulgare*, psilocybin in the Mexican hallucinogenic mushroom, *Psilocybe semperviva*, and serotonin and bufotenine in a number of plant and animal species.

The drugs and their alkaloids classified as alkaloidal amines are ephedra, ephedrine, colchicum seed, colchicum corm, colchicine, khat, and peyote.

Ephedrine

Ephedra or ma huang is the entire plant or the overground portion of *Ephedra sinica* Stapf (Fam. Gnetaceae). In Chinese characters, "ma" means astringent and "huang" means yellow, probably referring to the taste and color of the drug. It has been used as a medicine in China for more than 5000 years. Its use in modern medicine began in 1923 with the discovery of the valuable properties of ephedrine. The plant is found near the seacoast in southern China, and this source formerly supplied most of the American market. At the present time, northwestern India and Pakistan represent the areas from which ephedra is obtained.

The plant is a low, dioecious, practically leafless shrub that grows 60 to 90 cm high. The stem is green, slender, erect, small ribbed, and channeled. It is 1.5 mm in diameter and usually terminates in a sharp point. At the nodes, which are 4 to 6 cm apart, the leaves appear as whitish, triangular, scarious sheaths. Small blossoms appear in the summer.

Ephedrine or (−)-*erythro*-α-[1-(methylami-

no)ethyl]benzyl alcohol is an alkaloid produced commercially either by the extraction of plant material (*Ephedra* spp.) or by a chemical procedure involving a reductive condensation between L-1-phenyl-1-acetylcarbinol and methylamine. This yields L-ephedrine essentially free from the D-isomer. The carbinol precursor used in the reaction is produced biosynthetically by the fermentative action of brewer's yeast on benzaldehyde.

Ephedrine occurs as white, rosette or needle crystals, or as an unctuous mass. It is soluble in water, alcohol, chloroform, ether, and in liquid petrolatum. The latter solution is turbid if the ephedrine is not dry.

Ephedrine is a potent sympathomimetic that stimulates alpha, beta$_1$, and beta$_2$ adrenergic receptors. It is believed that β-adrenergic effects result from stimulation of production of cyclic adenosine 3',5'-monophosphate (AMP) by activation of adenyl cyclase, whereas α-adrenergic effects result from inhibition of adenyl cyclase. Ephedrine relaxes bronchial smooth muscle by stimulation of β_2-adrenergic receptors when administered parenterally or orally, and its action on β_1-adrenergic receptors in the heart produces a positive inotropic effect. Its effect on α-adrenergic receptors results in vasoconstriction in the skin and mucous membranes.

In large doses ephedrine may cause hypertension, headache, dizziness, palpitations, vomiting, and because it is a central nervous system stimulant, nervousness and insomnia.

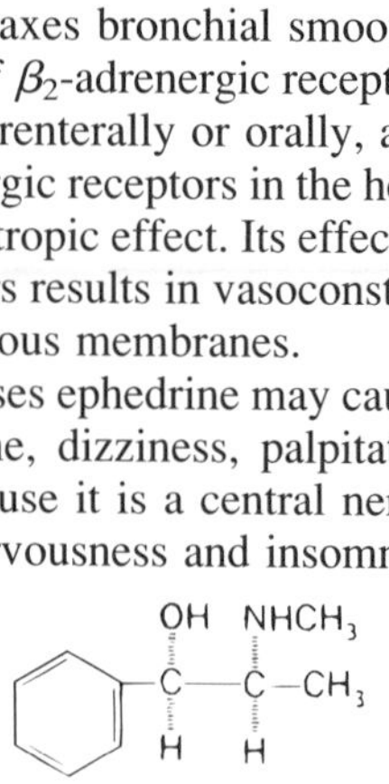

(−)-Ephedrine

Ephedrine sulfate is the sulfate of the alkaloid obtained from the natural sources or prepared synthetically. It occurs as fine, white, odorless crystals or as a powder and darkens when exposed to light. Ephedrine sulfate is used to combat hypotensive states and for allergic disorders, such as bronchial asthma, as well as for local treatment of nasal congestion.

Ephedrine hydrochloride also occurs as fine, white, odorless crystals or as a powder and is affected by light.

It has the same pharmacologic properties as ephedrine and is used as a sympathomimetic. Both of these salts are readily soluble in water and in hot alcohol but not in ether.

Allied Plants. In addition to *Ephedra sinica* (the source of ma huang) and *E. equisetina* Bunge (the chief source of the extracted alkaloid), *E. distachya* Linné also yields ephedrine. These plants grow in northern China, India, and Spain in sandy and clay soil.

Colchicine

Colchicum seed is the dried, ripe seed of *Colchicum autumnale* Linné (Fam. Liliaceae). **Colchicum corm** is the dried corm of the same species.

The genus name is from Colchis on the Black Sea, where the plant flourishes; *autumnale* refers to the season when the plant blooms. The plant is cultivated in England, central and southern Europe, and northern Africa, where it grows in moist meadows. It is also cultivated as an ornamental in the United States. Two to six flowers with long perianth tubes develop from the corm buds in the fall (hence, the name **autumn crocus**). The seed is collected in July and August and the corm in the spring before leaf development. Italy and the former Yugoslavia produce most of the supply of the seed and the corm.

Dioscorides mentions *Colchicum*. The Arabs recommended the used of the corm for gout in medieval times, but the drug was abandoned because of its toxicity. It again came into use in Europe about the middle of the 17th century.

Colchicum contains the alkaloid colchicine, up to 0.8% in the seed and 0.6% in the corm.

Colchicine is an alkaloid obtained from various species of *Colchicum*, usually *Colchicum autumnale*. It has also been found in other genera of the lily family. Colchicine has one amido nitrogen atom. The compound lacks pronounced basicity and does not form a well-defined series of salts as do other alkaloids. Nevertheless, it is precipitated by many alkaloid reagents and is conventionally considered an alkaloid. (See Fig. 9-12 for the structural formula.)

Colchicine occurs as pale yellow, amorphous scales or powder that gradually turns darker when exposed to light. It is soluble in water and ether and is freely soluble in alcohol and chloroform.

The exact mechanism of action of colchicine in the treatment of gout is not known. It does inhibit leukocyte migration and reduces lactic acid production by leukocytes which results in a decreased deposition of uric acid. In addition, there is a reduction in phagocytosis which decreases the inflammatory response. Colchicine is used as a suppressant for gout.

Colchicine has antimitotic activity. In its presence the chromosomes of the cell will continue to divide without the formation of spindle fibers and subsequent cell division to form daughter cells. Any numeric change in chromosome number in a cell entails a mutation that becomes evident in a number of the characteristics of the experimental plant. New varieties of plants of economic and pharmacognostic value may result from further research. The interrelationship between the action of colchicine and mitosis is being investigated in animals; preliminary experiments show that injections of colchicine can affect the dispersal of tumors; thus, it has been employed experimentally in the treatment of various neoplastic diseases.

Other Alkaloidal Amine Drugs

Khat or Abyssinian tea consists of the fresh leaves of *Catha edulis* Forskal (Fam. Celastraceae). The plant is a small tree or shrub native to tropical East Africa. It is cultivated extensively in the Ethiopian highlands near Harar and to a lesser extent in other parts of East Africa, in South Africa, and Yemen. Fresh leaves are regularly transported by air to areas distant from the centers of cultivation.

The leaves are chewed habitually by many people in East African and the Arabian countries to alleviate the sensations of hunger and fatigue. Authorities disagree as to the safety of the practice. The Expert Committee on Addiction-Producing Drugs of the World Health Organization does not classify khat as a drug that produces habituation or addiction, but the French government considers it a narcotic. Regardless, khat-chewing is a theologically accepted and lawful custom in Arabian and African countries today.

Khat contains a potent phenylalkylamine alkaloid called (−)-cathinone. It has pharmacologic properties analogous to those of (+)-amphetamine and is of similar potency with a similar mechanism of action, namely, the induction of catecholamine release from storage sites. The young, fresh leaves that come from the tips of the branches contain the optimum amount of cathinone. In older leaves, it is converted to the weakly active compounds (+)-norpseudoephedrine (80%) and (−)-norephedrine (20%). This conversion also occurs rapidly during the drying of young leaves.

(−)-Cathinone

Peyote or mescal buttons consist of the dried tops of *Lophophora williamsii* (Lemaire) Coulter (Fam. Cactaceae), growing in northern Mexico and the southwestern United States. The main axis of the plant lies beneath the ground, and from it arise a number of aerial shoots that are button-shaped or disklike and reach 20 to 50 mm in diameter. In the center of each disk are a tuft of hairs and usually one or more pink flowers.

This plant has been associated with Indian ceremonies for many years. It disturbs normal mental function and causes concomitant hallucinations and euphoria. Ingestion of mescal buttons results in mydriasis accompanied by unusual and bizarre color perception. Flashing lights and vivid configurations characterize the visions at first; later, the colors become dim and the subjects become drowsy; eventually, sleep is produced. The drug contains several alkaloids, including mescaline (the most active of the peyote constituents), anhalanine, anhalamine, and anhalidine. Mescaline (3,4,5,-trimethoxy-β-phenylethylamine) also occurs in other cacti, e.g., *Trichocereus* species, or it may be produced synthetically.

Mescaline

Mescaline is regarded as the first of a series of hallucinogens or psychotomimetics. Others are psilocybin (obtained from the mushroom *Psilocybe mexicana* Heim) and lysergic acid diethylamide (LSD). All of these drugs have proved valuable in experimental psychiatry.

PURINE BASES

The purines are derivatives of a heterocyclic nucleus consisting of the 6-membered pyrimidine ring fused to the 5-membered imidazole ring. Purine itself does not occur in nature, but numerous derivatives are biologically significant. The pharmaceutically important bases of this group are all methylated derivatives of 2,6-dioxypurine (xanthine). Caffeine is 1,3,7-trimethylxanthine, theophylline is 1,3-dimethylxanthine, and theobromine is 3,7-dimethylxanthine.

The methylxanthines competitively inhibit phosphodiesterase, which results in an increase of cyclic adenosine monophosphate with a subsequent release of endogenous epinephrine. This results in a direct relaxation of the smooth muscles of the bronchi and pulmonary blood vessels, a stimulation of the central nervous system, an induction of diuresis, an increase in gastric acid secretion, an inhibition of uterine contractions, and a weak positive chronotropic and inotropic effect on the heart.

Caffeine is synthesized from the same precursors in *Coffea arabica* as are the purine bases in all other biologic systems that have been investigated. Carbon atoms 2 and 8 derive either from formate or from any compound that can give rise to an active 1-carbon fragment (serine, glycine, formaldehyde, and methanol). These same compounds, as well as methionine, are active precursors of the *N*-methyl groups of the molecule. Carbon atom 6 is derived from carbon dioxide, and carbons 4 and 5, together with the nitrogen at 7, are derived from glycine. The nitrogen atom at position 1 derives from aspartic acid, but those in positions 3 and 9 originate from the amide nitrogen of glutamine.

The drugs of this group are coffee, caffeine, guarana, kola, maté, tea, theophylline, cocoa, and theobromine.

Caffeine

Caffeine-Containing Drugs

Kola, cola, or kolanuts is the dried cotyledon of *Cola nitida* (Ventenat) Schott et Endlicher, or of other species of *Cola* (Fam. Sterculiaceae). It yields not less than 1% of anhydrous caffeine. Kolanut is important because of its caffeine content and its flavor. Its principal use in the United States is in the manufacture of nonalcoholic beverages. In the tropical countries where it grows, the fresh nut is chewed as a stimulant, similar to the betel nut. *C. nitida* is a large tree indigenous to West Africa between Sierra Leone and the Congo. It is also cultivated in East Africa, Sri Lanka, Indonesia, Brazil, and the West Indies, particularly in Jamaica. The commercial supplies come chiefly from cultivated plants that grow in West Africa and in the West Indies.

Kolanuts in Jamaica are harvested twice a year when the pods ripen (May and June and again in October and November). The chocolate-colored pods, which range from 5 to 10 cm in length, are shaken from the tree and gathered immediately. The seeds are removed from the pods, and the outer coat is cut off, exposing the bare cotyledons. These cotyledons are then carefully graded because only sound cotyledons do not deteriorate quickly. Fresh kolanuts tend to mold and spoil rather easily; they must be transported to the markets quickly for local consumption. Kolanuts prepared for shipment to the United States are split in half, dried in the sun, and shipped in bags.

Kolanuts contain caffeine, up to 3.5%, and theobromine, less that 1%. In the fresh nuts, these purine derivatives are bound to the tannin kolacatechin. During the drying process, the complex is split, yielding free caffeine and theobromine and converting the colorless kolacatechin to the red-brown kola red.

Kola possesses the central stimulating action of caffeine. It is an ingredient in several carbonated beverages.

Coffee bean or coffee seed is the dried, ripe seed of *Coffea arabica* Linné or *C. liberica* Hiern (Fam. Rubiacae), deprived of most of the seed coat.

Roasted coffee is coffee roasted until it acquires a dark brown color and develops the characteristic aroma.

The plants are small evergreen trees or shrubs with lanceolate, acuminate, entire, slightly coriaceous, dark green, short petiolate leaves, which are partly united with the short interpetiolar stipules at the base. The name *Coffea* is from the Turkish *gahveh* or the Arabic gahuah, the name of a beverage. The coffee plant is indigenous to Ethiopia and other parts of eastern Africa and is widely cultivated in tropical countries, notably in Indonesia, Sri Lanka, and Central and South America, particularly Brazil. The yield from one tree is between 0.5 and 5 kg.

The fruit is a small spheroidal or ellipsoidal drupe with two locules, each containing one seed or coffee bean. There are two methods of freeing the seeds from the parchmentlike endocarp: (1) the fruits are allowed to dry and are then broken, and (2) the wet method in which the sarcocarp is removed by means of a machine, and the two seeds with the parchmentlike endocarp are allowed to dry in such a manner as to undergo a fermentation; after drying, the endocarp is removed. The green seeds are sent into commerce and roasted.

Coffee seeds contain from 1 to 2% of caffeine; about 0.25% of trigonelline (N-methylbetaine of nicotinic acid); from 3 to 5% of tannin; about 15% of glucose and dextrin; 10 to 13% of a fatty oil consisting chiefly of trioleoylglycerol and tripalmitoylglycerol; and 10 to 13% of proteins.

When the coffee is roasted, the seeds swell, change in color to dark brown, and develop the characteristic odor and flavor. The aroma is caused by an oil known as caffeol, consisting of about 50% furfurol with traces of valerianic acid, phenol, and pyridine. It is produced during the roasting process. At the same time, the caffeine is freed from its combination with chlorogenic acid with which it exists in the unroasted seed. The caffeine may be partially sublimed during this roasting process; much of the caffeine of commerce is collected in condensers attached to coffee roasters.

The action of coffee depends principally on the caffeine, which acts on the central nervous system, the kidneys, the muscles, and the heart. However, chlorogenic acid and caffeol are also physiologically active, and some of the unpleasant side effects connected with coffee consumption, at least in certain persons, have been attributed to these constituents. The usual cup of brewed coffee contains about 100 to 150 mg of caffeine, and a cup of instant coffee contains about 85 to 100 mg of caffeine. For comparative purposes of caffeine content, a cup of tea contains 60 to 75 mg; of cocoa, 5 to 40 mg; and 12 oz of cola drink, 40 to 60 mg. The estimated maximum daily dose of caffeine is 1.5 g. Although coffee is mainly a dietetic, it is also a

Purine   Xanthine

Caffeine   Theophylline   Theobromine

stimulant and a diuretic. It is of value in the treatment of poisoning by certain central nervous system depressants.

Decaffeinized coffee is prepared by extracting most of the caffeine from the coffee bean yet retaining the pleasant characteristic aroma of coffee. Such preparations normally contain up to 0.08% of caffeine. Decaffeinized coffee has an extensive American market and brings a higher price than the ordinary roasted coffee.

Guarana is a dried paste composed chiefly of the crushed seed of *Paullinia cupana* Kunth (Fam. Sapindaceae). The plant is a climbing shrub native to Brazil and Uruguay. The seeds are collected by the Indians and roasted over fires for about half a day; the kernels are ground with water to a pasty mass in crude stone mortars and molded into cylindric sticks that are dried in the sun or over fires.

Guarana enters into the preparation of a stimulating beverage that is used like tea and coffee by the people of Brazil. Guarana was introduced into France from South America in 1817, and caffeine (2.5 to 5%) was discovered as its principal constituent in 1840. The drug also contains 25% of tannin (cathechutannic acid).

In recent times, guarana has been extensively promoted as a stimulating drug. Its action is caused by the caffeine present, but it also possesses astringent properties.

Maté or Paraguay tea consists of the leaves of *Ilex paraguariensis* St. Hil. (Fam. Aquifoliaceae). Maté contains caffeine (up to 2%) and tannin. It is used in large doses as a laxative or purgative; it also has diaphoretic and diuretic properties. It is employed in South America in the preparation of a tealike beverage.

Caffeine

Caffeine or 1,3,7-trimethylxanthine occurs in coffee, tea, cacao, guarana, kola, and maté.

Although caffeine can be produced synthetically, it is usually prepared from tea, tea dust, or tea sweepings, or recovered from coffee roasters. Caffeine is anhydrous or contains one molecule of water of hydration.

Caffeine occurs as a white powder or as white, glistening needles matted together in fleecy masses. It has a bitter taste. Caffeine may be sublimed without decomposition when heated.

The solubility of caffeine in water is markedly increased by the presence of citric acid, benzoates, salicylates, and bromides; medicinal compounds of this class are citrated caffeine and caffeine and sodium benzoate. The latter is most suitable for intramuscular injection as an analeptic in the treatment of poisoning, as a stimulant in acute circulatory failure, and as a diuretic.

Caffeine and its related compounds are central nervous system stimulants.

Theophylline

Thea or tea consists of the prepared leaves and leaf buds of *Camellia sinensis* (Linné) O. Kuntze (Fam. Theaceae), a shrub or tree with alternate, evergreen leaves. The tea tree is indigenous to eastern Asia and is now extensively cultivated in China, Japan, India, and Indonesia. The generic name is Greek and means goddess; *sinensis* refers to its Chinese origin.

Green tea is prepared in China and Japan by rapidly drying the freshly picked leaves in copper pans over a mild artificial heat. The leaves are often rolled in the palm of the hand as they dry.

Black tea is prepared in Sri Lanka and India by heaping the fresh leaves until fermentation has begun. They are then rapidly dried artificially with heat.

Tea occurs as more or less crumpled, bright green or blackish green masses. Its odor is agreeable and aromatic; its taste is pleasantly astringent and bitter.

Tea contains 1 to 4% of caffeine (theine) and small amounts of adenine, theobromine, theophylline, and xanthine; about 15% of gallotannic acid; and about 0.75% of a yellow volatile oil that is solid at ordinary temperatures and has a strongly aromatic odor and taste.

The stimulating action of tea is essentially that of the contained caffeine; its astringent properties are owing to the tannin content. Tea leaf waste and tea dust represent important sources for the extraction of caffeine.

Theophylline or 1,3-dimethylxanthine is isomeric with theobromine and was first isolated from tea in 1885. It is prepared synthetically from caffeine or by other means. Theophylline occurs as a white, odorless, bitter crystalline powder that is soluble in about 120 parts of water. It is rendered more soluble when combined with basic compounds.

Theophylline and related compounds are utilized principally as smooth muscle relaxants for the symptomatic relief or prevention of bronchial asthma and for the treatment of reversible bronchospasm associated with chronic bronchitis and emphysema. In addition, theophylline possesses diuretic properties.

Theobromine

Theobromine or 3,7-dimethylxanthine is a compound prepared from the dried, ripe seed of *Theobroma cacao* Linné (Fam. Sterculiaceae), or is made synthetically. It occurs as a white, crystalline powder with a bitter taste and sublimes at about 260°C.

The base is slightly soluble in cold water or in alcohol but is readily soluble when mixed with salts that form basic solutions, such as calcium salicylate, sodium acetate, or sodium salicylate.

Theobromine is a diuretic and a smooth muscle relaxant. It has little stimulant action on the central nervous system.

SUGGESTED READINGS

Brossi, A., Manske, R.H.F., eds.: *The Alkaloids*, Vols. XXI-XXV, 26-40. New York, Academic Press, Inc., 1983–1991.

Brossi, A., Cordell, G. A., eds.: *The Alkaloids*, Vol. 41. San Diego, Academic Press, Inc., 1992.

Cordell, G.A.: *Introduction to Alkaloids. A Biogenetic Approach.* New York, John Wiley Sons, Inc., 1981.

Cordell, G. A., ed.: *The Alkaloids*, Vols. 42-45. San Diego, Academic Press, Inc., 1992-1994.

Dey, P.M., Harborne, J.B., eds.: *Methods in Plant Biochemistry,* Vol. 8: *Alkaloids and Sulphur Compounds.* London, Academic Press Limited, 1993.

Emboden, W.: *Narcotic Plants* (revised and enlarged). New York, MacMillan Publishing Co., Inc., 1979.

Glasby, J.S.: *Encyclopedia of the Alkaloids*, Vols. 1-4. New York, Plenum Press, 1975, 1977, and 1983.

Herbert, R.B.: *The Biosynthesis of Secondary Metabolites,* 2nd ed. New York, Chapman and Hall, 1989.

MacGregor, F.E., ed.: *Coca and Cocaine: An Andean Perspective.* Westport, Connecticut, Greenwood Press, 1993.

Manske, R.H.F., ed.: *The Alkaloids* Vols. V-XVI. New York, Academic Press, Inc., 1955-1977.

Manske, R.H.F., Holmes, H.L., eds.: *The Alkaloids,* Vols. I-IV. New York, Academic Press, Inc., 1950-1954.

Manske, R.H.F., Rodrigo, R.G.A., eds.: *The Alkaloids,* Vols. XVII-XX. New York, Academic Press, Inc., 1979-1981.

Mothes, K., Schütte, H.R., Luckner, M., eds,: *Biochemistry of Alkaloids.* Berlin, VEB Deutscher Verlag der Wissenschaften, 1985.

Pelletier, S.W., ed.: *Alkaloids*, Vols. 1-6. New York, John Wiley & Sons, Inc., 1983-1988; Vols. 7-8. New York, Springer-Verlag New York Inc., 1991-1992.

Phillipson, J.D., Roberts, M.F., Zenk, M.H., eds.: *The Chemistry and Biology of Isoquinoline Alkaloids.* Berlin, Springer-Verlag, 1985.

Saxton, J.E.: *The Chemistry of Heterocyclic Compounds: The Monoterpenoid Indole Alkaloids*, Vol 25. Part 4. New York, John Wiley & Sons, Inc., 1983.

Schober, S., Schade, C., eds.: *The Epidemiology of Cocaine Use and Abuse.* Research Monograph 110, Washington DC, U.S. Department of Health and Human Services, U.S. Government Printing Office, 1991.

Schultes, R.E., Hofmann, A.: *The Botany and Chemistry of Hallucinogens*, 2nd ed., Springfield, Charles C. Thomas, 1980.

Southen, I.W., Buckingham, J., eds.: *Dictionary of Alkaloids,* Vols. 1-2. London, Chapman and Hall Ltd., 1989.

Weiss, R.D., Mirin, S.M., Bartel, R.L.: *Cocaine*, 2nd ed., Washington, DC, American Psychiatric Press, Inc., 1994.

10

Proteins and Peptides

Proteins and peptides have been used as drugs for many years, long preceding the biotechnology revolution. However, because of the inaccessibility of human proteins (aside from blood proteins), for the most part, proteins used as drugs prior to the advent of modern biotechnology were derived from microorganisms, animals, and even plant sources. With some exceptions, most of these were used topically because of the antigenicity that resulted from administering foreign proteins systemically. The biotechnology revolution has made it possible to produce and administer human proteins, derived through recombinant technology, as drugs and pharmaceutical agents. Many of the previously used animal, plant, and microbial proteins are still in use today and will be discussed along with the recombinant proteins that are expanding our repertoire of useful therapeutic agents.

Recombinant techniques are also being used to produce some human proteins that previously were derived from human blood because of the increased risk in recent years of transmission of infectious agents, primarily viruses, with the components of human blood. Blood and blood-derived products are intensively screened for several infectious agents, but many practitioners prefer whenever possible to use recombinant proteins that carry no risk of viral contamination. Products that are available both in forms derived from human blood and from recombinant organisms will be identified in the monographs that follow.

Proteins are polymers of amino acids joined together by peptide bonds. The distinction between proteins and peptides is one of length of the amino acid chain and molecular weight and is somewhat arbitrary, but generally polypeptide chains in excess of 50 to 75 amino acids (molecular weight of 5000 daltons to 7500 daltons) are considered proteins instead of peptides. En-

zymes are proteins with catalytic capability and the smallest known enzymes are in the range of 7000 daltons. Proteins will have a secondary and tertiary structure, whereas small peptides may have a primary structure (the sequence of amino acids) but be quite flexible in their secondary and tertiary structure, especially in solution. Many scientists believe peptides assume an active conformation when they bind to their receptors, through interaction with the receptor amino acid functional groups, but are quite flexible prior to binding. The secondary structure of proteins involves the folding of the polypeptide's backbone chain without regard to the conformation of its side chains. The alpha helices, pleated sheets, and turns that make up the secondary structure, are determined by the rotation angles around the C_α-N bonds of the peptide chain and are held by hydrogen bonding between the hydrogen on the N-H group and the carbonyl oxygen of amino acids within the peptide chain being folded (in alpha helices) or between neighboring chains (beta-pleated sheets).

Tertiary structure involves further folding of the amino acid chain, including the alpha helices and beta sheets that have been formed as part of the secondary structure. Tertiary structure will establish the specific conformation of each amino acid side chain. With enzymes, this level of structure provides a catalytically active conformation, which is held by hydrogen bonds, disulfide bonds, hydrophobic interactions, and electrostatic charges. Loss of tertiary structure results in denaturation of the protein and loss of activity. Denaturation can be induced by any condition that disrupts the stabilizing forces such as salts, organic solvents, extremes of pH, heating and freezing, and detergents, although various proteins will have varied sensitivities to different denaturants. Some denaturation is reversible with the protein reassuming an active conformation when the denaturant is removed, but other proteins will be permanently denatured. If a denatured polypeptide chain can interact (aggregate) with other polypeptide chains in its denatured state, it is less likely to renature.

Many proteins have subunits assembled into larger proteins, and the arrangement of the subunits is termed the quaternary structure. The forces that provide for the association of subunits are similar to those providing tertiary structure. However, many multi-subunit proteins associate and dissociate in their quaternary structures reversibly in order to provide regulation of their activities.

Peptides can be synthesized using solid-phase peptide synthesis, which involves covalently coupling amino acids, one at a time, to the *N*-terminus of a growing polypeptide chain that is attached to a solid support. Oligopeptides (up to about 50 amino acid residues) can be efficiently synthesized using current techniques, but longer polypeptides are produced only in small yield because of the cumulative nature of less-than-quantitative yields. For instance, the synthesis of a 100 residue polypeptide will require 198 steps (a coupling step and a deblocking step for each added residue). Even with a 98% efficiency for each step, the overall yield would be 0.98^{198} × 100 or a 1.8% yield. With great attention to chemical detail, higher yields have been obtained, but the limitations are clear. However, a strategy that allows the linkage of several solid phase-synthesized fragments to be joined in solution has yielded some of the longer polypeptides. Recent advances allow substitution of unnatural amino acids and are particularly useful for making analogs of natural peptides with improved properties. Of particular interest are substitutions that decrease the rate of hydrolysis of peptides in the body.

Longer proteins are made by biological means using ribosomal protein synthesis in microbes, human cells, and other tissue culture as discussed in Chapter 2. Although the structure of the protein can be altered using the 20 standard amino acids through manipulation of codons, it is not yet practical to substitute non-natural amino acids. However, research is progressing on ways to charge tRNAs with non-natural amino acids, and the generation of altered peptides (with non-natural amino acids) through ribosomal synthesis may not be many years away.

Although the ability to produce human proteins commercially has decreased the problem of antigenicity in the use of proteins as drugs, it has not completely eliminated antigenicity problems. Proteinaceous products used systemically may still elicit allergenic reactions for several reasons. Contamination with minor amounts of proteins from the producing species and the creation of new epitopes in the therapeutic protein, either through sequence modifications or changes in glycosylation, may cause allergenicity. The body's recognition of a protein as foreign may lead to anaphylaxis or other allergic reactions, but it is often observed as a decrease in efficacy over time as antibodies combine with the protein in the body, making it unavailable for therapeutic effect.

Because of the potential for antigenicity, proteins that are used systemically, i.e., reach the blood stream, must be rigorously purified away from other proteins of the producing organism. The process of extracting the proteins from the cells or organisms in which they were produced and purifying them to homogeneity (the processes are collectively called "downstream processing"), as well as testing to confirm purity, can add significantly to the cost of proteins used as drugs. Proteins that are used in the gastrointestinal tract, topically, or outside the body altogether do not need the same degree of purity and are often used as mixtures of proteins (for examples, see "Malt Extract" and "Pancreatin" below), because that reduces cost and allergenicity is not an issue.

A variety of quality-control tests are applied to each batch of a purified protein to ensure that it is indeed the expected protein in its active conformation. Polyacrylamide gel electrophoresis will confirm that it is the appropriate size (and has not been degraded by proteases or formed covalent dimers or larger polymers); isoelectric focusing (IEF) will confirm that the charge is correct (an incorrect IEF result might indicate mutation of some amino acid residues or deamination of glutamines or asparagines or other chemical changes in amino acids); biological testing will confirm the correct specific activity of the correct protein; high-performance liquid chromatography will confirm the correct lipophilicity, usually indicative of proper folding; capillary electrophoresis will usually detect small contaminant proteins; and if the protein is used as a crystal (e.g., insulin), the crystals will be examined microscopically. Several (though probably not all) of these tests will be applied to a given protein product, and each batch will be tested prior to distribution.

Problems remain in the use of proteins as

drugs—problems with stability, drug delivery, and cost—but despite these problems there is enormous growth in the use of proteins and peptides as drugs. Some of the problems may be eliminated in the future by identifying the elements of a protein that are essential for its activity and synthesizing peptides or peptidomimetics to have the same activity with improved properties, but the realization of this approach is, for the most part, still in the future.

Enzymes are often named in a manner that describes the substrate or the product of the reaction. The suffix "ase" is used generally to designate an enzyme, although some enzyme names end in "in" (e.g., fibrinolysin). For hydrolytic enzymes, the activity will be labeled with the suffix "olytic" (e.g., proteolytic enzymes hydrolyze proteins), and the enzyme common name usually designates the substrate (e.g., collagenase is a proteolytic enzyme that hydrolyzes the specific protein, collagen). There are exceptions to these general rules, especially when generic names are being assigned to enzymes used as drugs. Proenzymes (also called zymogens) are inactive precursors of active enzymes. They are usually designated by the suffix "ogen" attached to the name of the active enzyme (e.g., chymotrypsinogen).

Proteins and peptides used as drugs fit into many therapeutic classes, some of which were available before the developments in biotechnology, and others are new. This chapter is organized by therapeutic classes, with a miscellaneous section added for some protein drugs that are a single entry in a therapeutic class.

DIGESTANTS

Digestion, which occurs throughout the gastrointestinal tract, is mediated by a series of hydrolytic enzymes. Carbohydrates are hydrolyzed into the constituent monosaccharides by carbohydrases; proteins are hydrolyzed into constituent amino acids by proteases; and fats are hydrolyzed into fatty acids and glycerol by lipases. Digestion begins in the mouth with a starch-hydrolyzing carbohydrase (amylase) in the saliva and proceeds through the stomach, where the pH is acidic because of gastric acid and pepsin is the predominant protease. A major component of digestion occurs in the duodenum (small intestine), where the pH is about 8. Most of the enzymes involved—amylase, the proteolytic enzymes chymotrypsin and trypsin, lipase,

nuclease—come from the pancreas in response to hormonal signals. The proteolytic enzymes are secreted as the proenzymes chymotrypsinogen and trypsinogen. Once they reach the duodenum, an enzyme called enterokinase, which is secreted from the duodenal mucosa, activates trypsinogen to trypsin and active trypsin cleaves chymotrypsinogen to yield active chymotrypsin. Some absorption occurs in the small intestine, and additional absorption, particularly of fats, occurs in the large intestine.

Digestive enzymes are used therapeutically, primarily in patients with pancreatic deficiencies. Children with cystic fibrosis have pancreatic deficiencies. The enzyme activity whose absence causes the most problems is the pancreatic lipase, and children with cystic fibrosis are characterized by fatty stools (steatorrhea). The amount of pancreatic enzymes secreted into the intestine over a day's time is large, and it is difficult to administer an amount of enzymes that would accomplish complete replacement. However, it is estimated that malabsorption and steatorrhea occur only when pancreatic secretion is reduced more than 90%, so supplementation with pancreatic enzymes, usually from animal sources, will help the nutritional status of such patients. It is estimated that delivery of 8000 units per hour of lipase for 3 postprandial hours will provide sufficient enzyme to provide a major improvement in absorption.

Oral administration of pancreatic enzymes so that they reach the intestine in active form requires protection from gastric acidity. This has been accomplished by enteric coating tablets of enzymes, although this solution is less than completely satisfactory because release varies widely from patient to patient. Microencapsulation with an enteric coating has proven somewhat more satisfactory, and patients are often treated simultaneously with antacids or drugs that block gastric acid secretion, such as cimetidine.

Digestive enzymes are usually administered as mixtures of enzymes obtained from pork or beef. "Pancreatin" is a mixture of pancreatic enzymes in approximately the ratios they are secreted into the intestine (2 units/mg lipase: 25 units/mg protease: 25 units/mg amylase). The lipase in pancreatin is commonly called "steapsin," and because this a critical activity, some products are enriched for lipase and are called "pancrelipase," but still contain the other activities with the following ratio specified by the United States Pharmacopeia (USP) as minimal standards: 24 USP units/mg lipase: 100 USP units/mg protease: 100 USP units/mg amylase. The specific pancreatic products are as described below.

Pancreatin is a substance containing enzymes, principally amylase, lipase, and protease. It is obtained from the pancreas of the hog, *Sus scrofa* Linné var. *domesticus* Gray (Fam. Suidae), or of the ox, *Bos taurus Linné* (Fam. Bovidae). The pancreas is a gland that lies directly inside the posterior wall of the abdomen. The fresh glands are minced and extracted, and the extract is dried to form a cream-colored amorphous powder with a faint, characteristic, but not offensive, odor. Its greatest activity is in neutral or faintly alkaline solution. More than traces of mineral acids or large amounts of alkali hydroxides render pancreatin inert, and an excess of alkali carbonates inhibits its action.

As mentioned previously, pancreatin contains, in each milligram, not less than 25 USP units of amylase activity, not less than 2 USP units of lipase activity, and not less than 25 USP units of protease activity. Pancreatin of a higher digestive power may be labeled to indicate its strength in whole-number multiples of the three minimum activities or may be diluted by appropriate admixture to conform to afore-mentioned specifications. One USP unit of amylase activity digests 1 mg of dry USP Potato Starch Reference Standard, 1 USP unit of lipase activity liberates 1 μEq of acid per minute at a pH of 9 and at 37° C, and 1 USP unit of protease activity digests 1 mg of casein, all under specified conditions.

Pancreatin is a digestive aid and is also used in the preparation of predigested foods for invalids.

Pancrelipase is essentially a more concentrated form of pancreatin, with the lipase component enriched relative to the other enzymatic activities. In each milligram it contains not less than 24 USP units of lipase activity, and 100 USP units of protease activity. Thus, the lipase activity is increased twelvefold, but the activity of amylase and protease only fourfold when compared with pancreatin.

Employed as a digestive aid, pancrelipase increases the intestinal absorption of fat, thus aiding in the control of steatorrhea. Steatorrhea is a particular problem in children with cystic fibrosis or other pancreatic deficiency. Pancrelipase is available in the form of capsules, powder packets, and tablets. The usual dose range is 8000 to 24,000 USP units of lipolytic activity prior to each meal or snack, to be determined by the practitioner according to the needs of the patient suffering from pancreatic insufficiency. Enteric coated microspheres appear to be the most reliable drug delivery vehicle, and the dose reaching the intestine in active form increases when gastric acidity is reduced with cimetidine or antacids.

Various other digestive enzymes are used either as digestive aids or for *in vitro* digestion of food. The enzymes include diastase and lactase, both of which act on carbohydrates, and the proteolytic enzymes pepsin and papain. These are described in detail below.

Diastase is a carbohydrase found in barley that has amylolytic activity, i.e., it converts starch into the disaccharide maltose, which is easily digestible. It can convert 50 times its weight of potato starch into sugars. Products contain diastase at various stages of purity, i.e., in the dried barley grain (called ''malt''), extracted from the grain (called ''malt extract''), or purified as ''diastase.'' The less pure products will contain sugars and other proteins in addition to the amylolytic enzyme. The enzyme is most active in solutions that are approximately neutral, and acidity of pH 4 destroys the activity. These conditions will apply to the enzyme whether it is in crude form in malt or in purified form.

Barley is the dried grain of one or more varieties of *Hordeum vulgare* Linné (Fam. Poaceae). Barley is grown throughout the world wherever the climate is favorable.

Malt or malted barley is dried, artificially germinated barley grain. To prepare malt, heaps of barley grain are kept wet with water in a warm room and allowed to germinate until the caulicle protrudes. The grain is then quickly dried. The enzyme diastase in the moist warm grains converts the starch to maltose, thereby stimulating the embryo to grow. The embryo is killed when the grain is dried.

Dry malt resembles barley but is more crisp, has an agreeable odor, and has a sweet taste. It contains 50 to 70% of the sugar, maltose, 2 to 15% of dextrins, 8% of proteins, diastase, and a peptase enzyme. Malt is used extensively in the brewing and alcohol industries.

Malt extract is the product obtained by extracting malt. The malt is infused with water at 60° C, and the expressed liquid is concentrated at a temperature not exceeding 60° C, preferably under reduced pressure.

Malt extract may be mixed with glycerin, 10% by weight. It contains dextrin, maltose, a small amount of glucose, and amylolytic enzymes. It can convert not less than five times its weight of starch into water-soluble sugars.

Malt extract is used as an easily digested nutritive and as an aid in digesting starch. Many commercial extracts of malt do not contain diastase, which is destroyed by the heat used for their sterilization. Such extracts should not be confused with this product. They are used as bulk-producing laxatives. An example is Maltsupex.

Lactase is an enzyme that hydrolyzes lactose to galactose and glucose. It is obtained commercially from the yeast, *Saccharomyces lactis*, and is used as LactAid powder to help patients with lactose intolerance to digest the lactose in milk or milk products.

Pepsin is a proteolytic enzyme obtained from the glandular layer of the fresh stomach of the hog, *Sus scrofa* Linné var. *domesticus* Gray (Fam. Suidae). It is used in partially purified form, and products will contain other proteins and cell constituents.

Pepsin is prepared by digesting the minced stomach linings with hydrochloric acid. This solution is clarified, partially evaporated, dialyzed, concentrated, and either poured on glass plates to dry, thus forming **scale pepsin**, or carefully evaporated in a vacuum, forming **spongy pepsin**.

Pepsin occurs as lustrous, transparent, or translucent scales, as granular or spongy masses ranging in color from light yellow to light brown, or as fine white or cream-colored amorphous powder. It is free from offensive odor and has a slightly acid or saline taste.

Pepsin digests not less than 3000 and not more than 3500 times its weight of coagulated egg albumin. A pepsin of higher digestive power may be reduced to the standard by admixture with a pepsin of lower power or with lactose. (Note: Pepsin produced commercially, especially spongy pepsin, often is four to five times as active as that used medicinally.)

Pepsin is administered to assist gastric digestion. Because pepsin is normally active in the acidic environment of the stomach, its pH optimum is quite acidic. It should preferably be given after meals. It is often combined with cellulases, amylase, and pancreatic enzymes, although the combination with pancreatic enzymes makes little sense because they will not survive the acidic environment of the stomach unless administered with antacids or cimetidine, and agents that increase the pH of the stomach will greatly reduce pepsin activity. Pepsin has a long history of use in medicine, but its actual beneficial contribution is poorly documented.

Papain is the dried and purified latex of the fruit of *Carica papaya* Linné (Fam. Caricaceae). The papaya tree is indigenous to tropical America and is cultivated in Sri Lanka, Tanzania, Hawaii, and Florida. It attains a height of about 5 to 6 meters. The fruit grows to a length of about 30 cm and a weight of 5 kg. The epicarp adheres to the orange-colored, fleshy sarcocarp that surrounds the central cavity. This cavity contains a mass of nearly black seeds.

The full-grown but unripe fruit is subjected to shallow incisions on the four sides. The latex flows freely for a few seconds but soon coagulates. After collection, the coagulated lumps are shredded and dried by the sun or by the use of artificial heat, the latter method yielding the better grade of crude papain. Incisions and collections are made at weekly intervals as long as the fruit exudes the latex. The crude papain is purified by dissolving in water and precipitating with alcohol. Papain has been referred to as ''vegetable pepsin'' because it contains enzymes somewhat similar to pepsin; however, unlike pepsin, papain acts in acid, neutral, or alkaline media.

Papain contains several enzymes: one or more proteolytic enzymes, among which is peptidase I, capable of converting proteins into dipeptides and polypeptides; a renninlike, coagulating enzyme that acts on the casein of milk; an amylolytic enzyme; a clotting enzyme similar to pectase; and an enzyme that has a feeble activity on fats. It is quite apparent that more than one proteolytic enzyme is present, because a single sample of papain yields variable results depending on the protein used. Although differing in strength in accordance with the method of manufacture, papain can digest about 35 times its own weight of lean meat. For this reason, it is used to tenderize meats. The best grade of papain digests 300 times its own weight of egg albumin.

Papain is used as a digestant for proteins because it has an action much like that of pepsin. It is combined with other enzymes such as amylases in products intended for use as digestive aids, much as has been described for pepsin. However, its broader pH range may make it more useful. Another use of the enzyme is as an ingredient in cleaning solutions for soft contact lenses. In the meat packing industry, papain is used extensively for tenderizing beef.

α-**Galactosidase** (found in Beano) is an enzyme derived from the fungus *Aspergillus niger*, which is classified as a food and sold without prescription in pharmacies and food stores. It is recommended for decreasing intestinal gas produced by eating foods such as beans, lentils, cabbage, and broccoli. These ''high-fiber'' foods contain many oligosaccharides with α-galactoside linkages that human intestinal enzymes cannot hydrolyze. Therefore, they move on to the large intestine where they are digested by intestinal bacteria, which liberates hydrogen, carbon dioxide, and methane gas and ultimately causes flatulence, bloating, diarrhea, and abdominal cramps. Some individuals are much more likely to suffer these effects than others. The enzyme hydrolyzes the oligosaccharides and makes the sugars available in the stomach and small intestine where they are absorbed.

The Beano preparation consists of partially purified *Aspergillus niger* protein in liquid form. At least two other enzymes, β-galactosidase and β-hexosaminidase, are also present. Five drops contain 0.25 g of *Aspergillus* protein and 160 galactosidase units of enzymatic activity. The recommended dosage is three to eight drops of the enzyme preparation to the first bite of the offending food after cooling (temperatures greater than 130° F may inactivate the enzyme). However, controlled studies of the efficacy of the enzyme showed that efficacy increased with increasing dose up to 70 drops. The safety of higher doses has not been established.

DEBRIDEMENT

Debridement is the removal of dead tissue or the components of tissue, i.e., proteins, nucleic acids. After trauma, in some infections such as bed sores, and after some surgical procedures, there will be dead tissue, dead microorganisms, and dead white blood cells, and sometimes pus that need to be removed in order to stimulate the growth of healthy tissue. Debridement of these dead cells is often done surgically. Enzymes can be used as an adjunct to surgery, or in some cases, as the primary mode of debridement. If the primary protein present is the skin protein collagen, a proteolytic enzyme that can digest collagen will be required. However, in dead skin, the collagen is partially denatured and will be more easily degraded than intact skin. Nevertheless, with some enzymes it is necessary to protect healthy skin when the product is applied to avoid irritation. When purulent secretions are present, nucleic acids are a major component of the material that needs to be removed, and nucleases will be applied. If blood clots are present, a proteolytic enzyme that can hydrolyse fibrin will be used.

Most of the products are applied topically and are formulated either as ointments or solutions. A few are used inside the body, specifically chymotrypsin for lens extraction from the eye, chymopapain for removal of ruptured vertebral discs, and dornase alpha for liquefying purulent secretions in cystic fibrosis patients. Antigenicity of foreign proteins is a particularly important issue when the proteins are used internally. Descriptions of the specific products follow.

Collagenase is an enzyme preparation obtained from fermentative cultures of *Clostridium histolyticum*. It cleaves collagen, the protein that accounts for 75% of the dry weight of skin tissue. It is used topically to debride dermal ulcers and severely burned areas, and thus contributes to the formation of granulation tissues and subsequent epithelialization. Complete debridement occurs in 10 to 14 days. Collagen in healthy tissue and newly formed granulation tissue is not attacked.

Collagenase is most active between pH 6 and 8. Enzymatic activity is inhibited by detergents, benzalkonium chloride, hexachlorophene, nitrofurazone, tincture of iodine, and heavy metals. Burow's solution should be avoided because of the heavy metal and low pH, although this solution has been used to stop the enzyme action. Other cleansing solutions such as hydrogen peroxide, Dakin's solution, or normal saline do not inhibit the collagenase activity and can be used. If infection is present, an appropriate antibacterial agent needs to be used in conjunction with the collagenase. Ointment preparations (Santyl ointment) contains 250 units of collagenase enzyme per gram.

Sutilains is a substance containing a mixture of proteolytic enzymes derived from the bacterium *Bacillus subtilis*. It contains not less than 2.5 million USP casein units of proteolytic activity per gram. This cream-colored powder is applied topically in ointment form three to four times daily for wound debridement in much the same way as described above for collagenase. Like collagenase, it is inactivated by heavy metals, detergents, and antiseptics, and the area must be cleansed of these materials before applying the enzyme ointment. The ointment must be refrigerated. The product, Travase ointment, contains 82,000 casein units of proteolytic activity per gram.

Subtilisin is a purified proteolytic enzyme that is found in the sutilains mixture. Subtilisin is produced as a single gene product via genetic engineering and is used in contact lens cleaning solutions. Its structure has been modified to increase its heat stability. As previously mentioned, papain and purified pancreatin are also included in some brands of enzymatic cleaners for contact lenses.

Trypsin is one of the intestinal proteolytic enzymes that can be prepared from animal sources, usually pancreases of oxen. It is used primarily topically by aerosol application for wound and ulcer cleansing to remove necrotic tissue and debris. The available preparations also contain balsam of Peru and castor oil, which serves as a protective covering and prevents premature epithelial desiccation.

Papain has been previously described. It is also used in 10% concentration in ointment form for wound debridement. Unlike collagenase and some of the other proteases used for wound debridement, it is inactivated by hydrogen peroxide solutions.

Fibrinolysin and desoxyribonuclease are a combination of enzymes that are used in topical ointment or solution preparations for debriding general surgical wounds, ulcerative lesions, second- and third-degree burns, episiotomy wounds, and infected abscesses or sinus tracts. The combination is based on the observation that purulent wound secretions have high concentrations of nucleoproteins and blood clots made up of fibrin. The mixture of enzymes (Elase) is available as a powder for mixing with normal saline to make irrigating solutions or as an ointment. The product is used intravaginally, topically (either as a wet dressing or the ointment), or for irrigating abscesses, empyema cavities, or sinus tracts. The individual enzymes are described below.

Fibrinolysin (also called "plasmin") is a protease normally found in blood serum as a proenzyme ("profibrinolysin" or "plasminogen"), which is activated to proteolytic capability by a kinase at the site of blood clots, which are primarily composed of a protein called "fibrin." It is selective for proteolysis of fibrin and involved in the normal resolution of clotted blood in the body. The commercially used fibrinolysin is obtained from bovine serum and is activated *in vitro* with a kinase derived from *Streptococcus* called "streptokinase." In dried form, fibrinolysin retains proteolytic activity almost indefinitely; however, in solution form it rapidly deteriorates. Its enzymatic activity is lost completely when it is exposed to room temperature for 6 to 8 hours.

Desoxyribonuclease is a nucleolytic enzyme that is obtained in a highly purified state from pancreatic glands of bovine origin. Like fibrinolysin, it is stable in dry form but rapidly loses its activity in solution form. It can catalyze cleavage of the giant molecules of desoxyribonucleic acid into numerous fragments of smaller size (polynucleotides); thus, it acts against devitalized tissues in purulent states. It is available only as a combination product with bovine fibrinolysin.

Dornase alfa (Pulmozyme) is another desoxyribonuclease product. It is a highly purified solution of recombinant human desoxyribonuclease I (sometimes abbreviated as "rhDNase"), an enzyme that selectively cleaves DNA. The protein is produced by genetically engineered Chinese Hamster Ovary (CHO) cells containing the human gene for desoxyribonuclease I. The protein is a glycoprotein of 260 amino acids and has a molecular weight of 37,000 daltons. It is indicated for the management of respiratory complications in patients with cystic fibrosis. Dornase alfa will reduce the viscoelasticity of sputum in cystic fibrosis patients by hydrolyzing the extracellular DNA that accumulates from degenerating leucocytes that have responded to infections. Reduction of the viscosity of the sputum improves pulmonary function and reduces the need for parenteral antibiotics for pulmonary infections.

Dornase alfa is routinely administered to cystic fibrosis patients once or twice daily by oral inhalation in an air-driven nebulizer. Although dornase alfa enzyme is present in the airway secretions for up to 6 hours following inhalation, concentrations in the sputum decline quickly at the end of the aerosol treatment. Dornase alfa must be stored in the refrigerator and protected from strong light. It should be refrigerated during transport as well. The solution needs to be discarded if it is cloudy or discolored. The ampule contains no preservatives, so once opened the entire ampule must be used or discarded. Patients need to be advised on the handling of the product and the use and maintenance of the nebulizer system. Patients can continue receiving standard cystic fibrosis therapies (antibiotics, bronchodilators, corticosteroids) while taking dornase alfa, but the product should not be mixed with other drugs in the nebulizer.

Chymopapain is a nonpyrogenic proteolytic enzyme that has been highly purified from the latex of *Carica papaya* Linné (Fam. Caricaceae). It is a sulfhydryl enzyme and sodium L-cysteinate hydrochloride is added to product preparations as a reducing agent to maintain the sulfhydryl moieties in the -SH form. The pH of the reconstituted drug is 5.5 to 6.5.

Employed in the treatment of herniated lumbar intervertebral discs, chymopapain is injected into the nucleus pulposus to hydrolyze the noncollagenous polypeptides or proteins that maintain the tertiary structure of the chondromucoprotein. This relieves the compressive symptoms of lower back pain by lessening osmotic activity and thereby decreasing fluid absorption and reducing intradiscal pressure. About 75% of the patients so treated respond favorably.

The principal problem with chymopapain is the incidence of potentially fatal anaphylactic reactions, a risk whenever a foreign protein is injected into the body. The overall mortality rate following chymopapain injection is 1 in 5000 patients or 0.02%. This is in comparison to a mortality rate from surgical intervention of 0.02% to 0.1%. Clearly conservative treatments need to be tried first. Because of the potential for anaphylaxis, patients should be asked about known sensitivity to chymopapain or other papaya derivatives, such as papain in contact lens cleaner. Patients with multiple allergies (to a variety of allergens) probably are not good candidates. A preoperative screening test for chymopapain-specific IgE antibody can also be used. Patients should never be treated more than once with chymopapain, because the first exposure may have led to sensitization. Pretreatment with a histamine receptor antagonist (e.g., cimetidine plus diphenhydramine) in the 24 hours prior to chemonucleolysis may be helpful. An open intravenous line should be in place, and epinephrine should be available to manage immediate hypersensitivity reactions.

The unit of chymopapain activity is the nano-Katal (nKat), and 1 mg of the enzyme contains at least 0.52 nKat units. Chymopapain is marketed in 2-mL and 5-mL sterile vials containing 4 or 10 nKat units respectively in powder form. This is equivalent to 2 units/mL following reconstitution. The powder should be reconstituted with Sterile Water for Injection (Bacteriostatic Water for Injection may inactivate the enzyme). Chymopapain can be shipped unrefrigerated, but it should be stored at refrigerator temperatures until reconstitution and must be used within 2 hours of reconstitution.

Chymotrypsin is a proteolytic enzyme crystallized from an extract of the pancreas gland of the ox, *Bos taurus* Linné (Fam. Bovidae). It contains not less than 1000 USP chymotrypsin units in each milligram. The enzyme occurs as a white to yellowish-white, odorless, crystalline or amorphous powder. Chymotrypsin is available as **chymotrypsin for ophthalmic solution**.

This proteolytic enzyme is administered in solution to the posterior chamber of the eye, under the iris, to achieve zonal lysis for extraction of the intracapsular lens prior to lens replacement. The proteolytic activity is specific for the zonular fibers and ocular tissues that hold the lens in place. The equatorial pericapsular membrane is destroyed in 5 minutes and zonular fibers are lysed within 10 to 15 minutes following application of the enzyme.

Chymotrypsin's potency is measured in Armour proteolytic activity units, and the product is sold in 150, 300, and 750 unit vials of powder that should be reconstituted immediately prior to use. One or two mL of a solution containing 75 or 150 units/mL are usually applied.

BLOOD CLOTTING

A variety of proteins and enzymes are used to either promote blood coagulation in patients who lack the ability to form blood clots or to degrade blood clots that have formed and are blocking critical blood vessels, e.g., of the heart or lungs. The coagulation cascade process consists of a series of linked protease reactions that convert inactive coagulation factor proenzymes (designated by Roman numerals) into enzymatically active forms. The final step involves the conversion by thrombin of soluble fibrinogen into insoluble fibrin. The coagulation cascade is capable of tremendous amplification as the linked reactions progress. Blood coagulation is essential to survival in cases of trauma and surgery, and patients with hemophilia who lack one or more of the factors in the cascade are at constant risk of bleeding.

On the other hand, there is another system in the body, the fibrinolytic system, that is the functional antithesis of the coagulation cascade. It serves to restrict clot propagation and to remove fibrin as wounds heal. In this system a proenzyme called plasminogen is activated by phosphorylation to plasmin (or fibrinolysin) that degrades fibrin. The activating kinases in the human body are tissue plasminogen activator (t-PA) and single-chain urokinase-type plasminogen activator (scu-PA). These bind to fibrin in clots, and then plasminogen will bind to the activator-fibrin complex and be activated. This complexation process allows fibrinolysis to be localized to the blood clot, which is particularly important because plasmin has low substrate specificity and can degrade fibrinogen, plasminogen, and other proteins of the coagulation and fibrinolytic systems. In providing pharmacological intervention to effect fibrinolysis (in situations where the physiological fibrinolytic system cannot degrade the clot rapidly enough to restore blood flow to a critical organ), the activators are used instead of plasmin itself because of this lack of specificity. Also, activators that do not bind to the clot were thought to be more likely to cause generalized bleeding, but this has not necessarily been found to be true in clinical trials. The localization of plasmin protease activity to thrombi (clots) is also promoted by a serine protease called α_2-antiplasmin that forms an inert complex with circulating plasmin but not with fibrin-bound plasmin.

Pharmacologically, heparin and the thrombolytics, t-PA, streptokinase, and urokinase and their derivatives (all activators of the fibrinolysis system) are used to effect anticoagulation. On the other side, protamine sulfate is used to counteract the effects of heparin, and replacement factor VIII is available for treatment of classic hemophilia (hemophilia A).

Heparin sodium is a mixture of highly electronegative acidic mucopolysaccharides of molecular weight 5,000 to 50,000 that contain numerous *N*- and *O*-sulfate linkages. It is usually obtained from the intestinal mucosa or other suitable tissues of domestic animals used for food by humans. It works to decrease blood coagulation by binding to a specific glycoprotein inactivator of thrombin called antithrombin III. Antithrombin III forms a complex with and irreversibly inhibits the activity of thrombin (which activates fibrinogen to fibrin) and other clotting factors. Heparin catalytically accelerates the interaction of antithrombin III and the proteolytic clotting factors. Lesser amounts of heparin are needed to inhibit the formation of thrombin from prothrombin than are required to accelerate the antithrombin-thrombin interaction and this is the basis of "low-dose" prophylactic therapy with heparin. Salts of heparin (calcium or sodium)

are the drugs of choice when an immediate anticoagulation effect is desired. Strengths of heparin sodium are labeled in USP units per mL, but the USP unit is not equivalent to international units (IU). Administration is by deep subcutaneous injection, direct intravenous injection, or intravenous infusion. Heparin sodium is commercially available in concentrations ranging from 1000 to 40,000 USP units/mL. Bleeding (e.g., nosebleeds) is the principal sign of overdose. Heparin can be antagonized with protamine sulfate, which is described below.

A low-molecular-weight heparin product, enoxaparin, has recently been approved by the FDA for prevention of deep vein thrombosis following hip replacement. Low-molecular-weight heparin is composed of fragments with a molecular weight of 4000 to 6500 and is formed by depolymerization of standard heparin (average molecular weight of 12,000 to 15,000). Low-molecular-weight heparin fragments have relatively more anti-factor Xa activity than standard heparin, which could lead to an increased antithrombotic effect. They cause less inactivation of thrombin, less inhibition of platelets, and less vascular permeability, which could lead to less bleeding. They also have a longer half-life than standard heparin and are more bioavailable.

Streptokinase was the first available agent used for dissolving blood clots. It is a purified bacterial protein elaborated by group C β-hemolytic streptococci. Streptokinase has no direct enzymatic action on plasminogen; rather it binds to plasminogen in a 1:1 ratio and causes a molecular conformational change such that the complex becomes an active enzyme that cleaves bonds on other plasminogen molecules, thus activating them to the fibrinolytic enzyme, plasmin. Plasmin degrades not only fibrin clots but also fibrinogen and other plasma proteins. The plasminogen-streptokinase complex also can be formed *in vitro* and chemically modified (anisolylated) to ensure the stability of its enzymatic properties. The **anisolylated plasminogen-streptokinase activator complex** (APSAC) is officially called **"anistreplase"** and is used similarly to streptokinase. The major difference is in the half-life of the drug; the half-life of streptokinase is 23 minutes, compared to 90 minutes for anistreplase.

Use of streptokinase and anistreplase is indicated in the treatment of pulmonary embolism, deep vein thrombosis, arterial thrombosis and embolism, arteriovenous cannula occlusion, and coronary artery thrombosis. At present, it is particularly widely used for the last condition, often producing a prompt recanalization of the involved vessel. The route of administration, dosage, and duration of treatment vary for each of the above conditions. The greatest benefits are derived from streptokinase and anistreplase when they are administered early in the course of a myocardial infarction or other clotting episode. In recent studies, heparin is administered along with the thrombolytic agents to counteract a paradoxical increase in local thrombin that is observed with all plasminogen activators. The major side effect of concern is bleeding, either peripherally or intracranially. Serious peripheral bleeding occurred in 5 to 6% of patients in recent clinical trials, but it was not clear to what extent the plasminogen activators contributed because all patients also received heparin. Some patients also experienced allergic reactions including anaphylaxis (0.1 to 0.2%) or became refractory to streptokinase or anistreplase because of preexisting antibodies. Repeat doses of streptokinase or anistreplase are not usually recommended between 5 days and 6 months following an initial treatment because of the likelihood of circulating antistreptokinase antibodies, which could either decrease efficacy or lead to allergic responses. Streptokinase is marketed as a lyophilized powder in sterile vials containing 250,000 to 750,000 IU. Streptokinase is considerably less expensive than the recombinant plasminogen activators and although some studies show a slight edge in efficacy for recombinant tissue-plasminogen activator (t-PA), there is considerable debate whether the increased cost is warranted.

Urokinase is an enzyme isolated from human urine or obtained from human kidney cells by tissue culture techniques or by recombinant DNA technology. There are two forms. Both have similar clinical effects, but they differ in molecular weight. There is a two polypeptide-chain form and a single-chain form. A fragment of the double-chain form is available in the United States; the single-chain form, produced by recombinant techniques and known as **scu-PA**, is available in Europe. Both are serine proteases that act on the endogenous fibrinolytic system, converting plasminogen and other plasma proteins. Use of urokinase is indicated in the treatment of pulmonary embolism, coronary artery thrombosis, and in restoring the patency of intravenous catheters. It appears to have a reduced probability of serious allergic reactions, presumably owing to its human origin but should be used with appropriate caution. Neither product is as widely used as streptokinase and tissue-plasminogen activator (t-PA). The usual dosage regimen is a priming dose followed by administration of 4400 units/kg of body weight per hour for 12 hours by intravenous infusion. The half-life after intravenous dosage is 10 to 16 minutes.

Tissue plasminogen activator or t-PA (Alteplase) is a glycosylated enzyme produced by recombinant techniques in Chinese hamster ovary cells and is a native human plasminogen activator. It occurs as both a single-chain and double-chain form, but the recombinant product is a single-chain form. It acts by cleaving plasminogen to yield plasmin and has a high binding affinity for fibrin. However, the selectivity is not absolute, and it does cause some hydrolysis of fibrinogen, as do the other thrombolytic agents. It causes less general fibrinogenolysis than streptokinase, but interestingly, bleeding occurred in clinical trials with about the same frequency with either agent. It should have a lower frequency of allergic reactions than streptokinase because it is a human enzyme; in clinical trials a small percentage of patients had mild hypersensitivity reactions (e.g., urticaria).

t-PA is slightly more efficacious than streptokinase in establishing coronary reperfusion and lowering mortality in patients with myocardial infarction, as shown by a 1993 clinical trial in which either drug was administered with heparin. The heparin may be particularly important with t-PA, because t-PA has a short half-life (4 to 8 minutes) and reocclusion must be prevented. Continuous infusion may also help prevent reocclusion. t-PA can also be used for pulmonary embolism. Like the other agents, the best results are obtained when the drug is administered early in the course of the clot.

It is available as a powder for reconstitution with water in sterile vials.

New thrombin inhibitors that are more specific than heparin are under investigation. **Hirudin** is a polypeptide that occurs naturally in the saliva of the medicinal leech but is now produced by recombinant technology. **Hirulog** is a synthetic hirudin-like polypeptide. Unlike heparin, the polypeptides are direct inhibitors of only thrombin and are not neutralized by activated platelets. Although they have not been thoroughly tested yet, it is thought that they may be superior to heparin in preventing reocclusion and would be administered along with the plasminogen activators.

Several proteins are used to cause clotting rather than dissolving clots. Protamine is a protein used to counteract the effects of heparin, and antihemophiliac factor is used specifically in patients with hemophilia.

Protamine sulfate is a purified mixture of simple protein principles obtained from the sperm or testes of suitable species of fish, usually those belonging to the genera *Oncorhynchus* Suckley, *Salmo* Linné, or *Trutta* Jordan et Evermann (Fam. Salmonidae). It has the property of neutralizing heparin. Protamines are basic, low molecular weight, positively charged proteins that have a high affinity for the negatively-charged heparin molecules. The binding is immediate and results in an inert complex. Each milligram of protamine sulfate neutralizes not less than 80 USP units of heparin activity derived from lung tissue and not less than 100 USP units of heparin activity derived from intestinal mucosa.

Protamine sulfate is a fine, white or off-white, amorphous or crystalline powder that is sparingly soluble in water. It is an antidote to heparin and is administered intravenously. The usual intravenous dose is 1 mg for each 90 or 115 USP units of heparin activity, derived from beef lung tissue or porcine intestinal mucosa, respectively, in 1 to 3 minutes, up to a maximum of 50 mg in any 10-minute period, repeated as necessary.

Two products are available for treating classic hemophilia (hemophilia A). Both are recombinant forms of clotting factor VIII, a glycoprotein that is part of the clotting cascade, and are called "**antihemophilic factor**." KoGENate is produced in baby hamster kidney cells, while Recombinate is produced in Chinese hamster ovary cells. Both are administered intravenously to prevent and control hemorrhagic episodes associated with hemophilia in which the genetic deficiency is factor VIII. Dosing is calculated based on a formula that considers body weight and the desired percentage increase in factor VIII. The products are unstable in solution and must be administered within 3 hours of reconstituting the concentrate with diluent. The principle advantage of the recombinant products is the fact that they are free of blood-borne contaminants such as HIV and hepatitis that have been so devastating to hemophiliacs. Although screening has greatly decreased the incidence of contamination in our blood supply, it can not eliminate it entirely. The frequency with which hemophiliacs receive blood products and the number of donors required to generate a dose of nonrecombinant factor VIII, make it dangerous to use factor VIII derived from donated blood, thus stimulating the need for a recombinant form of the protein.

MISCELLANEOUS ENZYMES AND OTHER PROTEINS

Asparaginase is the enzyme L-asparagine aminohydrolase obtained from cultures of certain strains of *Escherichia coli*. The enzyme works to treat acute lymphocytic leukemias, including the induction of remissions in children, by depriving malignant cells of the asparagine they need for protein synthesis. Malignant cells require an exogenous source of asparagine (i.e., the blood stream) whereas normal cells can synthesize sufficient asparagine for their needs. Thus the enzyme, by hydrolyzing asparagine in the blood stream to form aspartic acid and ammonia, selectively inhibits tumor cell proliferation. It is most effective in the postmitotic (G1) phase of the cell cycle.

A number of serious adverse reactions are noted with asparaginase, including allergic reactions and fatal anaphylaxis. There is an increased risk of hypersensitivity reactions with retreatment. Hepatotoxicity occurs in a majority of patients. Asparaginase is used primarily in combination with other chemotherapeutic agents, such as prednisone and vincristine. Administration is intravenous or intramuscular.

A modified version of asparaginase called **pegaspargase** (PEG-L-asparaginase) is now available that has improved properties. Pegaspargase is manufactured by covalently conjugating polyethylene glycol (PEG), a polymer with a molecular weight of 5000, to the asparaginase enzyme derived from *E. coli*. The polyethylene glycol extends the half-life of asparaginase in the bloodstream from 1.24 days for asparaginase alone to 5.73 days for pegaspargase. More importantly, it reduces hypersensitivity reactions and allows some patients who have developed allergic reactions to asparaginase to receive continued treatment. However, hypersensitivity, including potentially fatal anaphylactoid reactions, remains a major side effect of pegaspargase. Pancreatitis occurs in about 1% of patients and can be serious.

The product can be administered intravenously or intramuscularly. It is important to store the product at refrigerator temperatures. Freezing destroys the enzyme activity, but the instability can not be detected visually. Excessive agitation must be avoided; the vial should not be shaken. The vial should be entered only once and unused portions discarded.

Asparaginase derived from another organism, *Erwinia*, is available from the National Cancer Institute for selected cases. Some patients who are hypersensitive to the *E. coli* enzyme may be able to tolerate the enzyme from *Erwinia*.

Adenosine deaminase bovine or pegademase is an enzyme used for enzyme replacement for the treatment of severe combined immunodeficiency disease (SCID) associated with a genetic deficiency of adenosine deaminase. The enzyme has been prepared from bovine intestine and modified by covalent attachment of multiple units of monomethoxypolyethylene glycol (PEG). The PEG serves to prolong the half-life and reduce the antigenicity of the product.

SCID is a rare, inherited, and generally fatal disease that results from a deficiency in adenosine deaminase, an enzyme that hydrolyzes adenosine and deoxyadenosine to form inosine (or deoxyinosine) and ammonia. Adenosine, when it accumulates, is toxic to lymphocytes, resulting in the immunodeficiency that makes the patients extremely susceptible to opportunistic infections. Replacement of the enzyme results in improved immune function and a decrease in frequency of opportunistic infections, although there is a lag of a few weeks to as long as 6 months between administration of the enzyme and improvement in the immune function.

Pegademase is administered every 7 days as an intramuscular injection. Peak blood levels are achieved within 2 to 3 days and the half-life varies from 3 to 6 days. Antibody to the enzyme may develop over time, resulting in more rapid clearance of the drug and a decreased response. This may be addressed by more frequent, higher doses of the enzyme. The product should be stored in the refrigerator and not frozen.

Gene replacement therapy for SCID is under investigation and may eventually take the place of direct replacement of the enzyme.

Hyaluronidase for injection is a sterile, dry, soluble, enzyme product prepared from mammalian testes and capable of hydrolyzing mucopolysaccharides of the type of hyaluronic acid. Its potency is expressed in USP hyaluronidase units. Hyaluronidase for injection contains not more than 0.25 μg of tyrosine for each USP hyaluronidase unit.

Hyaluronidase is a mucolytic enzyme capable of depolymerizing and catalyzing hyaluronic acid and similar hexosamine-containing poly-saccharides. It is also a spreading and a diffusing factor. It occurs in human testes, in various bacterial cultures as a metabolic product, in heads of leeches, and in snake venoms. Because of its action on hyaluronic acid, this enzyme promotes diffusion and hastens absorption of subcutaneous infusions.

Hyaluronidase for injection is a spreading agent and used in hypodermoclysis.

Imiglucerase (β-glucocerebrosidase or Cerezyme) is an analog of a human lysosomal glycoprotein that catalyzes the hydrolysis of the glycolipid glucocerebroside, yielding glucose and ceramide. Patients with the genetic disease called Type I Gaucher's disease are lacking the β-glucocerebrosidase enzyme. The resulting syndrome results from accumulation of glucocerebroside in tissue macrophages that become engorged and deposit in the liver, spleen, and bone marrow, and sometimes the lung, kidney, and intestine. Patients develop severe anemia and thrombocytopenia, progressive hepatosplenomegaly, and skeletal complications. Treatment with the recombinant enzyme improves anemia and thrombocytopenia, reduces spleen and liver size, and relieves the symptoms of the bone disease. The drug must be administered as long-term replacement therapy.

β-Glucocerebrosidase is an intracellular glycosylated enzyme that does not easily enter its target cell, the macrophage. Therefore, the native enzyme is modified so that the oligosaccharide chains at the glycosylation sites terminate in mannose sugars. These mannose-terminated oligosaccharide chains are specifically recognized by endocytic carbohydrate receptors on macrophages and facilitate the enzyme's entry into the cells.

Imiglucerase is administered by intravenous infusion over 1 to 2 hours. Dosage is individualized to each patient, but 60 units/kg every 2 weeks is the initial dosage for which the most clinical data have been derived. Maintenance doses may range from every day to monthly, depending on the severity of the deficiency and the patient response. As with many of the protein drugs, imiglucerase should be stored in the refrigerator as the lyophilized powder for injection. Once it is reconstituted it is stable for up to 24 hours at refrigerator temperatures. The vial contains no preservative, so once a vial is entered for use any remaining product must be discarded and not kept for subsequent use.

Another product that is used for replacement therapy for a genetic disease is α_1-**antitrypsin or α_1-proteinase inhibitor** (Prolastin). The currently available product is prepared from pooled human plasma, but because of the risk of blood-borne diseases (despite the fact that the plasma is tested for HIV and hepatitis B surface antigen), development of a recombinant enzyme is underway.

α_1-Antitrypsin deficiency is a chronic hereditary, usually fatal, autosomal recessive disorder that results in a slowly progressive, severe emphysema that usually manifests itself in the third and fourth decades of life. Although the pathogenesis is not completely understood, it is thought that lung tissue is unprotected from the effects of elastase, a naturally occurring protease released by neutrophils in the respiratory tract, and the elastase destroys elastin-containing cells in the epithelial lining of the respiratory tract, resulting in emphysema. Replacement therapy involves intravenous injection of the product usually on a once-weekly basis. Like other protein products, the lyophilized, preservative free powder should be refrigerated prior to reconstitution, used within 3 hours of reconstitution, and unused solution discarded.

OTHER PROTEINS

Gelatin is a product obtained by the partial hydrolysis of collagen derived from the skin, white connective tissue, and bones of animals. Commercially, gelatin is prepared from the suitable by-products of slaughtered cattle, sheep, and hogs. Bones are first decalcified by treatment with hydrochloric acid. The materials are extracted with boiling water and steam under pressure until the collagen is hydrolyzed. The solution is then filtered by electro-osmosis, concentrated under reduced pressure, allowed to gel, and rapidly dried on netting in currents of warm air.

Gelatin occurs in sheets, flakes, shreds, or as a coarse or fine powder. It is faintly yellow or amber and has a slight, characteristic odor and taste. When dry, gelatin is stable in the air, but when moist or in solution, it is subject to bacterial decomposition. Gelatin is insoluble in cold water but swells and softens when immersed in cold water, gradually absorbing from five to ten times its weight of water. It is soluble in hot water and insoluble in most immiscible solutions and in volatile and fixed oils.

Commercially, gelatin is available as two types: A and B. Type A exhibits an isoelectric point between pH 7 and 9 and is incompatible with anionic compounds such as acacia, tragacanth, and agar. Type B, on the other hand, should be used when such mixtures are desired because it exhibits an isoelectric point between pH 4.7 and 5.

If gelatin is intended for use in the manufacture of capsules to contain medication or for the coating of tablets, it may be colored with a certified color, may contain various additives, and may have any suitable gel strength.

Gelatin contains amino acids: alanine, arginine, aspartic acid, cystine, cysteine, glutamic acid, glycine, histidine, hydroxyproline, isoleucine, leucine, lysine, methionine, phenylalanine, proline, serine, threonine, tyrosine, and valine. Because only traces of other important amino acids are present and tryptophan is absent, gelatin is an incomplete nutritional protein. The gelatinizing constituent is known as chondrin, and the adhesive substance is known as glutin.

Gelatin is a pharmaceutic aid (encapsulating agent, suspending agent, tablet binder, and coating agent). Combined with glycerin, it forms glycerinated gelatin; as such, it is employed as a vehicle and also for the manufacture of suppositories. Zinc oxide is added to form zinc gelatin, which is used as a topical protectant. In addition, gelatin is a nutrient and is extensively used for the preparation of commercial food products and for bacteriologic culture media.

Absorbable gelatin sponge (Gelfoam) is a sterile, absorbable, water-insoluble, gelatin-base sponge. It consists of a light, nearly white, porous, pliable, nonantigenic matrix prepared from purified, specially treated gelatin, and is sterilized by heat. Even when handled roughly, this product shows little tendency to disintegrate. It absorbs about 50 times its weight of water and about 45 times its weight in blood.

Control of capillary oozing and of bleeding from veins is effected through the use of absorbable gelatin sponge applied in the dry form or saturated with sterile isotonic sodium chloride solution or sterile thrombin solution. The sponge is applied to the bleeding area and held for 10 to 15 seconds; it is then left in place.

Absorbable gelatin sponge is a local hemostatic. It is applied topically in operative wounds.

Absorbable Gelatin Film (Gelfilm) is a specially prepared gelatin product used in neurosurgery and in thoracic and ocular surgery. It consists of a thin, pliable, nonantigenic absorbable film of purified gelatin. In the dry state it resembles cellophane in appearance and stiffness, and occurs in pieces about 25 × 50 mm or 100 ×

125 mm in size and about 0.075 mm in thickness. When moistened by immersion in salt solution, it is easily cut into the shape needed to fit into the contours of the incision.

GROWTH FACTORS

A number of therapeutically important proteins produced by recombinant technology are growth factors. These proteins stimulate or otherwise regulate the growth of a variety of tissues in the body with substantial specificity. Although some of these proteins that are in experimental stages of development, such as nerve growth factors and epidermal growth factor, may eventually have applications for wound healing, the ones that are currently available on the market stimulate the immune system (see Chapter 12). The exception is erythropoietin, which stimulates red blood cell development. However, because a description of its action depends on the hematopoietic pathway, which is presented in Chapter 12, it will also be addressed in that section.

HORMONES

Hormones are mammalian metabolites that are produced by endocrine or ductless glands, are released directly into the blood, and are involved in eliciting responses by specific body organs and tissues. These biologically active metabolites either are steroidal or are derived from amino acids. The latter group of hormones consists primarily of peptides of various sizes, but a few nonpeptide metabolites (epinephrine, thyroxine) are known.

The nonpeptide, nonsteroidal hormones are nevertheless derived biosynthetically from amino acids and are included in this peptide and protein chapter for the sake of completeness. In addition to the pertinent details about the nonsteroidal hormones, general aspects of endocrine products used as therapeutic agents will be discussed in this chapter. Specific details about the steroid hormones are presented in Chapter 7.

Present therapeutic use of endocrine products is an outgrowth of the primitive practice of organotherapy. The use by Magnus in the 13th century of powdered hog testis to treat male impotence and of rabbit uterus to treat female sterility was a direct progenitor of the present therapy. The basic philosophy for the use of mammalian

organs was ably expressed by Vicary in the 16th century when he said, "In what part of the body the faculty you would strengthen lies, take the same part of the body of another creature in whom the faculty is strong, as a medicine."

The origin and early development of endocrine therapy were empiric, but most of the present knowledge of endocrine function and therapy is the result of intensive investigations conducted over the past 50 years. Standardized powdered glands and glandular extracts initially provided more reproducible effects and better therapeutic control than did randomly selected glands, and isolated hormonal substances have offered additional advantages in most cases. Modern technology has permitted the chemical or biotechnology-based synthesis of many hormones including a number of peptides, and the preparation of substances that mimic the actions of natural hormones (e.g., prednisone-cortisone).

Much of the obvious progress in the endocrine area is reflected in the nature of available products. However, a more precise comprehension of their physiologic functions and improved diagnostic procedures have contributed significantly to therapeutic advancement.

Hormones function as chemical transmitters of selective stimuli between the various endocrine glands and specific body organs and tissues. Sufficient information is available to permit some generalizations about the modes by which hormones influence the metabolism of target cells and maintain homeostasis. The size and lipophilic character of steroids permit penetration of cell membranes, but often peptide hormones bind to receptors on the surface of the cell and act in one of two ways: (1) to directly induce changes in membrane permeability for ions, glucose, and amino acids or (2) to induce the production of a secondary messenger such as cyclic AMP, which transmits the signal of the hormone within the cell. Hormones that control membrane permeability, either directly or indirectly, include the estrogens, growth hormone, glucagon, glucocorticoids, insulin, testosterone, and vasopressin. Induction of enzyme formation and modification in the rate of enzymatic reactions are other known mechanisms of hormonal action.

Physiologic control of hormone formation or release to regulate hormone level is a vital aspect of maintaining metabolic homeostasis and integrity of body function. Two general regulatory mechanisms are currently recognized. There is a feedback mechanism that responds to change in concentration of some substance in the blood. The key substance may be a hormone or some other metabolite. For example, an increase in levels of triiodothyronine-thyroxine causes a decrease in thyrotropin secretion, owing to an inhibition of the secretion of thyrotropin-releasing factor by the hypothalamus. The second mechanism involves external stimuli and is mediated by the hypothalamus; the hypothalamus secretes releasing factors that act on the anterior pituitary to increase the release of specific tropic hormones.

Some manifestations of hormonally controlled processes are rather subtle, and their significance in the normal individual is usually recognized only by people trained in the health sciences. However, the widely recognized influence of the gonadal hormones on the development and function of the reproductive organs and sex characteristics illustrates the general type of fundamental involvement of hormones.

There is appreciable interaction among the functions of the various endocrine glands and a close correlation between the endocrine system and the central and autonomic nervous systems. Thus, a primary disturbance in an endocrine gland or therapy with a hormone may have far-reaching effects. Caution must be exercised in therapeutic management of such complex situations to avoid dangerous or irrational developments.

Disturbance in the function of an endocrine gland may take the form of excessive activity (hyperfunction) or diminished activity (hypofunction) to any degree. The most frequently encountered therapeutic situations involve the hypofunctioning gland. Replacement therapy merely uses endocrine preparations to supplement or totally replace abnormally low levels of endogenous hormone. Early diagnosis and treatment are essential in this type of therapy to avoid irreversible changes that can occur, such as cretinism, giantism, and other comparable conditions. Use of hormones for replacement purposes is usually long-term therapy, and because these potent substances are normal body metabolites, serious side effects are usually minimal if caution is taken to balance the administered dosage with replacement needs. Insulin use provides a good example of this type of approach to a hypofunctioning endocrine system.

Hypofunctioning glands that retain some degree of activity can potentially be stimulated to approach normal activity by the use of drugs that are not hormones per se, or by the inhibition of the normal catabolic processes to conserve the limited supply of hormone. There are many variations to this type of therapeutic approach, but they all require metabolic capability in the glandular tissue and a thorough knowledge of biochemical detail. This general approach will probably become more useful in the future when greater knowledge is available.

Hormonal substances are generally not employed in treatment of hyperfunctioning endocrine glands. Antimetabolites may offer some potential for eliminating the deleterious effects of abnormally high levels of hormones. Also, as our capability to synthesize peptides has increased, there have been analogs of peptide hormones synthesized that serve as antagonists at hormone receptors, thus reducing the impact of a hyperfunctioning gland. Alternate approaches to this kind of problem include surgical removal of part of the hyperfunctioning gland or selective destruction of some of the glandular tissues. Various radiation treatments, including the use of Iodine 131 in certain thyroid conditions, represent the latter approach.

Sometimes, hormones have therapeutic use for pharmacologic actions that are not directly related to normal endocrine functions. The use of glucocorticoids for anti-inflammatory and antirheumatic purposes falls into this category. The potential danger of serious side effects is considerably greater when hormones are used for specific pharmacologic actions than when they are used for replacement therapy. Prolonged therapeutic use of a hormone, such as cortisone, may cause irreversible atrophy of the endocrine gland that normally produces the hormone or may induce other undesirable secondary responses. The safest use of a hormone as a therapeutic agent involves a short duration of therapy, e.g., the use of oxytocin to control postpartum hemorrhage. This short-term approach avoids problems associated with prolonged upset of the delicate balance among various endocrine systems.

Hormones and hormone analogs are also used extensively for diagnostic purposes in that often the best way to diagnose a misfunctioning hormonal system is to perturb the system by administering a regulatory hormone or a hormone analog and observe the response. A separate section is included for these diagnostic agents.

Traditionally, many drugs employed in medical practice and generally classified as endocrine products are by-products of the meat-packing industry. Thyroid, pancreas, adrenal, and pituitary glands of bovine and porcine origins are used for such purposes. The active principles obtained from such glands may vary in quantity and quality depending on species, so that specific manufacturing processes are developed and used with particular species in mind.

Glands used in the manufacture of pharmaceutic products are collected in government-inspected packinghouses and must conform to the regulations of the Meat Inspection Department of the United States Department of Agriculture. Only glands from carcasses that are classified by federal inspectors as edible may be used.

Endocrine glands are technically fresh meat and must be processed in a manner that prevents deterioration. Glands are normally quick-frozen as soon as they are removed from the animal carcasses and maintained in a frozen state until processed. Processing varies with the nature of the ultimate endocrine product. The glands in many cases are subjected to extraction and fractionation treatments to yield purified hormones. However, the continued therapeutic acceptance of desiccated thyroid is a pragmatic reminder that satisfactory results sometimes can be achieved without costly isolation of the active principles. The frozen thyroid gland is simply dehydrated, defatted, powdered, standardized, and made into suitable dosage forms.

However, in some cases the hormones derived from nonhuman mammals are not effective in humans or cause antigenicity over time that may lead to allergic reactions or decreased efficacy. For these situations, the capability to synthesize a peptide drug via solid-state synthesis or to produce the human protein from human genes via biotechnology has provided new options for therapy. Gene replacement therapy may someday prove useful for hormone deficiencies, but the problems involved in proper regulation of hormone release and action are so critical that it seems unlikely that this will be an early target of gene therapy.

Chemical synthesis is a logical approach to ensuring the ready availability of adequate supplies of any natural metabolite of known structure and therapeutic use. The feasibility of synthetic procedures is governed to a large degree by the complexity of the molecule and by the technical knowledge relating to the given type of compound. Hormones present no exception to these generalizations. Perhaps the only unusual feature that is applied commercially in the production of certain hormones involves the action of selected biologic systems on foreign substrates. Various microorganisms metabolize certain steroids to give useful compounds. An indication of the significant contribution of microbial biotransformation of steroids is included in the steroid chapter.

The Merrifield solid-phase synthesis of peptides is a technologic development of the 1960s of major significance for endocrine therapy. This technique involves basically attaching a carboxy-terminal amino acid to a resin column and synthesizing a polypeptide by passing a programmed sequence of reacting solutions through the column. There is no need to isolate each intermediate; the process can be automated, and commercially feasible synthesis has been extended to peptides containing more than 30 amino acid residues. A number of peptide hormones that were previously isolated from glandular materials are now prepared synthetically, and as mentioned previously, solid state synthesis allows the synthesis of peptide hormones not available from an animal source and of analogs of peptide hormones that can be used as agonists and diagnostic agents. Analogs (peptidomimetics) may also be synthesized with unusual amino acids or nonpeptide linkages in order to increase the half-life of a hormonal analog. Peptides and proteins are, of course, subject to proteolysis both in the gastrointestinal tract (necessitating a non-oral dosage form for most of them) and within the body. Analogs with slower rates of proteolysis will have longer half-lives and may even be orally absorbed.

Biotechnology-derived hormones on the market include human insulin and human growth hormone. The former is an example of a hormone that had been available from animal sources but with problems in some patients arising from the differences in structure of beef or pork insulin from the human hormone. The latter (growth hormone) is an example of a hormone that is more species specific; beef and pork growth hormone is not active in humans. Furthermore, the pituitary-derived hormones are difficult to obtain in any quantity from animal sources because of the small amount in an animal, so the ability to overexpress the gene in a host organism or cell-line is a great advantage.

Adrenal Gland Hormones

The **adrenals** (suprarenals) in humans are a pair of small glands; one is situated over the superior medial aspect of each kidney. Each average gland measures $5 \times 25 \times 50$ mm; together, the adrenals weigh 4 to 18 g.

The adrenals were first described by Eustachius in the 16th century and were for a long period of time thought to function in the inhibition of fetal urination and in the prevention of renal stones in the adult. Knowledge of adrenal function began with Addison in 1849 and is still far from complete.

Each adrenal consists embryologically, histologically, and functionally of two distinct glandular entities that are grossly combined into one organ. Cells of the adrenal cortex secrete steroid hormones, which were discussed previously.

The adrenal medulla is composed of cells that migrated out from the embryonic neural crest and are analogous to the peripheral sympathetic neurons of the autonomic nervous system. The adrenal medulla secretes epinephrine and norepinephrine (normally in a ratio approximately 17:3) and functions as a sympathetic postganglionic structure.

The adrenal medulla is not essential for life, and no diseases of deficiency are known. Therapeutic use of these hormones is based on the pharmacology of sympathomimetic amines and not on the principle of replacement. The pharmacological effects of each of the adrenal hormones (called "catecholamines" because of their chemical structure) are based on their interaction with the various receptors of the sympathetic nervous system. There are four major subtypes of adrenergic receptors (also called "adrenoceptors"), α_1, α_2, β_1, and β_2. A third β subtype, β_3, has also been found and is thought to be involved primarily in lipolysis in adipocytes. Cloning of the receptor proteins has shown that each of these subtypes represent separate and distinct molecular entities, although there is a high degree of amino acid homology for receptor subtypes within a given adrenoceptor family. All of the adrenoceptors possess seven hydrophobic regions, and the proteins are thought to transverse the membrane seven times.

The actions of the cells in response to receptor stimulation involves second messenger systems. α_2-Adrenoceptors are coupled to the inhibition of adenylate cyclase, while β-adrenergic receptors (both major subtypes) activate adenylate cyclase. In each case, the receptor is coupled to the catalytic enzyme adenylate cyclase through a G protein (guanine nucleotide regulatory protein), and the nature of the G protein determines whether activation or inhibition occurs. α_1-Adrenoceptors are also linked to a G-protein, but in this case the coupling produces effects through increases in intracellular phosphatidylinositol turnover resulting in increased intracellular calcium levels and activation of protein kinase C.

Various tissues (e.g., smooth muscle of vasculature and the respiratory tract and cardiac tissue) have various combinations of adrenoceptors, and the effect of each compound on each tissue reflects the response of those receptors. Epinephrine has a high affinity for all the adrenergic receptors, but norepinephrine will activate α_1-, α_2-, and β_1-adrenoceptors with relatively weak activity at β_2-adrenoceptors. The effects on tissues with mixed receptors will vary. For example, low doses of epinephrine result in vasodilation as β-adrenergic receptors are activated, and increasingly larger doses lead to eventual vasoconstriction as more and more of the α_1-adrenergic receptors are activated. Epinephrine also stimulates cardiac contraction and heart rate and leads to bronchodilation caused by activation of β_2-adrenergic receptors of the bronchial smooth muscle. This action is particularly useful pharmacologically during acute asthmatic or anaphylactic reactions. Epinephrine is also used pharmacologically for its vasoconstricting effects: to prolong the actions of infiltration anesthetics by reducing local blood flow in the region of the injection and to control localized hemorrhage. It is used in cardiac arrest to restore cardiac activity. Side effects result from heart stimulation (palpitations) and the fact that it can cross into the central nervous system (CNS), stimulating apprehension, restlessness, and increased respiration. Epinephrine action has a rapid onset but a short duration of action.

Similarly, the effects of norepinephrine can be explained by the fact that it acts on α_1- and α_2-adrenoceptors and β_1-adrenoceptors but has relatively low affinity for β_2-adrenoceptors. It is not useful to treat bronchoconstriction but increases the force of the heart beat and causes vasoconstriction. It can be used like epinephrine for local vasoconstriction, and because it has strong peripheral vasoconstrictive properties, it is used intravenously to restore blood pressure during spinal anesthesia when peripheral resistance is low. It is not used for most types of shock because renal circulation is already compromised and perfusion of the kidneys would be jeopardized. Norepinephrine also causes cardiac palpitations accompanied by bradycardia as its principal side effect. It does not cross into the CNS well and is less likely to cause the CNS side effects associated with epinephrine.

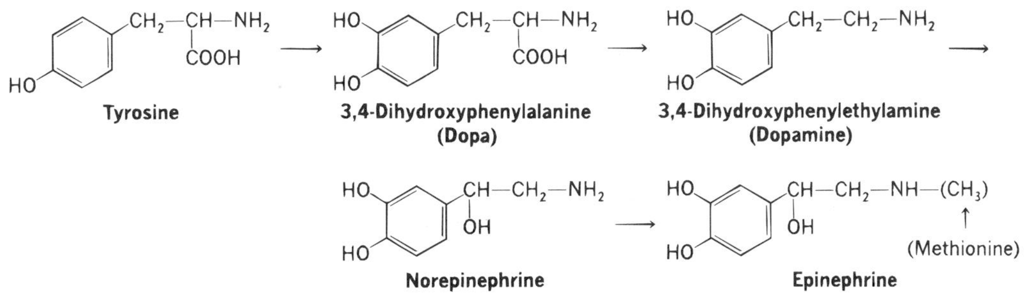

Fig. 10–1. Biosynthesis of epinephrine.

Dopamine (3,4-dihydroxyphenethylamine) is a biosynthetic precursor to norepinephrine and epinephrine as discussed below. It has actions in both the periphery and in the CNS where it plays a physiological role as a neurotransmitter, acting upon D_1 and D_2 receptors. The physiologic role of peripheral dopamine has not been conclusively established. When administered exogenously for pharmacologic purposes, it does not pass into the CNS. Peripherally, its actions result from the direct action on the receptors, but also from an indirect action resulting from synthesis of norepinephrine and release of stored norepinephrine. It is used in the treatment of shock resulting from inadequate cardiac output caused by myocardial infarction or congestive heart failure, and also in the treatment of septic shock. Its advantage is that it increases cardiac output while also dilating renal blood vessels, thus increasing renal blood flow.

The catecholamine hormones are metabolically inactivated in several ways. A major pathway involves catechol *O*-methylation, but oxidative deamination with monoamine oxidase is especially significant owing to the therapeutic use of monoamine oxidase inhibitors.

Biosynthesis of Epinephrine. From a biosynthetic viewpoint, epinephrine may be considered an alkaloidal amine of the phenylpropanoid type. Its derivation from tyrosine has been demonstrated experimentally. Tyrosine is oxidized to dihydroxyphenylalanine (dopa), which is decarboxylated and oxidized in the side chain. The norepinephrine thus produced is converted to epinephrine by transfer of a methyl group from active methionine (Fig. 10–1). The rate-limiting step appears to be the conversion of tyrosine to dopa.

Epinephrine (Adrenalin) is (−)-3,4-dihydroxy-α-[(methylamino)methyl]benzyl alcohol. It may be isolated as a hormone from the adrenal medulla or may be prepared synthetically. Dextrorotatory epinephrine is almost completely inactive, and optically inactive mixtures have approximately half the activity of natural epinephrine. The specific rotation of epinephrine is not less than −50° and not more than −53.5°. Epinephrine occurs as a white to nearly white, microcrystalline, odorless powder that gradually darkens when exposed to light and air.

The labile catechol function precludes oral administration of epinephrine, which must be administered by subcutaneous or intramuscular injection or absorbed through a mucous membrane.

Epinephrine is incorporated into a variety of pharmaceutic formulations for therapeutic use. The hormone is frequently solubilized in aqueous preparations using hydrochloric acid or tartaric acid (bitartrate), and a water-soluble borate complex is sometimes used in ophthalmology. Acidity favors the stability of this labile compound, but no epinephrine-containing solution should be used if a brown color or a precipitate has formed. Formulations for therapeutic use of this hormone include a 1:1000 aqueous solution for topical purposes, a 1:100 aqueous solution for inhalation, metered-dose aerosol products, sterile aqueous solutions (1:1,000, 1:10,000, and 1:100,000) for parenteral administration, a sterile 1:200 suspension in oil for prolonged systemic action, and several ophthalmic solutions (1:50 to 1:400) for use in open-angle glaucoma and for other ophthalmic purposes.

Levarterenol or (−)-norepinephrine is (−)-α-(aminomethyl)-3,4-dihydroxybenzyl alcohol. It is usually used as the bitartrate salt, which is a white or faintly gray, crystalline powder. It slowly darkens when exposed to air and light. Solutions of this hormone should not be used if they are brown in color or contain a precipitate. Levarterenol is a sympathetic stimulant with predominantly α-receptor adrenergic activity. It is a strong peripheral vasoconstrictor and is especially useful in restoration of blood pressure in acute hypotensive situations such as may result from spinal anesthesia.

Levarterenol bitartrate is usually administered by intravenous infusion. Usually, the equivalent of 4 mg of levarterenol is placed in 1000 mL of 5% dextrose injection and infused at a rate adjusted to maintain blood pressure.

Dopamine is used to treat cardiac decompensation and patients with acute hypotension. It is administered by intravenous infusion. Initial infusion rates are 0.5 to 5 μg/kg of body weight per minute; most patients can be maintained on a dose of 20 μg/kg of body weight per minute or less.

Thyroid Hormones

The **thyroid gland** in humans consists of two lobes that are lateral and inferior to the anterior aspect of the larynx and are connected across the larynx by an isthmus to produce a U-shaped structure averaging 30 g in weight. Galen vaguely described the thyroid in the second century, but its identity as a ductless gland was first described by Holler in 1776. Interestingly, Roger of Palermo used sponges and seaweed, high in iodine content, in the treatment of goiter (thyroid enlargement) in the 12th century.

Thyroid gland mobilizes dietary iodine, converting it to an organic compound that can accelerate metabolic processes. It is necessary to the development and function of all body cells. The actual molecular form of the thyroid hormone or hormones exclusive of calcitonin, which has a hypocalcemic action that is distinct from the physiologic responses usually associated with this gland, remains unclear. The iodine-containing levorotatory amino acids, thyroxine and triiodothyronine, occur in the gland and are physiologically active upon oral administration. These metabolites also occur in the gland bound with globulin (thyroglobulins), and the exogenously administered amino acids could conceivably bind with serum protein to form physiologically active molecules that are responsible for the ultimate hormonal action. The thyroid gland can store thyroglobulins and other iodometabolites. The release of these thyroid hormones appears to be controlled by thyrotropin (thyroid-stimulating hormone or TSH) a hormone of the anterior pituitary.

Manifestations of hypothyroidism may be caused by an iodine deficiency and a resulting lack of precursor moieties for the hormonal substances (simple hyperplastic goiter, which is characterized by a compensatory enlargement of the gland), by a deficiency of thyrotropic factors, or by other metabolic irregularities. The first two causes may be corrected by adding iodine to the diet or administering thyrotropin, respectively. Naturally, replacement therapy with thyroid hormones can be used for a deficiency of any origin.

A hypothyroid condition results in some degree of cretinism in infants and of myxedema in adults. Cretinism is characterized by retarded and abnormal growth, arrested sexual development, mental deficiency, thickened and dry skin, thickened tongue, coarsened features, and a fall in the metabolic rate. The features of myxedema include general lethargy, retarded mental processes, increased body fat, susceptibility to cold and fatigue, cardiac dilatation, dry and thickened skin, coarsened features with a thickened and protruding tongue.

Thyroid hyperactivity results in thyrotoxicosis characterized by increased heart rate, blood pressure, nervous excitability, and metabolic rate, muscular weakness with tremor, loss of body weight and fat, and an increased tolerance to cold but intolerance to heat. When accompanied by protrusion of the eyeballs (exophthalmos), the condition is known as exophthalmic goiter (Graves' or Basedow's disease). The course of the disease is marked by occasional crises or ''storms,'' which may result in abrupt death. These symptoms of thyroid hyperactivity may result from overdose of thyroid preparations; thus, the rationality of using thyroid preparations in obesity ''cures'' is questionable. Treatment of organic hyperthyroidism is principally surgical, aided by radioactive iodine and by antimetabolites such as propylthiouracil. Improved manipulation of the latter approaches may supplant surgery in selected cases.

Preparations of thyroid hormones are useful for replacement therapy in cretinism or myxedema. Early diagnosis and treatment are essential in cretinism to avoid irreversible body and mental retardation. These preparations are also employed to prevent myxedema in cases in which the thyroid gland must be surgically removed. Preparations from the thyroid gland are sometimes used as pharmacologic agents for their influence on various metabolic processes, but the success of such therapy is difficult to predict.

The responses elicited by exogenous thyrox-

Thyroxine (T₄)

Triiodothyronine (T₃)

ine and triiodothyronine differ quantitatively. Triiodothyronine exhibits a more rapid onset and a shorter duration of action. This difference appears to be related to the extent of ionization of the 4′-phenolic group in the respective substances at physiologic pH. Thyroxine is approximately 90% ionized and is predominantly protein-bound in the blood. The reversible binding to plasma proteins is apparently electrostatic, and the strength of the bond varies among the different plasma proteins. Drugs such as salicylates and phenytoin disrupt the weaker bonds (potential drug-drug interaction) to increase the physiologic impact of thyroid hormones.

Relative binding and biopharmaceutic properties of thyroxine and triiodothyronine are also illustrated by their normal serum levels. The normal human serum levels of triiodothyronine range from 60 to 160 ng/mL, but the concentration of thyroxine is approximately 60 times higher.

Biosynthesis of Thyroid Hormone. Our understanding of thyroid hormone biosynthesis has increased in recent years. The first step is the active transport and concentration of inorganic iodine in the thyroid epithelial cells and is stimulated by TSH, thyroid stimulating hormone, an anterior pituitary hormone. In turn, TSH release from the pituitary is controlled by positive effectors from the hypothalamus, thyrotropin-releasing factor, somatostatin, and dopamine, and by negative input from the thyroid hormones. Once iodide is trapped by the thyroid gland, it is rapidly oxidized in a peroxidase-dependent reaction to iodine (I_2). Thyroid peroxidases also catalyze the iodination of the large thyroglobulin molecule to form monoiodotyrosine and diiodotyrosine. Thyroglobulin is a large (600,000 daltons) glycoprotein that contains 120 tyrosyl groups, which are sites for the iodination. T_3 (3,5,3′-triiodothyronine) is then formed by coupling of monoiodotyrosine and diiodotyrosine moieties through an ether linkage while they are still part of the thyroglobulin molecule. Similarly, T_4 is formed by ether coupling of two diiodotyrosine moieties. T_3 and T_4 are stored in the gland's follicles as part of thyroglobulin until TSH stim-

ulates their release through proteolysis of the peptide linkages in thyroglobulin. The active circulating thyroid hormones are T_3 and T_4. T_4 arises solely as described above, but some T_3 is also generated peripherally by monodeiodination of T_4. Approximately one third of the thyroxine excreted by the normal thyroid gland undergoes metabolic deiodination to triiodothyronine in peripheral tissues. Such considerations suggest that triiodothyronine is truly the active molecular form responsible for thyroid activity, but the significance of its metabolic relationship with thyroxine relative to biologic control processes needs further clarification.

Deiodination in various body tissues is the major catabolic pathway for thyroxine and triiodothyronine. However, other metabolic pathways are known, including deamination and oxidation in the kidney to form acetic acid analogs and conjugation in the liver followed by biliary excretion. Some differences have been detected in the latter pathway. The β-glucuronide is the major conjugation product of thyroxine, but the sulfate ester is more common for triiodothyronine. None of the catabolic pathways is especially rapid, and manipulation of these processes offers no significant potential for achievement of therapeutic objectives.

Thyroid is the cleaned, dried, and powdered thyroid gland previously deprived of connective tissue and fat. It is obtained from domesticated animals that are used for food by humans. Thyroid contains not less than 0.095% and not more than 0.125% of total thyroxine and triiodothyronine, and the ratio of thyroxine to triiodothyronine is not less than 5:1. It is free from inorganic iodine or iodine in any combination other than that peculiar to the thyroid gland.

Thyroid is effective in oral therapy. The effect of a single dose of thyroid orally, or of thyroxine orally or intravenously, is not manifest for some 24 to 48 hours; it reaches a maximum in 8 to 10 days and decreases slowly over a period of several weeks. Hence, accumulation may occur, and dosage schedules must be adjusted individually to the needs of the patient.

Thyroglobulin is obtained by fractionation of porcine thyroid gland. It contains thyroxine and triiodothyronine in a ratio of not less than 2.8:1. The source is restricted to *Sus scrofa* Linné var. *domesticus* Gray (Fam. Suidae), because the hog accumulates especially high levels of the thyroid hormones and has a higher proportion of triiodothyronine. Thyroglobulin is used in essentially the same manner as thyroid.

Sodium levothyroxine is the sodium salt of the levo isomer of thyroxine, an active physiologic principle obtained from the thyroid gland of domesticated animals used for food by humans. It can also be prepared synthetically.

Sodium levothyroxine is classed as a thyroid hormone. It is used for replacement therapy of reduced or completely absent thyroid function (manifested as myxedema, cretinism, and mild forms of hypothyroidism). Consistent potency, prolonged duration of action, and easily monitored plasma levels prompt many authorities to consider levothyroxine the agent of choice for thyroid replacement therapy. It is also used as adjunct therapy to suppress thyrotropin release in adenoma goiter and thyrotropin-dependent thyroid gland carcinoma. Its use to treat such vague symptoms as dry skin, fatigue, habitual abortion, obesity, and sterility in the absence of confirmed hypothyroidism is inappropriate and may be dangerous.

Sodium liothyronine is the sodium salt of the levorotatory isomer of 3,3′,5-triiodothyronine. This physiologically active compound is a naturally occurring thyroid hormone, but quantities needed for commercial purposes are provided by chemical synthesis. Sodium liothyronine is used for the same purposes as sodium levothyroxine. Liothyronine, compared to other thyroid agents, has better gastrointestinal absorption, a more rapid onset of action, and a shorter duration of action.

Liotrix is a 4:1 mixture of synthetic sodium levothyroxine and sodium liothyronine. The effects of this mixture are claimed to resemble closely those of endogenous thyroid secretion and to give laboratory protein-bound iodine test results that are more consistent with clinical response than are the results obtained with other preparations. However, recognition of the conversion of thyroxine to triiodothyronine in peripheral tissues raises questions about any therapeutic advantage of this mixture over its individual components.

Consensus equivalents for comparison of the various thyroid preparations, based on 65 mg of thyroid are thyroglobulin, 65 mg; sodium levothyroxine, 100 μg; sodium liothyronine, 25 μg; and liotrix formulations containing 50 or 60 μg

of levothyroxine and 12.5 or 15 μg of liothyronine.

Sodium dextrothyroxine is the salt of the synthetically prepared dextrorotatory isomer of thyroxine. Dextrothyroxine reduces serum cholesterol and low-density lipoproteins, and it has been classed as a hypocholesterolemic agent. Its greatest therapeutic use is in this area, but patients must be monitored carefully for ischemic myocardial changes and other adverse reactions.

Pancreatic Hormones

The bulk of the **pancreas** is an exocrine gland that supplies digestive enzymes to the duodenum. Isolated groups of cells, the islets of Langerhans, constituting about 3% of the gland, produce the hormonal substances. **Glucagon** is produced by the α-cells, and **insulin** is formed by the β-cells. Glucagon and insulin, both polypeptide hormones, exert counterbalancing actions on carbohydrate metabolism in the body.

Glucagon elicits a hyperglycemic response by increasing adenyl cyclase, which in turn increases liver phosphorylase activity, a key factor in glycogenolysis. The hypoglycemic action of insulin appears to involve glucokinase, membrane transport, and perhaps other factors associated with normal metabolism of blood glucose. In the normal individual, these hormones function to maintain blood glucose within a physiologically tolerated balance by increasing or decreasing, respectively, the glucose level.

Pathologic conditions related to a deficiency in glucagon formation either do not occur, have an insufficient survival factor to create a medical problem, or are unrecognized. The typical case of a hypofunctioning pancreas gland results in insulin deficiency and the condition known as diabetes mellitus. This condition was described by Auretaeus in the first century as a siphoning of flesh into urine; it is characterized by a high blood-glucose level (hyperglycemia), excess glucose in the urine (glucosuria), and diuresis, resulting in dehydration and constipation. The primary impairment of glucose metabolism induces a number of secondary metabolic changes. Accumulation in the blood of such metabolites as β-hydroxybutyric acid, ketone bodies, and other breakdown products of fats is common. The untreated diabetic, as a result of such metabolic irregularities, suffers from severe acidosis, depression, coma, and ultimately death.

Treatment of diabetes mellitus with insulin is replacement therapy. Insulin prolongs life in the diabetic and permits a fuller and happier life, but its use does not cure or prevent the pathologic condition. Insulin is especially valuable in preventing the complications of diabetes that are frequently the cause of death: arteriosclerosis with hypertension, nephritis, superficial ulcers and infections, gangrene of the extremities, and gallstones.

Conditions of hyperinsulinism may result from overdosage of insulin, underfeeding, tumors of the pancreas, or certain pituitary or adrenal disturbances. Outstanding symptoms are fatigue, hunger, marked sweating, and convulsions.

In the management of diabetes mellitus caused by insulin deficiency, an adequate diet is determined, and the amount and spacing of insulin dosage are established to keep the patient symptom-free and free from glucosuria. The plasma half-life of insulin is approximately 10 minutes; therefore, continuous delivery of the hormone is needed in replacement therapy. This is accomplished by subcutaneous administration of a suspension that is formulated to provide slow release of the insulin. Insulin is a potent drug, and the therapeutic considerations are relatively complex and sophisticated. Dosage must be coordinated with dietary intake, and a regularized eating schedule is necessary to accommodate the programmed delivery of insulin and to avoid drug-induced hypoglycemia. The over-the-counter status of insulin, compared with other drugs, is inconsistent with the inherent complexity and risks of the therapy, but it is indicative of what can be achieved by concerted patient education programs. Insulin pumps are available and are being further developed. They are designed with microcomputer chips that respond to the patient's need for insulin. It is hoped that such devices will help maintain a more constant glucose level and reduce the complications of diabetes. Recent studies have shown that complications are reduced as glucose levels are maintained at more constant levels, either by more frequent monitoring of glucose levels and more frequent administration of insulin if needed, or by the use of pumps.

One USP unit of insulin can cause the metabolism of approximately 1.5 g of glucose. Occasionally, insulin resistance or tolerance develops, and abnormally high doses of insulin are required to control diabetes. The resistance appears to involve antibody binding to restrict the biologic availability of much of the administered hormone; a high-potency insulin (500 units/mL) is available by prescription for such cases. Resistance caused by antibody formation occurs more frequently with nonhuman insulins, but can occur with human insulin as well. Resistance caused by antibody formation may be managed by changing the insulin species source, or if that is not effective, by administering corticosteroids that decrease IgG production or decrease insulin binding to the antibody. Resistance that involves receptor insensitivity (and not antibodies) may also occur in obese patients, patients with acanthosis nigricans, patients with insulin receptor defects, or during infections or pregnancy. These are usually managed with high doses of concentrated insulin (500 units/mL). The objective of high doses in resistant cases is distinct from such uses in treating schizophrenic states. An insulin overdose in the latter situation is used to induce therapeutically convulsive (hypoglycemic) shock.

Glucagon can be used in diagnosis and in the treatment of hypoglycemia associated with improper management of diabetes mellitus or with psychiatrically induced insulin shock. Intravenous administration of glucose can also be used to treat hypoglycemia, but glucagon is more convenient to use with unconscious or uncooperative nonhospitalized patients.

Glucagon is a straight-chained polypeptide containing 29 amino acid residues with a molecular weight of 3485. The amino acid sequence has been determined. The isoelectric point of the hormone is between 7.5 and 8.5. It is soluble in acids and bases, below 3.0 and above 9.5, respectively; these solutions are relatively stable. The alkali stability of glucagon can be used for the selective inactivation of insulin, which is a labile cystine-containing contaminant that is difficult to remove quantitatively in the isolation of this hormone.

Insulin is a polypeptide with a molecular weight of 5734. It contains 48 amino acid residues (including three cystine residues) that are arranged in two linear chains connected by disulfide linkages. Insulin tends to form dimeric and hexameric forms, a characteristic that resulted in an initial estimate of about 35,000 for the molecular weight of the hormone. This hormone has been studied more extensively than any other polypeptide hormone. One of the interesting observations resulting from these studies is the variation in amino acid residues 8, 9, and 10 depending on the origin of the insulin (Fig. 10–2). The amino acid sequence in these three positions has no effect on the normal physiologic properties of the polypeptide. Variations in this portion of the molecule cause some antigenic reactions, and this is the basis for selecting

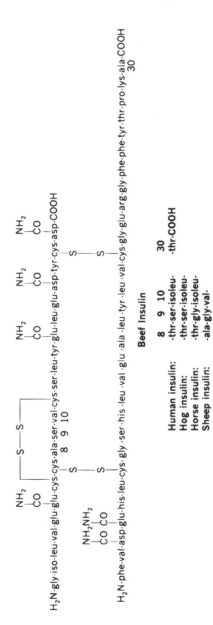

Fig. 10–2. Structures of insulin from several mammals.

human insulin in cases of suspected insulin hypersensitivity or tolerance. However, most of the early cases of hypersensitivity to insulin preparations can be explained by other foreign proteins that were present in the formulations. The distinctive amino acid residue 30 of the larger peptide chain of human insulin is apparently without physiologic significance, because an analog lacking amino acid residues 26 to 30 retains activity.

The disulfide bonds that link the two peptide chains are major obstacles to the feasible synthesis of insulin, and the biosynthetic accomplishment of this feat was made possible by the development of biotechnology tools. The elucidation of proinsulin significantly clarified the biologic formation of the hormone. Proinsulin is a straight-chain polypeptide containing 86 amino acid residues and all of the disulfide linkages inherent to insulin. The polypeptide sequences at the amino terminal and carboxylic acid terminal ends of the proinsulin molecule correspond to the two chains of insulin, and a proteolytic enzyme in the pancreas apparently cleaves peptide bonds to remove the connecting polypeptide sequence (called the "C-peptide") and to form the physiologically active two-chained insulin.

In the pancreatic cells, proinsulin is derived from a larger precursor, called preproinsulin, that has a signal peptide attached. The signal peptide is cleaved as the molecule is transported across the endoplasmic reticulum membrane of the beta cells. Both processed insulin and the C-peptide are stored in beta cell granules, and both are liberated during secretion. The exact function of the C-peptide is not currently understood. Normal secretion of insulin is a continuous process, although blood levels of the hormone can increase several-fold after a carbohydrate-rich meal.

Insulin was crystallized in 1926 by the addition of traces of zinc, and crystals of zinc insulin formed the original reference standard of the USP. The isoelectric point of zinc insulin is 5.1 to 5.3. Thus, it is soluble at the alkaline pH of tissue fluids and is rapidly absorbed from subcutaneous injection sites. Insulin is digested by proteolytic enzymes (a common property of polypeptide hormones), and it is ineffective when given orally.

Prior to the development of biotechnology techniques, all insulin and glucagon were derived from the pancreas glands of animals. Production from these sources is still used, although human insulin is used in many patients. One form of human insulin is produced by semisynthetic modification of pork insulin isolated from pork pancreas glands. The procedures for isolation of the proteins are relatively complex, a situation that is common for the isolation and purification of most peptide molecules. At least 20 major steps are accomplished before a form of insulin suitable for human use is finally developed. Immediately following their removal from slaughtered animals, the raw beef and pork pancreases are frozen to prevent enzymatic destruction of the insulin in the gland. About 8000 lb of animal pancreases are needed to yield 1 lb of pure zinc insulin crystals.

The first step in actual production involves grinding of the frozen powder with acidic alcohol to obtain the insulin and to suppress enzyme activity, centrifuging the crude extract to separate the liquid extract containing the insulin and impurities, evaporating in vacuum to remove the alcohol, treating the concentrate to separate the fat, filtering to remove residual fat, adding salt water to precipitate the insulin, redissolving the precipitate, reprecipitating by isoelectric means, buffering to obtain a uniformly soluble product, washing, drying, and pooling the insulin obtained from other lots prepared in the same manner, and determining the potency. Insulin prepared in this manner may be subjected to further purification by ion-exchange chromatography to yield a purified insulin product (not more than 10 parts per million proinsulin contaminant).

Contaminating proinsulin can cause immunogenic responses. All insulins contain less than 25 parts per million (ppm) proinsulin; "improved single peak" insulin contains < 20 ppm, and "purified" insulin contains < 10 ppm proinsulin. Purified pork insulins have about 1 ppm, and human insulin prepared by recombinant DNA techniques or semisynthetically (these approaches are described below) have 0 and 1 ppm, respectively.

Commercial production of human insulin has been achieved using three approaches. Pork insulin is converted to human insulin by replacing enzymatically the terminal alanine amino acid residue with threonine. Two recombinant DNA techniques have also been used for microbial synthesis. In the first rDNA approach, the genes (DNA) that direct the biosynthesis of the A and B polypeptide chains of human insulin are expressed in separate clones of *E. coli*. In each clone the gene for the A or B chain was fused to a bacterial promoter and inserted into a plasmid. The plasmids were transformed into separate strains of *E. coli*. Once appropriate recombinant colonies were identified, the peptide chains were overexpressed in large scale fermentation. The individual peptides ended up in inclusion bodies in the respective *E. coli* cells. Inclusion bodies are opaque structures that are often formed in *E. coli* in response to large scale production of protein, probably as a way of protecting the cell from the produced material. Inclusion bodies will precipitate as the cells are broken, aiding in the purification of the proteins. However, the recovered proteins will have been wrongly folded and cross-linked within the inclusion bodies and must be denatured and renatured in a more dilute solution to regain the individual insulin chains. Consequently, the A chain of 21 amino acids and the B chain of 30 amino acids are purified separately, and the complete insulin molecule is chemically synthesized from the chains by forming two disulfide bridges. It must be further purified to obtain crystalline, pure insulin, which is tested by a variety of criteria including crystal shape, biological activity, and electrophoresis to ensure that no contaminants are present.

In recent years, another procedure involving only one strain of recombinant *E. coli* has replaced the initial procedure. The messenger RNA for preproinsulin was isolated from cancerous pancreatic beta cells, which overproduce insulin (these "insulinoma cells" were used because the insulin mRNA is the predominant species of mRNA in the cell), and cDNA of the preproinsulin transcript was generated using reverse transcriptase. The signal peptide sequence of the native transcript was replaced with one that signals secretion in *E. coli*, specifically the signal sequence for β-lactamase. This modified gene was cloned into an *E. coli* plasmid under the control of an *E. coli* promoter and overexpressed. The proinsulin is secreted into the periplasmic space of the *E. coli* organisms. Lysis of the cell wall without disruption of the cell membrane yields almost pure proinsulin. It is isolated and treated with trypsin to generate active A and B chain insulin with the disulfide bonds already in place. The second approach is less expensive because it involves only one fermentation and the downstream processing and purification is substantially less involved.

The absolute therapeutic indication for human insulin may be rare. It produces a lower incidence of allergic reactions than many of the products from animal pancreas glands, and it may have special use in the small proportion of diabetes allergic to purified pork insulin.

Nevertheless, the availability of human insulin from non-meat sources is an advantage. Human insulins are particularly indicated when there is local insulin allergy or lipodystrophy at the injection site, in patients with insulin resistance, for temporary insulin administration (e.g,. gestational diabetes), and in newly diagnosed diabetes.

Glucagon for injection is a mixture of the hydrochloride with one or more suitable, dry diluents. When the aqueous injection is reconstituted, it has a pH between 2.5 and 3.0 and is usually formulated to contain 1 mg/mL.

Insulin injection or insulin is a sterile, neutral solution of the active principle of the pancreas that affects the metabolism of glucose. It is a prompt-acting preparation with an onset within 30 minutes to 1 hour, a peak of action at 2 to 5 hours, and a duration of 6 to 8 hours. This is the preparation of choice when glucose tolerance fluctuates rapidly; such situations may include the presence of a severe infection, shock, surgical trauma, or unstable diabetes. Insulin preparations, including insulin injection, must be labeled to indicate the nature (e.g., beef and pork, beef, pork, or human) of the insulin; when a product meets the standards for purified insulin, this must also be indicated on the label. The usual dose, for diabetic acidosis, intravenously, is 1 to 2 units/kg of body weight, repeated in 2 hours as necessary; for diabetes, 10 to 20 units, subcutaneously, 3 or 4 times a day according to the needs of the patient.

With the recent emphasis on maintaining tighter control of glucose levels to reduce diabetic complications, patients are being advised to monitor blood glucose levels frequently and to administer more frequent doses of insulin if needed.

Preparations of insulin are marketed in multiple-dose ampules of varying unitage. The package color of commercial products varies with the unit value. Standard insulin formulations contain 100 units/mL but concentrated insulin containing 500 units/mL is also available.

Isophane insulin suspension, isophane insulin, or NPH insulin is a sterile suspension in a phosphate buffer of insulin made from zinc-insulin crystals modified by the addition of protamine in such a manner that the solid phase of the suspension consists of crystals composed of insulin, protamine, and zinc. It provides 100 USP insulin units in each milliliter. It is an intermediate-acting insulin preparation.

Isophane insulin is insoluble at the pH of tissue fluids and therefore has a slow absorption rate. The onset of action occurs in 1 to 1.5 hours, the maximum effect occurs at 4 to 12 hours with a 24 hour duration of action. A preparation containing 70% isophane insulin and 30% insulin is available in a 100-unit formulation to give a rapid onset of activity and a 24-hour duration of action.

Insulin zinc suspension or lente insulin is a type of intermediate-acting insulin preparation. It consists of a mixture of crystalline and amorphous materials (approximately a 7:3 ratio) suspended in an acetate buffer. It provides 100 USP insulin units in each milliliter.

The use of an acetate buffer provides a prolonged duration of action. Achievement of this objective without the addition of foreign proteins, such as protamine, circumvents occasional hypersensitivity problems associated with these additives. The ratio of crystalline and amorphous insulin is selected to give a convenient duration of action of approximately 24 hours.

Lente insulin has an onset of 1.5 to 2 hours and a peak between 7 and 15 hours.

Extended insulin zinc suspension or ultralente insulin is a sterile suspension in an acetate buffer of insulin modified by the addition of zinc chloride in such a manner that the solid phase of the suspension is crystalline. It provides 100 USP insulin units in each milliliter. It is a long-acting insulin preparation; the duration of action is determined by the particle size and persists for over 36 hours. Ultralente insulin has an onset of 4 to 8 hours and reaches peak levels between 10 and 30 hours.

Parathyroid Hormone and Calcitonin

Calcium homeostasis in the body is controlled by parathyroid hormone, calcitonin, and the various metabolites of vitamin D. Calcium levels in the blood are normally in the range of 4.5 to 5.7 mEq/L (10 to 11 mg/dL). Regulation occurs with parathyroid hormone and calcitonin having counterbalancing effects on the bone (the storage site of calcium), the intestine (absorption of dietary calcium), and the kidneys (excretion of calcium) to achieve the correct blood concentration. Parathyroid hormone is released in response to hypocalcemia and promotes resorption of calcium from bone and conversion of 25-hydroxy D_3 to 1,25-dihydroxy D_3 within the kidney. Parathyroid hormone and 1,25-dihydroxy D_3 promote calcium reabsorption within the kidney tubules, and the vitamin D_3 metabolite promotes intestinal uptake of calcium. On the other hand, calcitonin is released in response to hypercalcemia and has a hypocalcemic effect by suppressing bone resorption, inhibiting intestinal absorption of calcium, and increasing renal excretion of calcium.

The **parathyroid glands** in humans are usually four in number, oval, 5 to 6 mm in length, and situated upon or imbedded in the dorsal surface of the thyroid gland. They develop and function independently of thyroid tissue. For a number of years, after their discovery by Sandstrom in 1880, the parathyroids were considered to be remnants of embryonic thyroid tissue.

Acute parathyroid hormone deficiency results in tetany when the level of serum calcium falls from normal (10 to 11 mg/dL) to around 6 to 7 mg/dL. Fibrillary muscular twitching progresses to the convulsive state, culminating in death by tetanic spasm of the larynx and muscles of respiration.

Parathyroid hyperfunction produces a condition known as Recklinghausen's disease of bone (osteitis fibrosa cystica), characterized by bone pain, marked elevation of serum calcium with a fall in serum phosphate, and cystic rarefaction of bones with spontaneous fracture and deformity. The calcium removed from bone is excreted in the urine. A similar picture may result from overdose with extracts of parathyroid gland. In either case, renal stones and calcification of soft tissues occur.

The **parathyroid hormone** is a straight-chain polypeptide containing 83 amino acid residues and has a molecular weight of approximately 9500. A portion of the molecule that contains only 35 amino acid residues can elicit the significant physiologic activity of the hormone. The essential 35-amino-acid subunit of human parathyroid hormone differs in five or six of its amino acid residues from the animal parathyroid hormones that are available through the meat-packing industry. Immunologic recognition of this factor may contribute to the high incidence of tolerance noted in therapy. The hormone has a hypercalcemic action. Its principal effect involves bone resorption and calcium release, but it also promotes absorption of calcium from the gut and renal tubules.

Parathyroid hormone is inactivated in the intestinal tract, but it has been used parenterally in medicine for blood-calcium maintenance in cases of parathyroid tetany. Following injection, the blood calcium level rises in about 4 hours, reaching a maximum in about 16 hours and returning to the original level after 24 to 36 hours. Repeated or prolonged administration may establish a complete tolerance with abolition of therapeutic effect. To avoid this, dihydrotachysterol may frequently be substituted; this preparation may be given orally. Adequate intake of calcium, phosphate, and vitamin D must be assured. Some authorities question the justification for using parathyroid hormone for therapeutic purposes, and its current use is primarily in the diagnostic area (the synthetic 35-amino acid subunit of the human parathyroid hormone called teriparatide acetate is used for these diagnostic purposes; see its description under ''Diagnostics'' later in this chapter).

Calcitonin is a polypeptide containing 32 amino acid residues. The individual amino acid composition of calcitonin from different animal sources varies considerably. The key molecular features for biologic activity appear to include a prolinamide moiety at the carboxyl terminal end of the peptide and a cyclic subunit containing six amino acid residues, including the ring closing cystine, at the amino terminal end of the molecule. Reduction of the disulfide linkage causes a loss of activity.

Calcitonin can be used to treat Paget's disease (osteitis deformans) and postmenopausal osteoporosis, and to control hypercalcemia secondary to other osteolytic conditions. The preparation used in therapy is a synthetic salmon calcitonin. Salmon calcitonin elicits twentyfold or more activity on a molar basis than human or porcine calcitonins; the apparent increased potency may be caused, in part, by a greater affinity for receptor sites and thus a slower rate of degradation and a longer duration of action. Circulating antibodies to salmon calcitonin occur after 2 to 18 months of treatment in about half of treated Paget's disease patients, but calcitonin therapy remained effective in many of these cases. Occasionally patient's with high antibody titers will be found, and these patients are refractory to salmon calcitonin. Human calcitonin (also made synthetically) is usually effective in these patients. In general, the risk of diminishing efficacy and hypersensitivity reactions is less with the use of human calcitonin. Interestingly, however, the side effects of nausea and vomiting and flushing of the face or hands is somewhat more frequent with the human calcitonin.

Gastrointestinal Hormones

The intestinal mucosa secretes such peptide hormones as cholecystokinin, gastrin, and secretin. These hormones facilitate digestion by stimulating the release by the gastrointestinal tract or the pancreas of various enzymes and other exocrine substances. There is no therapeutic indication for these hormones, but several are used diagnostically, either as the complete hormone or, more frequently, as an active synthetic peptide subunit of the natural hormone. These diagnostic aids are addressed in the section devoted to those agents later in the chapter.

Cholecystokinin contains 33 amino acid residues in a linear chain, but the carboxylic acid-terminal octapeptide is fully active. Cholecystokinin stimulates the secretion of pancreatic digestive enzymes, the flow of bile, and the contraction of the gallbladder.

Secretin normally increases the bicarbonate content and volume of secretion from the pancreas. It is a linear polypeptide containing 27 amino acid residues; the amino acid sequence has a noticeable similarity to that of glucagon.

Gastrin increases gastrointestinal motility and stimulates the secretion of gastric acid, pepsin, and intrinsic factor.

Pituitary and Hypothalamic Hormones

The human **pituitary gland or hypophysis** is situated in a small cavity in the sphenoid bone at the base of the skull and is attached to the base of the brain by a short stalk. It weighs about 0.5 g. Galen considered it a strainer for spinal fluid, and Vesalius later thought it was the source of mucus that lubricated the nasopharynx. Pituitary is from the Latin *pituita*, meaning slime or mucus.

The pituitary body is in reality three glands by origin and function:

1. The anterior lobe is ectodermal in origin—derived from an outpouching from the primitive pharynx.
2. The intermediate lobe, which is not well developed in humans but does produce melanocyte-stimulating hormone (MSH).
3. The posterior lobe is neural in origin—derived from an outpouching of the base of the brain.

The hormones of the pituitary gland are as follows:

Anterior lobe
  Follicle-stimulating hormone (FSH)
  Luteinizing hormone (LH)
  Growth hormone (somatotropin, GH)

Prolactin
Adrenocorticotropic hormone (ACTH)
Thyroid-stimulating hormone (TSH)
Intermediate lobe
Melanocyte-stimulating hormone (MSH)
Posterior lobe
Vasopressin (antidiuretic hormone, ADH)
Oxytocin

Extracts of **posterior pituitary** lobe exhibit the following effects in experimental animals and in humans:

1. A pressor effect, owing to arteriolar and capillary vasoconstriction
2. Direct stimulation of smooth muscle, seen in the intact animal or in preparations of isolated muscles
3. An antidiuretic action, effected by increasing the tubular and collecting duct resorption of water in the kidney

The diversity of these effects complicated attempts at therapeutic use of unfractionated extracts of the posterior pituitary and the use of such preparations has been superceded by the use of oxytocin or vasopressin (antidiuretic hormone), the two hormonal substances that have been isolated from this gland. The two hormones are closely related octapeptides (Fig. 10–3) with five of the amino acid residues in a cyclic structure involving a labile cystine moiety. The hormones are prepared synthetically now. Their actions, especially those of vasopressin, show a degree of overlap.

Oxytocin is the uterine-stimulating fraction, and it is relatively free from action on other smooth muscle. It is especially active on the pregnant uterus, which has been sensitized by estrogens. Oxytocin appears to increase the permeability of uterine cell membranes to sodium ion with an effective augmentation of the contracting myofibrils. Some physiologic involvement by oxytocin in the normal onset of labor is suspected, but further scientific clarification is needed. Oxytocin is also released during lactation in response to the suckling stimulus and is responsible for milk ejection from the alveoli of the breast.

Vasopressin is the antidiuretic principle and is also called antidiuretic hormone or ADH. The pressor effects of this hormone are observed only when large quantities are administered. Vasopressin regulates the threshold for resorption of water by the epithelium of the renal tubules. The hormone is released into the blood when osmoreceptors in the hypothalamic nuclei detect an increased extracellular electrolyte concentration in the serum or a decreased blood volume. It interacts with specific receptor sites in the renal collecting ducts to enhance the reabsorption of solute-free water. The resulting fluid conservation contributes to maintenance of homeostasis.

No clinical conditions have yet been associated with hyperfunction of posterior pituitary. A deficiency state is seen only in the condition of diabetes insipidus, which follows a deficiency of antidiuretic hormone. The increased urine output when drinking alcoholic beverages is caused physiologically, in part, by a temporary deficiency state because alcohol inhibits the release of vasopressin.

Diabetes insipidus (literally an outpouring of tasteless urine) is characterized by a failure of renal resorption of water; there is a tremendous diuresis and associated tremendous thirst and

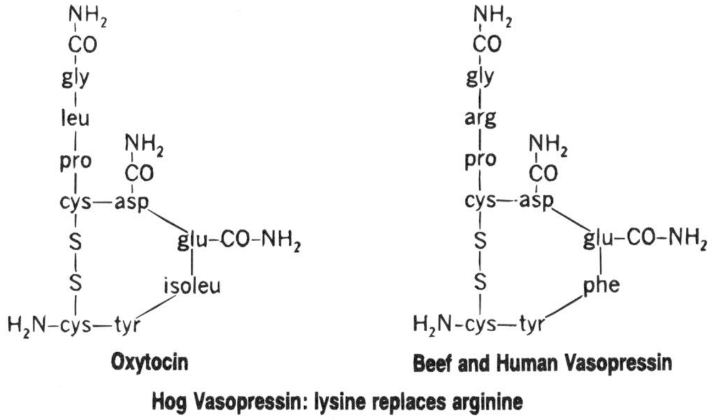

Oxytocin   **Beef and Human Vasopressin**

Hog Vasopressin: lysine replaces arginine

Fig. 10–3. Structures of oxytocin and vasopressin.

water intake. This condition must not be confused with the diabetes mellitus of insulin deficiency.

The biologic half-lives of oxytocin and vasopressin are short, a factor that can be considered an advantage or a disadvantage, depending on therapeutic objectives. Vasopressin is employed in replacement therapy for the management of diabetes insipidus, and one of the concerns in formulation is a need for an increase in the duration of action. Oxytocin is used as a pharmacologic agent for its oxytocic properties, and thus the desired duration of therapy is short.

The relatively small size of these polypeptides provided a focusing point for initial studies on chemical synthesis and structure-activity comparisons that undoubtedly have implications for all physiologically active polypeptides. It has been difficult to prepare analogs that are superior in therapeutic properties to the two naturally occurring hormones; most changes in the molecules result in a loss of activity. However, desmopressin, described below, is one synthetic analog with superior properties that has resulted from this effort.

Vasopressin injection is a sterile solution (of 8-L-arginine vasopressin) in water for injection. The water-soluble, pressor principle is prepared by synthesis (Pitressin Synthetic). It is also available as vasopressin tannate (Pitressin Tannate in Oil), a uniform suspension in peanut oil for intramuscular injection.

Vasopressin injection is standardized so that 1 mL possesses a pressor activity equivalent to 20 USP posterior pituitary units. It is administered intramuscularly or subcutaneously to control neurohypophyseal diabetes insipidus but is ineffective in the nephrogenic form of the disease. It is also used as a peristaltic stimulant in postoperative ileus and prior to abdominal radiography to dispel gas that would provide interfering shadows. It also is used to control acute hemorrhage in the gastrointestinal tract and esophagus.

The dosage of vasopressin must be adjusted to the needs of the individual patient, but convenient therapy is handicapped to a degree by the relatively rapid inactivation of the hormone in the body. The need to administer 5 to 10 USP units of vasopressin (vasopressin injection) 2 or 3 times daily is common. Formulation of vasopressin tannate in peanut oil was developed to give a gradual release of the hormone and a longer duration of action; an intramuscular injection of 2.5 to 5 USP units of this preparation may exert the desired action for 48 to 96 hours.

Lypressin or 8-lysine-vasopressin is a synthetically prepared peptide hormone that occurs naturally in the posterior lobe of the hog pituitary gland. It has the properties of causing the contraction of vascular and other smooth muscles and of producing antidiuresis. Slightly more stable than arginine-vasopressin, it is available as a nasal spray for treatment of diabetes insipidus. The onset of antidiuretic action is prompt, peaks in 30 minutes to 2 hours, and has a duration of action of 3 to 8 hours. Each milliliter of nasal spray contains 0.185 mg of lypressin, which is equivalent to 50 USP posterior pituitary pressor units, and each spray contains about two pressor units. The usual dosage is one or two sprays into each nostril four times daily, but patients can learn to control their own dosage based upon frequency of urination and thirst. An additional bedtime dose will help control nocturia. If more than two sprays every 4 to 6 hours are required, the dosing should be made more frequent, because more than two or three sprays per nostril results in drainage of the excess liquid through the nasopharynx into the digestive tract where it is inactivated.

Desmopressin or 1-deamino-8-D-arginine-vasopressin is a synthetic analog of arginine-vasopressin. It possesses little of the undesirable pressor effect of the parent hormone and has a prompt onset combined with a relatively long duration of action. A single dose of desmopressin produces an antidiuretic effect that persists for 8 to 20 hours. Desmopressin is used for the same purposes as vasopressin as well as treatment of primary nocturnal enuresis (along with behavioral conditioning). Desmopressin acetate is available as a solution for subcutaneous or intravenous injection and as a nasal solution. The antidiuretic effect of the injection is about ten times that of the equivalent intranasal dose. The nasal solution is available in nasal pipets containing 20 μg/0.2 mL or as a nasal spray with each spray containing 10 μg/0.1 mL (0.1 mg/mL). The solutions should be refrigerated, but the nasal solution will maintain stability for up to 3 weeks when stored at room temperature.

Oxytocin is a synthetically prepared peptide hormone that occurs naturally in the posterior lobe of the pituitary gland. Glandular material is no longer used as a commercial source of this hormone. The oxytocic principle is available as an injection for induction of labor for medical indications (use for elective induction is inappropriate) and for control of postpartum hemorrhage. A nasal spray is available to promote milk ejection on the infrequent occasions when this is a problem in breast feeding.

The dosage for induction of labor is determined by uterine response. Intravenous drip is the only appropriate method of administering oxytocin for induction of labor and must be done under constant monitoring of the strength of the contractions and the fetal heartbeat. The intravenous infusion is started at a rate of 0.001 to 0.002 units/min. The dose is increased in similar increments until a contraction pattern that resembles normal labor has been established. Overdosage can result in severe damage to both the mother and the infant, including infant brain damage or fetal death. The dosage for control of postpartum hemorrhage is 10 units intramuscularly after delivery of the placenta.

The **anterior lobe** of the pituitary exerts a profound influence on the growth and development of the body and on its sex characteristics through its stimulating actions on the other endocrine glands. The **anterior pituitary** has been referred to as the ''master gland,'' and the ''conductor of the endocrine symphony.'' Primary disturbances in anterior pituitary function may result in widespread endocrine involvement and generalized secondary disturbances. Therapy in such complex situations is far from simple and is associated with unusual potential for undesirable side effects. Effective therapeutic use of the hormones of the anterior pituitary is still in an early stage of development.

The secretion of hormones from the anterior lobe or adenohypophysis is regulated by the hypothalamus, which stores the regulatory hormones and releases them into the adenohypophyseal portal vasculature, causing the appropriate pituitary hormones to be released. The hypothalamic hormones are as follows:

Hormone	Structure
Gonadotropin releasing hormone (Gn-RH)	Decapeptide
Growth-hormone releasing hormone (GH-RH)	40 amino acids
Growth-hormone release inhibiting hormone (GH-RIH, somatostatin)	14 amino acids
Prolactin releasing factor (PRF)	Not known
Prolactin inhibiting factor (PIF)	Dopamine
Corticotropin releasing hormone (CRH)	41 amino acids
Thyrotropin releasing hormone (TRH)	Tripeptide

Most of the pituitary hormones (except ACTH) are large (20,000 to 40,000 MW) glycoproteins and are quite labile, whereas the hypothalamic hormones are peptides. Therefore, when the hypothalamic-pituitary axis is intact, the hypothalamic hormones make better therapeutic agents than the pituitary hormones. Also, analogs can be made that have antagonist instead of agonist activity. Hypothalamic hormones and their analogs are also used diagnostically to determine the site responsible for a hormonal deficiency. There are exceptions, of course, in that recombinant growth hormone, ACTH, and LH and FSH as they occur in urine are all pituitary hormones that currently are used therapeutically. It is likely that our understanding of both pituitary and hypothalamic function will increase in the next few years as a result of molecular biology tools as well as our ability to synthesize peptides and peptidomimetics, and new therapeutic opportunities are likely to arise.

The individual pituitary hormones and their releasing factors are described below. When a hormone, releasing hormone or analog is used therapeutically, the use is described. Diagnostic uses are described separately in the following section.

Adrenocorticotropin, ACTH, or corticotropin is a straight-chain polypeptide of approximately 4,500 molecular weight, containing 39 amino acid residues. A synthetic corticotropin, cosyntropin, consisting of the initial 24 amino acid residues has the full biologic activity of this hormone.

ACTH stimulates the production of glucocorticoids in the adrenal cortex by interacting with specific receptors and activating adenylate cyclase. ACTH can be used to increase glucocorticoid levels therapeutically, although it is less expensive to administer glucocorticoids directly; however, it does avoid the glucocorticoid associated problem of atrophy of the adrenal cortex.

Corticotropin injection is a sterile preparation of the peptide hormone that is derived from the anterior lobe of the pituitary of mammals used for food by humans. It is usually administered intramuscularly but can be administered by intravenous infusion if a rapid response is desired; however, this situation is uncommon, because the most frequent objection to the use of corticotropin injection is the short duration of action.

Repository corticotropin injection is corticotropin in a solution of partially hydrolyzed gelatin. This formulation has a prolonged therapeutic effect; its usual intramuscular dose is 40 USP units once daily. A similar, prolonged duration of action is obtained with a suspension prepared by adsorbing corticotropin on zinc hydroxide.

The gonadotropins, **follicle stimulating hormone (FSH)** and **luteinizing hormone (LH)** are anterior pituitary hormones responsible for aspects of sexual function in both males and females. FSH is a 32,000 molecular weight glycoprotein that is released in women in substantial amounts during the follicular stage of the menstrual cycle and is responsible for the development of the ovarian follicle. In males, FSH is thought to be responsible for maturation of the germinal elements of the testes and stimulates spermatogenesis and the production of testicular androgen-binding protein. In both the ovaries and the testes, FSH acts through binding to specific adenyl cyclase-linked receptors. LH is a 30,000 dalton glycoprotein that is released from the pituitary during the follicular stage of the menstrual cycle, and plasma levels rise abruptly just prior to ovulation. It stimulates estrogen production by the ovary and is required for progesterone production by the corpus luteum of the ovary. In the male, LH acts on the interstitial cells of the testes to stimulate testosterone production.

Supplies of LH and FSH from human pituitaries are limited, as one would expect, and animal-derived hormones are immunologically incompatible for therapeutic purposes. However, the urine of postmenopausal women contains high gonadotropin levels, and a purified preparation of these gonadotropins called **menotropins** or **urogonadotropins** (Pergonal) is used therapeutically. The urine gonadotropin levels are high in such women because atrophic ovaries cannot respond to tropic stimulation, thus precluding feedback suppression. The preparation contains approximately equal amounts of FSH and LH. It is used to enhance fertility in anovulatory women with functional ovaries and to stimulate spermatogenesis in hypogonadotropic males.

The usual dosage regimen for females involves intramuscular injection of 75 units each of FSH and LH daily for 9 to 12 days to stimulate follicular growth and maturation. One day after the last menotropins injection, 10,000 units of human chorionic gonadotropin is administered to simulate a preovulatory LH surge and to induce ovulation.

Approximately 75% of patients treated with combination gonadotropins ovulate, and conception results in 25% to 50% of those women. Multiple births occur in 20% to 30% of the suc-

cessful pregnancies, and 25% of the total pregnancies eventually terminate in spontaneous abortion. The incidence of congenital abnormalities is not increased.

The use of the gonadotropins can also result in a 0.5 to 2% incidence of ovarian hyperstimulation syndrome characterized by sudden ovarian enlargement and ascites. Therefore, patients receiving treatment need to be monitored.

The usual therapeutic regimen for males involves 4 to 6 months of pretreatment with human chorionic gonadotropin. Menotropin (75 units each of FSH and LH) is administered intramuscularly 3 times a week, and concurrent administration of human chorionic gonadotropin is continued at the rate of 2000 units twice weekly. The menotropin therapy should continue for at least 4 months.

Human chorionic gonadotropin (HCG) is not produced by the anterior pituitary, but is included here because of the similarity of its function to LH and its use therapeutically along with the menotropins. HCG is a gonad-stimulating hormone obtained from the urine of pregnant women and placental tissue. It is a 27,000 dalton glycoprotein that is immunologically similar to LH and is produced by the trophoblast of the placenta with maximum production occurring approximately 2 months after implantation. It is the hormone that is detected in modern over-the-counter pregnancy-testing kits and is usually detectable within a few days after implantation. Levels drop off after about 4 months of pregnancy.

HCG resembles LH in its actions and is used as replacement therapy to stimulate descent of the testes in cryptorchidism and to stimulate the development of interstitial cells of the testes in delayed adolescence and hypogonadotropic eunuchoidism. The major indication for withdrawal of therapy or reduction of dosage is sexual precociousness. Other degenerative side effects may be noted in females; hence, chorionic gonadotropin is infrequently used in females, although it can be used effectively in conjunction with menotropins to treat infertility and to maintain the functional integrity of the corpus luteum in some cases of habitual abortion. HCG has been used in weight-loss clinics, but its effectiveness in adjunct therapy for the treatment of obesity has not been demonstrated.

Chorionic gonadotropin is a relatively labile glycoprotein that contains about 12% of galactose. It must be administered parenterally and is formulated in a dry mixture with suitable diluents and buffers to give greater shelf life.

Somatropin, somatotropin, or growth hormone influences a number of essential growth processes. It stimulates linear growth of bones during development, and its anabolic effects include an increased intracellular transport of amino acids and a net body retention of nitrogen, phosphorus, and potassium. Hypofunction of the growth-stimulating activity in children results in the pituitary dwarf; in adults, such deficiency often produces an increased delicacy of structure, referred to as acromicria.

Growth hormones from various animal sources appear to be more species-specific in their activity than most other hormones. Human pituitary growth hormone contains 190 amino acid residues and two disulfide bonds. Lack of a feasible natural source or a feasible synthetic procedure for this pituitary hormone precluded consideration of therapeutic use for many years. However, recombinant DNA technology made possible the production of human growth hormone. The first recombinant human growth hormone (rHGH) was called somatrem (Protropin), and it contained an amino-terminal methionyl residue not found in natural HGH. The second rHGH was called somatropin (Humatrope, Nutropin) and had the same amino acid sequence as the native hormone.

When somatotropin is employed therapeutically, it is used to stimulate linear growth in patients with documented pituitary growth hormone deficiency. It is not indicated for use in patients with closed epiphyses. Many interactions, including influences of hormones of the adrenal cortex, gonads, parathyroid, and thyroid, contribute to growth. Therapy with somatropin must be monitored carefully. Use of this hormone is restricted to physicians experienced in the diagnosis and management of patients with pituitary growth hormone deficiency.

The usual dosage regimen of somatropin is 2 international units, intramuscularly, three times a week (a minimum of 48 hours between injections) for as long as growth continues. Treatment should be discontinued when the patient has reached a satisfactory adult height, when response to the therapy is no longer satisfactory. Five percent of the patients can be expected to develop neutralizing antibodies and to fail to respond to the hormone.

Growth hormone has been used for some other purposes in addition to growth hormone deficiency, some approved and some unapproved by the FDA. The use of somatropin for treatment of growth failure in children with chronic renal failure has been approved. It is also used widely to promote growth in female children with Turner's syndrome (a genetic disease resulting from a XO sex chromosome karyotype). In otherwise normal short children with normal levels of growth hormone, rHGH accelerates growth, but it is not clear that it increases final height. It also has been shown to accelerate wound healing in children with large cutaneous wounds and to increase lean body mass and decrease fat in growth hormone deficient adults, in the elderly, and in patients recovering from surgery. The safety of the use (especially long-term use) of growth hormone in patients not deficient in it is unknown, and use for these purposes is still controversial. This is especially true because of the high cost of the products.

Diagnostics

Because of the regulatory systems involved in hormone release and function, many of the aspects of hormonal function can be tested by administering hormones or hormone analogs and observing the effect on levels of other hormones. These products are described below.

Thyrotropin is the thyrotropic principle of the anterior pituitary. A glycoprotein in the 28,000 to 30,000 molecular weight range, it is obtained from bovine glands and is purified to remove significant amounts of corticotropic, gonadotropic, and other hormones. Theoretically, it can be used in replacement therapy, but it is used primarily as a diagnostic aid in evaluating thyroid function, including distinguishing between primary and secondary hypothyroidism. It is available as a lyophilized powder and is administered intramuscularly or subcutaneously.

Protirelin is a synthetic tripeptide that is identical to the natural thyrotropin releasing hormone produced by the hypothalamus. It stimulates the release of prolactin and TSH and is used as an adjunct in the diagnostic assessment of thyroid disease and patients with pituitary or hypothalamic dysfunction. Serum TSH in response to protirelin is measured to help establish the basic cause of hypothyroidism in a patient.

Pentagastrin is a synthetic pentapeptide corresponding to the C-terminus of the natural gastric hormone, gastrin. Like gastrin, it stimulates gastric acid production with peak responses occurring 20 to 30 minutes after subcutaneous injection. It is used to diagnose gastric acid secretory function in suspected pernicious anemia, atropic gastritis, or gastric carcinoma, all of which have reduced gastric acid production. It is also used to assess hypersecretion in diagnosis of Zollinger-Ellison tumor, duodenal ulcer, or postoperative stomal ulcer.

Secretin is a gastric hormone whose main natural function is to increase the volume and bicarbonate content of pancreatic juice. It is used intravenously to diagnose gastrinoma (Zollinger-Ellison syndrome) and pancreatitis. Patients with gastrinoma will release high levels of gastrin in response to secretin, whereas in normal patients only a small change or no change is observed in serum levels of gastrin. Patients with pancreatitis will secrete a lower volume of pancreatic juice with substantially lower amounts of bicarbonate than normal subjects. It should not be used in patients with acute pancreatitis until the attack has subsided.

Teriparatide acetate (hPTH 1-34) is a synthetic polypeptide consisting of the first 34 amino acid fragment of human parathyroid hormone and is the biologically active segment of the natural 84 amino acid hormone. It is used as a diagnostic agent to assist in distinguishing between hypoparathyroidism and pseudohypoparathyroidism (i.e., end organ resistance) in patients with hypocalcemia. Patients with hypoparathyroidism will show a tenfold or greater increase in urinary cAMP and phosphate in response to teriparitide, whereas those with pseudohypoparathyroidism will show a less than sixfold increase in the 0 to 30 minute postinfusion period, compared to a baseline collection.

Cosyntropin is a synthetically prepared peptide subunit of corticotropin and is used as a diagnostic aid in suspected adrenal insufficiency. It contains 24 amino acid residues and presents a lesser risk of allergenic reactions than the natural hormone. It is not used therapeutically because there is no repository form.

Gonadorelin HCl is a synthetic decapeptide that is identical to the gonadotropin-releasing factor of the hypothalamus. It is used diagnostically in suspected gonadotropin deficiency to evaluate the functional capacity and response of the gonadotropes of the anterior pituitary. The test in females should be conducted in the early follicular phase of the menstrual cycle.

Sermorelin acetate is an acetate salt of a synthetic 29-amino acid polypeptide that is the amino-terminal segment of the naturally occurring 44-amino acid polypeptide growth hormone-releasing hormone (called GHRH). It increases plasma growth hormone concentrations by direct stimulation of the pituitary gland. Sermorelin, also called GRH (1-29) or GHRH (1-29), is equivalent in activity to native GHRH. It is used as a single dose of 1 μg/kg to assess the ability of the pituitary to secrete growth hormone.

SUGGESTED READINGS

Anderson, H.V., Willerson, J.T.: Thrombolysis in Acute Myocardial Infarction. N. Engl. J. Med., *329*: 703, 1993.

Anon. Pegademase, Med. Lett. Drugs Ther. *32*:87, 1990.

Anon. Alpha-galactosidase to Prevent Gas, Med. Lett. Drugs Ther., *35*:29, 1993.

Anon. Recombinant Human Growth Hormone. Med. Lett. Drugs Ther., *36*:77, 1994.

Craig, C.R., Stitzel, R.E.: *Modern Pharmacology*, 3rd ed., Boston, Little, Brown & Co., 1990.

Esteve Foundation Symposium IV. *The Clinical Pharmacology of Biotechnology Products*. Amsterdam, Excerpta Medica; Distributor: New York, Elsevier, 1991.

Goodman, H.M.: *Basic Medical Endocrinology,* 2nd ed., New York, Raven Press, 1994.

Olin, B.R., Hebel, S.K., Gremp, J.L., Hulbert, M.K., eds.: *Drug Facts and Comparisons*. St. Louis, Facts and Comparisons, 1995.

Ruffolo, R.R., Jr., Nichols, A.J., Stadel, J.M., Hieble, J.P.: Structure and Function of α-Adrenoceptors, Pharmacol. Rev., *43*:475, 1991.

Ruffolo, R.R., Jr., ed.: β-*Adrenoceptors: Molecular Biology, Biochemistry, and Pharmacology. Prog. Basic Clin. Pharmacol*. Vol 7. Basel, Karger, 1991.

Voet, D., Voet, J.G.: *Biochemistry*. New York, John Wiley & Sons, 1990.

Wilson, J.D., Foster, D.W.: *Williams' Textbook of Endocrinology*. Philadelphia, WB Saunders, 1992.

11

Antibiotics

Antibiotics probably represent the greatest single contribution of drug therapy in the past half-century, a period characterized by unprecedented advancements in health care. This group of drugs provides effective control of many human microbial pathogens that previously caused prolonged incapacitation or death without appreciable regard for age, economic status, or physical fitness.

The word "antibiotic" is derived from the term antibiosis, which literally means "against life" (*anti*—against, *bios*—life). A measure of the significant and spectacular contribution of antibiotics to therapy is indicated by the common inclusion of the word in the layman's vocabulary. Most people have an accurate, or at least a functional, general concept of the word, but workers intimately involved in the antibiotic field find considerable difficulty in drafting a precise definition. The formal concept that is most widely accepted by scientific specialists defines an antibiotic as a chemical substance, produced by a microorganism, that has the capacity, in low concentration, to inhibit or kill, selectively, other microorganisms. The most critical component of this definition is the "selectivity" or "selective toxicity" which means that the compound inhibits or kills the microorganism without having a similar effect on the host organism (e.g., humans). Essentially all definitions limit antibiotics to compounds that exert their action in low concentrations. This definition excludes compounds such as ethanol that are active at higher concentrations and tend to have primarily a physical action on the microorganisms. (These compounds are generally referred to as "antiseptics.") The formal definition also excludes synthetic compounds. However, synthetic compounds are included equally with natural compounds and their derivatives in the term "antimicrobials" (which can

also be subdivided by the specific type of microbe being inhibited, e.g., antifungals, antibacterials, etc). For practical purposes, the term "antibiotic" and the term "antimicrobial" can be used interchangeably without regard to the source of the compound. For the purposes of this chapter, we have focused upon the natural antibiotics and their derivatives but have included a section on the synthetic antimicrobials in order to provide a complete picture of available agents.

DEVELOPMENTAL HISTORY

The history and development of antibiotics as therapeutic agents are similar to the patterns noted for other types of drugs. Relatively ineffective attempts to use materials that are now recognized as having antibiotic associations can be detected in folk medicine and in prepenicillin scientific literature. Development in the antibiotic field since 1940 is characterized by a practical blending of empiric observation and increasingly sophisticated manipulations of biologic and chemical factors. This familiar pattern is frequently overlooked because an aura of 20th-century miracle drugs has surrounded the antibiotics.

Reports, some dating back 2500 years, indicate that various ancient and primitive peoples applied moldy bread, soybean curds, and other materials to boils and wounds liable to infection; this can be considered a folk-medicine type of antibiotic therapy. Pasteur demonstrated bacterial antagonism shortly after he established the bacterial etiology of infectious disease. During the 1880s, attempts were made to utilize antagonism to achieve an ecologic control of the human microbial flora by introducing selected nonpathogenic organisms. Pyocyanase, a crude mixture of metabolites extracted from *Pseudomonas aeruginosa*, became available around the turn of the century and could be considered the first commercial antibiotic. Pyocyanase, at best, was a poor antibiotic by modern standards, but its failure to achieve wide acceptance as a therapeutic agent can be related, in part, to the variable composition of the crude mixture and the resultant lack of reproducible or predictable therapeutic responses.

Establishment of the therapeutic feasibility of penicillin antagonism in the early 1940s stimulated the intensive efforts that have culminated in the high level of current antibiotic development. Numerous approaches to the production and use of antibiotics have been used concurrently in the past, and practical considerations of biologic, chemical, and economic factors will undoubtedly dictate a similar situation in the predictable future.

The progressive trend in the logistic aspects of antibiotic development can be illustrated by the following sequence of objectives: (1) Screen diverse sources of microorganisms for detection of useful antagonism. (2) Select improved microbial mutants, determine optimal environmental and nutritional conditions, and develop suitable procedures for recovering antibiotics from cultures. (3) Direct or induce the formation of specific, desired metabolites. (4) Modify the fermentative metabolites by biologic or chemical manipulations to yield more useful antibiotic substances. (5) Develop procedures for total synthesis of antibiotics for possible economic advantage. (6) Use an adjunct agent to modify the availability or impact of an antibiotic. Interestingly, because of the complexity of the structures of most antibiotics, most of the useful compounds are produced fermentatively or semisynthetically, i.e., synthetic modification of a fermentatively-produced compound, even after a procedure for total synthesis has been developed. This is in sharp contrast to many other natural products which are identified from natural sources but then produced synthetically.

Initially, antibiotic therapy was commonly used in a wide range of microbial infections with only limited logic or design. However, with the accumulation of experience and the availability of a greater variety of antibiotics, the trend has moved toward a more precise diagnosis of the pathologic organism, including a consideration of sensitivity variations with certain pathogens, and a more conservative use of these valuable therapeutic agents.

Production of commercial quantities of the various antibiotics involves many different approaches and procedures to accommodate the individual biologic idiosyncrasies of the producing organisms and the chemical characteristics of the individual antibiotics. A detailed consideration of antibiotic production is obviously a subject for specialized study. Fortunately, the health-science practitioner only needs a general knowledge of the production procedures and of the significance of key manipulations. This background provides a basis for understanding the scientific limits and economic components of these therapeutic agents and for comprehending readily the types of research developments that will lead to future advances and change.

SCREENING FOR ANTIBIOTICS

In searching for new antibiotics, relatively simple and rapid methods have been developed for screening microorganisms for antibiotic-producing ability. Soil samples are commonly employed in the screen because they are a rich source of antibiotic-producing organisms. Most of these organisms are members of a group of branching, procaryotic microorganisms that occupy a position in their morphologic characteristics between fungi and bacteria. They are placed in the taxonomic order Actinomycetales and are given the common name actinomycetes. A compilation of the microbial sources of antibiotics discovered in the United States and Japan between 1953 and 1970 reveals that approximately 85% are produced by actinomycetes, 11% by fungi, and 4% by bacteria. The antibiotics currently used in therapy are produced by surprisingly few groups of distantly related organisms. The important genera and their taxonomic relations are as follows:

Phylum Schizomycophyta
  Class Schizomycetes
    Order Eubacteriales (bacteria)
      Family Bacillaceae
        Genus *Bacillus*
    Order Actinomycetales (actinomycetes)
      Family Streptomycetaceae
        Genus *Micromonospora*
        Genus *Streptomyces*
Phylum Eumycophyta (fungi)
  Class Ascomycetes
    Order Aspergillales
      Family Aspergillaceae

Genus *Penicillium*
Form-Class Deuteromycetes (Fungi Imper-
fecti)
Form-Order Moniliales
Form-Family Moniliaceae
Form-Genus *Cephalosporium*

This distribution reflects partly the fact that soil microorganisms tend to produce antibiotics and partly the fact that screening was focused upon soil samples during that period. Over time, fewer new compounds (and more of the already discovered ones) were identified from soil screening programs, and programs have moved on to screen unusual sources of microorganisms, e.g., from marine environments. Also, screening has become more focused upon pathogens for which we currently have inadequate therapy such as fungal and viral infections, as well as bacterial infections caused by difficult-to-kill pathogens (e.g., *Pseudomonas*, methicillin-resistant *Staphylococcus*).

A general method for screening first involves treating the soil sample (or sample from another source) with chemicals that inhibit the growth of interfering bacteria and fungi but do not affect actinomycetes. Cycloheximide is an antifungal antibiotic often employed for this purpose, and a 1 : 140 dilution of phenol is used as an antibacterial agent. Varying dilutions of the treated sample are streaked on agar plates containing medium that supports the growth of actinomycetes. After incubation for 3 to 7 days at 25 to 30° C, the plates are examined for characteristic colonies of actinomycetes. These colonies are then selectively transferred onto fresh medium. Giant colonies of the selected organisms are grown, and plugs are cut from the colonies that include not only the organism but also the underlying agar. If the organism produces an antibiotic, it should diffuse into the agar medium. The plugs are placed on an agar plate that has been seeded with a test organism that gives an indication of the potential usefulness of the antibiotic. The test plates are incubated under conditions appropriate for maximum growth of the test organism, and if after incubation there is a clear zone around the plug of the actinomycete, it can be assumed that an antibiotic in the plug inhibited the growth of the test organism.

The next step in the screening procedure is to determine whether the chemical substance that produced the inhibition is a new antibiotic or a known compound. This process is termed "de-replication." The compound is characterized by its chromatographic and spectroscopic properties, as well as by the microorganisms it inhibits (its antibiotic "spectrum"), and these data are compared to a database of previously identified compounds. Only if a compound is truly new and has interesting antibiotic activity will it be pursued further.

COMMERCIAL PRODUCTION

When a new antibiotic has been discovered, investigations into the chemical, physical, and biologic properties of the antibiotic are required before the decision to produce the antibiotic commercially can be made. Two important requirements for production are: (1) the organism must produce the antibiotic in submerged culture as opposed to surface culture, and (2) the organism must excrete the antibiotic into the culture medium. However, some antibiotics, such as those of the polyene group, are retained in the cells of the organism and require special extraction procedures for recovery. These requirements are important considerations in production costs which, in turn, determine whether the antibiotic can compete with other antibiotics for a portion of the market. Other considerations are chemical stability, the minimum inhibitory concentration against strains of pathogenic organisms, toxic manifestations in mammals, and activity *in vivo*.

The commercial production of antibiotics is an excellent example of the benefits that can be achieved from a multidisciplinary approach to solving a technologic problem. One must be impressed when one thinks, on the one hand, of an obscure microorganism growing in soil and, on the other hand, of the product of that microorganism—a pure crystalline chemical substance used to save human life. The transition from one to the other has required the most diligent application of the sciences of microbiology, chemistry, and engineering.

Commercial fermentative production of an antibiotic almost always involves growth of the producing organism in aerated tanks holding thousands of gallons of nutrient medium. Spores or occasionally vegetative growth from a stock culture of the organism are used to start the fermentation process. It is important to maintain stock cultures (e.g., by lyophilization) that require transfer as infrequently as possible because repeated transfer may select for those cells of the organism that are poor producers of antibiotic. The several hundred gallons of vegetative growth that are necessary for inoculating the large fermentation tanks are obtained by successively transferring the organism to increasingly larger volumes of nutrient. The use of a large standard inoculum reduces the incubation time required for production of the antibiotic, lessens the chance for costly contamination by foreign microorganisms, and provides the best possible opportunity for control of subtle environmental and nutritional factors that influence the antibiotic yield.

In the production of antibiotics, there are often distinct phases in the fermentative process. These phases can be divided into the growth phase of the organism, which is also termed the trophophase, and the antibiotic production phase, also termed the idiophase. Figure 11–1 illustrates these phases in the course of a typical penicillin fermentation carried out in a culture medium containing glucose and lactose as the sources of carbon nutrition, corn steep liquor for nitrogen sources, and phosphate buffer. During the growth phase, the culture becomes thick owing to the formation of aggregates of fungal cells called mycelium. Growth is indicated in the figure by the curve showing an increase in mycelial nitrogen and lasts from the beginning of the culture period to approximately 1 day later (0 to 24 hours). During the growth phase, glu-

cose rather than lactose is preferentially utilized because it can be used directly as a source of carbon. In the growth process, ammonia is liberated by deamination of amino acids of the corn steep liquor. This liberation raises the pH of the medium to 7, the optimum pH for penicillin stability, and buffers in the medium maintain the pH close to neutrality.

Penicillin production increases rapidly between 24 to 80 hours. At the start of the antibiotic production phase, glucose has been used up, and the fungus then uses lactose for a carbon source. Little additional growth occurs because the lactose cannot be utilized until it is hydrolyzed to glucose and galactose. The decreased availability of a carbon source is thought to be the triggering mechanism for penicillin production.

INCREASING COMMERCIAL YIELD

Considerable effort is devoted to determining the optimal environmental and nutritional conditions for antibiotic production. Optimal conditions for antibiotic formation are frequently quite different from those for maximum vegetative growth. Factors that are often observed to have qualitative or quantitative importance for antibiotic production include sources of nutri-

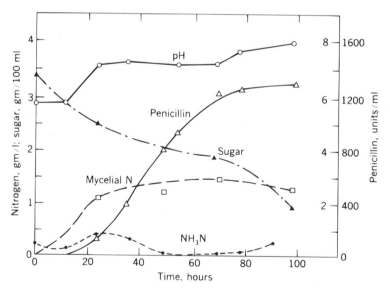

Fig. 11–1. Chemical changes, mycelial growth, and penicillin production in a typical penicillin fermentation. Reprinted with permission from Brown and Petersen, 1950 Industrial and Engineering Chemistry, *42*:1769-1774. Copyright by the American Chemical Society.

tional carbon and nitrogen, ratio of carbon/nitrogen nutrients, mineral composition of medium, incubation temperature, initial pH and control of pH during the fermentation period, rate and method of aeration, and addition and timing of addition of special growth- and antibiotic-promoting substances. Selection of optimal fermentation conditions is usually based on empiric observations, but careful attention to such factors is often critical. For example, some strains of *Bacillus subtilis* produce optimal yields of bacitracin when the C/N ratio is about 15; at lower ratios the yield is less, and when the ratio is reduced to approximately 6, licheniformin, a related but commercially undesired antibiotic, is produced.

The practical benefit of adding special chemicals to the fermentation cultures has probably achieved only a small fraction of its ultimate potential, but some examples will show the practical utility of this general approach. It was observed at a fairly early stage in the development of penicillin production that the addition of phenylacetamide or related compounds to the culture medium had a minor beneficial effect on the yield of penicillin substances and had a major influence on the composition of the penicillin mixture. The presence of phenylacetic acid derivatives in the nutrient mixture favored the formation of penicillin G; this reduced the problems of using a mixture of unknown or variable composition and the cost of separating the individual antibiotic substances. Use of various acyl moieties to direct the fermentative formation of other penicillins (e.g., penicillin V) achieved limited commercial success, but semisynthetic techniques have superseded this approach to the production of specialized penicillins.

The use of mercaptothiazole in cultures of *Streptomyces aureofaciens* emphasizes that additives can be beneficial without being incorporated into the antibiotic molecule. Strains of this actinomycete usually produce both chlortetracycline and tetracycline; the proportions depend to some degree on the availability of chloride ion in the culture medium. Tetracycline has the greater therapeutic utility, but the resolution of mixtures of these two tetracyclines is costly. Because the organism tends to be a chloride scavenger and because chloride ion is one of the most difficult ions to exclude quantitatively from water and nutrients, control of the presence of this ion in the nutrient medium to favor the production of tetracycline is not commercially feasible. However, the addition to the fermentation mixture of mercaptothiazole or any other compound that presumably inhibits chlorination favors tetracycline production.

Some additives may increase antibiotic production through an enzyme induction effect. For example, the addition of methionine to a cephalosporin C fermentation during the trophophase stimulates the production of the antibiotic. Because methionine does not serve as a biosynthetic precursor to the antibiotic, as compared to the role of phenylacetic acid in penicillin G biosynthesis, it is assumed that methionine stimulates the production of the cephalosporin C biosynthetic enzymes.

Conversely, it has been demonstrated that in penicillin fermentation, lysine in the culture medium inhibits antibiotic production. Penicillin and lysine are end products of a branched biosynthetic pathway in which α-aminoadipic acid is a common precursor. Lysine production is regulated either by inhibition or repression of the enzymes required for the production of α-aminoadipic acid, so addition of lysine blocks α-aminoadipic acid formation and ultimately results in a decrease in penicillin formation.

Another important approach to increasing the yield of antibiotic is mutation and strain selection. Mutation induced by exposing the parent strain to ultraviolet light, x rays, or various mutagenic chemicals, such as nitrogen mustards and analogs of purines and pyrimidines, is the major approach for selecting improved strains, but a search of natural sources for new wild-type or different species that produce the antibiotic in higher yield than the original producing organism is also employed. In the case of induced mutations, lethal levels of the mutagen are adjusted so that approximately 90 to 99% of the cells of the organism are killed. Mutants that produce a higher yield of antibiotic are selected from the surviving cells. Penicillin production offers a good illustration of the potential success of these approaches. Penicillin antagonism was observed originally with a culture of *Penicillium notatum* Westling, which produced in surface culture 4 mg of penicillin per liter of culture medium. In the early selection process, no mutants of *P. notatum* were found that would give a satisfactory yield of penicillin in submerged fermentation; however, in 1944, through natural selection, a strain of *P. chrysogenum* Thom was discovered that yielded penicillin in the amount of 40 mg per liter. Subsequently, by utilizing procedures of mutation and strain selection, the yield has been increased to 21,000 mg per liter.

With the recent advances in molecular biology, our knowledge of the molecular regulation of antibiotic biosynthesis has increased substantially. Such information will allow the rational manipulation of the producing organisms to increase yields, perhaps by deregulating rate-limiting biosynthetic enzymes or by introducing extra copies of genes corresponding to rate-limiting steps. It also will allow rational introduction of genes for alternate biosynthetic steps, thus leading to "hybrid" antibiotics which are fermentatively-produced analogs of the natural antibiotic molecules.

RECOVERY AND ISOLATION

Most of the commercially important antibiotics are excreted readily into the nutrient medium where they accumulate. In cases such as certain of the peptide antibiotics, in which the antibiotic is retained endocellularly until the cells reach an advanced physiologic age, the fermentation period is terminated when most of the cell membranes have undergone lysis or have lost their selective retention property. Thus, isolation of antibiotic substances is basically recovery from the culture broth. The fundamental approaches that are usually considered are selective precipitation, selective adsorption, or selective extraction with an immiscible solvent. The chemical characteristics of various antibiotics and their accompanying metabolites govern the manipulations that will be effective in any given situation. Ideally, the initial isolation procedure should be as efficient and selective as possible to give the best yield and to facilitate subsequent purification, but economic considerations commonly dictate a compromise procedure.

Liquid-liquid extraction using some water-immiscible organic solvent is the approach utilized for most antibiotics. This procedure lacks a high degree of selectivity with most solvents that are sufficiently inexpensive to be employed on a commercial scale. It is also relatively inefficient because antibiotic substances tend to be fairly polar molecules. However, the economic advantage of easy adaptation to a chemical engineering flow process more than offsets these

limitations in most cases unless the antibiotic molecule is so polar that the partition coefficient favors the aqueous phase.

Highly polar antibiotics, such as neomycin and other aminoglycoside antibiotics, are usually recovered from the culture broth by adsorption on some suitable adsorbent. Many adsorbents remove antibiotics of this type from culture broths with varying degrees of selectivity. The major limitation to selecting adsorbents is the need to recover the antibiotics by reversing the adsorption process without using extreme conditions that would be destructive. Use of charcoal of controlled activity grades and elution of the antibiotic with dilute acid is a typical example of this isolation approach.

Once the crude antibiotic has been recovered from the nutrient broth, it is subjected to chromatography, recrystallization, or other standard manipulations to effect an appropriate degree of purification. It should be noted that attainment of chemical purity is usually considered impractical and unnecessary for therapeutic purposes. Extraneous metabolites, such as foreign proteins that cause undesirable side effects, are routinely excluded during purification, but separation of closely related antibiotic molecules is often unfeasible. Most fermentatively produced antibiotics used in therapy are actually mixtures of closely related compounds with one of the metabolites constituting the majority of the mixture. This practical approach permits reproducible therapeutic responses because a given antibiotic molecule always accounts for most of the mixture; it also provides the most economic materials for drug formulations because the inefficiency and expense of total separation of similar chemical molecules, the relative concentrations of which are unequal, can be avoided. The presence of up to 6% chlortetracycline in commercial tetracycline represents a practical application of such purification considerations. Accepted standards of purity for antibiotics and antibiotic preparations are controlled by the *United States Pharmacopoeia*. Qualitative and quantitative evaluations of antibiotic preparations for adherence to established standards utilize both biologically and chemically based tests. Colorimetric and spectrophotometric approaches and definitive measurements have largely replaced microbiologic assay and arbitrary units for quantitative purposes. However, biologic tests are still employed to detect the presence of pyrogens in parenteral antibiotic formulations. The objectives and approaches of most tests for evaluation of antibiotic preparations are not significantly different from those used to ensure the standards of other drugs.

However, in some instances the purity of an antibiotic is important to reducing side effects. A primary example is the glycopeptide antibiotic, vancomycin, which for many years was limited in its usefulness by nephrotoxicity. However, once purification procedures were improved and impurities were removed, the incidence of nephrotoxicity was reduced dramatically.

The one unusual aspect of evaluating antibiotics is associated with the need to guarantee sterility in parenteral preparations. Masking of the presence of microbial contaminants through bacteriostatic action of the antibiotic must be precluded. Three basic approaches can be used to eliminate the antibiotic masking of microbial contaminants. Preparations containing antibiotics that are inactivated readily by biologic or chemical means may be subjected to the appropriate treatment before testing for sterility. Penicillinase inactivation of penicillin G and hydroxylamine hydrochloride inactivation of streptomycin illustrate this approach. Parenteral solutions of all antibiotics, especially those containing the more stable ones, can be evaluated by diluting the preparation such that the antibiotic level is below the minimum threshold concentration for activity or by initially removing any microorganisms with a sterile Millipore filter in a manipulation that separates the organisms from the antibiotic.

MANIPULATIVE FORMULATIONS

Effective use of many drug substances can be enhanced through various manipulations in pharmaceutic formulations. Antibiotics are no exception. Chemical and physical approaches for the protection of labile antibiotic molecules in gastric acid, the use of insoluble derivatives to eliminate objectionable tastes and thus gain patient acceptance for certain oral formulations, and the use of either soluble or insoluble salts to facilitate the desired delivery of the therapeutic agent illustrate the practical utilization of manipulative formulations for various antibiotics.

Buffers in oral penicillin G preparations reduce the destructive effect of gastric acidity, and enteric coatings of some oral erythromycin formulations protect the macrolactone ring of this antibiotic until it passes through the acidic environment of the stomach and into the small intestine where it is absorbed. Erythromycin estolate (the lauryl sulfate salt of the propionyl ester) and erythromycin ethylsuccinate are much more insoluble than the parent macrolide antibiotic. This property makes a dual contribution to oral suspensions of these antibiotic substances. The insolubility helps to avoid the extremely bitter taste of these drugs and to protect them until they reach the lower intestine.

The glucoheptonate and lactobionate salts of erythromycin are used to increase the solubility of the antibiotic sufficiently to permit intravenous administration. The insoluble benzathine and procaine salts of some penicillins are used intramuscularly for repository effects. When benzathine penicillin G is used in oral suspensions, this insolubility characteristic contributes a stability factor.

The use of an adjunct agent is another sophisticated approach to modifying the therapeutic availability or impact of an antibiotic. The classic example is probenecid, which inhibits the tubular excretion of penicillins. Concurrent administration of penicillins and probenecid is used to achieve prolonged blood levels of these antibiotics. Recent examples are the addition of clavulanic acid, a β-lactamase inhibitor without significant antibiotic activity per se, to a formulation of amoxicillin or ticarcillin; the result of the combinations is an expanded therapeutic spectrum.

RATIONAL ANTIBIOTIC THERAPY

Various antibiotics are widely employed for the effective control of most serious infections, but prophylactic administration of antibiotics to individuals is justified only under certain circumstances. Effective antibiotic therapy involves the correct diagnosis of the pathogen and the proper selection of an antibiotic. Diagnostic bacteriologic examination is usually a minimum basis for rational therapy. Exceptions include diseases such as scarlet fever, typhoid fever, or other conditions characterized by clinical symptoms that are indicative of a specific microbial etiology especially when the organism is always (or almost always) sensitive to the first-choice antibiotic. Interim antibiotic therapy (''empirical therapy'') is usually initiated on a calculated judgment basis in acute cases of meningitis, pneumonia, urinary tract infections, and similar conditions with multiple possible causes pending bacteriologic diagnosis; the therapeutic ap-

Table 11–1
A Summary of Common Pathogens That Cause Infections Treatable with Antibiotics

Pathogenic Organism	Disease Produced
Gram-positive cocci	
Enterococcus faecalis	subacute endocarditis, urinary tract infection
Staphylococcus aureus	cellulitis, impetigo, septicemia, endocarditis, osteomyelitis, pneumonia, food poisoning, furunculosis, wound infections
Streptococcus pneumoniae	pneumonia, meningitis, otitis
Streptococcus pyogenes *β*-hemolytic group A	scarlet fever, rheumatic fever, erysipelas, pharyngitis, impetigo, otitis
Gram-positive bacilli	
Bacillus anthracis	anthrax
Clostridium botulinum	food poisoning (botulism)
Clostridium difficile	pseudomembranous colitis
Clostridium perfringens	gas gangrene
Clostridium tetani	tetanus
Corynebacterium diphtheriae	diphtheria
Gram-negative cocci	
Neisseria gonorrhoeae	gonorrhea
Neisseria meningitidis	meningitis
Gram-negative bacilli	
Bacteroides fragilis	abscesses of abdomen, lung, brain
Bordetella pertussis	whooping cough
Brucella abortus, B. melitensis, and *B. suis*	brucellosis
Enterobacter aerogenes	pneumonia, wound infections, urinary tract infection, septicemia
Escherichia coli	urinary tract infection, septicemia, respiratory infections, peritonitis
Haemophilus influenzae	respiratory infections, meningitis, otitis
Klebsiella pneumoniae	pneumonia, urinary tract infection, septicemia
Legionella pneumophila	Legionnaire's disease
Proteus vulgaris	urinary tract infection, septicemia
Pseudomonas aeruginosa	urinary tract infection, pneumonia, burn-wound infection, septicemia
Salmonella species	food poisoning (salmonellosis)
Salmonella typhi	typhoid fever
Shigella dysenteriae	bacillary dysentery
Vibrio cholerae	Asiatic dysentery
Yersinia pestis	bubonic plague
Acid-fast bacilli	
Mycobacterium leprae	leprosy
Mycobacterium tuberculosis	tuberculosis
Spirochetes	
Borrelia burgdorferi	Lyme's disease
Treponema pallidum	syphilis
Fungi	
Blastomyces dermatitidis	North American blastomycosis
Candida albicans	candidiasis (moniliasis)
Coccidioides immitis	coccidioidomycosis (San Joaquin fever)
Cryptococcus neoformans	cryptococcosis
Histoplasma capsulatum	histoplasmosis
Epidermophyton, Microsporum, and *Trichophyton* (various species)	dermatomycoses (ringworm, athlete's foot)

Table 11–1
A Summary of Common Pathogens That Cause Infections Treatable with Antibiotics *(Continued)*

Pathogenic Organism	Disease Produced
Miscellaneous, Rickettsiae, Large Viruses	
Chlamydia psittaci	psittacosis (parrot fever)
Chlamydia trachomatis	trachoma, postgonococcal urethritis
Chlamydia psittaci	psittacosis (parrot fever)
Chlamydia trachomatis	trachoma, postgonococcal urethritis
Mycoplasma pneumoniae	respiratory infections
Pneumocystis carinii	respiratory infections
Rickettsia prowazekii	epidemic typhus
Rickettsia rickettsii	Rocky Mountain spotted fever
Rickettsia typhi	endemic typhus

proach is modified as necessary upon confirmation of the causative organism.

Knowledge of the bacteriologic statistics of infection, i.e., what organisms most often produce a certain type of infection in particular areas of the body and in patients at a particular age, is important for proper clinical judgment for empirical or interim therapy. For example, in cases of bacterial meningitis in adults, the most common causative organisms are *Neisseria meningitidis* and *Streptococcus pneumoniae*. In children under 10 years of age, *Haemophilus influenzae* is also a common causative agent; however, in infants less than 1 month of age, coliform bacteria such as species of *Escherichia*, *Klebsiella*, and *Enterobacter* are added to the list of common causative agents (Table 11–1).

It should be emphasized, however, that rational antibiotic therapy depends first on isolating and identifying the pathogenic organism from the focus of infection and then on determining the sensitivity of that strain or organism against properly selected antibiotics known to be potentially active against the organism.

Cultures should be taken and susceptibility tests performed whenever the site of infection is accessible or fluids (blood, urine, sputum) which may contain the pathogenic organism are available. Exceptions occur when obtaining a sample is invasive to the patient and a single antibiotic will kill most of the likely pathogens (e.g., in otitis media). Antibiotics with antibacterial activity are often classified into two broad categories on the basis of inhibiting predominantly gram-negative or gram-positive bacteria.

Knowledge that a given antibiotic or group of antibiotics is characterized by a gram-negative or a gram-positive spectrum has some therapeutic utility, especially for selecting an antibiotic for initiating therapy in the absence of definitive bacteriologic data and for considering alternate antibiotic approaches. When the pathogen is known or strongly suspected, selection of an effective antibiotic can frequently be based on the knowledge that the spectrum of an antibiotic includes a specific microorganism. However, judicious selection of an effective antibiotic for control of many pathogenic species, including most gram-negative microorganisms, necessitates individual determination of susceptibility because various strains of these pathogens have different antibiotic sensitivities.

Susceptibility tests are performed either by Kirby-Bauer testing or by turbidity testing to determine a minimum inhibitory concentration (MIC). In Kirby-Bauer testing, the patient's organism is spread on an agar plate, disks containing specified amounts of each antibiotic are placed on the agar plate, and the plates are incubated for a specified period of time. Clear zones around the disks indicate that the antibiotic is active against the pathogen (Fig. 11–2) since the growth of the organism is inhibited as the antibiotic diffuses into the agar. The zones are measured and compared to a standard table which correlates the zone of inhibition with clinical efficacy. It is very important to control all parameters of the test, including the amount of inoculum, the temperature and time of incubation, etc., if an accurate result is to be obtained.

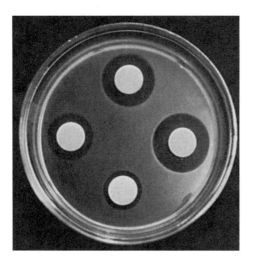

Fig. 11–2. A microbiologic assay plate showing zones of inhibition of varying size owing to different concentrations of antibiotic on the filter paper discs. The disc on the right contains the greatest concentration of antibiotic. Photo courtesy of Eli Lilly & Co.

The Kirby-Bauer test does not yield an MIC value directly.

Turbidity testing involves two-fold dilutions of the antibiotics in series of tubes, which are subsequently inoculated with the patient's microorganism and incubated at a specified temperature for a specified period of time. As can be seen in Figure 11–3, the organism will grow in tubes containing concentrations of antibiotic below the MIC which is, by definition, the concentration of antibiotic in the first clear tube. The MIC value is useful clinically since it is important to reach a peak antibiotic level that is minimally four to eight times the MIC. In recent years, clinical laboratories have moved toward automated turbidity testing which involves the use of multiwell plates and automated plate readers in place of the Kirby-Bauer test, coupled with a secondary MIC determination if needed. The concept involved with the multiwell plates is the same as when individual test tubes are used. Again, strict control of conditions of the test is critical for accurate information to be obtained. Isolation of the patient's organism and susceptibility testing usually take about 48 hours. Thus, rational empirical or interim therapy is critical, particularly in serious infections, and that therapy can then be modified once full information is obtained.

At the MIC, the antibiotic has inhibited the growth of the organism, but has not necessarily killed it. Usually, if aliquots from the tube corresponding to the MIC and from the next higher concentration are plated on non-antibiotic-containing agar plates, some organisms will grow. The concentration of antibiotic that results in complete killing of the organism (no organisms on the non-antibiotic-containing plate) is called the minimum bactericidal concentration (MBC) and may be important, particularly in serious infections or immunocompromised patients whose immune system cannot remove inhibited organisms from the site of infection.

Many pathogens are susceptible to more than one commercially available antibiotic. The choice of antibiotic for any given therapeutic situation must be based on composite considerations of a number of factors and is rarely unequivocal. In addition to the activity against the pathogen, the antibiotic must be able to get to the site of infection, and it must be available via the appropriate route of administration (parenteral for serious infections; oral for less serious, outpatient infections). Other properties which favor the use of a given antibiotic include freedom from acute and chronic toxicities; an optimal activity near pH 7 that is not influenced by serum, other body fluids, or pus; sufficient solubility in aqueous fluids to facilitate good distribution to all body tissues; chemical stability; efficient absorption following oral administration; no tendency to induce the development of resistant strains of pathogens; and a low expense factor. No known antibiotic possesses all of these ideal characteristics. The naturally occurring penicillins probably most nearly approach many of these properties for therapeutic situations in which their spectrum is adequate because they tend to have a rapid onset of systemic activity when orally administered, cause a low incidence of toxicity, and are inexpensive. However, serious penicillin hypersensitivities contraindicate the use of these antibiotics in some individuals, and the development of resistance by some pathogens is a definite therapeutic concern. Cost is never a major or exclusive criterion for selection of a first-choice antibiotic for therapeutic purposes, but if all other factors are equal, the least expensive therapeutic approach (not necessarily the least expensive unit formulation) serves the best interests of the patient.

Properties of the antibiotic per se are not the only considerations in selecting the best therapeutic agent. Such patient factors as age and secondary debilitating conditions may influence the use or choice of antibiotics in specific situations.

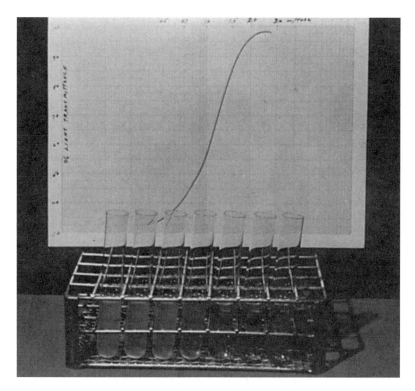

Fig. 11–3. Turbidimetric assay tubes with curve illustrating the relationship of increasing percent of light transmittance on the *y* axis and increasing concentration of antibiotic on the *x* axis. The minimum inhibitory concentration is the antibiotic concentration in the first clear tube; in this case, the fifth from the left. Photo courtesy of Eli Lilly & Co.

Serious infections or infections in immunocompromised patients may require a bactericidal antibiotic (one that actually kills rather than inhibits the pathogen). Serious infections of patients with gastrointestinal complications usually require a parenteral route of administration, and compromised liver or renal function generally indicates the adjustment of dosage or dosage interval or the use of antibiotics that are not metabolized and/or eliminated via those routes. Gradual development of normal renal and liver function during the neonatal period necessitates adjustment of dosage and administration interval and influences the choice of antibiotic. Pregnant patients experience unique toxicities to themselves or the fetus from some antibiotics, and some antibiotics are contraindicated in pregnancy. Patient allergies must always be considered.

Data are being accumulated on the modes and mechanisms of action of various antibiotics, on the bases for toxicities in antibiotic therapy, and on the details of resistance. The available information is sufficient to rationalize scientifically many developments that may be observed during therapy. A consideration of these factors will undoubtedly provide a basis for more effective and precise antibiotic therapy in the future when more complete knowledge becomes available.

MODES AND MECHANISMS OF ACTION

A number of different classification schemes could be used to categorize the selective toxicity of antibiotics for susceptible microorganisms. The recognition of five general modes of action, namely, inhibition of microbial cell-wall formation, inhibition of protein synthesis, disruption of deoxyribonucleic acid metabolism, alteration of normal function of the cellular membrane, and inhibition of synthesis of some essential metabolite (antimetabolite), is satisfactory pending the accumulation of more data. It is frequently difficult to distinguish primary from referred re-

Table 11–2
Modes of Antimicrobial Action

Inhibition of cell wall formation	Inhibition of protein biosynthesis
Bacitracin	Aminoglycosides
Cephalosporins	Chloramphenicol
Cycloserine	Lincosamides
Penicillins	Macrolides
Vancomycin	Spectinomycin
Other beta-lactam antibiotics	Tetracyclines
Disruption of nucleic acid metabolism	Alteration of cell membrane function
Fluoroquinolones	Amphotericin B
Rifampin	Nystatin
Actinomycin D	Polymixin
Bleomycin	Azole antifungal agents
Doxorubicin	Antimetabolites
Mitomycin	Sulfonamides
Zidovudine	Trimethoprim
Didanosine	Methotrexate
Acyclovir	
Ganciclovir	

sponses in preliminary attempts to determine the mode of antibiotic action. When more detailed information becomes available, current concepts on the mode of action of a few antibiotics (Table 11–2) may be altered, and the relative therapeutic importance of alternate modes of action will be clarified.

Knowing the mode of action is important for determining the clinical utility of various agents. The more selective the antibiotic for the pathogen metabolism, the less toxicity the human host will experience. For instance, human cells have no cell walls, and cell wall inhibiting antibiotics such as the penicillins tend to be very safe with wide therapeutic ranges. In contrast, cell membranes are common to both procaryotic and mammalian cells, and cell membrane disrupting antibiotics tend to be very toxic. Also, the mechanism of action will determine whether an antibiotic is bactericidal or bacteriostatic. For the most part, cell wall synthesis inhibitors will be bactericidal since the cells will lyse in the absence of an intact cell wall. On the other hand, most protein synthesis inhibitors have a reversible action and will be bacteriostatic in that the cells will continue to grow once the antibiotic is removed. An exception is the class of aminoglycoside antibiotics which cause irreversible inhibition of protein synthesis and are bactericidal. Finally, whether or not combination therapy will result in synergism, independent action, or antagonism depends upon the mechanisms of the interacting antibiotics. A well-known and often used synergistic combination is the combi-

nation of a β-lactam antibiotic and an aminoglycoside where the β-lactam antibiotic inhibits cell wall synthesis and allows better penetration of the aminoglycoside. An example of antagonism is observed with antifungal agents amphotericin B and ketoconazole. Amphotericin B works by associating with ergosterol, a sterol component of fungal membranes. Ketoconazole inhibits the synthesis of ergosterol, thus antagonizing the effect of amphotericin B.

The specific mechanism of action of an antibiotic, as contrasted with the general mode of action, is frequently an individualistic feature, and distinctive mechanisms of action are often observed for two antibiotics with the same general mode of action. Precise knowledge of the mechanism of action offers tremendous potential for sophisticated developments in antibiotic therapy. Sufficient information is available on the mechanism of action of certain antibiotics that interfere with cell-wall formation and protein biosynthesis to show representative patterns of biologic involvement.

Inhibition of cell-wall formation involves the disruption of mucopeptide synthesis. Gram-positive bacteria are particularly susceptible to antibiotics that inhibit mucopeptide formation because they possess a cell wall that contains a relatively thick mucopeptide layer to provide structural support of the cytoplasm. The mucopeptide layer is known variously as murein, glycopeptide, or peptidoglycan, and because of the nature of its chemical structure, it is tough and fibrous. Support is required because gram-positive bacteria concentrate low-molecular-weight metabolites such as amino acids and nucleotides, which impart a high internal osmotic pressure. On the other hand, gram-negative bacteria have a relatively low internal osmotic pressure with a thin layer of mucopeptide.

The synthesis of mucopeptide occurs in distinct steps. The first step is a series of reactions inside the cell that result in the production of the basic building units (uridine diphospho-*N*-acetyl-muramylpentapeptide). Cycloserine inhibits the formation of the pentapeptide portion of the building block. In the next step, the building units are carried to the outside of the cell membrane. During this process, the units are linked covalently to the preexisting cell wall. Vancomycin and bacitracin inhibit this step of the biosynthesis. The final stage of the biosynthesis is the cross-linking of linear molecules to form the highly cross-linked, three-dimensional mucopeptide. The last reaction in mucopeptide formation is catalyzed by transpeptidases that split the terminal D-alanine residues of the pentapeptide of the building unit and, in the case of *Staphylococcus aureus*, form a peptide bond between the terminal glycine of a pentaglycine bridge and the penultimate D-alanine of a mucopeptide strand (Fig. 11–4). Therefore, each

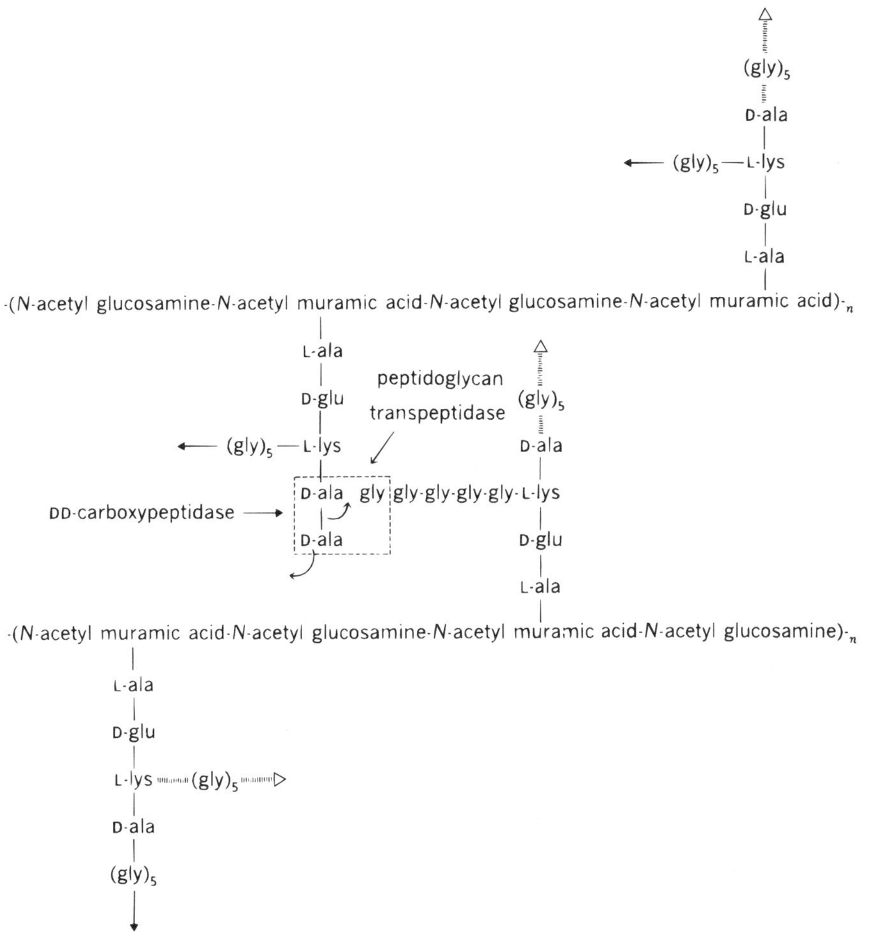

Fig. 11–4. Partial structure of bacterial cell wall mucopeptide showing polysaccharides composed of polymeric chains of alternating units of *N*-acetylglucosamine and *N*-acetylmuramic acid. The peptide chains cross-link the polysaccharide chains to make a rigid three-dimensional structure. The last steps in mucopeptide formation are catalyzed by a DD-carboxypeptidase that splits off the terminal D-alanine and peptidoglycan transpeptidase that forms a peptide bond between the penultimate D-alanine and, in the case of *Staphylococcus aureus*, the glycine of a pentaglycine bridge.

polypeptide side chain of each repeating building unit becomes covalently linked to the side chains of neighboring mucopeptide strands. The cross-linking process has two steps: carboxypeptidation, followed by transpeptidation. The penicillins and the cephalosporins are competitive inhibitors of this cross-linking.

It appears that the penicillin or cephalosporin molecule occupies the D-alanyl- D-alanine substrate site of the DD-carboxypeptidase and/or the peptidoglycan transpeptidase, forming a covalent adduct that is stable to subsequent hydrolysis and, therefore, irreversibly inactivates the enzyme. These penicillin-sensitive enzymes are also known as penicillin-binding proteins (PBPs). The PBPs are found in the cell membrane of all bacteria examined to date. Bacterial membranes yield multiple PBPs ranging in number from three in gonococci to ten or more in *Escherichia coli*. On sodium dodecylsulfate-polyacrylamide gels, PBPs have molecular weights usually ranging from 40,000 to 120,000 and are numbered in order of decreasing molecular weight. The currently used nomenclature involves assigning numbers to the protein, with 1 being the highest molecular weight; therefore, the numerical connotation of PBPs is strictly a reference to their relative molecular size within the group of PBPs detected in a microorganism. Thus, PBP-1 of *Escherichia coli* need not have anything in common with PBP-1 of gonococci.

The physiologic function of PBPs in the formation of cell wall has been assigned in a limited number of bacteria by studying mutants lacking one or another of the PBPs and by studying the effects of antibiotics that selectively bind to some of the PBPs. In *Escherichia coli*, PBP-1, PBP-2, and PBP-3 all have transpeptidase activity and are involved, respectively, in elongation, shape, and septation during growth. β-Lactam antibiotics that bind to PBP-1 cause cell lysis, whereas binding to PBP-2 produces giant spherical shaped cells which eventually lyse; those binding to PBP-3 produce filamentation prior to lysis. Most β-lactam antibiotics bind most tightly to PBP-1 and PBP-3, whereas amdinocillin binds preferentially to PBP-2. The rapid lysis caused by imipenem is thought to be due to its ability to bind tightly to PBP-1B and PBP-2, and the gram-negative spectrum of aztreonam results from its ability to bind selectively with high affinity to the PBP-3 of gram-negative organisms.

Formation of an essential protein may be blocked at any of the basic stages of protein biosynthesis. The antibiotic could adversely influence the replication and synthesis of DNA, the transcription of the genetic code and the specific sequential synthesis of DNA, the transcription of the genetic code and the specific sequential synthesis of mRNA, or the synthesis and assembly of the ribosomes. All of these biologic processes are fundamental for the eventual synthesis of a protein, but many constituents that act at these levels tend to be relatively toxic. Most of the therapeutically useful (more selectively toxic) antibiotics that act on protein biosynthesis influence in some manner the normal assembly of the amino acids into proteins within the mRNA-ribosome complex.

The ribosomes found in bacteria have a sedimentation coefficient of 70S, and they are composed of two particles of different size, the 50S and the 30S ribosomal subunits. Each subunit is composed of ribosomal RNA and a number of different proteins. Antibiotic action to inhibit protein biosynthesis can be focused on the events that take place on the ribosomes. These are initiation, binding of aminoacyl-tRNA, peptide bond formation, translocation, and termination (Fig. 11– 5).

The selective toxicity of protein synthesis inhibitors results from the fact that the human host cells have 80S ribosomes rather than 70S ribosomes, and the antibiotics that are used are selective for the 70S ribosomes. Human cells do have 70S ribosomes in their mitochondria, and some very lipophilic antibiotics will cause toxicity at high doses related to the ability of the antibiotics to penetrate the mitochondrial membrane and inhibit mitochondrial protein synthesis.

Streptomycin, an aminoglycoside antibiotic, affects initiation as well as elongation and termination of protein synthesis. The antibiotic binds to the 30S subunit and causes a breakdown of the initiation complex, resulting in the release of f-met-tRNA. Other aminoglycoside antibiotics such as kanamycin, gentamicin, and neomycin interfere with initiation of protein synthesis; however, these antibiotics affect elongation of the peptide chain more markedly through inhibition of translocation than through initiation. In addition, the aminoglycoside antibiotics with a streptamine or 2-deoxystreptamine moiety provoke codon misreading or induce the uptake of incorrect amino acids that do not correspond to the codon. The tetracyclines interfere with the binding of aminoacyl-tRNA to the acceptor site of the 70S ribosome. Experimental evidence points to a single strong binding site for tetracycline located on the 30S subunit; however, it

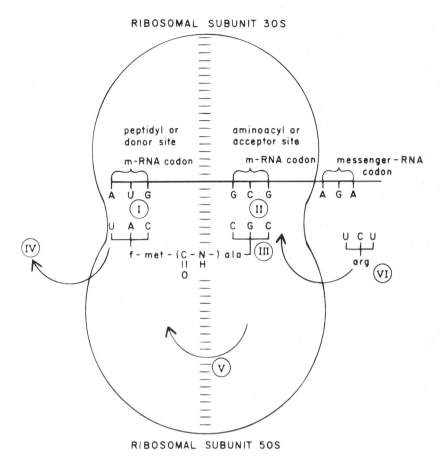

Fig. 11–5. Sequence of events of protein synthesis on the 70S ribosome: I. Formation of initiation complex involves the binding of the first aminoacyl-tRNA to the ribosome. In bacteria, the first amino acid bound is formylmethionine (f-met). II. Binding of the next aminoacyl-tRNA to aminoacyl site. III. Formation of peptide bond catalyzed by a ribosome-bound peptidyl transferase. IV. Release of formylmethionine-specific tRNA. V. The peptidyl-tRNA (f-met-ala-tRNA) moves to the peptidyl site. This is called the translocation step, and the mRNA shifts to the next codon. VI. The aminoacyl site is free and available for the next addition of aminoacyl-tRNA which, in this case, is arginine-tRNA.

has not been completely ruled out that the 50S subunit might also be involved in the binding. Chloramphenicol binds to the 50S subunit where it disrupts the function of peptidyl transferase. Erythromycin also binds to the 50S subunit. It does not inhibit peptide bond formation, but it does block translocation.

DNA metabolism has much in common between procaryotes and higher organisms, so most antibiotics that interfere with DNA metabolism are very toxic and are used as antitumor agents. Selectivity is obtained by the fact that cancer cells are replicating much more rapidly than normal cells. A few instances are known of selective inhibition of some specific enzymes of nucleic acid metabolism, the primary example

being the fluoroquinolone antibacterial agents which inhibit the DNA gyrase (topoisomerase) of bacteria but do not affect the analogous enzymes in human cells. Similarly, rifampin inhibits the DNA-dependent RNA polymerase of bacteria but has no effect on the human enzyme except at very high concentrations. Also, some selectivity may be obtained through differential activation of compounds inside the cells. The antiviral agent acyclovir is phosphorylated to its active form by herpes virus-infected cells (by a virally encoded thymidine kinase) but not by normal cells. Similarly, the antifungal agent 5-fluorocytosine (5-FC) is activated (by deamination) to 5-fluorouracil by the target fungal cells but has little effect as 5-FC on the host cells.

Other antibiotics affect the permeability of the cell membrane in a way that causes leakage of cytoplasmic solutes. The two most important groups of these drugs are the polyene antibiotics, amphotericin B and nystatin, and the peptide antibiotics, such as the polymyxins. The polyene antibiotics are antifungal agents that affect the membranes of eucaryotic cells but have no activity on bacteria. This difference in sensitivity of different organisms to these antibiotics is determined by the presence of sterols in the cell membrane of eucaryotic cells. The polyenes bind to the membrane, and the extent of binding is proportional to the amount of sterol present. The selectivity for fungi is based upon selective bindings to ergosterol, a sterol found in fungi but not human cells. The selectivity is not complete, and the polyenes are relatively toxic agents. Molecular models show the polyenes to have a rodlike structure held rigid by an all-*trans* extended conjugated system that is equal in length to a sterol molecule. One surface is lipophilic, and the opposite, studded with hydroxyl groups, has a hydrophilic face. There is evidence that there is a packing of alternating sterol and polyene molecules, which creates a pore through the cell membrane. The pore is thought to be a hollow cylinder with a polar interior surface caused by the hydrophilic hydroxyl groups of the polyene molecules and an exterior surface composed of sterols being attracted to the lipophilic side of the polyenes (Fig. 11– 6). Ions from the cytoplasm such as K^+ would leak through the polar pore, causing damage to the cell by the upset of the ion balance. Selective antifungal activity is also obtained by the azole antifungal agents which inhibit the biosynthesis of ergosterol, leading to leaky membranes. Like the polyenes, these compounds have no effect on bacteria. The peptide antibiotics also bind to the cell membrane and disturb membrane function; however, these antibiotics are active against bacteria since sterols are not required for binding.

Antimetabolites inhibit the growth of bacteria through selective inhibition of some essential biosynthetic pathway. The primary examples in clinical use are the folic acid synthesis inhibitors, the sulfonamides and trimethoprim, all of which are synthetic antimicrobials and not true antibiotics. The biosynthesis of the active form of folic acid, tetrahydrofolate, which is an essential contributor of 1-carbon units in the biosynthesis of amino acids and nucleic acid bases, involves the joining together of *p*-aminobenzoic

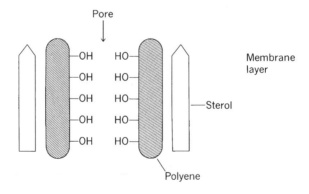

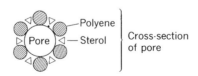

Fig. 11–6. The possible interaction of polyene antibiotics in a eucaryotic cell membrane. The polyenes complex with membrane sterols to form a pore through the membrane through which ions may pass.

acid (PABA) and pteroylglutamic acid. The sulfonamides are structural analogs of PABA and competitively inhibit the enzymes which catalyze the reaction. The competitive inhibition is reversible, and these compounds are bacteriostatic. Trimethoprim inhibits a later step in the pathway, dihydrofolate reductase, and the combination of a sulfonamide and trimethoprim is synergistic. Methotrexate is an inhibitor of human dihydrofolate reductase that is used as an anticancer agent.

BASES OF TOXICITY

One limitation to the therapeutic use of an antibiotic substance is mammalian toxicity. The manifestation of such adverse reactions varies greatly with different antibiotic molecules. As mentioned in the previous section, toxicity may be associated with a lack of selectivity for the pathogen versus the host associated with the basic mechanism of action. However, more often, toxicity is due to hypersensitivity, alteration of normal microbial flora, or a pharmacologic action that is independent of the antibiotic activity of the molecule. Theoretically, the safest antibiotic inhibits an essential process, such as cell-wall formation, that is unique to the microorganism. Actual situations usually follow the theoretical considerations, as illustrated by the relative safety of the penicillins and the relative toxicity of chloramphenicol. However, some degree of deviation from the ideal is probably universal because antibiotic molecules normally lack absolute specificity or the ability to influence only one biochemical reaction. In the case of penicillins, hypersensitization with serious consequences precludes the use of these antibiotics in some individuals. Many antibiotic molecules are characterized by reactive functional groups, and hypersensitivity may be a problem with molecules containing functional groups that can react with proteins to yield potentially antigenic hapten-protein molecules. Toxicity caused by some independent pharmacologic property of the antibiotic is usually difficult to predict; this type of complication must be evaluated individually for each antibiotic.

In addition to any adverse pharmacologic action of an antibiotic per se, indirect toxicities can be observed with these therapeutic agents. The most common type of indirect antibiotic-induced toxicity is associated with an alteration in the ecologic balance of the intestinal flora. This problem is greatest with the broad-spectrum antibiotics because a major portion of the intestinal flora may be suppressed. *Candida albicans* is an example of the slow-growing, unsusceptible microorganism that may become a dominant component of the intestinal flora following the administration of antibiotics. The body frequently has no prior adaptation or tolerance to the level of foreign metabolites resulting from the unusual proliferation of such organisms; the toxicity is usually manifest as gastrointestinal disturbances rather than as acute toxicities. Enterococcal overgrowth following therapy with third-generation cephalosporins and the pseudomembranous colitis caused by *Clostridium difficile* in some patients receiving clindamycin or other antibiotics can be life-threatening.

MODES OF RESISTANCE

Antibiotic resistance is a major therapeutic concern. One practical way to circumvent this problem, at least for short-term purposes, is to develop and use new antibiotics, but experts are concerned justifiably about the practicality of long-term developmental aspects of this approach. Resistance to antibiotics may result through spontaneous or induced genetic mutation. However, many of the practical problems have developed via the process of selection or, in other words, favoring through the use of antibiotics the low frequency of organisms of antibiotic-resistant genotype that exists naturally in the antibiotic-sensitive, wild population. Spontaneous mutation is believed to make only a minor contribution to the total problem of antibiotic resistance. Bacterial cells can acquire genetic material from other bacterial cells through the processes of transformation, transduction, and conjugation. Transformation, which is a process by which DNA from a lysed bacterial cell is inserted directly into a recipient cell, makes no substantial contribution to the clinical problem of drug resistance. Transduction, or the phage- induced transfer of resistant determinant sections of bacterial DNA, is believed to be an important factor in the emergence of drug-resistant strains of *Staphylococcus*. Conjugation is a widely recognized mechanism for transmitting resistance among gram-negative bacilli of clinical concern. Conjugation of compatible cells (which may represent different species or even genera) provides a means for direct transfer of R-factor genes residing on bacterial plasmids, and great danger lies in the fact that bacterial plasmids may contain genetic information for multiple resistance.

The rapid spread of resistance genes on plasmids among gram-negative organisms accounts for the clinical phenomenon of widespread variability in sensitivity to various antibiotics among strains of these species. Hospital-acquired strains, which cause "nosocomial" infections, tend to have acquired the greatest resistance and are much more difficult to treat. Gram-positive organisms can also have R-factor resistance plasmids, but these are not spread by conjugation and the spread of resistant strains among the population is usually less rapid. Again, exposure to antibiotics in a hospital or institutional setting leads to selection of resistant strains, and nosocomial infections due to gram-positive organisms also are more likely to be resistant to a variety of antibiotics. Discontinuation of the use of a given antibiotic in a setting will remove the selection process and will result, over time, in a larger number of strains being sensitive to the antibiotic.

Multiple mechanisms of resistance to many antibiotics appear to exist, and the lack of precise information in many cases makes general categorization difficult. However, some modes of resistance that can be noted include:

1. Enzymatic inactivation of the antibiotic;
2. Altered permeability of the pathogen to the antibiotic;
3. Altered target site within the pathogen;
4. Loss of an activating enzyme in the pathogen;
5. Overcoming a metabolic block by increasing the target enzyme or competitive substrate, or by development of an alternate metabolic pathway in the pathogen.

The β-lactamase hydrolysis of the beta-lactam bond of penicillins and cephalosporins is by far the best documented mechanism leading to antibiotic resistance. β-Lactamases are produced by both gram-positive and gram-negative organisms and vary in their substrate specificity (penicillins and/or cephalosporins), their molecular characteristics, their sensitivity to inhibitors (clavulanate, sulbactam), whether they are encoded by chromosomal or plasmid-borne genes, and in which organisms they have appeared. The β-lactamase produced by strains of *Staphylococcus* is specific for the penam moiety and, therefore, hydrolyses penicillins but not cephalosporins, and is commonly called "penicillinase." The β-lactamases produced by gram-negative bacilli generally destroy both penicillins and some cephalosporins and have been categorized by Richmond-Sykes according to the above-described characteristics. Type III β-lactamases are the most common and are inhibited by clavulanic acid and sulbactam. The development of the semisynthetic penicillins was a direct result of efforts to avoid the specificity of the penicillinase enzyme, and similarly, the development of second- and third-generation cephalosporins was driven by the need to have antibiotics to kill β-lactamase-producing gram-negative pathogens. More recently, the combination of β-lactamase inhibitors with otherwise β-lactamase sensitive penicillins has expanded the usefulness of those antibiotics.

Enzymatic inactivation of antibiotics, leading to resistant organisms, can also occur by enzymes which add moieties to the antibiotic, thus making it unable to bind to its target. Gram-negative bacteria bearing any of several R-factors for multiple resistance can enzymatically inactivate aminoglycoside antibiotics by forming either phosphoryl, adenyl, or acetyl derivatives of these antibiotics.

Altered permeability is a frequently mentioned mode of resistance but is less frequently observed than enzymatic inactivation. Tetracycline resistance in some gram-positive organisms appears to be caused by the acquisition of a "pumping out" protein which rapidly removes antibiotic from the bacterial cell. In an analogous fashion, multidrug resistant (MDR) cancer cells have a membrane-associated protein called P-glycoprotein which rapidly pumps out xenobiotic molecules and makes the cancer cells resistant to a variety of anticancer agents. Another example of altered permeability is found in species of *Pseudomonas* which are often antibiotic resistant, partly through their ability to mutate to close the porins (protein-gated pores in their outer cell membranes), through which antibiotics must pass.

Alteration of the target molecule within the pathogen so that the antibiotic can no longer bind to it, thus allowing it to fulfill its cellular function, is another important mode of resistance. Such alterations can occur either through mutation or plasmid-encoded enzymes. An important example of the former is the development of methicillin-resistant *Staphylococcus aureus* (MRSA) which have a mutant PBP (PBP-2') which functions in cell wall formation but does not bind any β-lactam antibiotic, making MRSA resistant to all β-lactam antibiotics, resulting in a significant clinical problem. Enzymatic alteration of an antibiotic target is observed in macrolide resistance in gram-positive organisms. A plasmid-encoded methylase enzyme methylates an adenine residue at the target site on the 50S ribosome, resulting in a functional ribosome which does not bind erythromycin or other macrolides, thus making the organism resistant to those antibiotics. Interestingly, some of the genes encoding antibiotic resistance are thought to have arisen evolutionarily by gene transfer from antibiotic-producing soil organisms that have mechanisms of resisting the antibiotics they produce in order to avoid suicide.

Antibiotics which are activated by specific enzymes within the pathogens are unfortunately subject to resistance development since simple mutation of the activating enzyme will result in a loss of activation. The high rate of resistance to flucytosine is due to fungal organisms which have a mutated deaminase and therefore do not convert the flucytosine to 5-fluorouracil which normally kills the cells.

Resistance to antimetabolites which act as competitive inhibitors also can develop readily since deregulation of the amount of target enzyme or overproduction of the normal substrate will counteract the competitive inhibition and allow product to be formed. Organisms resistant to sulfonamides through this mode are frequently observed. Theoretically, resistance could also be caused by development of altered metabolic pathways, but the therapeutic significance of this type of resistance is relatively unknown.

CLASSES OF ANTIBIOTICS

The remainder of the chapter will be devoted to discussion of specific antibiotics, antimicrobials, antifungal agents, antiviral agents, and anticancer antibiotics. In each case, the natural antibiotics and their derivatives will be discussed in detail, but synthetic compounds will be discussed briefly for the sake of completeness in considering the choice of an antiinfective agent. For the anticancer agents, only the microbially-produced antibiotics will be included. For each class, the common properties of the class will be stressed, and the individual derivatives will be described with a focus on how each differs from the prototype compounds.

β-LACTAM ANTIBIOTICS

The β-lactam antibiotics include the penicillins, the cephalosporins, imipenem, and aztreonam. They have in common the four-membered β-lactam ring but vary in the way the highly-strained β-lactam ring is stabilized. Penicillins have a 5-membered thiazolidine ring attached to the β-lactam ring, and the combination comprises what is known as the ''penam'' nucleus. Similarly, cephalosporins have a 6-membered dihydrothiazine ring fused to the β-lactam ring, forming a ''cephem'' nucleus. The sulfur atom in either the penam or cephem nuclei has been replaced in some compounds by an oxygen atom, forming oxapenams (e.g., clavulanic acid), or oxacephems (e.g., moxalactam). Imipenem is a carbapenem, lacking a heteroatom in the fused ring, and aztreonam is an example of a monobactam, a class of antibiotics isolated initially from organisms found in the cranberry bogs of New Jersey and modified synthetically, which has only the β-lactam ring stabilized by an adjacent sulfonic acid moiety.

Penicillins

Penicillin antagonism attracted the attention of Sir Alexander Fleming in 1928. Fleming was studying staphylococci at St. Mary's College in London when he noticed a zone of inhibition surrounding a *Penicillium* contaminant in one of his cultures. The *Penicillium* was initially identified as *P. rubrum* but was later determined to be *P. notatum*. Interest in this antagonism remained largely academic until after 1940. In 1938, Florey and Chain at Oxford University first isolated a crude penicillin mixture from the mold, and during the early 1940s the therapeutic potential of penicillin was demonstrated.

Conditions in England during the first half of World War II were such that efforts to determine suitable procedures for producing commercial quantities of the antibiotic were conducted primarily in the United States. Significant early discoveries included the influence of nutrient composition on penicillin production and the discovery of a strain of *P. chrysogenum* that would produce the antibiotic in submerged fermentation. The presence of phenylpropanoid or phenylacetyl derivatives in the nutrient medium favored the formation of benzylpenicillin (penicillin G). Other penicillins could be formed by adding the appropriate precursor moieties to the fermentation cultures; penicillin V is an example of a therapeutically useful penicillin that was

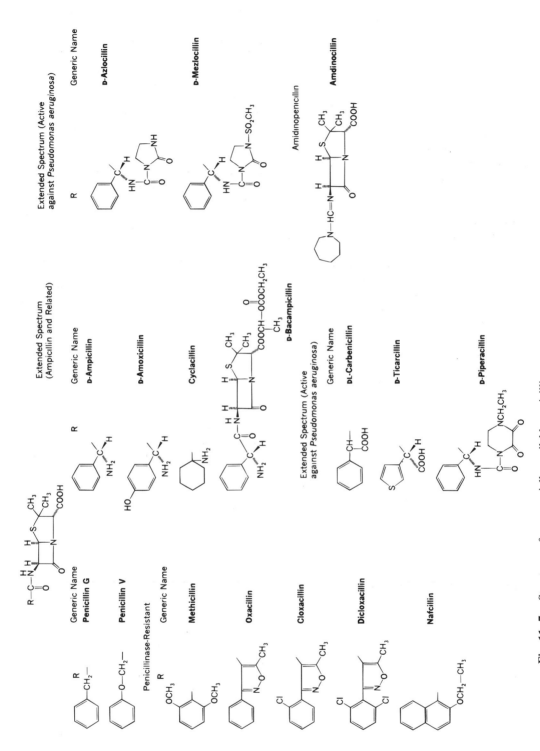

Fig. 11-7. Structures of commercially available penicillins.

prepared initially by this type of manipulated biologic process.

Discovery in the late 1950s of a strain of *P. chrysogenum* that accumulated high yields of 6-aminopenicillanic acid provided an alternate approach to preparing unusual penicillins, such as penicillin V, and provided an opportunity for even greater modification in the antibiotic molecules. 6-Aminopenicillanic acid has no significant antibiotic activity per se, but this biologically prepared substance can be chemically acylated to give a wide variety of active molecules. Amdinocillin, ampicillin, amoxicillin, azlocillin, bacampicillin, carbenicillin, cloxacillin, cyclacillin, dicloxacillin, methicillin, mezlocillin, nafcillin, oxacillin, piperacillin, and ticarcillin are therapeutically utilized semisynthetic penicillins that have been selected for various advantages offered by their chemical, physical,

or spectral properties. Structures of the commercially available penicillins are shown in Figure 11–7.

Biosynthesis of Penicillins. The amino acids cysteine and valine are incorporated into the 6-aminopenicillanic acid portion of penicillin molecules, and the acyl group of penicillin G is derived from phenylacetic acid. Many of the details of the biosynthetic pathway have been elucidated in recent years. As illustrated in Figure 11–8, the tripeptide, δ-(L-α-aminoadipyl)-L-cysteine-D-valine, is synthesized from L-α-aminoadipate, L-cysteine, and L-valine by an enzyme called ACV synthetase. The tripeptide is the precursor of isopenicillin N. Epimerization of the side chain yields penicillin N. In penicillin-producing pathways, the side chain is subsequently cleaved at the amide bond and replaced with phenylacetic acid to yield penicillin G. In

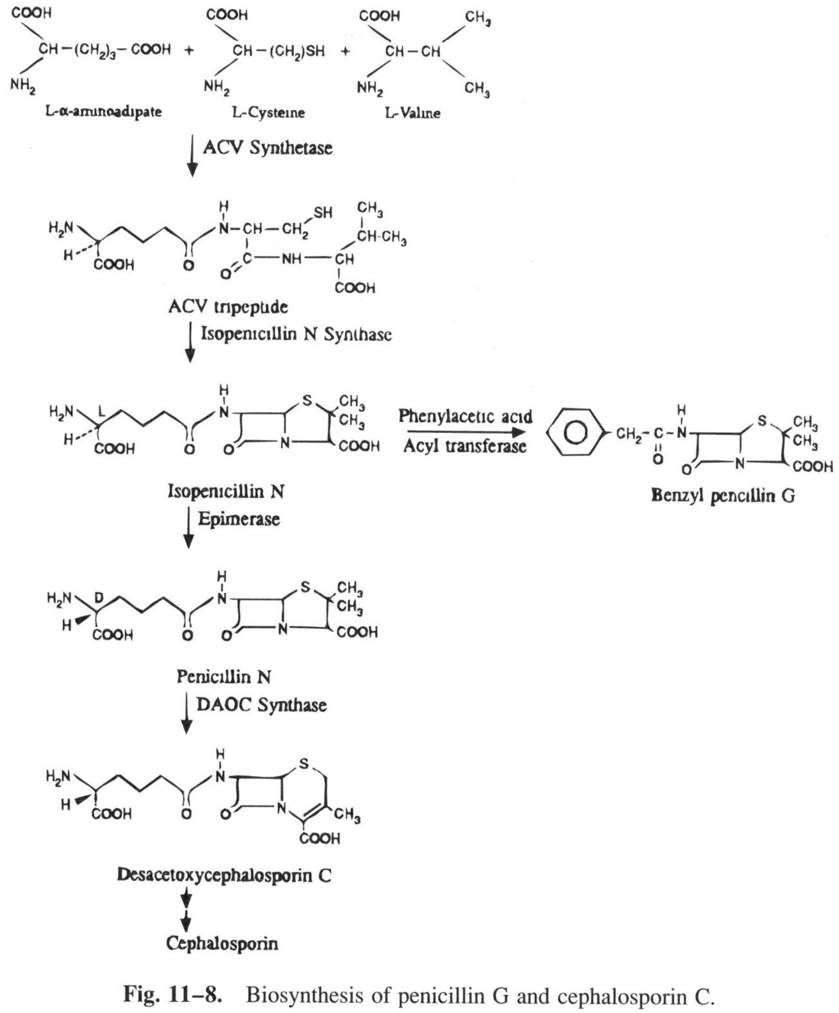

Fig. 11–8. Biosynthesis of penicillin G and cephalosporin C.

cephalosporin biosynthetic pathways, an enzyme called desacetoxycephalosporin C synthase (DOAC synthase or "expandase") acts upon penicillin N to generate the six-membered ring characteristic of cephalosporins. Further modification of the methyl group on this ring eventually yields cephalosporin C which is generally the starting point for semisynthetic production of the clinically useful cephalosporins. The genes and many of the enzymes of these pathways have been isolated and studied. While it originally was thought that antibiotics containing the β-lactam nucleus were solely the domain of fungi (*Penicillium* and *Cephalosporium*), we now know that many types of β-lactam metabolites are found also in several species of streptomycetes and some non-actinomycete procaryotes as well.

Properties of the Penicillins. The chemical structure of the penicillin nucleus is unusual and is characterized by a 4-membered β-lactam ring fused to a thiazolidine ring. This ring system contains three asymmetric carbon atoms in a fixed spatial arrangement, and any disruption of this arrangement by rupturing either the β-lactam ring or the thiazolidine ring results in a complete loss of antimicrobial activity. Unfortunately, the 4-membered β-lactam ring has considerable biologic and chemical lability, which has created a number of problems in the therapeutic utilization of these antibiotics. Biologically, microorganisms resistant to the action of penicillin G produce a β-lactamase (penicillinase) which hydrolyze the β-lactam ring to form inactive penicilloic acid (Fig. 11–9).

Chemically, penicillin G is rapidly inactivated when the pH is more acidic than 5.0 or more alkaline than 8.0. In acidic conditions, penicillin G is converted to penillic acid and to penicilloic acid in alkali (Fig. 11–9). Ideally, aqueous solutions of penicillin G salts should be buffered at pH 6.8 for maximum stability. Penicillins are also inactivated by metal ions, such as zinc and copper, and by oxidizing agents. The need for penicillin antibiotics with inherent stability in gastric fluids and with resistance to penicillinase prompted the search for and development of other penicillins. Penicillin V, ampicillin, and the penicillins chemically related to ampicillin (amoxicillin, bacampicillin, cyclacillin), as well as the indanyl derivative of carbenicillin, are characterized by a significant degree of acid stability, and cloxacillin, dicloxacillin, nafcillin, and oxacillin are both acid-stable and penicillinase-resistant. In the case of the penicillins with increased stability in gastric acid, the introduction of a hetero atom on the α-carbon of the side chain inhibits the participation of the side-chain amide carbonyl in the electron displacement caused by the acid proton. Penicillins resistant to the action of penicillinase possess side chains with acyl groups that protect the β-lactam ring through steric hindrance.

Definite proof of the structure of penicillin was not established until 1949. The need for quantitation of penicillin antibiotics prior to complete elucidation of their chemistry and prior to feasible approaches for resolving or avoiding mixtures of penicillins resulted in the use of microbiologic assay. Microbiologic assay still has

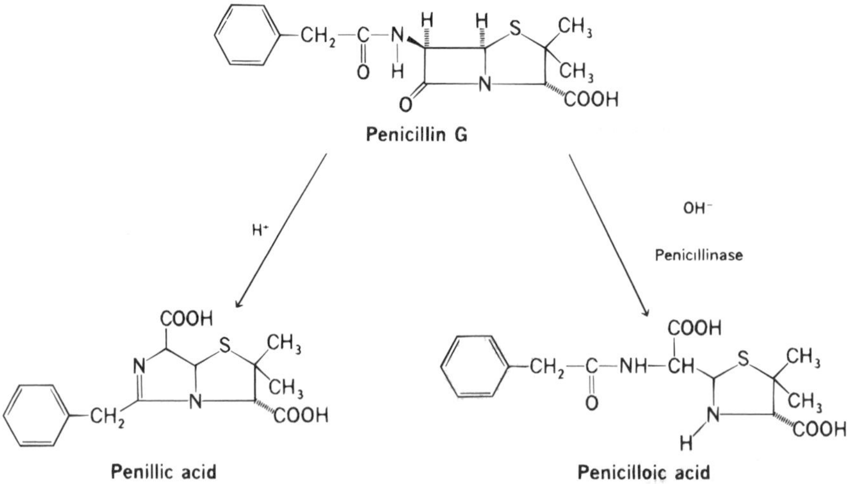

Fig. 11–9. Hydrolysis of the β-lactam system of penicillin G.

some utility in evaluating certain antibiotics, and biologic units are used to express quantitation for penicillin G and penicillin V. Sodium penicillin G is currently accepted as the reference standard; 1 unit is the antibiotic activity of 0.6 μg of sodium penicillin G reference standard. Microbial assays must be conducted under carefully controlled conditions, and alternate procedures frequently offer some advantages at the present time for quantitation of chemical availability. However, therapeutic efficacy is best determined biologically. In addition, a reduction in antimicrobial activity will reveal subtle chemical changes not demonstrable by chemical methods. Accordingly, microbial assays generally remain the standard for resolving doubt with respect to possible loss of activity.

Use of Penicillins. Penicillin G is considered the agent of first choice against many pathogenic gram-positive bacteria. These include *Bacillus anthracis, Clostridium tetani, Clostridium perfringens, Enterococcus faecalis, (Streptococcus faecalis),* β-hemolytic group A *Streptococcus,* and *Streptococcus pneumoniae.* In addition, penicillin is the drug of choice in treating syphilis *(Treponema pallidum)* and infections caused by the gram-negative coccus, *Neisseria meningitidis.*

Intramuscular or intravenous injection is the usual method of administration for penicillin G. The water-soluble sodium or potassium salts are available for this purpose, as are the repository forms, which are water-insoluble salts of high-molecular-weight amines such as procaine and benzathine.

Penicillin G is destroyed by gastric acid, and therefore absorption after oral administration is irregular and variable; consequently, the penicillin of choice for oral administration is penicillin V, which is less susceptible than penicillin G to degradation by gastric acid and produces blood levels two to five times higher than penicillin G. The patient should also be cautioned to take the antibiotic on an empty stomach (1 hour before or 2 hours after eating), because food inhibits its absorption.

In vitro sensitivity tests have shown that strains of group A *Streptococcus* have a sensitivity to penicillin G as low as 0.006 μg per ml; and the MIC range for other bacteria causing infections in which penicillin G is recommended is 0.01 to 2.0 μg per ml. The rapid intravenous administration of sodium or potassium penicillin G results in an immediate high blood level; however, after 1 hour, only 10% of the original dose remains in the blood owing to both distribution and elimination of the drug. Therefore, to maintain therapeutic blood levels in life-threatening infections, the antibiotic is administered by continuous infusion, preferably with a constant infusion pump rather than by the constant drip method.

Penicillins cross readily into the cerebrospinal fluid when meninges are inflamed but penetrate less readily in the absence of inflammation. This property makes them useful in treating meningitis due to sensitive organisms but one must be careful to maintain high blood levels as the meninges heal so that CSF levels do not drop below therapeutic concentrations.

After intramuscular injection of sodium or potassium penicillin G, a peak blood level is obtained within 30 minutes. Then the serum level falls rapidly, with a usual half-life of only 30 minutes. It is important to remember that the height of the blood level peak and the length of time during which penicillin may be demonstrated in the blood depend on the dose and also can vary from person to person.

To maintain therapeutic blood levels of penicillin G, two approaches are utilized. One approach interferes with the excretion of the antibiotic in the tubules of the kidney. When probenecid is used with penicillin, penicillin serum concentrations are approximately doubled. The supposed mechanism involves the hydrolysis of probenecid in the body to yield benzoic acid, which, in turn, competes with penicillin for renal excretion. Very high blood levels of penicillins are associated with seizures. The patient should be monitored for seizure activity especially when probenecid is being used to decrease renal elimination.

A more widely used approach for maintaining therapeutic blood levels delays absorption by employing repository penicillins. After intramuscular injection of an aqueous suspension of procaine penicillin G, a peak blood level is obtained in about 2 hours, and if an adult dose of at least 600,000 units is used, detectable levels are maintained in most patients for at least 24 hours. Benzathine penicillin G is less water-soluble than the procaine salt, and, following intramuscular injection of 600,000 units in an aqueous suspension, serum concentrations of 0.018 to 0.06 μg per ml persist for up to 2 weeks.

Resistance to penicillin G occurs very frequently among strains of *Staphylococcus aureus.* For this reason, if it is not known whether the infecting organism is a penicillinase producer, a penicillinase-resistant semisynthetic penicillin is normally the antibiotic of first choice until a culture-sensitivity test can be performed. The penicillinase-resistant semisynthetic penicillins have essentially equivalent antimicrobial activity against pathogenic gram-positive cocci with MICs of 0.05 to 1.0 μg per ml; however, they are less effective than penicillin G against these organisms.

Extended spectrum penicillins have activity against certain pathogenic gram-negative bacilli against which penicillin G has little activity at normal therapeutic doses. Based on microbial activity, these extended spectrum penicillins can be divided into two groups. One group, composed of ampicillin and the chemically related compounds amoxicillin, bacampicillin, and cyclacillin, is useful in the treatment of *Escherichia coli, Haemophilus influenzae, Salmonella,* and *Shigella* infections, as well as of those infections caused by gram-negative cocci and gram-positive organisms. The second group, which includes carbenicillin, ticarcillin, mezlocillin, piperacillin, and azlocillin, is important in treating non-β-lactamase producing *Enterobacter, Escherichia coli, Bacteroides, Proteus,* and *Pseudomonas aeruginosa* infections. In addition, mezlocillin, piperacillin, and azlocillin are indicated against *Klebsiella pneumoniae.*

A possible explanation for the extension of the antimicrobial spectrum of some of the penicillins such as ampicillin is that these antibiotics penetrate to the site of action more readily than does penicillin G. The mucopeptide layer of the cell wall of gram-negative organisms lies behind layers of polysaccharide, protein, and lipid, which serve as a penetration barrier to penicillin G but not to the extended spectrum penicillins. In the wild-type *Escherichia coli* with an intact penetration barrier, the MIC for penicillin G is 200 μg per ml as opposed to 2 μg per ml for ampicillin; however; if the penetration barrier is removed through mutation, penicillin G exhibits an MIC of 5 μg per ml and ampicillin an MIC of 0.5 μg per ml against the mutant strain.

The penicillins act by inhibiting mucopeptide formation in bacterial cell walls. Presumably, the lack of comparable metabolism in zoologic systems contributes to the relatively low incidence of serious side effects with these antibiotics. The most frequent adverse reactions are allergic responses, and the occasional incidence of anaphylactic shock can be fatal in the absence of emergency treatment. Epinephrine is usually administered for symptomatic control in penicillin shock.

In the early years of penicillin therapy, many cases of hypersensitivity were attributed correctly to foreign proteins, and the frequency of such reactions was reduced by improved purification procedures. However, impurities are not responsible for all penicillin reactions. Penicillin acts as a hapten and combines with body proteins to form an antigen which, in this case, is an allergen. Several breakdown products of the penicillin molecule also serve as minor antigenic determinants. Sensitization is usually owing to a previous treatment with penicillin, but some people get an allergic reaction when first treated owing to a hidden contact such as consumption of milk containing penicillin as a result of veterinary treatment. Allergic reactions vary from fatal anaphylactic shock to laryngeal edema and urticarial rashes to delayed reactions such as serum sickness (drug fever). The incidence of penicillin-allergic patients in the general population is estimated at 5% with the incidence of anaphylactic reactions only a small fraction of that. Because of the danger of a progressive hypersensitivity reaction, no repository penicillin formulation should be used in patients without a history of the patient taking penicillins safely. Although generally a history of hypersensitivity to penicillin is an indication to use alternate antibiotics for control of penicillin susceptible pathogens, sometimes a desensitization protocol is employed when no proven safe and effective alternatives exist. A skin test containing benzylpenicilloyl-polylysine, a synthetic analog of the major antigen, is reasonably predictive of penicillin allergy. The use of a combination of the benzylpenicilloyl-polylysine with a mixture of minor antigenic determinants in a skin test is more predictable but is available only on an experimental basis at this time.

All antibiotics with the penicillin nucleus are cross-allergenic. A patient history must take into account all penicillin derivatives. Ampicillin can cause an independent urticarial reaction which produces confusion in the patient drug history. The use of the skin test in such a situation would be indicated. Cephalosporins are often good alternatives in penicillin allergic patients since cross-allergenicity occurs in only about 10% of these patients, and it usually is seen as a rash rather than anaphylaxis. Imipenem has the same incidence of cross-allergenicity as cephalosporins. Aztreonam is the only β-lactam antibiotic with no documented cross-sensitivity in penicillin-allergic patients.

Penicillin G potassium or potassium benzylpenicillin is normally formulated with suitable buffer systems. Solid formulations have an expiration date that is not later than 5 years from the time the lot was released by the manufacturer. Sterile aqueous solutions may be stored in a refrigerator for up to 7 days (if an approved sodium citrate buffer is used) without significant loss of potency, and are stable at room temperature for 24 hours.

Penicillin G potassium may be administered orally, intramuscularly, or intravenously. One mg of pure penicillin G potassium is equivalent to 1595 units. Daily doses of 10 million units or more are given by intravenous infusion, and up to 100 million units daily may be administered by this method. The dose range varies widely, from 3 million to 100 million units/day, depending on the pathogen being treated, the extent of the infection, and other clinical conditions. Penicillin G potassium contains 1.7 mEq potassium and 0.3 mEq sodium per million units when prepared as directed. Electrolyte balance is an important consideration at high doses.

Penicillin G sodium or sodium benzylpenicillin is normally formulated with suitable buffer systems. Solid preparations have an expiration date that is not later than 5 years from the time the lot was released by the manufacturer, and sterile aqueous solutions may be stored in a refrigerator for 3 days without significant loss of potency. Pure penicillin G sodium is used as the reference standard for microbial assays of the penicillins, and 1 mg is equivalent to 1667 units. Penicillin G sodium is used orally, intramuscularly, or intravenously in the same manner as the potassium salt. A wide range in dosage will also be encountered with sodium benzylpenicillin. Penicillin G sodium contains 2 mEq sodium per million units, and sodium overload can occur at high doses.

Penicillin G procaine is the slightly soluble procaine salt of penicillin G. One mg of pure penicillin G procaine is equivalent to 1009 units.

This antibiotic is used intramuscularly and has the advantage of prolonged action because of slow absorption. It is formulated in an aqueous suspension. The usual intramuscular dose is 600,000 to 1.2 million units, one or two times a day. As mentioned above, procaine penicillin G should not be used in patients who have not previously received penicillin or a penicillin derivative without a hypersensitivity reaction. Occasionally a patient will be allergic to the procaine component of the preparation.

Penicillin G benzathine or *N, N′*-dibenzylethylenediamine dipenicillin G is a slightly soluble salt of penicillin that is used intramuscularly for its unusually prolonged duration of action. One mg of pure penicillin G benzathine is equivalent to 1211 units, and commercial material must have a potency of not less than 1050 units per mg. The usual dose, intramuscularly, is 1.2 million to 2.4 million units as a single dose. A single intramuscular dose results in low blood levels for up to a month and is used when prolonged low levels are needed, e.g., in the treatment of syphilis and in prevention of recurrent rheumatic fever.

Penicillin V or phenoxymethylpenicillin and penicillin V potassium or phenoxymethylpenicillin potassium are relatively acid-stable. The potassium salt is soluble in water, and this appears to favor better absorption following oral administration. However, both forms of this penicillin gave good blood levels, the average ranging from two to five times higher than the levels obtainable with comparable oral doses of penicillin G. One mg of pure phenoxymethyl penicillin is equivalent to 1695 units, and 1 mg of the pure potassium salt equals 1530 units. Quantities are usually expressed on a weight basis for preparations of these penicillins, and the usual oral dose is 125 to 500 mg (200,000 to 800,000 units), three or four times a day.

Penicillinase-Resistant Penicillins

Cloxacillin, dicloxacillin, methicillin, nafcillin, and oxacillin are semisynthetic penicillins that are not inactivated by penicillinase. They are recommended primarily for treatment of staphylococcal infections resistant to other penicillins. Methicillin is acid-labile and must be administered parenterally. Methicillin is often not the penicillinase-resistant penicillin of choice because it causes a higher incidence (than other penicillins) of a non-dose-related, reversible nephropathy that is thought to be a hypersensitivity reaction. Any *Staphylococcus* resistant to methicillin (or the other penicillinase-resistant penicillin derivatives) will be resistant to all β-lactam antibiotics. The other four penicillins are stable in gastric acidity. Nafcillin and oxacillin are available in formulations for oral and parenteral administration; cloxacillin and dicloxacillin are only used orally. All of these penicillins are employed as sodium salts.

Cloxacillin, dicloxacillin, nafcillin, and oxacillin are characterized by a high degree of binding to serum protein, but approximately only 20% of methicillin in blood is bound to serum proteins. Dicloxacillin is absorbed more readily than the other penicillinase-resistant penicillins administered orally. However, food interferes sufficiently with the absorption of all these penicillins, including dicloxacillin, to prompt the recommendation that they be administered on a fasting stomach in order to obtain satisfactory blood levels. A 500-mg oral dose of oxacillin results in a peak blood level of 2.6 μg/ml in 1 hour. When compared with oxacillin at the same dose, cloxacillin provides a two-fold higher blood level, and dicloxacillin effects a four times higher blood level. Nafcillin's oral absorption is inferior to the other penicillinase-resistant derivatives, but it is an excellent parenteral antibiotic. Nafcillin differs from other penicillin derivatives in that it is eliminated via biotransformation and biliary excretion. The dosage will not have to be adjusted in patients with renal dysfunction.

Extended-Spectrum Penicillins (Amino-penicillins)

Ampicillin or aminobenzyl penicillin is an acid-stable, readily absorbed semisynthetic penicillin. It is inactivated by penicillinase but has an unusual spectrum of activity for a penicillin. It is active against most of the bacteria sensitive to penicillin G but also has greater activity against certain gram-negative bacilli than penicillin G. The L-isomer of ampicillin is only about as active as penicillin G against gram-negative bacteria. The D-isomer shows increased activity; therefore, the D-isomer is used in therapy. Ampicillin has special clinical value for treatment of infections caused by non-penicillinase producing *Haemophilus influenzae, Salmonella* species, and *Shigella* species. This antibiotic effectively controls nonpenicillinase-forming strains of *Proteus mirabilis* and *Escherichia coli*, but the high frequency of penicillinase formation by these pathogens limits the clinical effectiveness of ampicillin with respect to these species. However, the recent availability of an ampicillin-sulbactam combination (the sulbactam inhibits Type III β-lactamases and penicillinase) has once again expanded the clinical utility of ampicillin. Ampicillin has two toxicities that are not observed in other penicillin derivatives in that it causes gastrointestinal disturbances in a high percentage of patients receiving it, and it sometimes will cause an urticarial rash independent of other penicillin allergy. The sodium salt of ampicillin is used in parenteral formulations, and oral dosage forms normally utilize the free acid. The usual dose varies widely, from 1 to12 grams daily in divided doses every 4 to 6 hours in adults, depending upon the sensitivity of the organism, the severity of the infection, and other factors. The usual oral dosage is 250-500 mg, four times a day. The ampicillin/ sulbactam combination is administered intravenously or intramuscularly.

Amoxicillin is the *p*-hydroxy derivative of ampicillin. It is stable in the presence of gastric acid and better absorbed from the gastrointestinal tract in the presence of food than ampicillin. It also produces less gastrointestinal disturbance than ampicillin, and since it has antibacterial activity similar to that of ampicillin, it is rapidly replacing this drug in therapeutics. Amoxicillin is available in an amoxicillin/potassium clavulanate combination (Augmentin) that is very useful when β-lactamase producing pathogens are suspected or identified, especially in respiratory tract infections in children in which *Haemophilus influenzae* is an important contributor. A 250-mg oral dose of amoxicillin gives a peak blood level of 4.3 μg/ml. The usual dose is 250 to 500 mg, orally, three times a day.

Bacampicillin hydrochloride is hydrolyzed to ampicillin during absorption from the gastrointestinal tract. Because it is more completely absorbed than ampicillin, it is administered in lower total daily dosages, with 400 mg chemically equivalent to 280 mg of ampicillin, and it sustains effective serum levels when given every 12 hours. Food does not interfere with the absorption from the tablets, but the suspension should be administered on a fasting stomach. The usual dose is 400 to 800 mg every 12 hours.

Extended-Spectrum Penicillins (Active Against *Pseudomonas aeruginosa*)

Carbenicillin disodium is a carboxybenzylpenicillin with increased antibacterial activity against non-β-lactamase-producing gram-negative bacilli, particularly *Pseudomonas aeruginosa*. The D- and L-isomers display only slight differences in biologic activity and undergo rapid interconversion when in solution; therefore, the racemic mixture is used. The antibiotic can be administered in sufficient dosage (up to 40 g daily) to obtain serum concentrations exceeding 50 to 60 μg/ml. Such concentrations inhibit most *Pseudomonas aeruginosa* strains. Clinical efficacy may be enhanced by combination therapy of carbenicillin disodium with gentamicin or tobramycin in full therapeutic dosages, although a chemical interaction between aminoglycosides and β-lactam antibiotics (the amino functionalities on the aminoglycoside molecules serve to attack the β-lactam ring, resulting in a covalent adduct and inactivation of the antibiotics) necessitates their administration by separate routes of administration. Carbenicillin has an α-carboxy moiety that requires a sodium salt so each molecule of carbenicillin carries two sodium atoms. This can result in sodium overload in patients with renal dysfunction or sodium restriction. Also the α-carboxy functionality is linked to a platelet dysfunction that can result in abnormal bleeding in some patients. Carbenicillin is particularly effective in urinary tract infections because of very high urine levels achieved by intramuscular injection. Carbenicillin disodium is not absorbed orally, but carbenicillin indanyl sodium, the indanyl ester of the α-carboxy moiety, is available for oral administration for urinary tract infections. It is absorbed orally but only achieves therapeutic levels as it is concentrated in the urine.

Ticarcillin disodium is the thienyl analog of carbenicillin and has the same antimicrobial spectrum and indications. It is more active than carbenicillin, particularly against *Pseudomonas aeruginosa*. It therefore can be used in lower doses, thus alleviating to some degree the problem of sodium overload. It is also used in combination with gentamicin and tobramycin. The combination of ticarcillin and clavulanate potassium (Timentin) is particularly useful against β-lactamase-producing gram-negative organisms although it must be noted that not all gram-negative β-lactamases are inhibited by clavulanate. Ticarcillin disodium is administered intramuscularly (in doses less than 2 grams per infection) and intravenously, and ticarcillin/clavulanate is available only for intravenous dosage.

Mezlocillin sodium is an ureidopenicillin similar to carbenicillin and ticarcillin in its antibacterial spectrum. It is active against gram-positive cocci, and non-β-lactamase-producing strains of *Haemophilus influenzae* and gonococcus are highly susceptible to mezlocillin. It is more active *in vitro* than carbenicillin and ticarcillin against susceptible strains of enteric gram-negative bacilli such as *Escherichia coli, Klebsiella*, and *Enterobacter*. The activity of mezlocillin against *Pseudomonas aeruginosa* is comparable to that of ticarcillin. It is available for intravenous or intramuscular use.

Piperacillin sodium is an aminobenzylpenicillin derivative with an antibacterial spectrum similar to that of mezlocillin. It is active *in vitro* against gram-positive cocci, non-β-lactamase-producing, enteric gram-negative bacilli and many anaerobes. It is more active *in vitro* than carbenicillin, ticarcillin, or ampicillin against *Escherichia coli, Klebsiella,* and *Enterobacter*; and it is 4 to 16 times more active than carbenicillin, ticarcillin, or mezlocillin against *Pseudomonas aeruginosa*. Like ticarcillin and amoxicillin, piperacillin is available in combination with a β-lactamase inhibitor, tazobactam. Piperacillin is available for intramuscular or intravenous use. For serious infections, the maximum dose is 3 to 4 g every 4 to 6 hours. No more than 2 g should be given intramuscularly at any one site.

Azlocillin sodium is an ureidopenicillin with a spectrum of activity similar to those of mezlocillin and piperacillin. Against *Pseudomonas aeruginosa*, it is more active *in vitro* than carbenicillin, ticarcillin, or mezlocillin, and is similar to piperacillin, but is less active against other gram-negative organisms than piperacillin. After equal doses, serum levels of azlocillin are higher than those obtained with mezlocillin or ticarcillin. Since azlocillin, mezlocillin, and piperacillin are all monosodium salts, these agents are less likely to cause fluid retention than carbenicillin or ticarcillin, which are disodium salts. Azlocillin is available only for parenteral administration.

Amidinopenicillin

Amdinocillin represents a new class of β-lactam antibiotics. It is a semisynthetic 6-amidinopenicillanic acid. Since it contains the β-lactam-thiazolidine fused ring structure, it can be considered a close relative of the penicillins. This change in the chemical structure, however, is associated with a marked alteration in its antibacterial spectrum and mechanism of action. Amdinocillin is considerably more active against gram-negative bacilli than against gram-positive cocci, whereas the reverse is true for penicillin G. Amdinocillin interferes with bacterial wall synthesis in *Escherichia coli* by binding principally to penicillin binding protein 2 (PBP-2). Other β-lactam antibiotics bind mostly to PBPs-1 and -3, which suggests that concurrent use of amdinocillin with other β-lactams might have a synergistic effect on susceptible bacteria. However, while amdinocillin has been very useful for elucidating the roles of the various PBPs, it is not currently in clinical use.

β-lactamase Inhibitors

Clavulanic acid is a fermentation product of *Streptomyces clavuligerus*, structurally related to the penicillins. Although only weakly antibacterial on its own, clavulanic acid is capable of irreversibly inactivating bacterial β-lactamases responsible for antibiotic resistance. Clavulanic acid acts synergistically with β-lactamase-sensitive penicillins and cephalosporins, and clavulanic acid concentrations of 5 μg/ml or less may decrease the *in vitro* MICs of these antibiotics against bacteria normally resistant to therapeutically attainable levels. The synergy mainly results from the protection afforded to the sensitive antibiotic caused by the inactivation of β-lactamase by clavulanic acid.

Clavulanic Acid

The combination of **amoxicillin and potassium clavulanate** (Augmentin) is a β-lactam antibiotic with a β-lactamase inhibitor. The addition of clavulanic acid extends the *in vitro* activity of amoxicillin to include β-lactamase-producing strains of *Haemophilus influenzae*, *Escherichia coli*, *Proteus mirabilis*, and *Staphylococcus aureus*. It is important to note that it will not extend the spectrum to organisms not normally killed by amoxicillin (e.g., *Pseudomonas aeruginosa*) in the absence of β-lactamase resistance or to organisms resistant to amoxicillin by mechanisms other than β-lactamase production. The combination is available in tablets for oral use containing 250 and 500 mg of amoxicillin. Each tablet strength contains 125 mg of potassium clavulanate; therefore, two 250-mg tablets are not equivalent to one 500-mg tablet, and the higher dose of clavulanic acid is more likely to cause diarrhea. The usual adult dosage is 250 mg every 8 hours, and 500 mg every 8 hours is recommended for severe infections.

A combination product of **ticarcillin disodium and potassium clavulanate** (Timentin) is available for parenteral treatment of urinary tract, skin and soft tissue, and lower respiratory tract infections, and sepsis due to susceptible organisms. When clavulanic acid is added to ticarcillin, a striking increase in activity occurs against β-lactamase-producing strains of *Staphylococcus aureus*, *Haemophilus influenzae*, gonococcus, *Escherichia coli*, and *Klebsiella*. It does not, however, inhibit the β-lactamases produced by most strains of *Pseudomonas*, *Enterobacter*, and some other gram-negative bacilli; and β-lactamase-producing strains of those organisms remain resistant to ticarcillin. The usual adult dosage is 3 g of ticarcillin and 100 mg of clavulanic acid every 4 to 6 hours administered by intravenous infusion over 30 minutes.

Sulbactam

Sulbactam is also structurally related to the penicillins but possesses only weak antibacterial activity of its own. However, in the combination of **ampicillin sodium and sulbactam sodium** (Unasyn) it inhibits irreversibly a variety of β-lactamases and restores ampicillin activity against a variety of β-lactamase-producing strains of bacteria that would be sensitive to ampicillin if they did not produce β-lactamase. The ampicillin sodium and sulbactam sodium combination includes 1 gram of ampicillin plus 0.5 gram of sulbactam or 2 grams of ampicillin plus 1 gram of sulbactam. Administration is via intramuscular or intravenous routes. Daily dosages should not exceed 4 grams of sulbactam.

Sulbactam

Tazobactam

Tazobactam sodium was recently approved for administration in combination with piperacillin sodium (Zosyn) for the same general approach of expanding the spectrum to include some β-lactamase-producing strains. The combination product is administered by intravenous infusion over 30 minutes. The usual total daily dose is 12 grams of piperacillin and 1.5 grams of tazobactam given as 3.375 grams every 6 hours.

Tazobactam

Cephalosporins and Other β-Lactam Antibiotics

In 1945, Brotzu isolated a microorganism from sea water collected near a sewage outlet off the coast of Sardinia and noted its antagonism to both gram-positive and gram-negative bacteria. The organism was identified as *Cephalosporium acremonium*. Abraham and his coworkers at Oxford reported the isolation of three substances with antibiotic activity from cultures of this organism during 1955 and 1956. These metabolites were a steroid (cephalosporin P) that has achieved no therapeutic significance, penicillin N, and cephalosporin C. Cephalosporin C is biosynthetically related to the penicillins and resembles these antibiotics in many of its biologic and chemical properties. The major difference is a 7-aminocephalosporanic acid nucleus which has a fused dihydrothiazine β-lactam ring system rather than the fused thiazolidine β-lactam system of 6-aminopenicillanic acid. The degree of antibacterial activity of cephalosporin C is only moderate, and it is not used therapeutically. However, it is produced by fermentation in large quantities to serve as a starting material for the chemical production of the semisynthetic cephalosporin antibiotics (Fig. 11-10).

The cephamycins are β-lactam antibiotics that are closely related chemically to the cephalosporins. They are produced by actinomycetes rather than fungi and are 7-α-methoxycephalosporins. Cephamycin C, which is produced by *Streptomyces lactamdurans*, serves as starting material for the chemical synthesis of cefoxitin, the first cephamycin antibiotic available for therapeutic use.

A new group of antibiotics related to the cephalosporins has been obtained through partial synthesis from penicillin. In these antibiotics the dihydrothiazine ring of the cephalosporins has been replaced by a dihydrooxazine ring. Apparently the sulfur atom in the cephalosporin ring system is not a requirement for high antibiotic activity. These antibiotics have been designated oxalactams. In this group, moxalactam is a 7-α-methoxyoxalactam derivative in which the me-

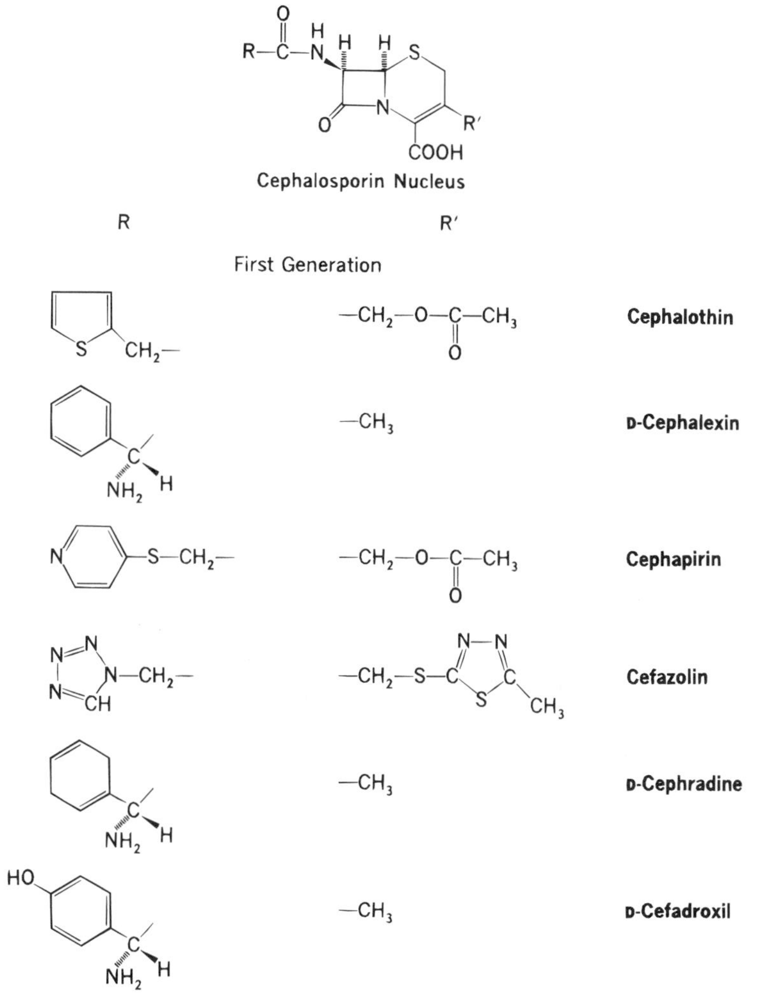

Fig. 11–10. Structures of commercially available cephalosporins and other β-lactam antibiotics.

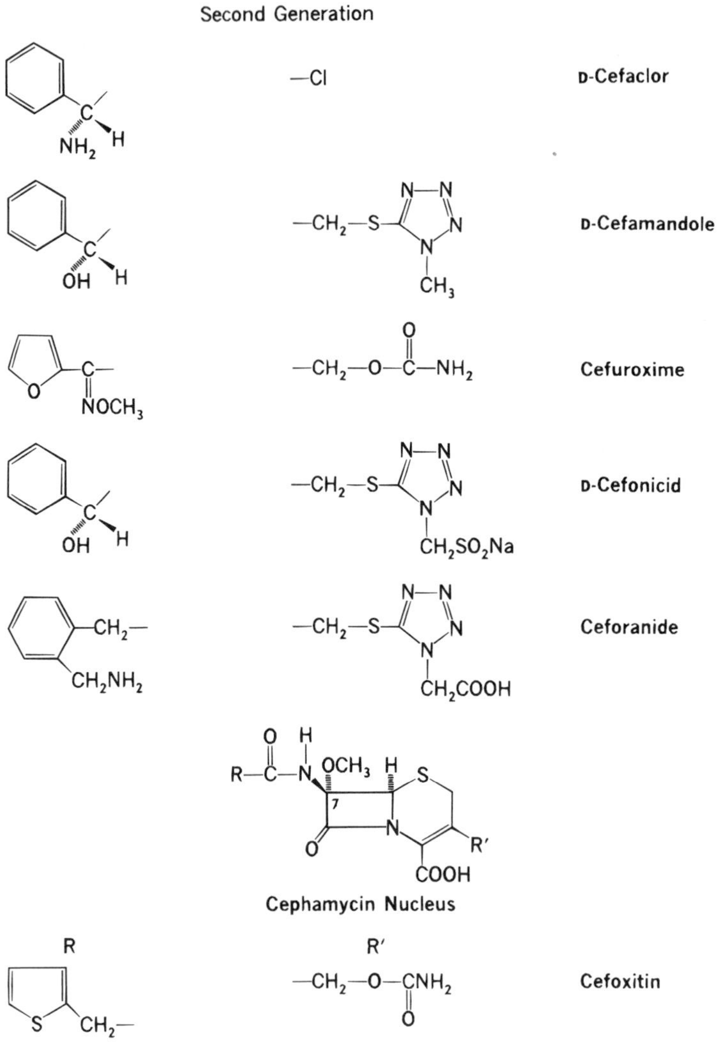

Second Generation

Fig. 11–10. *(Continued).*

thoxy group protects the oxalactam nucleus from β-lactamase hydrolysis.

Imipenem is another new type of β-lactam antibiotic. It is a member of a class of antibiotics containing the carbapenem nucleus in which the sulfur atom of penicillin has been replaced by a carbon atom. Thienamycin, which is a naturally occurring carbapenem compound produced by *Streptomyces cattleya*, serves as the starting material for the synthesis of imipenem (*N*-formimidoylthienamycin).

Another new class of β-lactams is the monobactam, of which aztreonam is the only clinically used representative. This antibiotic is active only against gram-negative aerobes but is resistant to β-lactamases.

The cephalosporins and related antibiotics can be divided into first, second, and third generation agents based on *in vitro* antibacterial activity. The first generation cephalosporins, such as cephalothin and cefazolin, are active against most gram-positive cocci, including *Staphylococcus aureus*, (but, notably, excluding *Enterococcus faecalis*), and some strains of gram-negative enteric bacilli, including *Escherichia coli, Klebsiella pneumoniae*, and *Proteus mirabilis*. The second generation group includes cephalosporins related to cefamandole and cefaclor, which have expanded activity against *Haemophilus influenzae, Neisseria gonorrhoeae*, and some enteric gram-negative bacilli, as well as cephalosporins related to cefoxitin, a cepha-

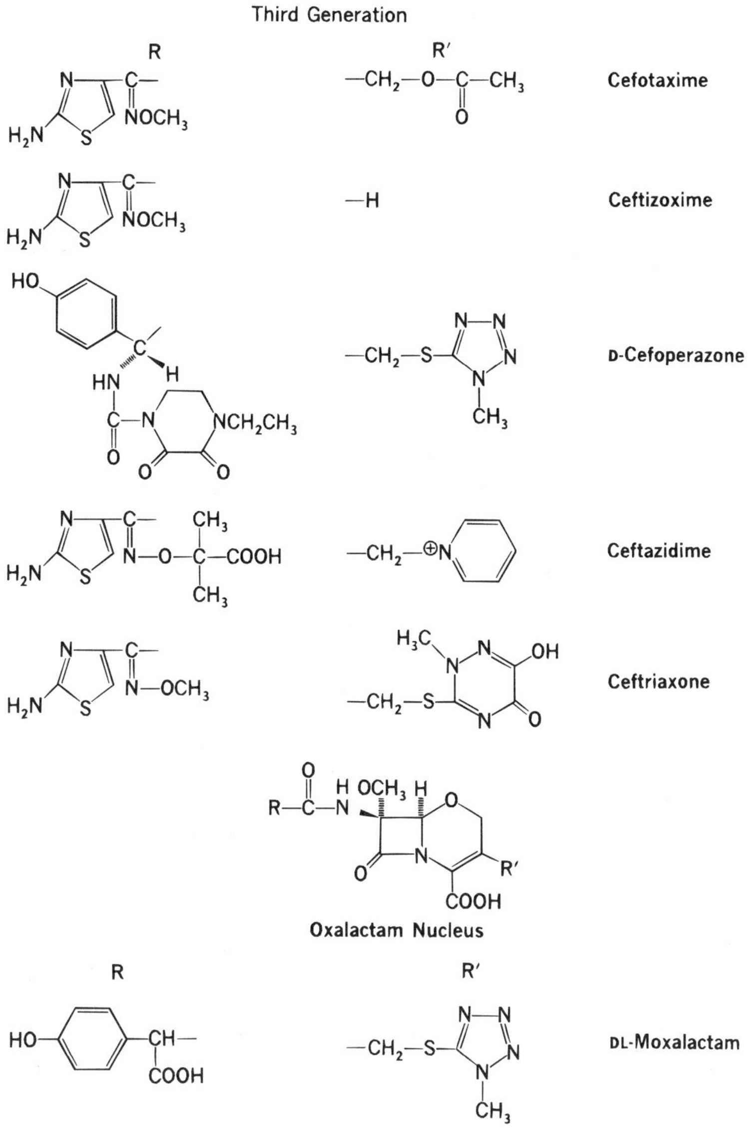

Third Generation

R   R'

—CH₂—O—C—CH₃   Cefotaxime

—H   Ceftizoxime

—CH₂—S—(tetrazole)   D-Cefoperazone

—CH₂—⊕N(pyridine)   Ceftazidime

—CH₂—S—(triazinone)   Ceftriaxone

Oxalactam Nucleus

R   R'

—CH₂—S—(tetrazole)   DL-Moxalactam

Fig. 11–10. *(Continued).*

mycin, which have expanded activity against strains of the gram-negative anaerobe, *Bacteroides*, and some gram-negative enteric bacilli. The third generation group, which includes moxalactam (an oxalactam) and many cephalosporins, is active against β-lactamase producing enteric gram-negative bacilli, gonococcus, meningococcus, and anaerobes such as *Bacteroides fragilis*. Only ceftazidime is particularly effective against *Pseudomonas aeruginosa*. No cephalosporins are active against *Enterococcus faecalis* (formerly called *Streptococcus faecalis*), and

penicillin G remains the antibiotic of choice for infections caused by this organism.

In general, progression from first to third generation drugs reveals a broadening gram-negative spectrum, a loss of efficacy against gram-positive organisms, and a greater efficacy against resistant organisms. First generation drugs are generally inactivated by β-lactamase-producing organisms (except staphylococci). Second and third generation agents are distinguished by an increasing resistance to β-lactamase inactivation.

The cephalosporins and related β-lactam antibiotics inhibit cell-wall formation, and this general mode of action explains their relatively low toxicity. Hypersensitivity is an occasional side effect of the cephalosporins. Some cross-sensitivity reactions in patients allergic to penicillin necessitate care in administering cephalosporins to individuals who are allergic to penicillin. Pseudomembranous colitis and enterococcal overgrowth have been reported with the use of cephalosporins.

First Generation Agents

Cephalothin, cefazolin, cephapirin, cephradine, cephalexin, and cefadroxil have antibacterial activity similar to that of ampicillin. They are effective against gram-positive bacteria, including penicillinase-producing *Staphylococcus*. The first generation cephalosporin antibiotics are resistant to penicillinase, but they are inactivated by another β-lactamase, cephalosporinase. Certain gram-negative organisms, including *Escherichia coli, Proteus mirabilis,* and *Klebsiella pneumoniae*, are sensitive to these cephalosporins. Species of *Enterobacter* and *Pseudomonas* as well as most indole-producing species of *Proteus* are resistant to this group. The susceptibility of *Haemophilus influenzae* is quite variable, and, generally, the first generation cephalosporins are less active against this organism than are the extended-spectrum penicillins such as ampicillin. The cephalosporins penetrate most tissues well except that, unlike the penicillins, they are unpredictable in the manner in which they cross the blood-brain barrier; consequently, the first generation cephalosporins should never be considered an adequate substitute for the penicillins in treating meningitis. The first generation cephalosporins used orally, namely, cephalexin, cefadroxil, and cephradine (the last is also used parenterally), are less effective than the parenteral cephalosporins against *Escherichia coli, Proteus mirabilis,* and species of *Klebsiella*. The orally effective cephalosporins can be used to treat infections caused by gram-positive bacteria, and because of the high concentration of these antibiotics excreted in the urine, e.g.,1000 μg per ml following a 250-mg oral dose of cephalexin, they are used to treat urinary tract infections caused by *Escherichia coli, Proteus mirabilis,* and *Klebsiella* species. Because of a prolonged excretion, cefadroxil has the advantage of providing more sustained serum and urine concentrations than are obtained with other oral cephalosporins. Clinical studies indicate that cefadroxil, 1 g twice daily, is as effective as cephalexin, 500 mg four times daily.

Cephalothin can cause thrombophlebitis when administered intravenously in doses larger than 6 g daily for periods longer than 3 days; also, intramuscular injection of this antibiotic may be painful. Cefazolin is the first cephalosporin marketed that seems to be devoid of these undesirable side effects.

Cefazolin has a longer half-life than cephalothin and can be administered three times a day instead of the every 4- to 6-hour administration schedule required for cephalothin.

Second Generation

Cefamandole nafate, cefaclor, cefuroxime, cefonicid, cefprozil, cefpodoxime proxetil, loracarbef, cefoxitin, cefmetazole, and cefotetan are classified as second generation cephalosporins. In general, they have the same spectrum of antibacterial activity as the first generation agents except that they are more active against *Haemophilus influenzae,* gonococcus, and some enteric gram-negative bacilli. The parenteral drugs cefamandole, cefuroxime, and cefonicid are about equally effective against *Haemophilus influenzae*. Cefoxitin, cefmetazole, and cefotetan have activity against the anaerobe *Bacteroides fragilis*; the other second generation cephalosporins do not. This activity makes them particularly useful for abdominal infections, including gynecological infections.

Cefoxitin and cefuroxime have a high degree of resistance to many of the β-lactamases that can hydrolyze the commonly used cephalosporins. In the case of cefoxitin, this resistance is attributable to the steric hindrance around the 7 position of the cephamycin nucleus because of the 7-α-methoxy group. Cefuroxime has a methoxyamino group on its acyl side chain, which increases its resistance to β-lactamase.

Several of the second generation agents are absorbed orally. Cefuroxime axetil and cefpodoxime proxetil are prodrugs that are hydrolyzed once they are absorbed and their absorption is actually enhanced by food. Cefaclor, cefprozil, and loracarbef are also absorbed orally. Cefamandole, cefoxitin, cefmetazole, cefotetan, and cefonicid, as well as the non-axetil form of cefuroxime, are administered parenterally. Cefuroxime achieves some penetration into the cerebrospinal fluid while the other second generation agents do not. However, its use for meningitis has been supplanted by third-generation agents that achieve much better levels.

The serum half-life of several of the second-generation cephalosporins is prolonged, thus allowing for dosing every 12 to 24 hours. These long half-life agents include the parenterally administered cefonicid, which is administered once a day, and cefotetan, which is usually administered every 12 hours. Oral agents including loracarbef, cefprozil, and cefpodoxime proxetil are also administered on an every 12 to 24 hour schedule.

Cefamandole contains a methyltetrazolethiomethyl group at position 3 of the cephalosporin nucleus that has been associated with prothrombin deficiency and, sometimes, with bleeding. In addition, this group may inhibit aldehyde dehydrogenase, which may result in alcohol intolerance as a result of a disulfiram-like reaction. Several of the second and third generation cephalosporins have the methyltetrazolethiomethyl moiety, and these agents all have the same side effects as are observed with cefamandole.

Third Generation Agents

Cefotaxime, ceftizoxime, cefoperazone, ceftazidime, ceftriaxone, moxalactam, and cefixime are third generation agents. They are differentiated from first and second generation drugs by their extended activity against a wide variety enteric gram-negative bacilli, including β-lactamase-producing strains. Cefotaxime has superior *in vitro* activity against *Escherichia coli, Klebsiella, Enterobacter, Proteus, Haemophilus influenzae,* and *Neisseria*, with 90% of the strains of these organisms inhibited at an MIC of 0.5 μg per ml or less. Cefotaxime maintains good activity against gram-positive organisms although with higher MICs (i.e., less activity) than first generation cephalosporins. It achieves reasonably good penetration through inflamed meninges which makes it useful for gram-negative meningitis. Cefotaxime is administered only by parenteral routes.

Ceftizoxime is the desacetyl active metabolite of cefotaxime and therefore has properties and a spectrum of activity very similar to that of cefotaxime. It has a slightly longer half-life that permits 8- to 12-hour dosing as compared with 6 to 8 hours for cefotaxime. Cefoperazone is less active than cefotaxime against enteric gram-negative bacilli but more active against *Pseudomonas aeruginosa*, although ceftazidime is a much superior agent for use against strains of *Pseudomonas*. Cefoperazone is administered parenterally and is excreted partially through the bile, thus achieving high biliary levels. Ceftazidime has activity similar to that of cefotaxime and ceftizoxime *in vitro* but is much more active against *Pseudomonas aeruginosa* and less active against staphylococci and *Bacteroides fragilis*. It is an agent of choice for empirical antibiotic therapy when *Pseudomonas* is among the suspected pathogens. Most strains of meningococcus, gonococcus, and *Haemophilus influenzae* (including ampicillin-resistant strains) are highly susceptible to ceftriaxone. It penetrates inflamed meninges well and is an important agent in the treatment of meningitis due to sensitive organisms. As β-lactamase producing strains of *Neisseria gonorrhoeae* have become more prevalent, ceftriaxone has become important in the treatment of gonococcal infections. It can be administered intramuscularly or intravenously, depending upon the specific circumstances. Its longer half-life allows for once a day dosing in many situations. It also is excreted in the bile and occasionally its relative insolubility will lead to "biliary sludging."

Moxalactam has a spectrum of activity similar to that of cefotaxime; however, its use is limited because of the occurrence of serious bleeding disorders. This agent, as well as cefamandole and cefoperazone, contains the methyltetrazolethiomethyl group, which may cause hypoprothrombinemia, as well as the α-carboxyl group previously seen in carbenicillin, which can result in platelet dysfunction. Both effects lead to bleeding disorders.

Cefixime is an orally-absorbed third generation cephalosporin. It has a spectrum of activity that includes β-lactamase producing strains of *Haemophilus influenzae,* and it maintains activity against gram-positive cocci. It is used primarily for outpatient treatment of respiratory tract infections on an every 12-hour dosing schedule.

Other β-Lactam Antibiotics

Imipenem/cilastatin sodium (Primaxin) is a fixed-dose combination product in a 1:1 ratio. Imipenem is a member of a class of antibiotics containing the carbapenem nucleus. It is prepared synthetically as the *N*-formimidoyl derivative of thienamycin, an antibiotic produced by *Streptomyces cattleya.* The *N*-formimidoyl derivative was formed to prevent the rapid intermolecular inactivation of thienamycin which occurs as the terminal amino group on the side chain attacks the β-lactam bond.

The N-formimidoyl derivative was formed to prevent the rapid intermolecular inactivation of thienamycin which occurs as the terminal amino group on the side chain attacks the β-lactam bond.

When imipenem is administered alone, it is rapidly hydrolyzed to an inactive metabolite by dehydropeptidase-I which is present on the brush border of the proximal renal tubular cells; consequently, adequate antibacterial levels are not reached. This disadvantage has been overcome by the coadministration of the dehydropeptidase inhibitor cilastatin sodium, the sodium salt of a derivatized heptenoic acid.

Cilastatin

Data from both *in vitro* and *in vivo* studies suggest that imipenem/cilastatin inhibits 90% or more of the clinically important bacterial pathogens at an MIC of 8 μg per ml or less, including *Enterococcus faecalis, Bacteroides fragilis, Pseudomonas aeruginosa, Serratia* sp., and other difficult-to-kill pathogens. It has a high degree of stability in the presence of most β-lactamases. Imipenem is less likely to kill some of the more unusual pseudomonads such as *Pseudomonas cepacia*, and it, like all other β-lactam antibiotics, will not kill methicillin-resistant *Staphylococcus*. It is not active against nonbacterial pathogens. Imipenem/cilastatin is usually reserved for initial therapy of serious infections when resistant organisms are suspected, therapy of serious infections due to organisms resistant to other antibiotics, and in the treatment of mixed infections that would otherwise require multiple antibiotics.

Imipenem/cilastatin is administered intramuscularly or intravenously. It achieves wide distribution, including penetration through inflamed meninges. It is administered in doses up to 4 g/day in divided doses, but the usual dose is 250 to 500 mg every 6 hours. Side effects include some hypersensitivity reactions and seizures, particularly in patients with CNS disorders.

Aztreonam is the first available member of a class of compounds called the monobactams which have a monocyclic β-lactam ring. It has bactericidal activity against gram-negative aerobes (but not anaerobes or gram-positive bacteria) due to its ability to bind tightly to the PBP-3 of gram-negative organisms. It is highly resistant to hydrolysis by β-lactamases. Aztreonam is useful for serious infections due to susceptible organisms, and since it does not appear to have cross-sensitivity with penicillins and cephalosporins, it may be of particular use in patients allergic to both these classes of antibiotics. It is administered intramuscularly or intravenously in usual doses of 1 to 2 grams every 8 to 12 hours for moderately severe infections in adults with normal renal function.

Aztreonam

MACROLIDE ANTIBIOTICS

Macrolide antibiotics are characterized by a macrolactone ring that is glycosidically linked to one or more sugars. Biosynthetic studies have established that the macrolactone ring is formed by a condensation of acetate and/or propionate units, apparently via malonyl-CoA and 2-methylmalonyl-CoA. Methyl substituents on the lactone ring appear to be residual from incorporation of propionate units rather than from terminal biologic methylation. The sugar components of these antibiotics are usually deoxysugars, at least one sugar residue is routinely an aminosugar, and both *N*-methyl and *O*-methyl groups of methionine origin are common. Experimental data suggest that these uncommon sugars are derived from glucose. Thus, the macrolides must be considered products of both acetate and carbohydrate metabolism. It is suspected that glycosidation is a terminal reaction in the pathway.

Erythromycin, clarithromycin, and azithromycin are the three macrolide antibiotics in clinical use. Erythromycin was initially isolated in 1952 from cultures of *Streptomyces erythreus* (now reclassified as *Saccharopolyspora erythreus*). The commercial product is primarily erythromycin A (Fig. 11–11), but also contains small amounts of two related antibiotics that have been designated erythromycins B and C. It is produced by fermentation, and the large number of asymmetric centers (19 in erythromycin A) suggests that chemical synthesis is not feasi-

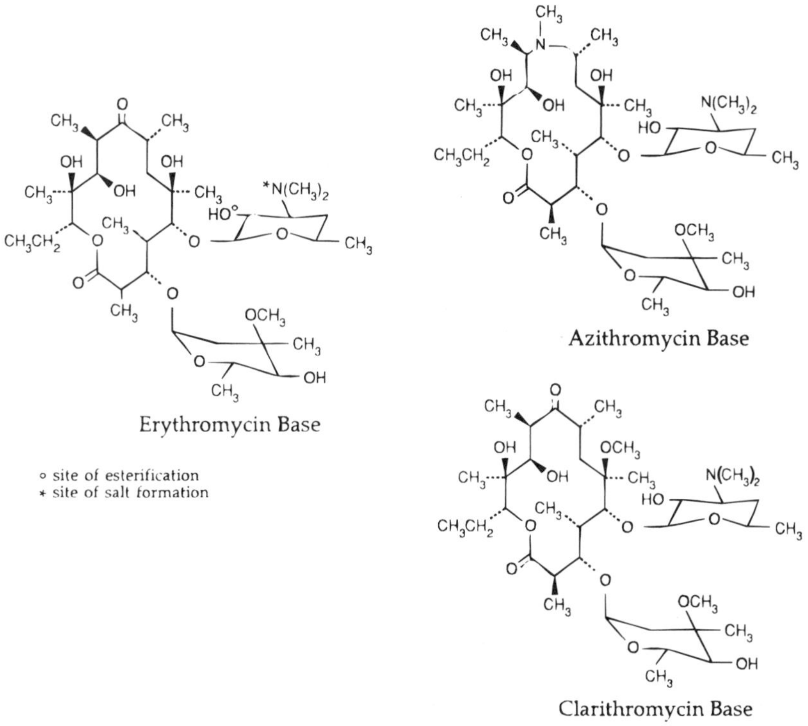

Fig. 11-11. Structures of erythromycin, clarithromycin, and azithromycin.

ble. However, this class of antibiotics has been the target for both semisynthetic modification (yielding clarithromycin and azithromycin) and genetic manipulation of the producing organisms to produce "hybrid" antibiotics with improved properties. Azithromycin is an "azalide" antibiotic, a subclass of the macrolides in which a methyl-substituted nitrogen atom has been incorporated into the lactone ring of erythromycin. Alkylation of the hydroxyl group at C-6 of erythromycin yields clarithromycin.

Macrolides all have the same mechanism of action, i.e., binding reversibly to the 50S ribosomal subunit of susceptible organisms thus inhibiting RNA-dependent protein synthesis by blocking the translocation of the peptidyl t-RNA from the acceptor site to the donor site. They have similar, but not identical, antibacterial spectra and side effects and differ primarily in their pharmacokinetics. They are bacteriostatic or bactericidal depending upon the specific pathogen and the concentration of antibiotic.

Several mechanisms of bacterial resistance to macrolides appear to exist. A lack of effective antibiotic penetration explains the relative insensitivity of most gram-negative bacteria, and similar permeability considerations seem to charac-

terize some resistant strains of normally susceptible species. In staphylococci, which readily develop resistance to macrolides, thus limiting the therapeutic utility of macrolides against this important pathogen, and perhaps in other gram-positive organisms, a plasmid-mediated enzymatic modification of the target site on the ribosome is responsible for resistance development.

Erythromycin has primarily a gram-positive spectrum but also inhibits some other pathogens. It does not inhibit any gram-negative enteric bacilli. It is active against various species of *Streptococcus* and *Corynebacterium*, and the gram-negative coccus *Neiserria gonorrhea*, although the minimal inhibitory concentrations are quite high for the latter. Erythromycin inhibits the spirochaete *Treponema pallidum* and is an alternative to penicillin in the treatment of syphilis. It is the drug of choice for undiagnosed pneumonias since it is active against both *Legionella* and *Mycoplasma pneumoniae*, as well as *Streptococcus pneumoniae*. It also has activity against strains of *Chlamydia*. Erythromycin is sometimes combined with sulfonamides in the treatment of respiratory tract infections due to *Haemophilus influenzae*, but it is less effective when used alone for this purpose. Overall, erythromycin is used most often as an alternative to β-lactam antibiotics in respiratory and skin and soft-tissue infections in penicillin-allergic patients, and as first choice for treatment of infections due to *Legionella* or *Mycoplasma pneumoniae*.

Erythromycin is a weak base, and the macrocyclic ring is unstable in gastric acidity, a factor that must be considered when devising pharmaceutic formulations. Enteric coating of the free base can be used to deliver the antibiotic to the intestinal tract where it is absorbed in its lipid-soluble non-ionized form, but these products tend to leave more unabsorbed drug in the intestine than other formulations, leading to a greater possibility of GI side effects. However, the blood levels achieved are adequate for most infections. The use of insoluble salts (erythromycin stearate) and esters [erythromycin estolate (the lauryl sulfate salt of the propionate ester) and erythromycin ethylsuccinate], which are hydrolyzed in the intestine and elsewhere in the body, also protects erythromycin from gastric acidity and allows oral administration. Soluble salts [lactobionate and glucoheptonate (also called gluceptate)] are used for intravenous administration. The various oral formulations vary in their absorption in the presence of food. The enteric coated base and the stearate formulations should be taken on an empty stomach, while the estolate and the ethylsuccinate can be taken with food. Erythromycin is a relatively safe antibiotic with gastrointestinal upset being the predominantly encountered side effect, which can be reduced by administering the antibiotic with meals. However, the estolate formulation does have an additional side effect of hepatotoxicity, observed as cholestatic jaundice, primarily in adults after 10 to 14 days of therapy. This side effect is observed infrequently in children, and the estolate is commonly prescribed as the oral suspension for children. Other macrolides can cause hepatotoxicity as well, but with lower frequency, and occasional hypersensitivity reactions are observed with all macrolides.

Normal peak serum levels that have been reported for the usual oral dosage regimens of erythromycin are between 0.3 and 5.0 μg per ml which is well above the MICs for most susceptible organisms. The antibiotic is well distributed into most tissues except for the cerebrospinal fluid and the urine. Only a small percentage (2.5 to 10%) is excreted by the kidney, and most is metabolized by the liver prior to elimination via the bile. The key involvement of hepatic metabolism may prompt the need for dosage reduction in cases of severe liver disease, and there are drug interactions observed with some other P-450 hepatically-metabolized drugs (e.g., the antihistamine terfenadine). Erythromycin preparations are administered with usual oral doses in adults equivalent to 250 mg of free base four times a day (e.g., 400 mg of the stearate salt is equivalent to 250 mg of free base).

Clarithromycin has about the same antimicrobial spectrum as erythromycin but exhibits significantly increased potency against those organisms. In particular, it has useful activity against *Haemophilus influenzae*, where erythromycin cannot be used alone. The parent compound is readily metabolized to an active metabolite, 14-hydroxyclarithromycin, which is twice as potent as the parent compound against *H. influenzae*. It also has activity against *Mycobacterium avium* and *Mycobacterium intracellulare* and is used as a primary agent for the treatment of disseminated mycobacterial infections. It is rapidly absorbed from the gastrointestinal tract after oral absorption and can be given with meals. The improvement in absorption relative to erythromycin dramatically reduces the incidence of gastrointestinal side effects. Clearance of the antibiotic and its active metabolite is primarily through the kidney.

Azithromycin is less active than erythromycin against some gram-positive organisms but is still useful for most streptococcal infections. It has improved potency against *Haemophilus influenzae*. It is readily absorbed but should not be given with meals. It is widely distributed into tissues, yielding tissue concentrations higher than that observed in plasma or serum, although it is not clear that the high tissue concentrations are quantitatively related to clinical efficacy since the antimicrobial effect of azithromycin is pH related. It is eliminated by biliary excretion, predominantly as the unchanged drug. It has an extended half-life which appears to be related to uptake and subsequent release of drug from tissues. Azithromycin has been administered as a single 1-gram dose and as a multiple dose regimen of a 500 mg loading dose followed by daily single doses of 250 mg. The most common side effects are gastrointestinal disturbances.

TETRACYCLINES

The **tetracyclines** are a group of actinomycete antibiotics that have a broad spectrum and considerable therapeutic utility (Fig. 11–12). Chlortetracycline was discovered by Duggar in 1948 from *Streptomyces aureofaciens. S. rimosus*

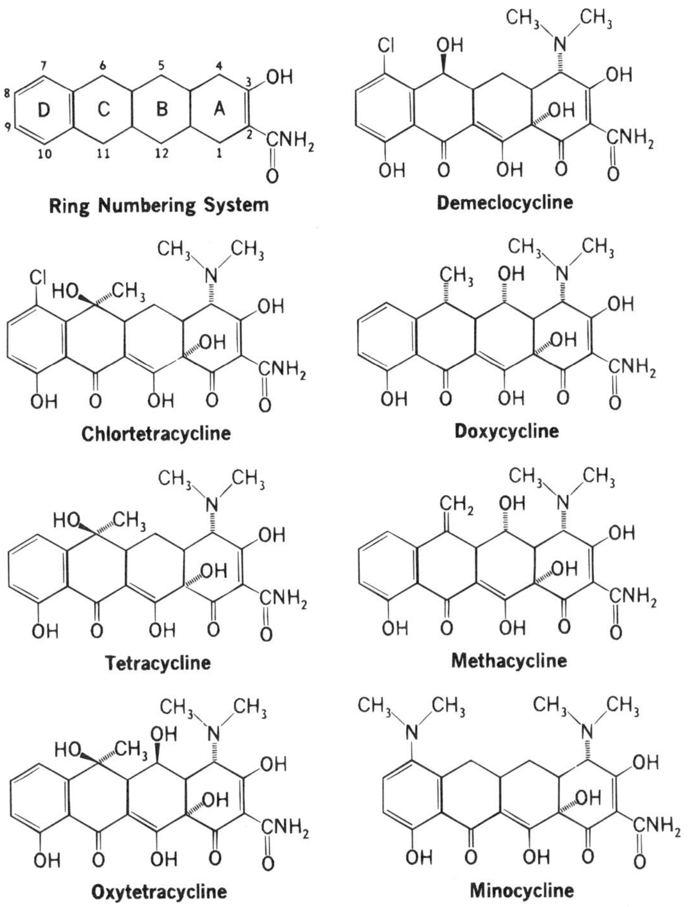

Fig. 11–12. Structures of commercially available tetracyclines.

yielded oxytetracycline in 1950, and tetracycline was found in the antibiotic mixture from *S. aureofaciens* in 1953. The latter observation resulted in patent problems, cross-licensing agreements, a number of legal challenges, and a major governmental investigation. Other minor tetracyclines occur in fermentation mixtures, but only 7-chloro-6-demethyltetracycline (demeclocycline) is currently used in therapy.

Developments in the selection of mutant strains and in manipulations to control chlorination and methylation have proved useful in the fermentative production of various tetracyclines. The presence of aminopterin or other methylation inhibitors in the nutrient mixture favors the formation of 6-demethyltetracyclines, and compounds such as mercaptothiazole aid tetracycline production by inhibiting chlorination. Initially, tetracycline was prepared in commercial quantities by catalytic dehalogenation (hydrogenolysis) of chlortetracycline, but fermentation procedures are currently more advantageous. Doxycycline, methacycline, and minocycline, however, are semisynthetic antibiotics that are prepared by chemical modification of oxytetracycline or tetracycline.

Biosynthesis of Tetracyclines. Studies with radioactive compounds have confirmed that tetracycline antibiotics originate through acetate-malonate metabolism. These pathways involve head-to-tail condensation of two carbon units to from intermediates termed "polyketides." Their formation deviates from the fatty acid pathway by a disruption or lack of a normal reduction-dehydration-reduction sequence as the chain elongates. Subsequent metabolic steps yield the characteristic constituents. Mutant strains of tetracycline-producing organisms have been selected for genetic blocks in the biosynthetic pathway and have been used to clarify a number of the sequential steps.

It is believed that a malonamyl-CoA residue

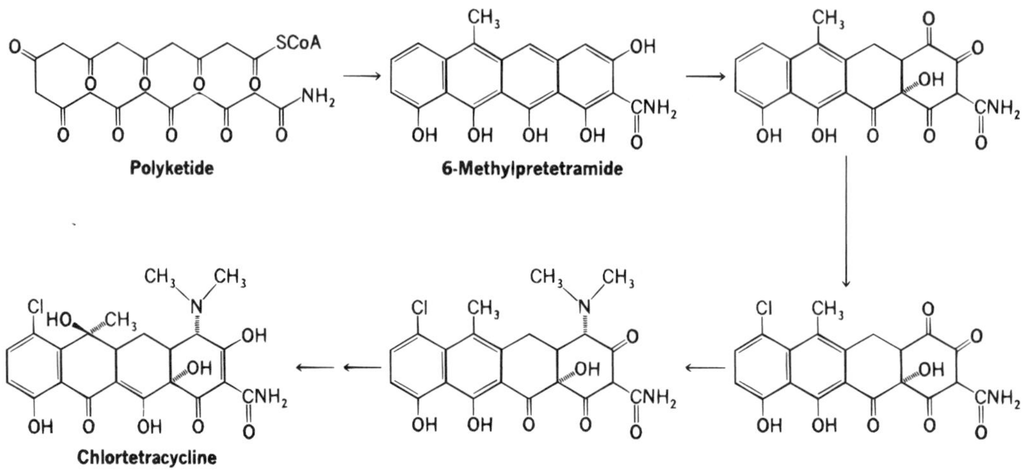

Fig. 11–13.   Biosynthesis of chlortetracycline.

serves as a primer and that eight malonate units undergo stepwise condensations with the addition of C_2 units and decarboxylation to yield a linear C_{19} polyketide (Fig. 11–13). Carbonyl-methylene condensations yield the tetracyclic pretetramide nucleus. Methylation of the C-6 position of the pretetramide is an early step in the biosynthesis of most tetracyclines, but this step is omitted in the formation of the naturally occurring demethyltetracyclines. Hydroxylation of the C-4 position and dearomatization to yield a 4-keto intermediate appears to precede 7-chlorination. Halogenation must precede introduction of the 4-amino group, which is methylated stepwise. Terminal reactions in the biosynthetic sequence are hydroxylation at C-6 and reduction of a double bond in ring B. The 5-hydroxy group in oxytetracycline is probably introduced before the reduction of ring B; it is interesting to note that the presence of a 7-halogen substituent apparently inhibits 5-hydroxylation.

Properties and Uses of the Tetracyclines. All tetracyclines are reasonably stable and are absorbed adequately upon oral administration. These amphoteric substances are most stable in acid and least stable in alkali. The tetracycline antibiotics are usually employed as the HCl salts. Chlortetracycline is the least stable of these antibiotics, and it is no longer available in the United States for oral administration.

Calcium ions in dairy products, as well as other di- and trivalent cations, tend to cause erratic and unsatisfactory absorption of the tetracyclines. Best absorption is obtained when caution is used in scheduling the administration of these antibiotics to avoid interference from

heavy metal ions on absorption. Doxycycline and minocycline are absorbed more readily than the other tetracycline antibiotics; their absorption is influenced to a lesser degree by food and milk, and their slower renal clearance favors prolonged maintenance of blood levels. Doxycycline appears to be the tetracycline of choice when absorption is a problem or when gastrointestinal side effects or other circumstances make it desirable to take the antibiotic with a meal. The biologic properties of minocycline resemble those of doxycycline, but it is considered a specialty tetracycline at this time because of the side effect of vertigo which it causes. The indication for parenteral use of tetracycline antibiotics is uncommon.

The tetracyclines have a broad spectrum of activity that includes gram-negative and gram-positive bacteria, rickettsia, some of the larger viruses, and some intestinal amoebae. Tetracyclines are often considered the antibiotics of choice for treatment of brucellosis, cholera, relapsing fever, and infections caused by *Chlamydia, Mycoplasma, Yersinia (Pasteurella)*, and rickettsia. The tetracyclines are effective, alternate-choice antibiotics for treating a large number of other infections. The action spectra for the various tetracyclines are qualitatively comparable, but lower median MICs may favor the use of doxycycline in some cases. Normal serum levels on oral regimens are 2 to 4 μg/ml.

The usual serum half-lives of the various tetracyclines are 5 to 6 hours for chlortetracycline, 8 to 9 hours for tetracycline, 9 to 10 hours for oxytetracycline, 12 to 14 hours for demeclocycline and methacycline, and 17 to 19 hours for doxycycline and minocycline. These antibiotics are eliminated by biliary excretion, glomerular filtration, and metabolism. The proportion of a dose that is eliminated by each route varies with the specific tetracycline, with the short-acting tetracyclines having greater urinary excretion and, conversely, the long-acting ones being largely eliminated by metabolism and biliary excretion. There is extensive enterohepatic recycling of the tetracycline antibiotics, even after parenteral administration. Urinary excretion usually accounts for 20 to 50% of the tetracyclines; the rate of renal clearance is slowest for doxycycline and minocycline, which do not achieve therapeutically useful urine concentrations. Metabolic degradation of these antibiotics is relatively insignificant, except for chlortetracycline and doxycycline; doxycycline does not accumulate in patients with renal impairment and is the indicated tetracycline in such cases.

Resistance to the tetracyclines developed slowly, but it has become a serious clinical consideration, especially with pneumococci, staphylococci, and such gram-negative pathogens as *Escherichia coli* and *Shigella* species. It has been suggested that penicillins, unless specifically contraindicated, should be selected in preference to the tetracyclines for treating susceptible coccal infections. Tetracycline resistance is characterized by an increasing median MIC for strains of various pathogens; the mechanism appears to involve decreased cell permeability to the antibiotics.

Tetracyclines exert their action by inhibiting protein synthesis. The antibiotics interfere with the binding of aminoacyl-tRNA to acceptor sites on the 30S subunit of microbial 70S ribosomes. Tetracyclines can also attack mammalian 80S ribosomes, but preferential penetration and concentration of these antibiotics in bacterial cells presumably explain the infrequent occurrence of major side effects.

The most frequently encountered adverse effect of tetracycline therapy is alteration of the intestinal flora; this is usually manifested by an overgrowth of *Candida albicans* in the intestine, mouth, or vagina, and tetracycline staphylococcal enterocolitis also occurs. Hypersensitivities may occur; the most serious is a photosensitivity that occurs most often with demeclocycline and doxycycline. The staining of teeth by deposition of tetracyclines in the calcium complex is a basis for selecting alternate antibiotics when treating children during the dentition period (up to age 10) and when treating pregnant women. The same complexation can also cause bone malformations in fetuses of mothers treated with tetracycline. Hepatotoxicity can also occur in pregnant women and in patients who achieve high blood levels resulting from parenteral administration or renal deficiency. The ability of some tetracyclines to complex with calcium ion can depress plasma prothrombin activity, and patients who are also on anticoagulant drugs may require dosage adjustment.

Chlortetracycline or 7-chlorotetracycline was the first tetracycline antibiotic available for therapeutic purposes. Satisfactory results can be obtained with this antibiotic, and it is still available in formulations for topical use, including ophthalmic purposes. Therapeutic use of other tetracycline antibiotics has replaced its oral and intravenous uses in human medicine, but chlortetracycline is still employed in veterinary medicine.

Tetracycline is the least expensive and most commonly utilized tetracycline antibiotic. It is available in a large number of formulations of the tetracycline base, HCl salt, and phosphate complex. The usual dosage schedules are based on the equivalence to tetracycline HCl and are 250 to 500 mg, orally, four times a day; 250 mg, intramuscularly, once a day or 100 mg, three times a day by this route; and 250 to 500 mg, intravenously, two times a day. Preparations for topical use are also available.

Low oral doses of tetracycline (250 mg per day) have been used successfully to treat chronic severe cases of acne. The scientific basis for this therapeutic use is unclear. It may be a combination of antibiotic activity reducing slightly the skin population of *Staphylococcus epidermidis* and *Propionibacterium acnes* and of the potential inhibiting effect of tetracycline on bacterial lipase from the latter species. It is believed that acne lesions are related to the irritation caused by free fatty acids in the sebum. Risks of *Candida* superinfection or other toxic responses are minimal with the low dosage regimen, but the prospects for encouraging the selection of resistant strains should preclude the use of tetracycline in trivial cases of acne.

Oxytetracycline or 5-hydroxytetracycline is available in various formulations for oral, parenteral, and topical purposes. The insoluble calcium salt is used in oral suspensions, and the oxytetracycline base and the HCl salt are employed, as appropriate, in other dosage forms. The usual dosage schedule is the same as that for tetracycline.

Demeclocycline or 7-chloro-6-demethyltet-

racycline has greater acid stability than the tetracyclines with a 6-methyl substituent. The better absorption and slower excretion by the body of this tetracycline antibiotic provide blood levels that offer some minor therapeutic advantages. Demeclocycline is used orally as the HCl salt. The usual dose is 600 mg daily in two to four divided doses.

Doxycycline or 6-deoxy-5-hydroxytetracycline is prepared from oxytetracycline by chemical dehydration and reduction. It is readily absorbed following oral administration, even in the presence of food and milk, and is eliminated by liver metabolism and biliary excretion. Slow excretion gives prolonged blood levels, and no significant accumulation is noted with renal impairment. The lack of renal elimination, however, makes other tetracyclines better choices for urinary tract infections such as cystitis, when high urine levels are desirable. A suspension of doxycycline base is used orally, and formulations of the water-soluble doxycycline hyclate are available for oral and intravenous administration. The usual oral dosage regimen is the equivalent of 100 mg of the antibiotic two times a day for 1 day. The usual intravenous schedule is 200 mg on the first day, administered in one or two infusions, then 100 or 200 mg daily, depending on the severity of infection.

Methacycline is prepared from oxytetracycline by chemical dehydration; it has a methylene function in the 6-position. The utility of methacycline is associated with good oral absorption and a prolonged serum half-life.

Minocycline is prepared by reductive methylation of 7-metro-6-demethyl-6-deoxytetracycline. It is readily absorbed from the intestinal tract, has a slow renal clearance to give prolonged blood levels, and is characterized by lower MICs than other tetracycline antibiotics for some pathogens. Minocycline is used rarely, however, due to a high incidence of vertigo and accompanying nausea, vomiting, and ataxia. It is used as the HCl salt, and the usual oral or intravenous regimen involves a loading dose equivalent to 200 mg of the antibiotic, then 100 mg, two times a day.

AMINOGLYCOSIDE ANTIBIOTICS

The aminoglycoside antibiotics include amikacin, gentamicin, kanamycin, neomycin, netilmicin, streptomycin, and tobramycin. Spectinomycin is technically an aminocyclitol derivative rather than an aminoglycoside, but a number of key properties are similar to those of the aminoglycoside antibiotics, so it will be considered with this group.

The chemical and biologic properties of these antibiotics are similar. Common chemical properties include water solubility, a strongly basic character, and stability. The antibiotic molecules routinely have two to three uncommon sugars linked glycosidically to an amino-substituted cyclohexanyl aglycone. The designation, aminoglycoside antibiotics, is used as a generic term for these compounds. Normally, antibiotic mixtures of closely related molecules are obtained by fermentation, and resolution of the individual components is infeasible and unnecessary for therapeutic purposes. Amikacin and netilmicin are different because they are semisynthetic materials produced from kanamycin A and sisomicin, respectively.

The aminoglycoside antibiotics have an intermediate spectrum of activity, including most aerobic gram-negative bacilli and some grampositive bacteria. These antibiotics are not absorbed following oral administration, and their systemic use is limited by nephro- and ototoxicities. The consequences of ototoxicities may be unusually serious. These antibiotics tend to damage both the auditory and vestibular branches of the 8th cranial nerve. Vestibular involvement is observed more frequently, especially with gentamicin and streptomycin. Symptoms include nausea, vertigo, and vomiting. Damage of the auditory branch results in irreversible loss of hearing; auditory toxicity appears to be more common with amikacin, kanamycin, neomycin, and netilmicin, and damage may be irreversible.

The aminoglycoside antibiotics act on the 30S subunit of 70S ribosomal systems to induce specific misreading of the genetic codon and to inhibit the formation of essential bacterial proteins by interfering with the initiation complex between RNA and the 30S subunit or by disrupting translocation. The misreading of coded information yields proteins that lack the distinctive physiologic function of normal microbial proteins, but blockage of protein synthesis is believed to be the more therapeutically important mechanism of action. The aminoglycoside antibiotics are unusual among protein synthesis inhibitors in that they are bactericidal. This property greatly enhances the utility of aminoglycosides for treatment of serious infections.

Emergence of resistant strains, especially of gram-negative bacilli, staphylococci, and mycobacteria, is becoming an increasing problem with the aminoglycoside antibiotics and has contributed, in part, to a decreasing therapeutic utility for kanamycin, neomycin, and streptomycin. Known mechanisms of resistance include chromosomal involvement (alteration of the reactive site on the 30S ribosomal subunit), plasmid transfer of extrachromosomal R-factors, and exclusion of the antibiotic from the bacterial cell. The greatest clinical problems are associated with resistance caused by R-factor transfer; enzymatic inactivation of one or more of the aminoglycosides is accomplished by acetylation, adenylation, or phosphorylation of the hydroxyl and/or amino groups on the sugar moieties. Cross-resistance among the various aminoglycoside antibiotics is often complete, but no, or only partial, cross-resistance is observed with some bacteria, depending on the nature of the metabolic inactivation that is involved. For example, if streptomycin is inactivated by phosphorylation of the 3-hydroxyl function of 2-deoxy-*N*-methylglucosamine, cross-resistance can be expected with kanamycin and paromomycin; if the same position is adenylated, cross-resistance occurs with spectinomycin.

The need for therapeutic control of gram-negative organisms and mycobacteria contributes to the therapeutic importance of the aminoglycoside antibiotics. However, the high incidence of resistance and the potential toxicities of the antibiotics require efforts greater than normal with the administration of these drugs to ensure effective utilization. Strain sensitivity should be determined routinely, and blood levels should be monitored periodically. A serum plasma level between 4 and 16 μg/ml is usually desired for most aminoglycoside antibiotics and most pathogens, and dosage regimens should be adjusted individually as needed. Renal conditions have an unusually profound influence on their excretion, which is predominantly by glomerular filtration. Renal impairment can increase the biologic half-life from 2 or 3 hours to several days; in such cases, drastic adjustments in the dosage regimen must be made to avoid prolonged high serum levels and the associated increased risks of toxic reactions.

The aminoglycoside antibiotics are indicated only for the treatment of serious infections when less toxic antibiotics are ineffective or contraindicated. They are, however, commonly administered in combination with β-lactam antibiotics to obtain broad coverage of gram-negative organisms in the empirical initial treatment of serious infections and to achieve synergy against many difficult-to-kill organisms.

Recognition of the therapeutic potential of penicillin stimulated an intensive search for other antibiotic substances. A special objective of these efforts was the discovery of antibiotics antagonistic to gram-negative bacteria. **Streptomycin** was isolated from a strain of *Streptomyces griseus* by Waksman and coworkers in 1944 after they had noted the *in vitro* inhibitory effect of metabolites of this species on gram-negative bacteria.

Because streptomycin was the first aminoglycoside antibiotic to be discovered, studies of its origin and properties provide the basis for much of the current knowledge about this group or antibiotics. Components of streptomycin include streptidine and the disaccharide, streptobiosamine, which contains the sugar residues, 2-deoxy-2-methylamino-L-glucose and streptose. Biosynthetic studies have shown that all three of these components are derived from D-glucose. No definitive information is available on the linking of the three components, but it is probably a terminal phase of the biosynthetic sequence. Detailed knowledge on the formation of individual moieties of aminoglycoside antibiotics is limited, but a general indication of the metabolic relationships of glucose to the various moieties can be gained from the biosynthetic origins of the streptomycin components (Fig. 11–14).

The nephro- and ototoxicities common to the aminoglycoside antibiotics are encountered with the systemic use of streptomycin. The high incidence of hypersensitivity of streptomycin, even on topical contact, is less serious. Hypersensitivity is not a major adverse response to aminoglycoside antibiotics as a group, and it is probably related in this instance to hapten formation involving the formyl group of the streptose unit in streptomycin.

The potential toxicity associated with systemic use of streptomycin is such that the antibiotic is considered for therapeutic use only when satisfactory alternatives are unavailable. *Mycobacterium tuberculosis* is refractory to most antibiotic therapy, and tuberculosis is the major condition requiring systemic administration for which streptomycin is a first-choice antibiotic.

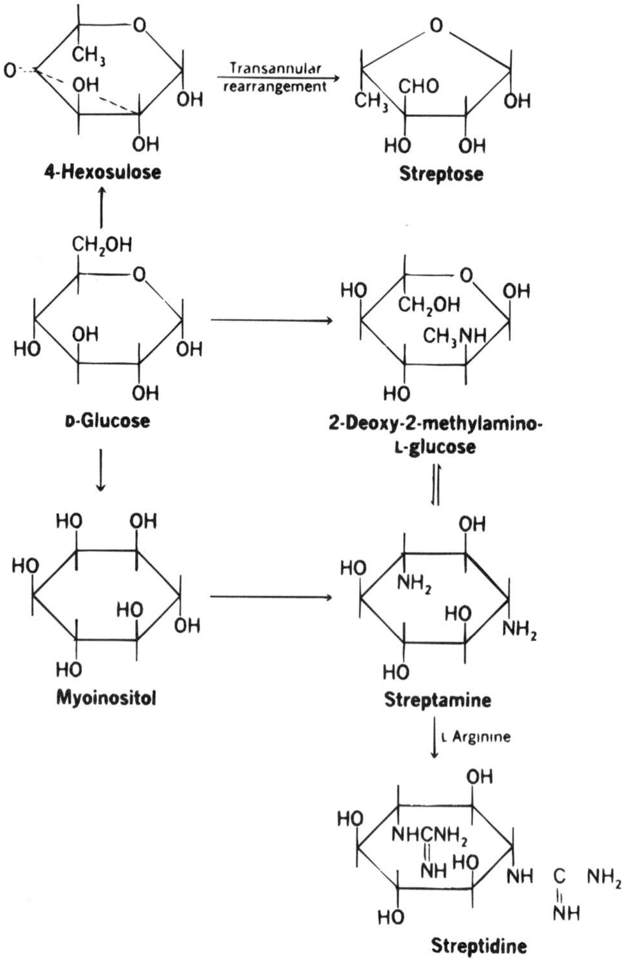

Fig. 11–14. Biosynthesis of components of streptomycin.

In treatment of tuberculosis, streptomycin is normally combined with rifampin, ethambutol, and/or isoniazid to achieve the best results. Justification is lacking for earlier claims that dihydrostreptomycin, which can be prepared fermentatively with *Streptomyces humidus* or chemically from streptomycin by catalytic reduction of the formyl substituent on the streptose unit, could be used with streptomycin to reduce toxicity. The incidence of serious auditory impairment is now recognized to be greater with dihydrostreptomycin than with streptomycin.

Streptomycin has some value in controlling *Yersinia pestis* (plague) and *Francisella tularensis* (tularemia); in such cases, it is usually combined with a sulfonamide. Combined streptomycin-penicillin and streptomycin-tetracy-

cline therapeutic approaches are sometimes indicated in bacterial endocarditis and

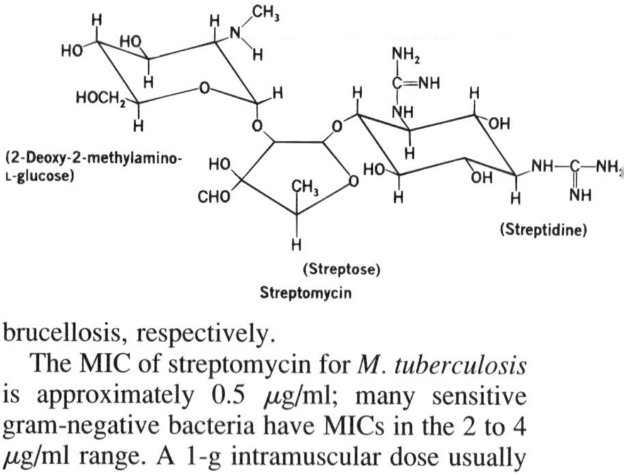

brucellosis, respectively.

The MIC of streptomycin for *M. tuberculosis* is approximately 0.5 μg/ml; many sensitive gram-negative bacteria have MICs in the 2 to 4 μg/ml range. A 1-g intramuscular dose usually

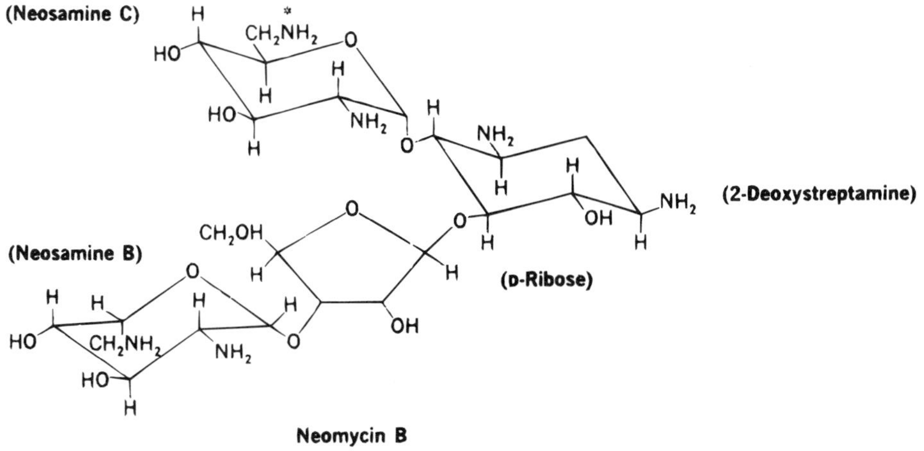

Fig. 11–15. Structure of neomycin B.

gives peak serum levels of 25 to 50 μg/ml in 1 to 2 hours; the normal half-life is 2.5 to 3 hours.

Streptomycin is available in formulations of its sulfate salt.

Neomycin is a mixture of chemically related aminoglycoside antibiotics that was isolated from *Streptomyces fradiae* in 1949 and *S. rimosus* var. *paromomycinus* in 1959. The antibiotic molecules contain a 2-deoxystreptamine unit and three sugar residues (see Fig. 11–15). Neomycin is a mixture of at least three antibiotic compounds. Neomycin B is the main component of the mixture. Neomycin C differs from neomycin B only in the stereochemistry of the aminomethyl group in the aminosugar that is linked to the ribose residue. Neomycin A or neamine has only a single sugar residue (neosamine C) linked to the deoxystreptamine aglycone.

Neomycin is stable, not absorbed following oral administration, and has the activity spectrum that is generally characteristic of the aminoglycoside antibiotics. Neomycin or other aminoglycoside antibiotics can be taken orally to control intestinal infections by susceptible organisms or for pre- or postoperative reduction of the intestinal flora. These antibiotics reduce the population of ammonia-forming bacteria in the intestinal tract, and they are used as effective adjunctive therapy in hepatic coma.

Oral administration of aminoglycoside antibiotics favors the emergence of resistant strains. Anaerobic bacteria, the major component of the bowel flora, are not sensitive to these antibiotics. Many authorities recommend restriction of oral administration to serious conditions and high

risk situations. Neomycin is available in formulations of the sulfate salt for oral and topical use. It is frequently a component (0.35%) in formulations for control of topical infections; these formulations are usually combinations of neomycin and such agents as bacitracin or polymyxin B, which discourage the emergence of resistant strains. The usual dosage for intestinal infections is the equivalent of 8.75 mg of neomycin per kg of body weight, every 6 hours, for 2 to 3 days. Preoperative use normally involves oral administration of 700 mg of neomycin every hour for four doses, then 700 mg every 4 hours for the balance of 24 hours.

Kanamycin was isolated from *Streptomyces kanamyceticus* in 1957 and is a mixture of at least three aminoglycoside antibiotics. These antibiotics contain two aminosugars that are linked individually to a 2-deoxystreptamine aglycone. Kanamycin A is the major component of the mixture (Fig. 11–16).

Kanamycin has an activity spectrum that is comparable to the other aminoglycoside antibiotics. It is used orally for control of infections and for preoperative treatment. The coliform bacteria are sensitive to kanamycin, and *Proteus* species are usually more susceptible to it than to the older aminoglycoside antibiotics. MICs for sensitive gram-negative bacilli usually fall in the 4 to 8 μg per ml range. Kanamycin can be used parenterally for treatment of serious gram-negative infections when susceptible strains are involved. Emerging resistance has become a problem, and amikacin, gentamicin, and tobra-

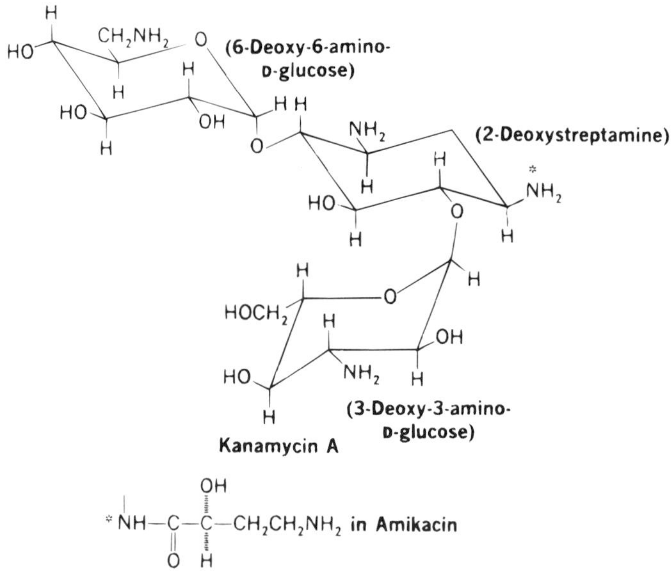

Fig. 11–16. Structures of kanamycin A and amikacin.

mycin have replaced kanamycin for systemic treatment of most gram-negative pathogens.

Kanamycin is available in formulations of the sulfate salt for intramuscular, intravenous, and oral use. The usual dose for control of intestinal infections is the equivalent of 1 g of kanamycin, three or four times a day. The usual dosage schedule for preoperative treatment is 1 g every hour for four doses, then 1 g every 6 hours for 36 to 72 hours. The usual parenteral dosage regimen is up to 15 mg per kg of body weight daily, intramuscularly or by intravenous infusion, in two, three, or four divided doses. Intramuscular administration gives peak serum levels of approximately 20 μg per ml in 1 to 2 hours; the normal half-life is between 2 and 4 hours.

Gentamicin is produced by *Micromonospora purpurea*, an actinomycete. The antibiotic mixture used in medicine consists primarily of gentamicins C_1, C_{1A}, and C_2. Gentamicin C_1 is the major component (approximately 60%). These antibiotic substances contain two aminosugar residues and a 2-deoxystreptamine unit. Gentamicin is inhibitory to pathogenic species of enterobacteria such as *Enterobacter, Escherichia,* and *Klebsiella* and to *Proteus* and *Serratia* species in lower concentrations (usual MIC, 1 to 2 μg/ml) than other aminoglycoside antibiotics, exclusive of tobramycin. It also has a clinically significant activity against *Pseudomonas aeruginosa* (MIC 2 to 8 μg/ml); combined β-lactam-

gentamicin therapy may have special utility in controlling systemic *Pseudomonas* infections. Gentamicin is available in formulations (0.1%) for topical use, but its principal use is parenteral for treatment of serious gram-negative infections caused by sensitive organisms.

Resistance to gentamicin occurs via plasmid-mediated modification of the structure by phosphorylation, acetylation, or adenylation of hydroxyl or amino moieties on the sugars. Cross-resistance with other aminoglycoside antibiotics is determined by the number of modifiable functional groups two antibiotics have in common. Organisms resistant to kanamycin or streptomycin often are sensitive to gentamicin presumably because the resistance is due to inactivation of a specific chemical site not found in the gentamicin molecule (e.g., inactivation by adenylation or esterification of the 3-hydroxyl function of a glucosamine moiety). Similarly, some, but not all, organisms resistant to gentamicin will also be resistant to tobramycin because they share many modifiable functional groups. The aminoglycoside with the fewest sites for inactivation, amikacin, is active against the greatest number of strains of gram-negative bacilli.

Gentamicin is rapidly absorbed on intramuscular administration and is readily distributed into various body tissues. Peak serum levels are often achieved in less than 1 hour, and the

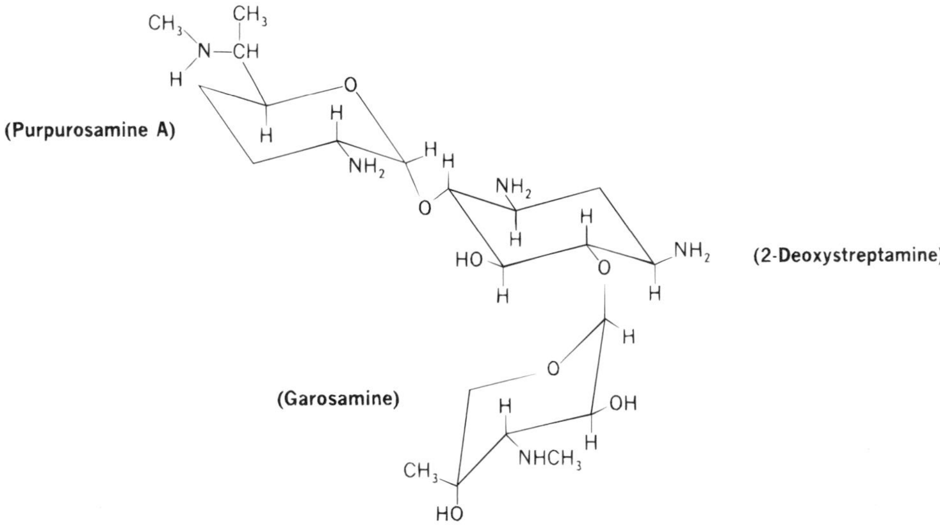

CH₃ and N—CH notation:

(Purpurosamine A)

(2-Deoxystreptamine)

(Garosamine)

Gentamicin C₂

normal serum half-life is approximately 2 hours. Dosage regimens based arbitrarily on mg per kg of body weight result in varying plasma levels that may be ineffectively low or dangerously high; for this reason, monitoring of plasma levels and individualization of dosage regimens are highly recommended with this antibiotic. The risk of ototoxicity increases greatly with prolonged serum levels greater than 10 to 12 μg/ ml, and trough levels above 2 μg/ml should be avoided. Trough levels are most important in relation to nephrotoxicity, which is thought to result from accumulation of antibiotic in the renal tubule cells. A patient receiving gentamicin must have an initial assessment of renal function and be monitored for renal function at least every 3 days during therapy. Since the antibiotic is eliminated renally, dosages must be adjusted for renal function. Nephrotoxicity is frequently, but not always, reversible.

Gentamicin is available as the sulfate salt, and the usual adult dose is the equivalent of 1 mg of gentamicin per kg of body weight, intramuscularly or intravenously, three times a day.

Tobramycin or nebramycin factor 6 is the single-component antibiotic that is separated from the nebramycin complex produced by *Streptomyces tenebrarius*. This antibiotic substance contains two aminosugar residues and a 2-deoxystreptamine unit; it is structurally related to kanamycin B, differing only in the absence of the 3-hydroxyl function in the kanosamine residue.

Tobramycin was approved in mid-1975 for general medical use. It has biologic properties and clinical indications that are similar to those for gentamicin. Tobramycin may give slightly lower tissue levels than gentamicin, and *Proteus vulgaris* and *Pseudomonas* species are more sensitive *in vitro* to tobramycin; however, these differences appear to lack significance in clinical situations. There is considerable debate in the medical literature concerning the relative toxicities of tobramycin and gentamicin; tobramycin appears to be somewhat less nephrotoxic, but the clinical significance of this observation on the choice between the two antibiotics is not clear.

Tobramycin is available as the sulfate salt, and the usual adult dose is the equivalent of 1 mg of tobramycin per kg of body weight, intramuscularly or intravenously, three times a day. The prescription product is Nebcin.

Amikacin is a semisynthetic aminoglycoside antibiotic derived from kanamycin A by acylation of the 1-amino group of the deoxystreptamine moiety to add an L-($-$)-4-amino-2-hydroxybutyryl substituent (Fig. 11–17). The terminal amino group in this substituent is apparently essential for activity. The added group sterically blocks one of the major sites of enzymatic *N*-acetylation by resistant organisms. Therefore, amikacin is active against many strains of pathogens that inactivate gentamicin, tobramycin, and other aminoglycoside antibiotics. Pathogens resistant to amikacin are invariably resistant to other known aminoglycoside antibiotics, a consideration that has prompted some authorities to recommend its conservative or restricted use.

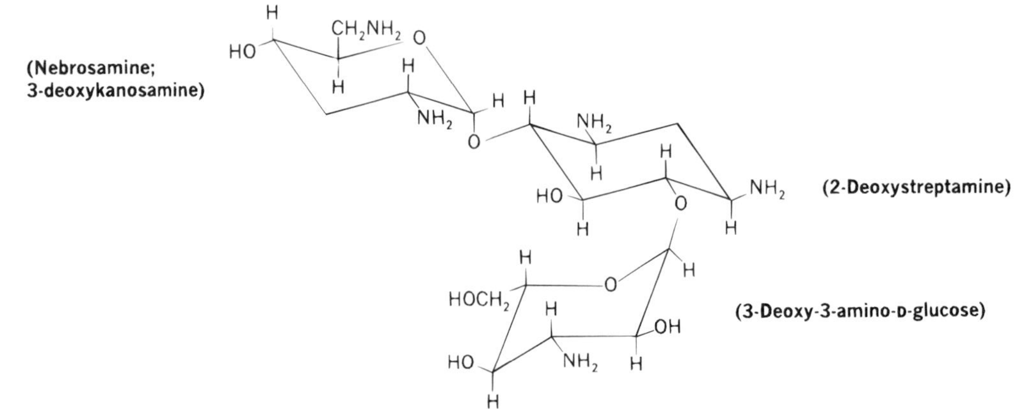

(Nebrosamine; 3-deoxykanosamine)

(2-Deoxystreptamine)

(3-Deoxy-3-amino-D-glucose)

Tobramycin

Amikacin is readily absorbed following intramuscular administration, and its normal serum half-life is approximately 2 hours. The MICs of sensitive organisms and the serum levels which cause toxicity are correspondingly larger for amikacin compared to gentamicin and tobramycin; therefore, amikacin is used in higher doses, and higher serum levels are observed. Risks of ototoxicity suggest that the peak serum level should not exceed 35 μg/ml and that trough levels should not exceed 10 μg/ml. A serum level of 8 μg/ml is adequate to exceed the MICs of 90% of the strains of *Escherichia coli, Enterobacter, Klebsiella,* and *Proteus.* Levels of 25 μg per ml are required to reach 90% of the MICs for strains of *Pseudomonas, Serratia,* and *Staphylococcus aureus.*

Amikacin is available as the sulfate salt. The usual dosage regimen for patients with normal renal function is 15 mg per kg of body weight daily, intramuscularly or by intravenous infusion, in two or three divided doses for 7 to 10 days.

Amikacin is also eliminated by the kidneys, so dosages and dosage regimens must be adjusted for renal function and serum levels of drug monitored regularly in order to avoid toxicity.

Netilmicin or N-ethylsisomicin is a semisynthetic aminoglycoside antibiotic derived from sisomicin, a product of *Micromonospora inyoensis.* It resembles gentamicin C$_{1A}$ chemically. It is effective against a number of the gram-negative pathogens that are resistant to amikacin, gentamicin, and tobramycin.

Netilmicin is rapidly distributed in body organs and tissues following parenteral administration. The normal serum half-life is approximately 2 hours. Ototoxicity considerations suggest that the peak serum level should not exceed 16 μg/ml and that the trough serum level should not exceed 4 μg/ml. Nephrotoxicity appears to be less of a consideration than with other aminoglycoside antibiotics, and urine concentrations of up to 800 μg/ml are attained. It is useful in treating complicated urinary tract infections

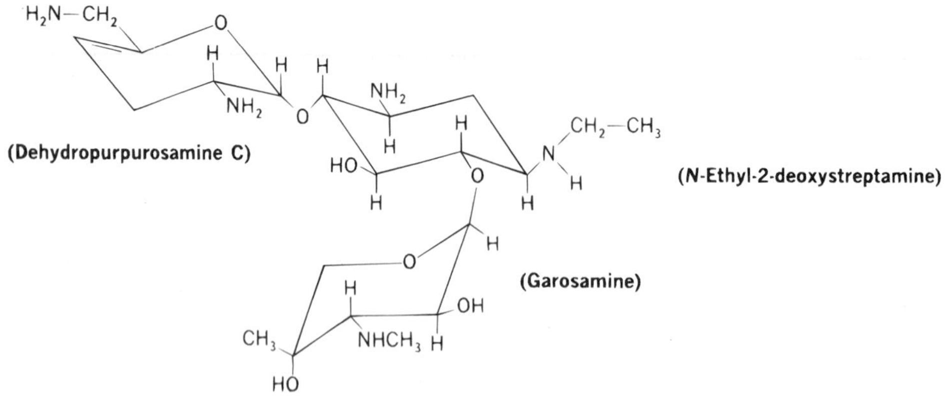

(Dehydropurpurosamine C)

(N-Ethyl-2-deoxystreptamine)

(Garosamine)

Netilmicin

and other serious infections caused by susceptible organisms.

Netilmicin is available as the sulfate salt. The usual dosage regimen for patients with normal renal function is 4 to 6.5 mg per kg of lean body weight daily, intramuscularly or by intravenous infusion, in two or three divided doses for 7 to 14 days. As with all aminoglycoside antibiotics, netilmicin is renally eliminated, so dosages and dosage regimens must be adjusted for renal function.

Spectinomycin is produced by *Streptomyces spectabilis* and *S. flavopersicus*. The antibiotic molecule is a glycoside, but it is not technically an aminoglycoside. An aminocyclitol aglycone is glycosidically linked to a neutral deoxysugar. The dry antibiotic powder is stable for long periods of time.

A number of the biologic properties of spectinomycin resemble those of the aminoglycoside antibiotics. It is not absorbed on oral administration, is excreted after injection in an active form by glomerular filtration, and acts by inhibiting protein synthesis through a mechanism involving the 30S subunit of the 70S ribosomal system. Spectinomycin has a broad antibacterial spectrum, but its only clinical indication is treatment of gonorrhea. Susceptible strains of *Neisseria gonorrhoeae* (MIC range of 7.5 to 20 μg/ml) are frequently controlled by a single parenteral dose of this antibiotic, a feature that is unusually advantageous for treatment of a venereal disease. This obviates many of the problems related to social stigma and mobile patient populations. Resistance to spectinomycin is known, and concern about facilitating the emergence of more resistance prompts some authorities to favor restricting the use of spectinomycin to cases in which penicillin is ineffective or contraindicated. Cross-resistance between penicillin and spectinomycin is unknown.

Spectinomycin

Spectinomycin is available as the pentahydrate of the dihydrochloride salt. The usual dose is 2 to 4 g intramuscularly; the higher dose is routinely recommended for female patients.

Peak serum concentrations of 100 to 160 μg/ml occur in approximately 1 hour; 8-hour serum levels are 15 to 30 μg/ml, and total elimination of the antibiotic normally occurs within 48 hours. The most frequently observed adverse response is pain at the site of injection; dividing the dose between two sites, especially with higher doses of the antibiotic, has reduced this problem. Nephro- and ototoxicities have not been reported; this may be an inherent property of spectinomycin, or it may reflect the short duration of the normal therapeutic regimen.

POLYPEPTIDE ANTIBIOTICS

A fairly large number of **polypeptides** of bacterial origin, which contain both D-and L-amino acids, have antibiotic activity. However, only a few of these metabolites have therapeutic utility. These antibiotics are not absorbed from the intestinal tract, and nephrotoxicity is a potential problem if they are used systemically. Most of the useful peptide antibiotics have a predominantly gram-positive spectrum; exceptions include the strongly basic polymyxins, which are active primarily against gram-negative organisms. These peptides have a surfactant property, and the polymyxins exert their effect by interacting with the lipid-rich anionic bacterial cell membrane. However, inhibition of mucopeptide synthesis in cell-wall formation by bacitracin appears to be more significant than membrane disruption for the action of this antibiotic.

The polypeptide antibiotics tend to occur as mixtures of closely related compounds. Components of these mixtures often differ in only one or two amino acid residues; resolution of such mixtures is not feasible for therapeutic purposes. The use of selected strains of producing organisms controls the composition of commercial mixtures to a degree, and use of microbial assay for quantitation provides a reliable indication of therapeutic response against susceptible organisms.

Polymyxin B is a mixture of antibiotics produced by *Bacillus polymyxa*. The mixture contains minimal amounts of the more toxic polymyxins A, C, and D, but the polymyxin B component is actually a mixture of polymyxins B_1 and B_2. Polymyxins B_1 and B_2 contain ten amino acid residues in common and differ only in a 6-methyloctanoic acid residue in polymyxin B_1 and an isooctanoic acid residue in polymyxin B_2. Both molecules have a cyclopeptidic structure and contain six residues of α,γ-diaminobutyric acid. This latter feature gives a strongly basic character to the polymyxin antibiotics. Polymyxin B is normally employed as the sulfate salt, which must have a potency of not less than 6000 units/mg.

Polymyxin B is not absorbed when administered orally and was formerly employed for control of infections of the intestinal tract caused by *Shigella, Pseudomonas aeruginosa,* and *Escherichia coli.* It is used topically in ointments (usually 5000 or 10,000 units/g) and ophthalmic solutions (10,000 units/ml). Nephro- and neurotoxicities occur frequently when polymyxin B sulfate is used systemically, and while it formerly had some limited utility in serious infections of *Pseudomonas aeruginosa* and certain coliform bacilli that do not respond to other antibiotics, systemic use is rarely justified now due to the development of less toxic antibiotics for these organisms.

Colistin is obtained from cultures of *Bacillus polymyxa* var. *colistinus* and contains primarily colistin A (polymyxin E) with a small amount of colistin B. This antibiotic has essentially the same spectrum and therapeutic utility as polymyxin B. The sulfate salt is used orally and topically. The sodium salt of a methane sulfonate derivative (colistimethate), which is inactive in itself but releases active polymixin in the body, was used parenterally, but its use today is rarely justified due to the availability of less toxic alternative antibiotics.

Bacitracin is produced by an organism of the licheniformis group of *Bacillus subtilis* and is a mixture of at least five polypeptides. The major component of the mixture is bacitracin A, which is a dodecylpeptide with five of the amino acid residues arranged in a cyclic structure. Bacitracin must have a potency of not less than 40 units per mg, unless it is intended for parenteral use; in the latter case, the potency must be not less than 50 units/mg.

This antibiotic is active against a wide range of gram-positive bacteria. Bacitracin or zinc bacitracin is a component in many ointment formulations for the control of topical infections; ointments usually contain 500 units/g. Parenteral formulations of bacitracin are available, but systemic use is rarely justified owing to problems of nephrotoxicity.

Vancomycin is a mixture of glycopeptides produced by *Streptomyces orientalis.* The structure of the primary component of the mixture has been determined to be a complex tricyclic aglycone linked glycosidically to glucose and vancosamine moieties. The molecule contains one free carboxylic acid residue, two chloro-substituted aromatic units, and seven amide bonds, one of which is a primary amide.

Vancomycin has a gram-positive spectrum. It acts on bacterial cell walls by inhibiting murein biosynthesis by complexing with the D-alanyl-D-alanine precursor and is bactericidal, which makes it particularly useful in serious infections and immunocompromised patients. It also has some secondary modes of action, i.e., impairing RNA synthesis and increasing cytoplasmic membrane permeability. Vancomycin, as its HCl salt, is being used increasingly for treatment of serious infections (e.g., septicemia, endocarditis, wound infections caused by gram-positive organisms, especially in patients allergic to β-lactam antibiotics) and of *Enterococcus faecalis* strains which are inadequately controlled by β-lactam antibiotics. Until recently one of the great advantages of vancomycin was that vancomycin-resistant organisms were virtually unknown. However, recent reports of plasmid-mediated resistant strains of *Enterococcus* have led to restriction of use of vancomycin in hospital settings in an attempt to control the spread of resistance.

Vancomycin is not absorbed orally, but oral administration is used for the treatment of staphylococcal enterocolitis and antibiotic-associated pseudomembranous colitis produced by *Clostridium difficile.* Intramuscular administration is painful and frequently associated with local necrosis; thus systemic therapy with vancomycin employs intravenous infusion over a period of 20 to 30 minutes. If vancomycin is administered too rapidly, it can cause a ''red-man'' or ''red-neck'' syndrome characterized by flushing and tingling around the head and neck, thought to be related to localized histamine release. The usual parenteral dose in adults with normal renal function is 500 g every 6 hours or 1 g every 12 hours. The drug is excreted by the kidneys, and dosage adjustment to maintain serum levels below 30 μg/ml is essential to avoid ototoxicity. Other side effects observed include rashes that are hypersensitivity reactions, and fever and chills upon administration. Nephrotoxicity used to be a significant adverse effect, but it is rarely observed with the currently available purified preparations. Vancomycin does not cross into the cerebrospinal fluid in the absence of inflammation, but therapeutic CSF levels may be achieved in some patients with meningitis.

Teichoplanin

Teichoplanin is a mixture of glycopeptides, with molecular weights ranging from 1562 to 1891, isolated from *Actinoplanes teichomycetius*. It is still investigational in the United States. Teichoplanin is similar to vancomycin in its chemical and antibiotic properties, but with some important differences. It is more lipophilic than vancomycin which leads to excellent tissue penetration and a longer elimination half-life.

The mechanism of action for teichoplanin is analogous to vancomycin, i.e., inhibition of cell wall synthesis, and it is generally bactericidal to most gram-positive organisms. This similarity in mechanism unfortunately means that most staphylococci and enterococci resistant to vancomycin are also resistant to teichoplanin.

Teichoplanin is administered intravenously or intramuscularly once a day and, unlike vancomycin, produces only mild pain at the site of injection. The "red-neck" syndrome observed upon rapid administration of vancomycin is rarely observed, and the incidence of ototoxicity also appears to be reduced. Initial trials used doses of 200 mg/day with limited success, but current studies are using 400 mg/day or more with substantial success and minimal toxicity. The higher therapeutic index compared to vancomycin may make teichoplanin a useful alternative to vancomycin in serious infections caused by gram-positive organisms.

LINCOSAMIDES

The class of antibiotics called the "lincosamides" includes two clinically used antibiotics, lincomycin and clindamycin. Both have some useful antibiotic properties, but their use is limited because of a potentially fatal side effect, pseudomembranous colitis.

Lincomycin is produced by *Streptomyces lincolnensis*. It has an amide function in the molecule and may be derived by a combination of amino acid and carbohydrate metabolites. **Clindamycin** (7-chloro-7-deoxylincomycin) is synthetically derived from lincomycin. These antibiotics have primarily gram-positive spectra, including pneumococci, staphylococci, and streptococci, with the exception of *Enterococcus faecalis*; the anaerobic spectra (both gram-negative and gram-positive) are also recognized as distinctive and significant. Clindamycin appears slightly more effective quantitatively than lincomycin; the MICs for most bacteria susceptible to clindamycin are in the 0.01 to 3.1 μg/ml range compared with a range of 0.02 to 6.2 μg/ml for lincomycin.

These antibiotics inhibit protein synthesis by a mechanism closely related to that of chloramphenicol and erythromycin. They all bind to the same site on the 50S subunit of 70S ribosomes. Erythromycin has a greater affinity for the site and thus effectively antagonizes the action of clindamycin or lincomycin. The absence of aerobic gram-negative spectra for clindamycin and lincomycin may relate to their inability to penetrate the cell walls of these bacteria. Microbial resistance to clindamycin and lincomycin slowly develops, but resistant strains are commonly resistant to multiple antibiotics, especially to erythromycin.

These antibiotics yield effective serum levels readily and exhibit no appreciable protein binding or accumulation, but their significant biologic properties show some variation. Both lincosamide compounds cause a high frequency of diarrhea. Clindamycin is also more readily eliminated from the body. The usual 500-mg dose of lincomycin gives a peak serum level of 1.8 to 5.3 μg/ml in 4 hours and has a normal half-life in the 4- to 6-hour range. Food does reduce the serum levels that are achieved with lincomycin, and administration on an empty stomach is recommended to avoid this problem; an extended half-life necessitates dosage adjustment in cases of renal disease or hepatic complication. Food does not influence the absorption of clindamycin, and the slight extension of antibiotic half-life with renal dysfunction tends to be insignificant clinically. The usual 300-mg dose of clindamycin gives a peak serum level of 2.6 to 3.6 μg/ml in 1 to 2 hours, and the normal half-life is between 2 and 4 hours.

Both clindamycin and lincomycin can cause severe colitis and pseudomembranous colitis, which may end fatally. Pseudomembranous colitis involves sloughing of the intestinal wall caused by a toxin produced by an overgrowth of *Clostridium difficile*. Treatment involves supportive therapy plus antibiotic therapy with metronidazole or vancomycin to eliminate the *Clostridium difficile*. Because of this serious side effect, it is recommended that use of the lincosamides be reserved for serious infections caused by susceptible anaerobic bacteria or by pneumococci, staphylococci, or streptococci in patients with mitigating considerations, such as penicillin hypersensitivity. Clindamycin is one of the most effective antibiotics against strains of *Bacteroides fragilis*, the gram-negative anaerobe which causes many abdominal infections, and it is used for these infections, often in combination with an aminoglycoside to kill accompanying gram-negative aerobes. The antianaerobic activity of clindamycin also makes it useful in pneumonias caused by anaerobes.

Distribution of these antibiotics in bone also favors their use in staphylococcal osteomyelitis. Clindamycin phosphate is used topically for treatment of serious acne and vaginally for bacterial vaginosis. Pseudomembranous colitis associated with the topical use of clindamycin is rare but has been reported.

Lincomycin is available in formulations of the HCl salt, and the usual adult dose is the equivalent of 500 mg of the antibiotic orally, three to four times a day, 600 mg intramuscularly, one or two times a day, and 600 mg by intravenous infusion (over a period of not less than 1 hour) every 8 to 12 hours.

Lincomycin

Clindamycin is available in formulations of the HCl salt (capsules) and of the HCl salt of the palmitate ester (suspension) for oral administration and of the phosphate ester for parenteral use. The palmitate and phosphate esters are inactive per se, but they are readily hydrolyzed to clindamycin in the body; gradual hydrolysis of the phosphate ester after intramuscular administration gives a flattened, delayed peak serum concentration and a half-life of approximately 5 hours. The usual adult dose is the equivalent of 150 to 450 mg of the antibiotic, orally, four times a day and 300 mg, intramuscularly or intravenously, two to four times daily. The topical preparations are available at a concentration of 10 mg/ml.

CHLORAMPHENICOL

Chloramphenicol was originally obtained by Burkholder from a culture of *Streptomyces vene-*

zuelae that was isolated in 1947 from a soil sample collected near Caracas, Venezuela. Because the organism had not been described previously, Burkholder applied the name *venezuelae* to the species. This antibiotic attracted considerable attention because it was the first truly broad-spectrum antibiotic discovered. Its spectrum of action includes gram-negative and gram-positive bacteria, a number of rickettsial pathogens, and a few viruses.

Chemically, chloramphenicol proved to be fairly simple. Its most unusual feature was the presence of a nitro group on a normal biologic metabolite. The molecular skeleton of the antibiotic suggested a biosynthetic origin via phenylpropanoid metabolism. Experimental studies with radioactive precursors have confirmed a shikimic acid-phenylpropanoid pathway for the biosynthesis of chloramphenicol, but the pathway apparently branches from normal phenylpropanoid metabolism prior to the formation of phenylalanine or tyrosine. *p*-Aminophenylpyruvic acid has been suggested as an early metabolite in the biosynthetic pathway, and subsequent steps involving transamination, hydroxylation, acylation, reduction of the carboxyl group, and terminal oxidation of the amino group are suspected (Fig. 11–17).

The relative simplicity of the chloramphenicol molecule led to the early development of feasible synthetic procedures for commercial production of the antibiotic. This ntibiotic is unique with respect to the successful development of totally synthetic means for commercial production. Four isomers exist; the active one is D(−)-*threo*-2,2-dichloro-*N*-[β-hydroxy-α-(hydroxymethyl)-*p*-nitrophenethyl]acetamide. Chloramphenicol has a broad spectrum of activity, including *Salmonella typhi, Haemophilus influenzae, Rickettsia*, and anaerobes such as *Bacteroides fragilis*. It is primarily bacteriostatic but is bactericidal against some organisms at therapeutically achievable levels. The MIC range for most clinically sensitive bacteria is 0.2 to 2.0 μg/ml.

Chloramphenicol acts by inhibiting protein synthesis at the ribosome level. It binds preferentially to the 50S subunit of microbial 70S ribosomes and disrupts peptidyl transferase, the enzyme that catalyzes peptide bond formation. Other types of involvement can be detected experimentally, but their significance for therapeu-

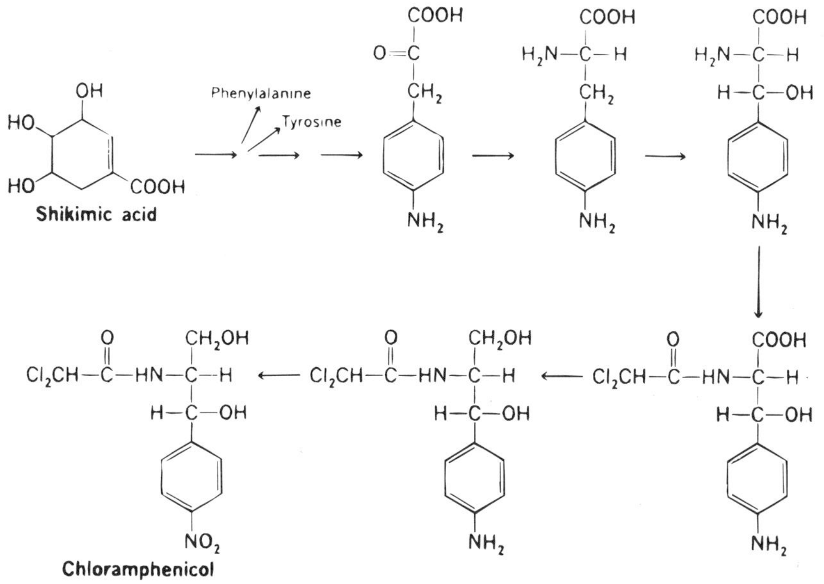

Fig. 11–17. Biosynthesis of chloramphenicol.

tic application of the antibiotic is unknown. Chloramphenicol has low affinity for 80S (mammalian) ribosomes although it is thought that because of its lipophilicity it penetrates mitochondria and inhibits mitochondrial 70S ribosomes, resulting in the dose-related bone marrow suppression, but not the idiosyncratic aplastic anemia, observed with this compound.

Chloramphenicol is very well absorbed orally and crosses readily into the cerebrospinal fluid. It is primarily eliminated by liver metabolism by conjugation with glucuronic acid followed by tubular excretion. About 5 to 10% appears in the urine as active drug. Patients with hepatic dysfunction and infants with undeveloped hepatic enzymes must have serum levels monitored carefully and dosages adjusted accordingly to keep serum levels below 25 μg/ml. Failure to do so in infants can result in a potentially fatal "gray-baby syndrome" characterized by cyanosis, circulatory collapse, and death.

Toxicities greatly restrict the use of chloramphenicol, and it now is indicated for only a few well-defined situations. Two types of bone marrow toxicity are observed. The first is a dose-related, commonly observed bone marrow suppression characterized by reticulocytopenia, thrombocytopenia, anemia, leukopenia, or some combination thereof. Serum iron increases as a consequence of decreased hemoglobin synthe-

sis. This form of toxicity occurs during therapy, particularly when serum levels exceed 25 μg/ml, and is generally reversible upon discontinuation of therapy. Patients receiving chloramphenicol should be monitored with complete blood counts at least twice a week during therapy.

The second form of bone marrow suppression is observed as aplastic anemia and is often irreversible and potentially fatal. Aplastic anemia is relatively rare (1:25,000 or less) and most often occurs weeks to months after the end of therapy. The mechanism of this toxicity is incompletely understood, but microbial reduction by the gut flora of the nitro function in a small percentage of those ingesting chloramphenicol may be a contributing factor. Optic neuritis and hemolytic anemia in patients with the Mediterranean form of glucose-6-phosphate dehydrogenase deficiency are additional toxicities.

Other antibiotics now provide alternate means of controlling many pathogens formerly controlled only by chloramphenicol, which should be used only in serious infections caused by susceptible organisms when other less dangerous antibiotics are ineffective or contraindicated. Third generation cephalosporins are frequently employed alternatives if parenteral administration is no problem. Chloramphenicol may still be the drug of choice for acute typhoid fever, other severe *Salmonella* infections, and rickettsial infections in children between 1 and 8 years of age. Penicillin hypersensitivity and renal insufficiency present considerations that could favor the use of chloramphenicol over ampicillin and tetracycline, respectively. Microbial resistance to chloramphenicol is characterized in many cases by acetylation of the antibiotic. The greatest resistance problem occurs with *Pseudomonas,* but plasmid R-factor transfer causes some resistance in other gram-negative bacteria. Multiple resistance to chloramphenicol and the β-lactam antibiotics is known in some gram-positive cocci and some strains of *Haemophilus influenzae.*

Chloramphenicol is stable, but esters of the antibiotic are employed in certain pharmaceutic formulations for solubility purposes. These esters are hydrolyzed in the body to release the physiologically active molecule. The insoluble palmitate ester is used in some oral formulations to avoid the bitter taste of the antibiotic, and the monosodium succinate ester is used for greater water solubility in preparations for intravenous use. Tissue esterases are not as efficient as pancreatic esterases, and approximately one third of parenterally administered chloramphenicol is eliminated by the kidneys as the inactive ester.

The usual dose is the equivalent of 50 mg of chloramphenicol per kg of body weight daily in four divided oral doses or intravenously in two or three divided doses.

RIFAMYCINS

Rifampin is a semisynthetic antibiotic that is derived from rifamycin B, a metabolite of *Streptomyces mediterranei.* Rifampin has a distinctive macrocyclic lactam structure attached to a conjugated "ansa" chromophore that is responsible for the red-orange color of the molecule. The antibiotic inhibits DNA-dependent RNA-polymerase activity in susceptible cells. It has a good gram-positive and a moderate gram-negative spectrum, but its clinical significance is based primarily on the sensitivity of *Mycobacterium tuberculosis* to the antibiotic. It is recommended for treatment of pulmonary tuberculosis; it should be used in combination with at least one other antitubercular agent to avoid selective development of resistant strains of the tubercle bacillus. The desire to avoid inadvertent selection of resistant *Mycobacterium tuberculosis* organisms has led to its restricted use in other infections. It is used in the treatment of asymp-

tomatic carriers of *Neisseria meningitidis* for individuals exposed to index cases of epidemic meningitis, especially when it occurs in tight quarters, such as military bases or college dormitories. Rifampin is particularly useful in this situation because it achieves high levels in the mucous membranes of the nasopharynx where the *Neisseria* organisms reside. Rifampin is also occasionally used in combination with other antibiotics for resistant strains of staphylococci, but resistance develops readily when rifampin is used alone.

Rifampin

Rifampin, in contrast to the naturally occurring rifamycins, is absorbed adequately on oral administration and is widely distributed through body tissues. Peak serum levels with usual dosage regimens are 4 to 32 μg/ml in 2 to 4 hours; the MICs of sensitive strains of *M. tuberculosis* have been reported to range between 0.006 and 0.5 μg/ml. The biologic half-life of rifampin is approximately 3 hours. Urinary excretion may account for elimination of up to 15% of the drug, but biliary excretion is the major pathway. Rifampin is deacetylated in the liver to give an antimicrobially active metabolite, and most of the antibiotic is in the deacetyl form when it is ultimately eliminated in the feces. Enterohepatic recycling of rifampin occurs, but the deacetyl form is not reabsorbed after biliary excretion.

The most serious adverse reactions involve hepatotoxicity, and the increased risk of toxicity in persons with liver damage, such as chronic alcoholics, may preclude the use of this antibiotic. Unfortunately, there is a high incidence of tuberculosis among alcoholics. Other side effects include a flu-like syndrome, with headache, dizziness, gastrointestinal side effects, and rashes. Rifampin is a potent inducer of hepatic microsomal enzymes, leading to drug interactions with a number of other drugs.

Rifampin is administered orally, and the usual dose for uncomplicated pulmonary tuberculosis is 600 mg, once a day. It should be taken 1 hour before or 2 hours after meals to avoid food interference with absorption. Patients should be advised that the antibiotic may color stools, urine, saliva, sweat, or tears a red-orange.

Rifabutin is a related antibiotic that is a semisynthetic derivative of rifamycin S. It shows good activity against most strains of mycobacteria, including most rifampin-sensitive *Mycobacteria tuberculosis* strains as well as some rifampin-resistant strains. It is also used as prophylaxis for *Mycobacterium avium-intracellulare* infections in AIDS patients.

MINOR ANTIBIOTICS

Novobiocin is produced by *Streptomyces niveus* and *S. spheroides*. The structure of novobiocin suggests an unusual biosynthetic origin for this antibiotic; it appears to involve moieties derived from amino acid, acetate, and carbohydrate metabolic pathways.

The activity spectrum for novobiocin is predominantly gram-positive. Staphylococci tend to be unusually sensitive to this antibiotic (MIC range of 0.1 to 2.0 μg/ml), but resistance develops rapidly. It has been used as an alternate means for controlling penicillin-resistant staphylococci. However, novobiocin has a high incidence of adverse reactions (hypersensitivity, hepatic dysfunction, and blood dyscrasias), and the penicillinase-resistant penicillins and other available antibiotics have obviated much of the former need for novobiocin; a number of authorities feel that its use can no longer be justified.

(Novinose)   Novobiocin

Cycloserine or D-4-amino-3-isoxazolidinone is probably the simplest metabolite with useful antibiotic activity. It can be produced by cultures of *Streptomyces orchidaceus* or by synthesis. Cycloserine has a fairly broad spectrum of activity, but its therapeutic utility is associated with its inhibitory effect on *Mycobacterium tuberculosis*. This antibiotic inhibits alanine racemase. The inhibitory action precludes the incorporation of D-alanine into the pentapeptide side chain of the murein component of bacterial cell walls,

and this presumably accounts for its antibiotic activity. Cycloserine sometimes causes an increase in the protein content of the cerebrospinal fluid, and this explains in part the CNS effects that may occur when doses exceed 1 g daily. Manifestations of these side effects are usually mental confusion, drowsiness, and coma; cases of psychosis or convulsions are known.

Cycloserine is considered an antibiotic of second choice and is most frequently employed in combination with isoniazid in treating tubercular patients who fail to respond to first-line agents. Cycloserine is readily absorbed following oral administration and is excreted rather rapidly via the kidneys, approximately 50% without metabolic alteration. The usual dose is 250 mg twice a day; the blood level should be monitored and the dosage adjusted to keep the serum level below 30 μg/ml.

Cycloserine

Capreomycin is a mixture of peptides produced by *Streptomyces capreolus*. Capreomycin I is the major component (not less than 90%); capreomycin II accounts for most of the balance of the mixture. Frequent nephrotoxicity is observed with therapeutic use of this antibiotic. Ototoxicity with irreversible auditory impairment and changes in hepatic function are also encountered.

The antibiotic is used as an alternate antitubercular agent in susceptible strains of *Mycobacterium tuberculosis* when other primary agents, such as streptomycin, isoniazid, and rifampin, are ineffective. It is administered intramuscularly as the sulfate salt, and the usual dose is the equivalent of 1 g of the antibiotic daily for 2 to 4 months, then 1 g, two or three times a week.

Mupirocin is a topically used antimicrobial with a structure unlike any other antibiotic. It is isolated from submerged fermentations of *Pseudomonas fluorescens* and used to be called pseudomonic acid. It inhibits bacterial protein synthesis by binding to isoleucyl-tRNA synthetase, thus preventing the incorporation of isoleucine into proteins. Its spectrum of action includes a variety of gram-positive aerobic cocci and bacilli, but few gram-negative organisms. It is active against staphylococci and streptococci responsible for most skin infections, although resistant organisms can develop. Mupirocin is used only topically because systemic administration leads to rapid metabolic inactivation.

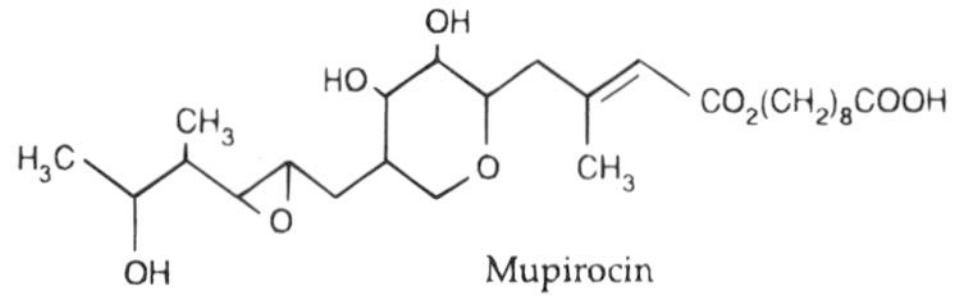

Mupirocin

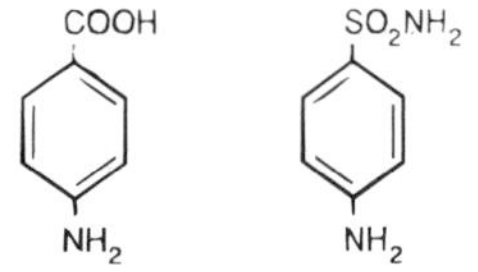

p-Amino-benzoic acid   Sulfanilamide

Fig. 11–18. Sulfonamides are structural analogs of *p*-aminobenzoic acid (PABA).

SYNTHETIC ANTIMICROBIAL AGENTS

Therapeutic use of antibiotics is not limited to natural products and their derivatives. While most of our useful antibiotics are natural products, a number of important classes are synthetic products. The following section is devoted to these agents so that they can be included for consideration when the health professional is making rational therapeutic decisions about antimicrobial therapy.

Sulfonamides and Trimethoprim

Sulfonamides, which were discovered and first used in the 1930s, were the first antimicrobial agents of the modern antibiotic era. All the compounds are derivatives of *p*-aminobenzenesulfonamide (sulfanilamide) which have been substituted at either the amide or the *p*-amino group to alter the physicochemical properties. Many sulfonamides have been synthesized, and many have been approved for clinical use, but only a few are in widespread use today.

Sulfonamides are considered antimetabolites in that they are analogs of *p*-aminobenzoic acid, a substrate in the biosynthesis of folic acid, an essential metabolite for bacteria who use it as a source of one carbon units for the biosynthesis of amino acids and purines and pyrimidines (Fig. 11–18). Sulfonamides competitively inhibit the enzyme tetrahydropteroyl synthetase which uses *p*-aminobenzoic acid as a substrate in the formation of the pteroyl moiety of folic acid (Fig. 11–19). They are bacteriostatic, and their effect can be reversed by high concentrations of the end product nucleic acids. However, unlike humans, sensitive bacteria do not transport dihydrofolate from their surroundings and must synthesize the cofactor in order to survive.

With a few exceptions, sulfonamides all have the same spectrum of activity. They inhibit a broad spectrum of gram-positive and gram-neg-ative bacteria, as well as *Chlamydia, Nocardia,* and *Pneumocystis.* However, plasmid-mediated resistance is widespread and greatly limits the utility of sulfonamides as single agents. Cross-resistance is common among the various agents.

Sulfonamides are orally absorbed (unless the *p*-amino moiety is substituted) and are widely distributed in the body. The various agents differ primarily in their half-life and degree of protein binding. Elimination is via liver metabolism (glucuronidation and acetylation) with subsequent renal excretion along with a portion of unchanged active drug. Dosage must be adjusted with either renal or hepatic insufficiency.

Sulfonamides cause a variety of side effects including gastrointestinal upset, hypersensitivity rashes (about 5% of patients), photosensitivity, hemolytic anemia in glucose-6-phosphate dehydrogenase deficient patients, and crystalluria. The latter is more common with agents which have lower solubility at urine pH and may be decreased in incidence by recommending that the drug be taken with a full glass of water. The most serious side effect is Stevens-Johnson syndrome, a potentially fatal hypersensitivity reaction that involves sloughing of skin and mucous membranes. Sulfonamides are contraindicated in the last trimester of pregnancy and in newborns because the compounds displace bilirubin from serum albumin and may cause kernicterus. This ability to bind to serum albumin also leads to drug interactions through displacement of other albumin-bound agents.

The specific sulfonamides that are used today are the following (Fig. 11–20). Sulfisoxazole is a short-acting sulfonamide particularly useful for urinary tract infections caused by susceptible organisms. Sulfamethoxazole is a medium-acting sulfonamide that is somewhat less soluble than sulfisoxazole and achieves higher blood levels. It is used frequently in combination with trimethoprim (see below). Salicylazosulfapyrimidine (sulfasalazine) is derivatized at the *p*-

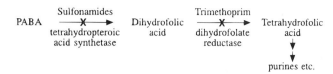

Fig. 11–19. Mechanism of action of the antimetabolites, sulfonamides and trimethoprim.

amino position with *m*-aminosalicylic acid to form a non-absorbable agent that is used in ulcerative colitis. It is cleaved in the intestine to yield *m*-aminosalicylic acid, which is supposed

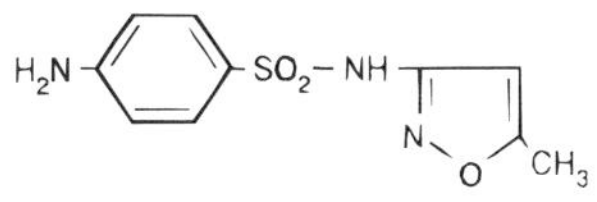

![Sulfamethoxazole structure]

Sulfamethoxazole

![Sodium sulfisoxazole structure]

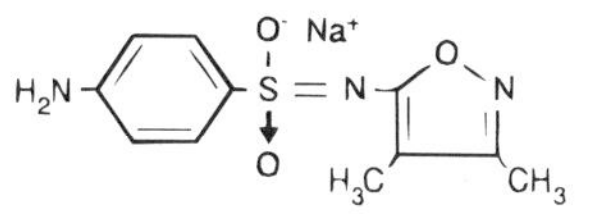

Sodium sulfisoxazole

Fig. 11–20. Unionized and ionized forms of sulfonamides.

to have a local anti-inflammatory effect, and sulfapyridine, which is absorbed. Mafenide and silver sulfadiazine are two derivatives used topically for prophylaxis of burn wounds. Sulfacetamide is a very soluble agent used in ophthalmic preparations. Some derivatives are also available for vaginal application.

Trimethoprim is 2,4-diamino-5-(3′,4′,5′-trimethoxybenzyl) pyrimidine, a synthetic compound that inhibits dihydrofolate reductase, the penultimate step in the synthesis of tetrahydrofolate, the active form of folic acid. The sequential inhibition of folic acid synthesis by sulfamethoxazole and trimethoprim provides for synergistic activity and reduced resistance development. The combination is active (and often bactericidal) against many gram-positive cocci and gram-negative rods. *Mycobacterium tuberculosis* and species of *Pseudomonas*, *Bacteroides*, and *Mycoplasma* are resistant, and resistance may develop among generally sensitive species.

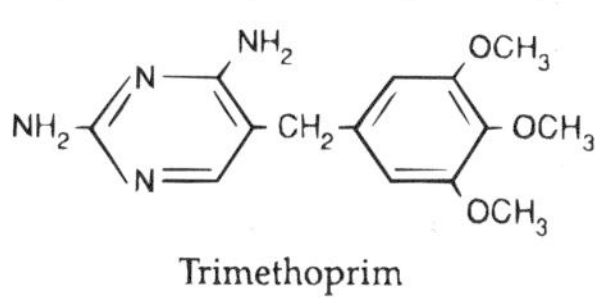

![Trimethoprim structure]

Trimethoprim

The adverse effects of the combination include all those discussed above for sulfonamides. In addition, a variety of blood dyscrasias are sometimes observed, particularly after prolonged administration. This side effect may be related to impaired folate utilization in the human cells. Patients with AIDS have a particularly high incidence of side effects, and hypotension and pulmonary infiltrates have been reported in these patients.

Trimethoprim-sulfamethoxazole (co-trimoxazole or TMP-SMZ) is available in a fixed ratio of 1:5 for oral use and intravenous administration. Trimethoprim, but not sulfamethoxazole, achieves particularly good prostate levels for treatment of prostate infections. The combination agent is useful for urinary tract infections, respiratory tract infections due to susceptible organisms, and is particularly useful in the reduction of acute exacerbations of chronic bronchitis. It is also used for traveler's diarrhea and chlamydial infections.

Metronidazole

Metronidazole is a synthetic nitroimidazole compound with an unusual spectrum of activity that makes it particularly useful in some situations.

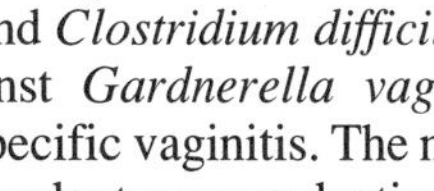

![Metronidazole structure]

Metronidazole

Metronidazole has bactericidal activity against a variety of pathogens, including, most importantly, *Trichomonas vaginalis*, *Giardia*, amoeba, and many anaerobes such as *Bacteroides fragilis* and *Clostridium difficile*. It also has activity against *Gardnerella vaginalis* which causes non-specific vaginitis. The mechanism of action is dependent upon reduction of the nitro group by nitroreductases since the cytotoxicity is due to the interaction with DNA of short-lived intermediates or free-radicals generated during the reduction. The end products are inactive. Only organisms with nitroreductases will be killed by metronidazole. The concentration of nitroreductases in human cells is low, providing for selective toxicity to pathogens.

There is some concern about tumorigenicity and/or teratogenic effects of metronidazole, but studies have not confirmed any increased incidence of cancer in humans who have received metronidazole. The current recommendations are to avoid long-term use and use during pregnancy, especially in the first trimester, and to discontinue nursing in nursing mothers during and for 2 days after therapy with metronidazole. Other adverse effects include gastrointestinal upset and central nervous system effects that can range from dizziness and headaches to seizures. It should be used with extreme caution in patients with seizure disorders. Metronidazole also causes an alcohol intolerance similar to that induced by the drug disulfiram.

Metronidazole is administered orally, intravenously, or intravaginally. Oral dosing is administered in two to four doses per day. Treatment of *Trichomonas vaginalis* infections requires treatment of both sexual partners.

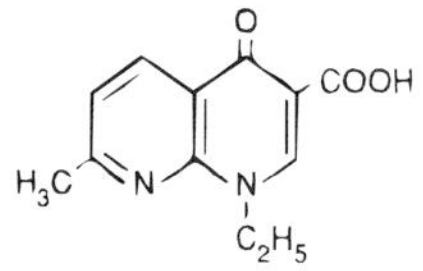

Quinolones

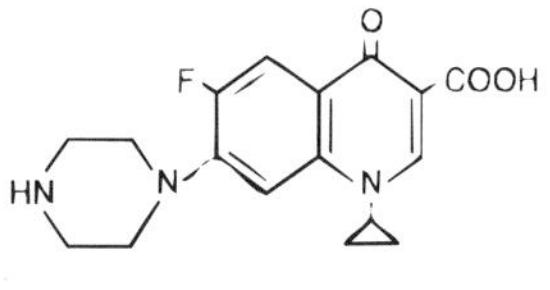

Nalidixic acid was the first member of the class of synthetic antimicrobials known as quinolones (Fig. 11–21). It has a 1,8-naphthyridine structure and was used only for urinary tract infections. Resistance development during therapy was a significant limitation. In the 1980s, the 6-fluoroquinolone compounds began to become available. These compounds have significantly improved activity and are now important compounds to consider in selecting appropriate antimicrobial therapy. The currently available fluoroquinolones are norfloxacin, enoxacin, ciprofloxacin, lomefloxacin, and ofloxacin. The individual agents differ in their spectra of action, particularly in activity against gram-positive bacteria, their oral bioavailability, and their half-lives.

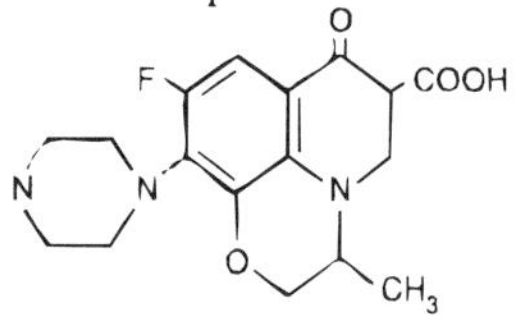

The **fluoroquinolones** are bactericidal agents whose mechanism of action involves inhibition of DNA gyrase, a member of the topoisomerase group of enzymes which regulate the superhelicity of DNA within the cells. Inhibition of DNA gyrase results in inhibition of DNA replication and cell death. Currently used antibacterial fluoroquinolones have only minimal activity against mammalian topoisomerases. The increased activity of the fluoroquinolones compared to nalidixic acid is due to their greatly increased affinity for binding to the DNA gyrase. Resistance developed readily to nalidixic

Fig. 11–21. Selected quinolone antimicrobial agents.

acid by small alterations in the DNA gyrase to reduce binding affinity; the new compounds can be used at concentrations that greatly exceed the binding affinity so small alterations will not lead to clinical resistance. Some acquired resistance has been observed infrequently with the new compounds, but thus far no plasmid-mediated resistance has been identified in clinical isolates.

The spectrum of activity includes most gram-negative aerobes, including, significantly, *Pseudomonas aeruginosa,* and other gram-negative enteric bacilli that are difficult to kill with many other agents. Anaerobes are mostly not sensitive. *Haemophilus influenzae, Salmonella* spp., *Neisseria meningitidis*, and *Neisseria gonorrhoeae* are all killed by the fluoroquinolones. Some of the newer compounds, specifically ciprofloxacin and ofloxacin, have improved activity against gram-positive organisms, specifically some staphylococci and streptococci. However, MICs are still relatively high compared to those of gram-negative bacteria, and resistance develops more quickly. Enterococcal infections are not effectively treated. This spectrum makes the fluoroquinolones particularly appropriate for urinary tract infections, prostatitis, gastrointestinal and abdominal infections, as well as respiratory tract and skin and soft tissue infections due to gram-negative organisms. Norfloxacin and enoxacin are used primarily for urinary tract infections and uncomplicated gonorrhea, while ciprofloxacin and ofloxacin are used for other systemic infections as well.

The fluoroquinolones are relatively safe agents but are not routinely used in children because of joint toxicity. In children with cystic fibrosis, the benefit of the antipseudomonal activity generally outweighs the risk of arthropathy. Adults experience mild gastrointestinal problems as the most common side effect, and allergic rashes occur in some patients. CNS symptoms ranging from dizziness and headache to seizures are thought to result from the ability of the fluoroquinolones to displace GABA from its receptors. Quinolones impair the elimination of methylxanthines such as caffeine and theophylline, and patients maintained on theophylline will require monitoring of serum levels and dosage adjustment if needed.

All the agents are available orally, and ciprofloxacin and ofloxacin are also available for intravenous administration. Oral bioavailability is excellent although antacids substantially impair absorption through the formation of cation-quinolone complexes. Other drugs that reduce gastric acidity, such as cimetidine and ranitidine, delay, but do not affect the completeness of, absorption. The agents are well-distributed in the body, including the prostate, a site which most antibiotics do not reach. Ofloxacin achieves the best cerebrospinal fluid levels. Ofloxacin and lomefloxacin are eliminated primarily by the kidneys; the other agents are partially metabolized prior to renal elimination, but all achieve therapeutic concentrations of active drug in the urine. Dosage adjustment in renal insufficiency is recommended. The half-lives vary from 3.2 hours for ciprofloxacin to 7.8 hours for lomefloxacin.

Synthetic Agents Used in Urinary Tract Infections

Methenamine and **nitrofurantoin** are two additional synthetic agents used only for urinary tract infections. Methenamine, hexamethylenetetramine, is orally absorbed and excreted in the urine where it is activated by the acidic pH of the urine to form formaldehyde, the active antibacterial product. It is used primarily for suppression of recurrent urinary tract infections and has few adverse effects.

Methenamine

Nitrofurantoin, a synthetic nitrofuran, is used for acute cystitis and suppression of recurrent urinary tract infections. Its spectrum includes *Escherichia coli, Citrobacter* spp., and *Enterococcus faecalis,* but many gram-negative bacilli, including *Proteus* species and *Pseudomonas* species, are usually resistant. Nitrofurantoin causes a number of adverse effects, the most serious of which is a hypersensitivity-based pulmonary infiltration.

Nitrofurantoin

Synthetic Agents Used for *Mycobacterium tuberculosis* Infections

The current first-line antimycobacterial agents include the natural products, streptomycin, rifampin, and rifabutin, which have already been discussed, plus several synthetic compounds including isoniazid (INH), ethambutol, and pyrazinamide. The second-line compounds are generally less effective or more toxic (or both) but are used in the case of organisms resistant to first-line agents or when adverse effects or patient characteristics prevent use of the first-line agents. These compounds include cycloserine and capreomycin, natural products that have already been discussed, *p*-aminosalicylic acid, and ethionamide. Tuberculosis is always treated with a combination of agents to minimize the emergence of resistance organisms. Isoniazid has been standardly used for prophylaxis of individuals with newly positive tuberculosis skin tests but without active disease, but the recent emergence of multiple-drug resistant organisms may alter that practice. The incidence of these resistant strains is rising and is of substantial public health concern. Patient compliance is also a major issue in the treatment of tuberculosis infections.

ANTIFUNGAL AGENTS

Fungi are an important cause of infections, particularly in immunocompromised hosts. Fungi are all eucaryotic organisms and as such are more like human cells than are bacteria. Antibacterial agents will not, for the most part, kill or inhibit fungi, and it has been difficult to identify selective targets within the fungal cells. Currently available systemic antifungal agents mostly target cell membrane synthesis or integrity. The fungal membranes are slightly different than human membranes because they contain a sterol, ergosterol, that does not appear in human cell membranes. Antifungal drug development is an area of significant need.

Fungi which cause human infections include: 1) filamentous dermatophytes, which cause skin infections such as ringworm (tinea corporis) and athlete's foot (tinea pedis) and nail infections (onychomycosis); 2) yeast (*Candida albicans*, a component of the normal flora which can overgrow in the intestine, vagina, bladder, or mouth, or on the skin, or can invade the bloodstream or organs, and *Cryptococcus neoformans*, which causes meningitis or pneumonia); or 3) dimorphic fungi (*Blastomyces, Histoplasma, Coccidioides, Paracoccidioides*), which have both filamentous and yeast-like forms and cause primary pulmonary or secondary disseminated infections, and 4) filamentous fungi such as *Aspergillus* which can invade a variety of sites in the body. Antifungal agents will have a characteristic spectrum that includes some or all of these fungi.

Of the antifungals used to treat dermatophytic infections, one, griseofulvin, is of natural origin, and undecylenic acid is derived from a natural fatty acid. Others are synthetic compounds. The classes of compounds used to treat systemic fungal infections are the polyenes, the azole derivatives, and 5-fluorocytosine. Of these, the polyenes are natural products and the others are synthetic. Natural products will be presented first, followed by a brief description of the synthetic agents.

Griseofulvin

Griseofulvin was isolated from cultures of *Penicillium griseofulvum* in 1939, and it was uti-

lized initially in plant pathology for its antifungal activity. Its value in therapeutic control of dermatophytes was not recognized until 1958.

Griseofulvin is also produced by a number of other *Penicillium* species, including *P. janczewski, P. nigrum,* and *P. patulum.* It arises biosynthetically from head-to-tail condensation of 7 acetate units. A polyketide is generally considered the basic precursor (Fig. 11-22), and griseophenone C has been identified as an early intermediate in the pathway. Subsequent methylation and chlorination are believed to precede the oxidative coupling of the benzophenone to the spiran, dehydrogriseofulvin. Presumably, the last step is reduction to yield griseofulvin.

Griseofulvin is stable and only slightly soluble in water. The insolubility of the drug leads to considerable variation in absorption upon oral administration. Formulations of microsize and ultramicrosize griseofulvin are used, and absorption can be facilitated further by administration with a high lipid meal. It is usually employed systemically for control of some dermatophytes belonging to the genera *Epidermophyton, Microsporium,* and *Trichophyton.* Griseofulvin is incorporated preferentially into keratin; this factor explains the unusual oral administration of an antibiotic for dermatomycoses and griseofulvin's lack of therapeutic efficacy in deep mycoses. Sensitive fungi exhibit an unusually narrow range of MICs (0.22 to 0.44 μg/ml).

Further studies are necessary to establish conclusively the means by which griseofulvin exerts its antifungal action. It appears to inhibit fungal cell mitosis by causing disruption of the mitotic spindle structure.

Griseofulvin is administered orally, and the

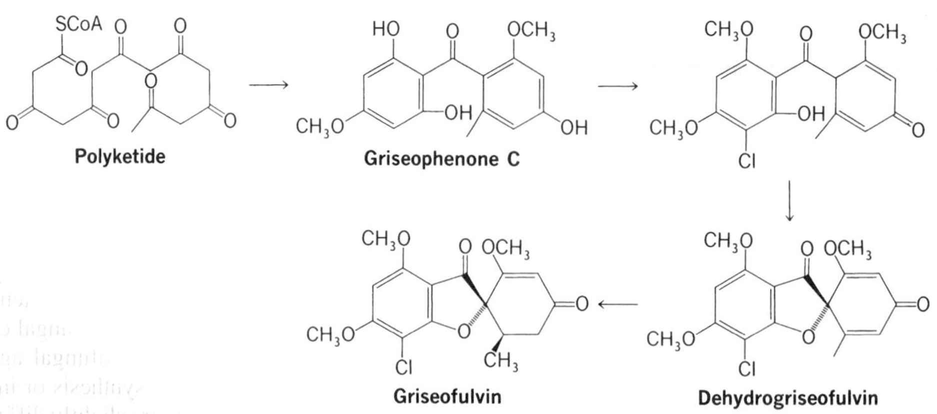

Fig. 11-22. Biosynthesis of griseofulvin.

usual dose of the microsize drug is 250 mg, two times a day. The ultramicrosize drug achieves about 1.5 times the effect of the microsize form on a unit weight basis. A 3- to 4-week treatment period is adequate for many conditions, but continued therapy for 6 to 12 months is necessary in some cases (e.g., infections of the fingernails or toenails). Griseofulvin is generally free of serious side effects; the most frequently encountered adverse reactions involve hypersensitivity, including occasional photosensitivity reactions.

Undecylenic Acid

Undecylenic acid (10-undecenoic acid; marketed as Desenex or Cruex) is derived from castor oil. Castor oil is hydrolyzed to yield its major fatty acid, ricinoleic acid, which is subsequently cleaved by pyrolysis to yield undecylenic acid. It is used in creams, ointments, powders, and solutions of 20-25% undecylenic acid in the treatment of fungal infections of the skin (athlete's foot, ringworm, etc.). Treatment should continue for 2 weeks to 1 month to prevent recurrence, although symptomatic relief should be observed in a few days. Severe cases of athlete's foot or other fungal skin infections and those involving hairy regions or nails should be referred to a physician for systemic therapy.

POLYENES

The designation **polyene**, for practical considerations in medicine and pharmacy, refers to a group of amphoteric actinomycete metabolites that are characterized by a series of conjugated double bonds. These metabolites are unsaturated macrolides with macrolactone rings that are considerably larger than those of erythromycin and oleandomycin. They are usually categorized on the basis of the number of conjugated double bonds in the molecules. Nystatin, a tetraene, and amphotericin B, a heptaene, are the polyenes used in therapy. The polyenes have no antibacterial activity, and their therapeutic utility is related to their antifungal action. The biologic activity of these antibiotics is determined with various strains of *Saccharomyces cerevisiae*.

The polyenes are fairly unstable, poorly absorbed from the intestinal tract, and reasonably toxic when administered systemically. They are insoluble, and this property sufficiently protects these antibiotics from inactivation to permit local action in the intestinal tract following oral administration. Limited solubility precludes intramuscular administration of amphotericin B, the only polyene currently recommended for systemic use; therefore, this antibiotic is given by slow intravenous infusion of a formulation that contains sodium deoxycholate to form a colloidal suspension of the polyene. Formulations with amphotericin B in liposomes have been tested recently and appear to substantially decrease the toxicity, particularly the nephrotoxicity, associated with the systemic use of amphotericin B.

The polyenes act by destroying the integrity of the cellular membrane of susceptible organisms, and this action may be related to the binding of the polyenes to steroids in the membrane and the formation of aqueous pores. Such a mechanism of action would explain the absence of antibacterial activity because bacterial membranes lack a steroid component. This type of interference with biologic processes may also account for at least one of the adverse reactions observed with systemic use of the polyenes; hemolytic anemia may result directly or indirectly from alteration in the formation or function of cholesterol-containing erythrocyte membranes.

Candida albicans is susceptible to the polyenes, and control of *Candida* overgrowth induced by broad-spectrum antibiotic therapy is a major use of these antifungal agents. Use of polyenes to control *Candida* infections of such origin is justified, but routine incorporation of a polyene in formulations of tetracyclines for prophylactic purposes has been challenged. The challenge is based, in part, on a concern for consequences of any increase in resistance to the polyenes and on a recognition that few alternate antifungal agents are currently available for treatment of systemic candidiasis.

Amphotericin B is produced by *Streptomyces nodosus*, and the commercial product must contain not less than 750 μg of amphotericin B per mg. The less active amphotericin A, a tetraene that is also present in the polyene fraction from cultures of this actinomycete, forms a soluble complex with calcium chloride; this manipulation is used in the commercial preparation of amphotericin B.

Amphotericin B can be used for topical purposes, but its special therapeutic utility is intravenous administration for treatment of potentially life-threatening, disseminated mycotic infections, such as blastomycosis, systemic

Amphotericin B

candidiasis, coccidioidomycosis, and monili-asis. The polyenes are less active against the der-matophytes and are used topically only when *Candida* is the likely pathogen. The MICs of susceptible fungi range from 0.03 to 1.0 μg/ml. This antibiotic is slowly eliminated from the body; the plasma half-life is about 24 hours, and the elimination half-life of this strongly protein-bound drug is estimated to be 15 days. Only a small percentage of the drug appears in the urine or bile, and dosage does not have to be adjusted for renal or hepatic dysfunction. Amphotericin penetrates poorly into the cerebrospinal fluid al-though the drug shows some efficacy for cryp-tococcal meningitis. Effective blood levels can be maintained with daily administration of a rel-atively low dose. The usual initial dose is 250 μg/kg of body weight daily, and most regimens call for an increase in the dose every 2 to 4 days for 4 to 8 weeks. Under no circumstances should a total daily dose exceed 1.5 mg/kg. The antibi-otic is administered by slow intravenous infu-sion over a period of 6 hours.

The side effects associated with amphotericin B administration are fever, chills, and hypoten-sion which are alleviated to some degree by the inclusion of hydrocortisone in the infusion or premedication with meperidine. Often a test dose of 1 mg is given before the first administra-tion to see how the patient will react. The most frequently observed toxicity with systemic use of amphotericin B is nephrotoxicity. Nephrotox-icity with this antibiotic is almost routine and is usually reversible upon cessation of therapy if the total amount of antibiotic administered does not exceed 5 grams. It can be decreased to some degree by hydrating the patient well and using the increasing dosage schedule described above. Three formulations under investigational use in the United States, a cholesterol sulfate-contain-ing colloidal dispersion, an amphotericin B lipid complex, and liposomal amphotericin B, appear to substantially reduce nephrotoxicity, perhaps by affecting the partitioning of amphotericin B

into fungal membranes instead of kidney cells. The toxicity associated with amphotericin B must be balanced with the need to control sys-temic mycoses in justifying the initiation and continuation of therapy in individual patients.

Nystatin is a tetraene produced by *Streptomy-ces noursei*. The commercial material must con-tain not less than 4400 units of activity per mg. It is available in formulations for treatment of cutaneous, intestinal, and vaginal infections of *Candida*. MICs range from 1.5 to 6.5 μg/ml. The usual dose is 500,000 to 1 million units, orally, three times a day or 100,000 units, intra-vaginally, one or two times a day.

Synthetic Antifungal Agents

In addition to the natural antifungal agents described above, there are some clinically im-portant synthetic agents to be considered. These can be grouped by their use as topical or sys-temic agents, although in the case of the imidaz-oles the compounds are used for both purposes.

Several compounds are used topically for der-matophytic infections. In addition to undecy-lenic acid, previously discussed, the compounds used are **tolnaftate, haloprogin,** and two new allylamines, **naftifine** and **terbinafine**, which inhibit squalene epoxidase. Several of the imid-azole compounds, discussed below, which have activity against the dermatophytes and *Candida*, are used either as topical preparations or as oral agents for skin and mucous membrane infec-tions.

Naftifine

Flucytosine (5-fluorocytosine, 5-FC) is an or-ally absorbed synthetic agent that has activity against yeasts, including *Candida* and *Cryp-tococcus*. Its mechanism of action involves con-version of the initial compound to 5-fluorouracil by a fungal deaminase. Subsequent metabolism yields 5-flurorodeoxyuridylic acid which inhib-its thymidylate synthetase and, thus, DNA syn-thesis. Mutation of the deaminase results in re-sistant cells, and resistant organisms are a major limiting factor in the use of 5-fluorocytosine. Flucytosine is well absorbed orally, achieves ex-cellent cerebrospinal fluid levels, and is excreted primarily in the urine. It is often used in combination with amphotericin B, both to achieve synergism and to reduce resistance development. The most important toxicities are diarrhea and leukopenia. These occur with much greater frequency when blood levels exceed 100-125 μg/ml, which occurs when patients have renal insufficiency. Therefore, toxicity and dosage levels should be monitored with particular care when flucytosine is combined with nephrotoxic agents such as amphotericin B.

5-Fluorocytosine   5-Fluorouracil

Compounds containing imidazole or triazole moieties are often grouped together and called "azoles." Included in these groups are the imidazoles, **miconazole, clotrimazole, econazole,** and **ketoconazole**, and the triazoles, **itraconazole** and **fluconazole**. They have broad spectrum antifungal activity, including the dermatophytes, *Candida*, and some of the organisms that cause deep mycoses. The mechanism of action involves inhibition of the demethylation of the 14-α-methyl group of lanosterol by binding to a cytochrome P-450 enzyme, thus inhibiting the synthesis of ergosterol, the sterol specific to fungal membranes. Azoles are antagonistic with amphotericin B since azoles decrease the content of ergosterol to which polyenes bind for their effect. The imidazoles also interfere with some P-450 enzymes in human metabolism, decreasing the synthesis of testosterone and cortisol. The newer triazole compounds are more specific and lack the hormonal side effects.

Several of the imidazoles, including miconazole, clotrimazole, and econazole, are used only topically for dermatophytic and *Candida* infections of the skin and mucous membranes. Ketoconazole is administered orally. Its absorption, as well as the absorption of the other orally absorbed azoles, is drastically reduced when patients are taking H_2-receptor blockers (e.g., cimetidine). Antacids also interfere with absorption and should be administered at different times than ketoconazole. Ketoconazole is widely distributed in the body including the skin and mucous membranes, but it does not achieve therapeutic cerebrospinal fluid levels. Ketoconazole is metabolized in the liver and excreted primarily in the bile. A number of drug interactions with other hepatically-metabolized drugs have been reported. In addition to the hormonal side effects, the common side effects of ketoconazole are anorexia, nausea, and vomiting. Hepatotoxicity occurs rarely but can be serious. Ketoconazole is effective for dermatophytic infections, candidiasis (including candidal infections of the skin and mucous membranes), non-meningeal histoplasmosis and blastomycosis, and paracoccidioidomycosis. It is not useful in cryptococcal infections or infections caused by *Aspergillus*.

Ketoconazole

Fluconazole

The newer triazoles have fewer side effects and drug interactions, as well as some other advantageous properties, and may replace ketoconazole for most uses. Fluconazole is administered orally and intravenously and, in contrast to ketoconazole, achieves excellent cerebrospinal fluid and urine concentrations. It is used as life-long maintenance therapy for AIDS patients whose cryptococcal meningitis has been treated initially with amphotericin B. Itraconazole is orally absorbed and has a broader spectrum than ketoconazole, including activity against *Aspergillus*. It is metabolized in the liver and does not achieve therapeutic levels either in the urine or the cerebrospinal fluid.

ANTIVIRAL AGENTS

Viral infections are among the most difficult to treat because viral replication utilizes many functions of the host cell, thereby allowing few selective targets for drugs to inhibit viruses without damaging the human host. Also, viruses are intracellular, making it necessary for antiviral agents to penetrate the human cell in order to act. Selectivity has been achieved in some cases, either by targeting viral-specific functions (e.g., amantadine and rimantadine inhibit viral uncoating and membrane fusion; several anti-HIV agents target reverse transcriptase) or by taking advantage of a virus-specific enzyme (e.g., acyclovir is activated to its active triphosphate form through a pathway which initially involves virus-specific thymidine kinase). Almost all antiviral agents are synthetic, and many are synthetic nucleoside derivatives which have some selectivity for the viral replication pathway. In addition to antiviral agents, viral infections are often prevented by vaccines, and immunomodulators are used alone or in combination with chemotherapeutic agents. The vaccines and immunomodulators are addressed in Chapter 12.

Acyclovir

ANTICANCER ANTIBIOTICS

Complete coverage of anticancer chemotherapy is beyond the scope of this text. However, a number of natural compounds with antimicrobial activity also are toxic to cancer cells and are used primarily as anticancer agents, usually in combination with other chemotherapeutic agents. The most important ones are presented below.

Dactinomycin or actinomycin D is obtained from selected strains of *Streptomyces parvullus* (formerly designated *S. antibioticus*). The molecule contains a phenoxazone chromophore that is linked to two cyclic polypeptides. The *N*-methyl amino acids, sarcosine and *N*-methylvaline, are present in the cyclopeptide portions of the antibiotic; this type of amino acid metabolite is uncommon in the plant kingdom. Biosynthetic studies indicate that the phenoxazone portion of the molecule arises from two molecules of tryptophan, presumably via the well-established pathway involving 3-hydroxyanthranilic acid.

Dactinomycin

Dactinomycin is an antineoplastic agent and is used for hospital treatment of Wilms' tumor and several other types of carcinoma and sarcoma. Nausea is common with intravenous administration of dactinomycin, and the best tolerance is obtained in isolated metastases when a perfusion technique can be employed. The drug is available as a lyophilized powder with mannitol. The usual adult dosage regimen is 10 to 15 μg/kg of body weight daily for 5 days by intravenous infusion; therapy is repeated at 4- to 6-week intervals and may involve concurrent administration of other antineoplastic agents.

Bleomycin is a mixture of antineoplastic glycopeptides produced by *Streptomyces verticillus*. The mixture can be separated into A and B fractions, and more than a dozen individual components have been reported. Bleomycin A_2 is the major constituent, composing between 55 to 70% of the mixture. Bleomycin B_2 (25 to 32%) is the second major constituent, and material intended for medicinal use must contain not more than 1% of bleomycin B_4. Bleomycin is standardized biologically, and the potency is expressed in units; bleomycin sulfate contains not less than 1.5 units and not more than 2 units of bleomycin per mg.

Bleomycin appears most useful for its palliative effect in some squamous cell carcinomas, but it is useful in lymphomas, testicular carcinomas, and some soft tissue sarcomas. Its low myelosuppressive action may offer clinical advantages. However, pulmonary toxicity frequently necessitates discontinuation of therapy. Bleomycin is preferentially concentrated in tumors, and a bleomycin-technetium 99m complex has diagnostic potential as a tumor-scanning agent.

Bleomycin is administered parenterally as the sulfate salt. The usual dosage regimen is 0.25 to 0.5 units/kg of body weight once or twice weekly.

The attention of medical investigators has been attracted to acetate-derived polycyclic metabolites of actinomycetes other than the tetracycline antibiotics. Daunorubicin and doxorubicin are two such metabolites; they occur as glycosides and have been judged to have utility in treating a variety of neoplastic conditions.

A variety of polyketide-derived **anthracycline derivatives** are produced by several species of *Streptomyces*. The two antineoplastic anthracyclines in current clinical use are doxorubicin and daunorubicin.

Doxorubicin: R = OH
Daunorubicin: R = H

Doxorubicin (Adriamycin) produced by *Streptomyces peucetius* var. *caesius* causes remission in a wide range of solid tumors, but unfortunately, the remission is short-lived in many cases. It shows promise in the treatment of some acute leukemias, soft tissue sarcomas, breast cancer, and several types of carcinoma. It is often used as a component in combination chemotherapeutic regimens.

Doxorubicin is rapidly metabolized in the liver (carboxyl reduction) to give an active alcoholic metabolite, adriamycinol. It inhibits DNA-dependent RNA synthesis. Doxorubicin exhibits a high incidence of bone marrow depression and other side effects, such as severe local tissue necrosis and serious irreversible myocardial damage. Complications associated with altered blood coagulation, leg vein thromboses, and pulmonary infarcts are claimed to present fewer problems with doxorubicin than with daunomycin.

Doxorubicin is administered intravenously as the HCl salt. It is excreted in the bile, and enterohepatic recycling gives an extended blood level. Slow renal elimination gives a red coloration to the urine for 1 or 2 days after administration of the drug. The recommended adult dose is 60 to 75 mg per square meter of body surface at 21-day intervals.

Daunorubicin (Cerubidine) is produced by *Streptomyces coeruleorubidus*. It is similar to doxorubicin in many of its biologic and chemical properties. Daunorubicin is used to treat acute lymphocytic and nonlymphocytic leukemias, usually as a component of combination chemotherapeutic regimens. It undergoes rapid reductive metabolism in the liver to give the active daunorubicinol.

Daunorubicin is administered intravenously as the HCl salt. The usual adult dose is 30 to 60 mg per square meter of body surface for 2 or 3 days at 3- to 4-week intervals. The pediatric dose is 25 mg per square meter of body surface once a week. The incidence of cardiotoxicity increases significantly for children and adults when the total cumulative doses exceed 300 and 550 mg per square meter of body surface, respectively.

Mitomycin C is one of the antineoplastic substances produced by *Streptomyces caespitosus*. It is not significantly more effective than other anticancer agents, and it causes more serious adverse reactions than most. It is considered useful in the treatment of disseminated adenocarcinoma of the stomach or pancreas and is an alternate drug in advanced metastatic conditions of various types that have become resistant to other chemotherapeutic agents. The response rate has been low, as anticipated in such high-risk situations, and remission is usually of short duration.

Mitomycin C

Mitomycin C is inactive per se; the active form is produced metabolically *in situ* and apparently acts as an alkylating agent to suppress DNA synthesis. Local tissue necrosis may occur, but severe bone marrow depression is the most serious side effect. The usual dosage regimen is, intravenously, 20 mg per square meter of body surface, either as a single dose or as divided doses over 10 days.

SUGGESTED READINGS

Appel, G.B.: Aminoglycoside Nephrotoxicity. Am. J. Med., *88* (suppl.C): 16S, 1990.

Cleary, J.D., Taylor, J.W., Chapman, S.W.: Itraconazole in Antifungal Therapy. Ann. Pharm., *26*:502, 1992.

Davies, J.E.: Aminoglycoside-aminocyclitol Antibiotics and Their Modifying Enzymes. In: Lorian, V., ed. *Antibiotics in Laboratory Medicine*, 3rd ed. Baltimore, Williams & Wilkins, 1991.

Eliopoulos, G.M., Moellering, R.C.: Antimicrobial Combinations. In: Lorian, V., ed. *Antibiotics in Laboratory Medicine*, 3rd ed. Baltimore, Williams & Wilkins, 1991.

Hooper, D.C., Wolfson, J.S., eds.: *Quinolone Antimicrobial Agents*, 2nd ed. Washington, D.C., American Society for Microbiology, 1993.

Janknegt, R. de Marie, S. Bakker-Woudenberg, A.J.M.: Liposomal and Lipid Formulations of Amphotericin B: Clinical Pharmacokinetics. Clin. Pharmacokinet., *23*: 279, 1993.

Kucers, A., Bennett, N. McK., Kemp, R.J. eds.: *The Use of Antibiotics.* Philadelphia, J.B. Lippincott, 1987.

Lin, R.: A Perspective on Penicillin Allergy. Arch. Intern. Med., *152*:930, 1992.

Mandell, G.L., Bennett, J.E., Dolin, R.: *Mandell, Douglas, and Bennett's Principles and Practice of Infectious Diseases*, 4th ed. New York, Churchill Livingstone, Inc., 1995.

Neu, H.C.: A Symposium on the Tetracyclines: A Major Appraisal. Introduction. Bull. N.Y. Acad. Sci., *54*:141, 1978.

Neu, H.C.: Oral Beta-lactam Antibiotics from 1960 to 1993. Infect. Dis. Clin. Pract., *6*:394, 1993.

Periti, P., Mazzei, T., Mini, E.: Pharmacokinetic Drug Interactions of Macrolides. Clin. Pharmacokinet., *23*:106, 1992.

Phillips, G., Golledge, C.L.: Vancomycin and Teichoplanin—Something Old, Something New. Med. J. Austral., *156*:53, 1992.

Piscitelli, S.C., Danziger, L.H., Rodvold, K.A.: Clarithromycin and Azithromycin: New Macrolide Antibiotics. Clin. Pharm., *11*:137, 1992.

Rosenblatt, J.E., Edson, R.S.: Metronidazole. Mayo. Clin. Proc., *62*:1013, 1987.

Sykes, R.B., Matthew, M.: The Beta-lactamases of Gram-negative Bacteria and Their Role in Resistance to Beta-lactam Antibiotics. J. Antimicrob. Agents Chemother., 2:115, 1976.

Utsui, Y.,Yokota, T.: Role of an Altered Penicillin-binding Protein in Methicillin and Cephem-resistant *Staphylococcus aureus.* Antimicrob. Agents Chemother., *28*:397, 1985.

Yunis, A.A.: Chloramphenicol Toxicity: 25 Years of Research. Am. J. Med. *87* (3N):44N 1989.

Zevos, M., Meunier, F.: Fluconazole (Diflucan): A Review. Int. J. Antimicrob. Agents, *3*:147, 1993.

12

Biologics and Immunomodulators

The inclusive term **"biologic"** may encompass any product derived from a living plant or animal source. However, strictly interpreted, biologics are substances defined by the Center for Drugs and Biologics of the Federal Food and Drug Administration (FDA) under the Public Health Service Act of 1944, as amended. The law refers to "any virus, therapeutic serum, toxin, antitoxin or analogous product," and it has been interpreted to include a lengthy list of such products as vaccines of bacterial, rickettsial, and viral origin, immune serums for the prevention or treatment of disease, various miscellaneous and diagnostic products, human blood, and products derived from human blood. Such substances as insulin, liver extract, and antibiotic products are not classified as biologics. Much of this reasoning depends on legal definitions and considerations.

The broad term "biologics" thus includes the immunizing biologics that are derivatives of animals (serums, antitoxins, globulins) or of microscopic plant organisms (vaccines, toxins, toxoids, tuberculins), which either directly or indirectly confer a state of protection against pathogenic microorganisms. Because these products do not affect the microorganisms directly, they cannot be considered chemotherapeutic agents; nor can they be classified with the antibiotics.

Biologics can be classified into two general categories, antigens and antibodies. An antigen is the material that provokes the immune response.

Biologically, an antigen is a substance that, when introduced into the tissue of humans or other vertebrates, causes the formation of antibodies. These antibodies then react specifically with the antigen that stimulated their production. Therefore, an antigen possesses two biologic properties: (1) immunogenicity, the capacity to induce antibody formation, and (2) specificity, governed by small chemical sites on the antigen molecule called the "antigenic determinants" or "epitopes." The antibody combines with one or more of these sites. Another important biologic concept of the antigen is that it must be considered foreign, by the antibody-forming host.

Antigens are usually protein; however, some high-molecular-weight polysaccharides are antigenic. Antigens must possess a high molecular weight. A weight of more than 10,000 daltons is required. The high molecular weight is associated with the biologic property of immunogenicity. Compounds with a molecular weight lower than 10,000 daltons can be partial antigens. They are called haptens. Because of their low molecular weight, they cannot induce the formation of antibodies by themselves. They lack the property of immunogenicity. However, they can attach to host proteins to form a complete antigen that will induce the formation of antibodies specific for the particular hapten. Drugs, or their breakdown products, may act as haptens, and this action is the basis of many drug allergies, e.g., penicillin allergy. In these cases, the drug molecule becomes the epitope.

Examples of antigens that are directly concerned in infectious disease are exotoxins, proteins and polysaccharides on the cell surface and capsules of bacteria, and the protein coat of virus particles. Microorganisms contain not one but many antigens, which in turn may contain many antigenic determinants or epitopes.

The number of distinct determinants on an antigen molecule usually varies with its size and chemical complexity. Aromatic amino acids contribute more to immunogenicity than nonaromatic residues. Studies have shown that the antibody recognizes the overall three-dimensional shape of the epitope rather than any specific chemical property, such as ionic charge. The epitope and antibody combining sites are structurally complementary and fit together in a lock-and-key arrangement.

Antibodies are found predominately in the serum fraction of the blood, although they also exist in other body fluids and in association with other tissues, such as lymph nodes and mucous membranes. When serum proteins are separated by electrophoresis, the four predominant fractions obtained are serum albumin and α, β, and γ globulins. The antibodies occur predominately in the γ globulin fraction and are called immunoglobulins. On the basis of their physical, chemical, and immunologic properties, the immunoglobulins can be separated into five subclasses: IgA, IgD, IgE, IgG, and IgM. IgM is the most abundant of the serum immunoglobulins, and the major part (up to 80%) of the serum antibody found after bacterial and viral infections belongs to this class of antibodies. IgG has a molecular weight of approximately 150,000 and contains about 1400 amino acids. These acids are not linked in one continuous chain but are arranged in four polypeptide chains, two heavy and two light. Each pair has identical structures. The chains are connected by disulfide bonds that help impart a tertiary structure to the molecule (Fig. 12–1). With papain, the peptides can be cleaved into two antigen-binding fragments (Fab) and a third fragment that cannot combine with antigen and crystallizes in neutral salt solutions (Fc). The two antigen-binding fragments are identical and arise from the amino-terminal ends of the four peptide chains. Each fragment contains the amino-terminal portion of one light chain and one heavy chain, and studies have shown that the amino acid composition of these portions of the peptide chains is variable from one antibody to another. The amino acid composition of the portion of the peptide chains representing the carboxy-terminal ends that make up the Fc fragment is relatively constant among different antibodies. The variability in the Fab region of the molecule may reflect the unique structure of each specific antibody against a specific antigen.

Because of the two combining sites on the IgG molecule, these antibodies are particularly well adapted to form macromolecular lattices with antigens and are usually good precipitating antibodies. The Fc fragments of human IgG contain various sites that are important in specialized functions of the immunoglobulin. One site facilitates placental transmission, one site fixes the antibody to macrophages, which allows them to function in a cytotoxic fashion, and one site fixes the complement. Complement is a complex of serum proteins and is required for the completion of certain antigen-antibody reactions, including the lysis of bacterial cells or erythrocytes by antibody.

When the newborn infant begins its own antibody production, the first immunoglobulin to appear is IgM. Molecules of IgM are pentamers of the basic four-chain immunoglobulin unit such as that found in IgG. The four-chain units are linked by disulfide bonds like a five-pointed star. The antigen-binding sites point outward. Because of the increased number of possible binding sites on a single antibody molecule, IgM can react with closely spaced antigenic determinants on the surface of cells, thereby making this antibody efficient in agglutinating or clumping erythrocytes and bacteria. For example, the ABO blood group antibodies are of the IgM type. IgM, with IgD, is the major immunoglobulin expressed on the surface of B cells. It is also the most efficient complement-fixing immunoglobulin.

IgA, IgD, and IgE are found in relatively low concentrations in the blood serum. IgA is the predominate immunoglobulin in external secretions, such as saliva and secretions of the respiratory and gastrointestinal tracts. These antibodies probably form a specific defense mechanism in these areas of the body. Each secretory IgA molecule consists of two four-chain basic units and one molecule each of secretory component and J chain, both of which are polypeptides with a molecular weight of approximately 70,000 and 15,000 daltons, respectively.

IgE molecules, also known as reagins, constitute only 0.004% of the total serum immunoglobulins but bind with high affinity to mast cells, which may be mediated by a cell attachment site on the Fc fragments in the molecule. Upon combination with certain specific antigens called allergens, IgE molecules trigger the release from mast cells of chemical mediators such as histamine, which are responsible for the symptoms of immediate hypersensitivity, such as asthma, hay fever, anaphylaxis, and skin eruptions. IgD is a monomer, and its main function has not been determined. It is found on the surface of B lymphocytes, suggesting that it may be involved in the differentiation of these cells. The specific role of IgD may be as an antigen receptor on antibody-producing cells that is designed for triggering the production of antibody.

Immunity is classified into two major types:

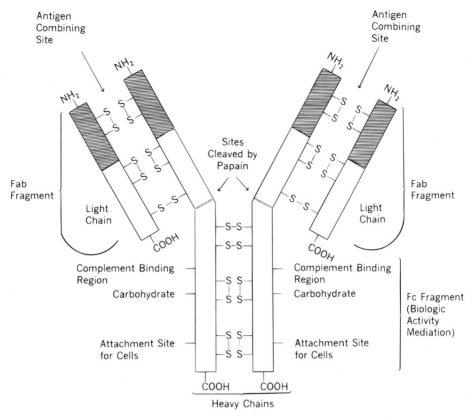

Fig. 12–1. A schematic representation of the structure of immunoglobulin G (IgG); ▨ designates amino acid variable region; ☐ designates amino acid constant region.

natural (innate) immunity and **acquired immunity.** The term natural or innate describes the defense mechanisms that are present in the body because of race, species specificity, and a multitude of other factors not easily defined, but it does *not* include any mechanisms especially developed during the lifetime of the individual. Thus, natural immunity is endowed at birth and is retained because of an individual's constitution.

On the other hand, acquired immunity is quite specific and generally is subdivided into two classes: **active immunity** and **passive immunity**, each of which is further subdivided as follows:

Acquired immunity
1. Active immunity
   a. Naturally acquired active
   b. Artificially acquired active
2. Passive immunity
   a. Naturally acquired passive
   b. Artificially acquired passive

Active immunity means the specific immunity developed by an individual in response to the introduction of antigenic substances into the body. In this type of immunity, the antigenic substances may be received by the body in a natural manner (naturally acquired active immunity), or they may be received by the body through the administration of a vaccine or toxoid (artificially acquired active immunity). In the first instance, recovery from an infection, such as measles or scarlet fever, produces an immunity that is acquired naturally, is developed rather slowly, and is usually long-lasting. In the second case, the immunity may be produced as the response to a series of injections (of typhoid or pertussis vaccine, for example), thus stimulating the body cells to make their own antibodies and producing an immunity that is acquired artificially, is developed gradually, and is usually long-lasting. The biologics that artificially induce active immunity are the vaccines and toxoids.

Depending on the nature of the antigen and

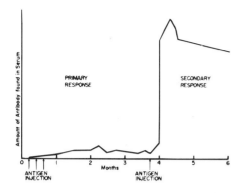

Fig. 12–2. An illustration of the recall or anamnestic phenomenon in antibody production.

the site of injection of antigen, antibody can be detected in the serum several days after the first injection of antigen. The antibody titer rises gradually to a low peak after the first and immediately subsequent injections and then falls slowly over a period of months (Fig. 12–2). A second injection of antigen administered while antibodies from the first stimulus are still present results in a rapid rise to a much higher peak than with the first injection. The second injection should not be too close in time to the first injection. If so, there is no additional effect on antibody production. The antibodies disappear much more slowly after the second stimulus than after the first. The rapid rise of antibody titer following a second administration of the antigen (the booster shot) presumably indicates that the antibody-producing cells have been primed by the first contact with antigen and, therefore, respond more effectively and more quickly when they encounter the antigen a second time. This phenomenon is termed the *recall* or *anamnestic* phenomenon and has great practical significance in immunization against infectious disease.

The major cellular components of the immune system are the macrophages and the lymphocytes. The origin of serum antibodies is now believed to be certain lymphocytes called B cells (so named because they were first described as originating from the bursa of Fabricius of chickens), which arise from the bone marrow in humans (Fig. 12–3). This is known as the humoral system of immunity because the B cells circulate in the body fluids, primarily in blood. The B-cell system handles most of the infectious organisms that are bacteria. Companion to the B-cell system is another lymphocyte population, the T cells. These cells originate in the bone marrow

but depend on the thymus gland for their differentiation. The T cells are the agents of cellular immunity, more stationary than the B cells, and seldom found circulating in the blood. Cellular immunity resists infections by fungi, acid-fast bacilli such as *Mycobacterium tuberculosis*, and viruses. T cells are also responsible for delayed hypersensitivity, e.g., tuberculin reactions and poison ivy dermatitis, and serve as the sentinels of immune surveillance against cancer and the mediators of graft rejection.

As each B cell matures in the bone marrow, it becomes committed to the synthesis of antibodies that recognize a specific antigen. All the progeny of each such cell retain the same specificity and thus form a clone of immunologically identical cells. The antibodies produced by B cells remain bound to the cell membrane, and when an antigen binds to an antibody in the membrane, the cell is stimulated to proliferate; this is the clonal selection process. The origin of this specialization involves complex gene rearrangement.

Some of the progeny of the selected clones remain as circulating B lymphocytes. They serve as the immune system's memory, providing a faster response to any subsequent exposure to the same antigen; hence, they are called B memory cells. Other members of the selected B-cell clones, called plasma cells, grow larger, stop reproduction, and continuously secrete large quantities of antibody. They have a short life of only 2 to 3 days.

There are four known subsets of T cells. They are identical in appearance but can be distinguished by function. Cell-mediated immunity is a function of two subsets of T cells: T_C cells, which are cytotoxic and attack cell membranes bearing their specific antigen, and T_D cells, which are delayed hypersensitivity cells. During clonal expansion of sensitized T_D cells, a number of biologically active protein factors called *lymphokines* are secreted, and these recruit and activate macrophages. Because several hours are required for synthesis of lymphokines, their effect is delayed.

The other population of T cells, T_H (helper) cells and T_S (suppressor) cells, have an immunoregulatory role over the entire specific immune system. Cellular interaction between T_H and B cells is essential for optimal humoral immune response to most antigens. When the T_H cells recognize an antigen, they stimulate B cells and other T cells specific for the same antigen, which results in their proliferation and differentiation.

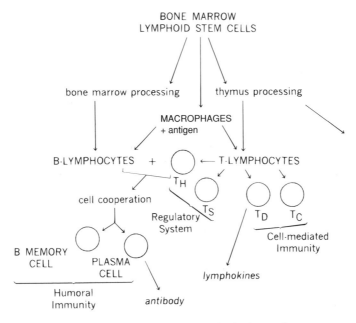

Fig. 12–3. Pathways for maturation of lymphocytes involved in the human immune system: T_H, helper cells; T_S, suppressor cells; T_D, delayed hypersensitivity cells; and T_C, cytotoxic cells.

The T_S cells have the opposite effect and diminish the activity of the same group of cells.

In addition to the lymphocytes (B and T cells), neutrophils and macrophages (collectively called phagocytes) are major cellular components of the immune system that also originate from the bone marrow. Neutrophils are polymorphonuclear white blood cells that are motile and are attracted to the site of infection where they phagocytize (engulf) infective organisms and destroy them in lysosomal vacuoles. The process, while serving as a first line of defense against infection, also can cause tissue damage leading to inflammation. Macrophages are mononuclear white blood cells that also can ingest and kill organisms. However, in addition, macrophages initiate and regulate the function of the lymphocytes through the secretion of *monokines*, protein factors analogous to the lymphokines (collectively the monokines and lymphokines are called *cytokines*). For instance, macrophages secrete interleukin-1 in response to interaction with an antigen, and interleukin-1 leads to T-cell proliferation. Other cytokines inhibit lymphocyte proliferation. Conversely, as mentioned previously, lymphokines secreted by T-cells can recruit and activate macrophages. Thus, the immune system is tightly regulated with the cytokines serving as the proteinaceous

messenger molecules. Failures in the regulation of the system can lead to autoimmune diseases and chronic inflammation, or to overwhelming infection.

Passive immunity is the type developed by the introduction of preformed antibodies (not antigens) into the body. In this type, the body cells are not stimulated to produce their own antibodies. Because the immunity acquired by the individual is not self-developed but is passed from one individual (or animal) to another, the term passive immunity is applied. The immunity developed in a newborn infant through transmission of the antibodies from the blood of the mother is an example of naturally acquired passive immunity; it is produced quickly but is not long-lasting. The injection of immunizing biologics containing preformed antibodies in forms such as diphtheria antitoxin or gamma globulin produces artificially acquired passive immunity, which again is produced quickly but is not long-lasting.

Obviously, certain biologics are intended for prophylactic or preventive therapy, whereas others are serviceable as therapeutic or curative measures. Vaccines and toxoids in their preventive capacities do not offer immediate protection to the patient; antitoxins, serums, and globulins give instant protection to the patient.

The importance of vaccination cannot be stressed too highly; its value has been proved beyond question. As a result of the judicious use of smallpox vaccine, the World Health Organization declared the world free of smallpox in May 1980. Typhoid fever and epidemic typhus fever were nonexistent among the personnel of the armed forces during recent wars, an outstanding medical accomplishment related primarily to rigid vaccination schedules maintained by military and naval medical staffs. Conceivably, any disease could be eradicated anywhere in the world if such proper preventive measures

as sanitation, vaccination, and education were instituted. At the present time, many childhood diseases can be effectively prevented by using the recommended immunization schedule illustrated in Tables 12–1 and 12–2.

Antibiotics are currently available for controlling many infectious diseases, but antitoxins and related passive immunologic agents are still useful in treating infections caused by viruses and other pathogens that fail to respond to antibiotics. Also, the unique use of antibody-containing biologics for prophylactic purposes must be emphasized. It is infeasible and undesirable to use

Table 12–1

Recommended Immunization Schedule for Children

Immunizing Agent	Preferred Age for Initial Dose	Dosage for Primary Immunization	Booster
Adsorbed diphtheria and tetanus toxoids and pertussis vaccine[1] (DTP)	2 to 3 months	0.5 mL, intramuscularly, repeated twice at 4- to 8-week intervals	0.5 mL 1 year after primary and 4 to 5 years later. Td every 10 years thereafter
Adsorbed tetanus and diphtheria toxoids for adult use (Td)	7 years and over	0.5 mL intramuscularly, repeated once after 4 to 8 weeks	0.5 mL 1 year after primary and every 10 years thereafter
Live oral poliovirus vaccine, trivalent	2 to 3 months	Two doses given at not less than 8-week intervals (in the volume indicated in the labeling), and a third, reinforcing dose 8 to 12 months later	One dose at entry into school
Live attenuated measles virus vaccine[2]	15 months of age or older	1000 $TCID_{50}$ subcutaneously[3]	At ages 4–6 and/or upon entry to middle school
Live rubella virus vaccine[2]	Between age 15 months and puberty	1000 $TCID_{50}$ subcutaneously[3]	At ages 4–6 and/or upon entry to middle school
Live mumps virus vaccine[2]	15 months of age or older	1000 $TCID_{50}$ subcutaneously[3]	At ages 4–6 and/or upon entry to middle school
Haemophilus b vaccine[4]	2 to 3 months	0.5 mL, intramuscularly, repeated twice at 8-week intervals	At 12–15 months of age
Hepatitis B vaccine	birth	0.25–0.5 mL, intramuscularly, repeat at 1–2 months and 6–18 months	No routine boosters recommended

[1] For primary immunization or boosters over age 6, use Td; the first 3 doses should be DTwP; the 4th and 5th doses may be DTaP (see text); the first three doses may be the combined DTwP-Hib product.

[2] May be given in bivalent or trivalent vaccine (MR or MMR); the trivalent vaccine, MMR, is preferred.

[3] Quantity of virus estimated to infect 50% of inoculated tissue cultures × 1000.

[4] Hib vaccines are capsular oligo- or polysaccharides conjugated to diphtheria toxoid, diphtheria CRM_{197} protein, tetanus toxoid, or *Nesseria meningitidis* serogroup B outer membrane complex. The diphtheria toxoid conjugate (ProHIBiT) is not recommended for primary immunization of infants.

Table 12-2
Recommended Immunization Schedule for Normal Infants and Children by Age of
Administration

Age	Vaccine	Comments
0–2 days	Hepatitis B—1st dose[1]	The current recommendation is that all infants receive Hepatitis B vaccine; infants born to hepatitis-antigen positive mothers should also receive Hepatitis B immunoglobulin
1 month	Hepatitis B—2nd dose	
2 months	DTwP—1st dose[2] OPV—1st dose Hib—1st dose	DTwP and Hib may be combined in a single product
4 months	DTwP—2nd dose OPV—2nd dose Hib—2nd dose	DTwP and Hib may be combined in a single product
6 months	DTwP—3rd dose Hib—3rd dose	DTwP and Hib may be combined in a single product
12 months	Hib—4th dose (if PedvaxHIB is used) Hepatitis B—3rd dose	
15 months	OPV—3rd dose DTwP—4th dose Hib—4th dose (if HibTITER or OmniHIB is used) MMR—1st dose	Can be anytime between 6 to 18 months May use DWaP
4–6 years	DTaP—5th dose OPV—4th dose MMR[3]	At entry to school
11–12 years	MMR[4]	At entry to middle school
14–16 years	Td	Repeat every 10 years throughout life

[1] An alternative acceptable schedule for hepatitis B immunization is to administer 3 doses at 1–2 months, 4 months, and 6–18 months.
[2] In the future, the wP component may be replaced by a new accellular pertussis vaccine.
[3] Recommended by the Center for Disease Control Advisory Committee on Immunization Practices (ACIP).
[4] Recommended by the American Academy of Pediatrics (AAP).

antibiotics for prophylaxis. These reasons suggest that biologics must be accorded a special place among medicinally useful materials obtained from natural sources.

All biologics are "dated," i.e., carry an expiration date on the label of the package, because they do not retain their potency for an indefinite period. Specific regulations govern the determination of the expiration date for given biologic formulations. For example, diphtheria antitoxin can have a 5-year expiration date, provided that the preparation has a 20% excess of potency. Whether the potency of the biologic still exists near the end of the expiration time depends on the methods of storage.

The nature of biologic products requires that they be refrigerated during storage. They represent either living or dead microorganisms or their metabolic products as well as the active components of the blood of animals. To ensure their activity as immunogenic materials, they should be stored at a temperature ranging from 2 to 8° C. In certain instances, lower temperatures are indicated. Yellow fever vaccine should be stored at a temperature no higher than 5° C and preferably lower than 0° C; live poliomyelitis vaccine should be preserved at a temperature below −10° C. Because biologics are usually stored in mechanically operated refrigerators, they may occasionally become frozen. Provided the container is not broken, such freezing does not affect the potency of the product unless the label states otherwise.

All immunizing biologics must comply with

the identity, safety, sterility, and potency tests and other requirements for the individual product in accordance with the Food and Drug Regulations—Code of Federal Regulations, as administered by the Bureau of Biologics of the FDA. Each lot of the product must be released individually before its distribution. The labeling must correspond to certain specifications. It must bear the name of the product, the lot number, and expiration date; the manufacturer's name, license number, and address; and a statement regarding storage and refrigeration. Biologics are to be dispensed in the unopened container in which they were placed by the manufacturer.

In addition to the commercially available biologics, the Centers for Disease Control (CDC), United States Public Health Service, can supply various rare immunologic agents in emergency situations. These products are available through the CDC Drug Service, Division of Immunologic, Oncologic, and Hematologic Diseases, Center for Infectious Diseases, CDC, Atlanta, GA, 30333.

VACCINES

Vaccines are used as inoculations to stimulate the production of antibodies. There are many types of vaccines, some of which have been made possible by the advent of biotechnology. Vaccines can be composed of (1) attenuated (weakened) live whole organisms (bacteria or viruses), (2) killed or inactivated organisms, (3) harmless organisms related to the pathogen that induce cross-immunity, (4) isolated structural components or products of organisms, which sometimes are conjugated to proteins to increase immunogenicity (called "conjugate vaccines"), (5) recombinant live vaccines; and (6) synthetic vaccines. The advantage to using live organisms is that they will set up an actual mild infection and lead to long-lasting immunity; the disadvantage has been that attenuated (weakened) organisms always carry the risk that not every cell or particle is attenuated, or if the organism is genetically altered, that reversion may occur. However, appropriate quality-control measures greatly decrease the risk of any breakthrough infection with the active pathogen. Recombinant technology has allowed a safer approach to live vaccines because it permits an immunogenic antigen from a given pathogen to be expressed in an immunogenic, but nonpathogenic, host organism, thus gaining the advantage of a live organism vaccine without any risk of infection with the pathogen. Synthetic vaccines use recombinant technology to produce antigenic components of pathogens in a host organism. The antigenic component is then isolated and used directly or conjugated to an immunogenic protein to generate a vaccine. This approach is analogous to covalently conjugating cellular components (e.g., capsular polysaccharides) that have been isolated by chemical extraction of pathogens to carrier proteins. *Haemophilus influenzae* b vaccines are generated in this manner. Table 12–3 describes the composition of a variety of currently used vaccines.

New approaches to developing vaccines are also under investigation with the goal of developing vaccines that are safe and highly immunogenic. One of the more intriguing experimental approaches is that of nucleic acid vaccines. DNA encoding an antigen is injected into muscle and is apparently taken up by the cells and expressed. The cytoplasmic antigen induces a cytotoxic T-lymphocyte response that confers a strong immunogenic response.

Primary active immunity from vaccination develops more slowly than the incubation period of most infections and must be induced prior to exposure to the infectious agent; therefore, the general action of vaccines should be considered prophylactic. One exception is the rabies vaccination. Because the rabies virus has a median incubation period of 35 days in humans, there is usually sufficient time for protective antibodies to develop when the vaccine is administered after exposure.

Recommendations concerning who should receive a given vaccine involves a balance of risk versus benefit. The benefit to be derived from the use of vaccines is affected by the chance that the patient will develop the disease, the consequences of the disease, the efficacy of the vaccine, and the availability of antibiotic therapy for the disease. With reference to cost or risk, one must consider the incidence and severity of side effects of the vaccines as well as the cost of producing and administering vaccines to a wide population. Many vaccines that are not used routinely will be administered to healthcare workers, travelers, or others at specific risk of infection. Herd immunity develops when a sufficient percentage of the population is immunized so that there is no reservoir of the pathogen to infect unimmunized persons. Herd immunity is a reasonable goal of widespread immunization

Table 12–3.
Composition of Currently Used Products for Active Immunization

Vaccine	Type
Measles (rubeola)	Live virus
Mumps	Live virus
Rubella	Live virus
Oral poliovirus (OPV)	Live virus
Inactivated poliovirus (IPV)	Inactivated virus
Influenza virus	Whole virus, subvirion (split virus), purified surface antigens
Yellow fever	Live-attenuated virus
Hepatitis B	Recombinant surface antigens
Varicella zoster	Live virus
Rabies	Inactivated virus
Pneumococcal	Extracted polysaccharides (23-valent)
Haemophilus b conjugate	Isolated polysaccharides conjugated to carrier proteins
Plague	Formaldehyde-inactivated *Yersinia*
Typhoid	Live attenuated *Salmonella typhi*
Meningococcal	Extracted polysaccharides from serogroups A, C, Y, and W of *Neisseria meningitidis*
Tetanus	Adsorbed toxoid
Diphtheria	Adsorbed toxoid
Pertussis (whole cell)	Killed whole cell (wP)
(acellular)	Inactivated toxin (toxoid) and filamentous hemagglutinin of *Bordetella pertussis*
BCG	Attenuated live *Mycobacterium bovis*.

programs and involves major efforts directed at routine childhood immunization programs in all parts of the population. Requirements for immunization of travelers will often change with time as herd immunity against particular pathogens develops in various places in the world. In the most dramatic example of this concept, widespread inoculation against smallpox led to its eradication worldwide and has made the need to immunize all children against smallpox a thing of the past.

Nonliving vaccines provide protection for only a limited time, and repeated vaccination is required to maintain protection against typhoid fever, cholera, plague, and typhus. Active immunization with living agents is generally preferable to immunization with killed vaccines because of a superior and more long-lived immune response. For example, a single vaccination of measles, rubella, or mumps vaccine is sufficient to produce a long-lasting if not permanent immunity, although recent recommendations are that children should be revaccinated at time of entry into elementary or middle school. Multiple immunizations are recommended for polio, because interference among the three administered virus types present in the trivalent vaccine could prevent completely successful primary immunization. The timing of multiple immunizations is based on studies that measure antibody response to vaccine administration and the longevity of antibody response. There usually is acceptable variability in the dosage schedule so that recommendations will include considerations of convenience to parents in order to increase compliance.

The benefits of active immunization far outweigh the dangers associated with the use of vaccines; however, precautionary measures should be followed to ensure optimum effectiveness with a minimum of adverse reactions. Use of vaccines is contraindicated under conditions in which the immune response may be depressed, such as during therapy involving corticosteroids, antineoplastic agents, immunosuppressive agents, or radiation; in patients with immunoglobulin deficiency (agammaglobulinemia and dysgammaglobulinemia); and in patients with latent or active infections. Also, patients receiving some live virus vaccines such as the oral poliovirus vaccine have the potential of transmitting the virus to immunosuppressed family members, so patients' medical histories should include the health status of family members and the inactivated poliovirus vaccine should be used in these cases.

Active immunization may cause fever, malaise, and soreness at injection sites. Some reactions are relatively specific for a particular vaccine, such as arthralgia and arthritis following rubella vaccine or convulsions following pertussis vaccine. During the 1976 "swine flu" immunization program in the United States, there was an eightfold increase in postimmunization Guillain-Barré syndrome (acute febrile polyneuritis) in comparison with unvaccinated controls. This complication arises within 8 weeks of immunization and has resulted in a 5% mortality rate among patients who developed the syndrome.

Allergic reactions may result either from the organism constituting the vaccine or from a protein incorporated into the vaccine during manufacture, e.g., egg protein from chick embryo tissue cultures. Consequently, a careful history of the patient should be taken before vaccination to detect possible hypersensitivity to the protein to be injected. Epinephrine (1:1000) should be available to counteract any anaphylactic reaction.

VIRAL VACCINES

Viral vaccines for prophylaxis against mumps, rubella, measles (rubeola), smallpox, and yellow fever contain living (attenuated) viruses. Inactivated or killed viruses are used in influenza and rabies vaccines. Preparations containing live attenuated or killed viruses are available for immunization against poliomyelitis.

The cultivation of viruses poses a problem because they are completely dependent on living cells for their sustenance. No method of growing viruses without cells is known. Viruses for smallpox vaccine and for rabies vaccine were obtained for years from vesicular tissues of vaccinated calves and brain tissues of infected rabbits, respectively, but this approach has limited utility for many viruses. The use of living chick or duck embryos for viral culture offers advantages in some cases, but the development of techniques for tissue culture of mammalian cells provided the major basic advancement necessary for significant expansion in the practical use of many viral vaccines. A number of viruses currently employed in viral vaccines are grown on tissue cultures prepared from chick embryo, monkey kidney, or human diploid cells. Primary tissue cultures have created some problems, especially because of the need for large numbers of monkeys, and because of the continuous need for extensive tests, with resulting expense and delays, to ensure the absence of undesirable simian viruses in each monkey kidney donor. It appears that advancements will be forthcoming and will permit indefinite propagation of suitable cell lines. The use of tissue cultures of human cells has now become a reality (see "Rabies Vaccine").

Smallpox vaccine is the living virus of vaccinia (cowpox) that has been grown in the skin of a vaccinated bovine calf. It is available in dried and in liquid form; the latter consists of a smooth, aqueous suspension of infected tissue that contains 40 to 60% of glycerin or of sorbitol and may contain not more than 0.5% of phenol as a preservative.

The pioneering work of Dr. Edward Jenner in England in 1796 documented that when a mild case of cowpox (vaccinia) is developed by a person, the same person is immune to smallpox. Using this information, Jenner inoculated a young boy with pus from a milkmaid infected with cowpox. Two months later, the boy was inoculated with pus from a patient infected with smallpox, but no disease developed. Immunity had been established.

Smallpox vaccine is a specific immunizing agent and is used as a prophylactic before the infection occurs. It creates active immunity that usually lasts for about 7 years. Because the disease has undergone complete worldwide eradication, smallpox vaccination of civilians is now indicated only for laboratory workers directly involved with variola virus or closely related orthopox viruses. The vaccine is not available commercially but can be obtained from the CDC.

Rabies vaccine, also known as **human diploid cell rabies vaccine (HDCV),** is a sterile lyophilized preparation of either the whole virion or subvirion rabies virus. The whole virion vaccine is prepared from Wistar rabies virus grown in cultures of human diploid embryo lung tissue and inactivated with tri-*N*-butyl phosphate and β-propiolactone. The subvirion vaccine is prepared from the Pasteur-derived Pitman-Moore virus grown on human diploid cell cultures developed in Europe and inactivated with β-propiolactone. Both vaccines are supplied as 1.0 mL, single-dose vials of lyophilized vaccine with accompanying diluent.

In addition to his other famous accomplishments, Louis Pasteur is associated with rabies. Pasteur was able to "fix" the virus of rabies by passing it from an infected dog to the brain of a rabbit and then from one rabbit to another until a uniformity was established that resulted in attenuated virulence for humans. In the first immunization against rabies in 1885, Pasteur used such a fixed virus to achieve active immunity.

The Pasteur treatment is not a curative treatment, but it actually accomplishes the same result, because immunization of a patient bitten by a rabid animal proceeds more quickly than the incubation period of the disease. Because the treatment consists of a series of injections for 28 days, the development of antibodies probably inhibits the growth of the virus.

Brain tissue, formerly used in the preparation of the vaccine, contains a significant amount of myelin, which is thought to be the "paralytic factor" that causes rabies treatment paralysis. With the advent of HDCV, problems with paralysis have been greatly reduced. Rare cases of Guillain-Barré syndrome have been reported; however, these patients recovered completely from the paralysis. There also has been a 6% incidence of an immune-complex-like reaction in persons receiving booster doses of HDCV. The illness is characterized by an onset 2 to 21 days post-booster and involves generalized urticaria, arthralgias, nausea, vomiting, fever, and malaise, but is not life-threatening.

The vaccine is an active immunizing agent and is recommended primarily for the prevention of rabies in persons bitten by an animal supposed or known to be rabid. However, the vaccine may be used for pre-exposure immunization for veterinarians or other high-risk individuals. The usual pre-exposure dose is three injections of 1.0 mL of reconstituted vaccine on each of days 0, 7, and 21. Booster doses of vaccine depend on risk categories. In high-risk patients, serology is performed and a booster dose is administered if the titer falls below 1:5. Postexposure immunization should be started as quickly as possible after the wound has been inflicted; the usual administration schedule is five injections of 1.0 mL of reconstituted vaccine on each of days 0, 3, 7, 14, and 28. Rabies immune globulin should be administered at the time of the first dose of vaccine for additional protection, particularly in the case of a bite from a wild animal.

Yellow fever vaccine is an attenuated strain of living yellow fever virus, selected for high antigenic activity and safety. It is prepared by culturing the virus in the living embryo of the domestic fowl (*Gallus domesticus*). The virus-infected, chick-embryo pulp is suspended in water and, after appropriate aseptic processing, is distributed in suitable quantities into ampuls and dried from the frozen state. Afterward, the vials are filled with dry nitrogen and flame-sealed. The expiration date of this vaccine is not longer than 1 year from the date of issue, and it must be stored at a temperature preferably below 0° C but never above 5° C. Yellow fever vaccine should be hydrated immediately before use. It does not contain human serum. Yellow fever vaccine should not be administered to individuals allergic to egg or chicken protein.

Yellow fever or "yellow jack" was considered an endemic disease in certain tropical regions, including the Caribbean Islands and Central America. Work on the Panama Canal was abandoned by the French because of the terrific death toll caused by yellow fever. Through the heroism of Walter Reed, Carlos Finlay, and numerous volunteers among the American troops stationed in Cuba during the Spanish-American war, The *Aëdes* mosquito finally was proven to be the vector of the disease. Further investigation was necessary to determine that the cause of yellow fever was a noncultivatable, filter-passing virus.

Yellow fever vaccine is an active immunizing agent that is used to develop active immunity against the disease. The usual dose, given subcutaneously, is 0.5 mL. The use of yellow fever vaccine in the United States is limited largely to persons planning to travel through parts of the world where yellow fever is endemic. Yellow fever vaccine is recommended for all travelers 6 months of age or older who are planning a trip to countries that require a certificate of vaccination against yellow fever and for persons living in countries in which yellow fever is endemic. Immunity develops by the 10th day following vaccination, and the certificate is valid for 10 years according to World Health Organization guidelines. The vaccine should be administered at least 1 month apart from other live virus vaccines.

Influenza virus vaccine is a sterile, aqueous suspension of suitably inactivated influenza virus types A and B, either individually or combined, or virus subunits prepared from the extra-embryonic fluid of influenza virus-infected chick embryo (called "split-virus" or "subvirion"), and/or purified surface antigens (hemagglutinin antigens). The strains of influenza virus used in the preparation of this vaccine are those designated for the particular season by the Center for Drugs and Biologics of the Federal FDA. It is important that influenza virus vaccines prepared for one influenza season be discarded prior to the next season. It contains a suitable preservative and may contain an adsorbent, such as aluminum phosphate or protamine. During the commercial preparation of the vaccine, the viruses are grown and collected, concentrated, refined by ultracentrifugation, and inactivated by ultraviolet irradiation.

Each lot of influenza virus vaccine must be tested to determine its potency; its power to stimulate the formation of specific virus-neutralizing antibodies in mice is correlated with the potency. Each milliliter is labeled according to the number of CCA units it contains; the unit refers to the chicken red-cell agglutination titer. This vaccine must be stored at a temperature between 2 and 8° C, and the expiration date is not longer than 18 months from the date of issue.

Influenza virus vaccine is an active immunizing agent. Its usual dose is 0.5 mL intramuscularly, preferably in the deltoid muscle. Annual vaccination is recommended for individuals in high-risk categories. This category includes any person older than 6 months of age who because of age or underlying medical condition is at increased risk of complications of influenza: (1) all persons greater than 65 years of age, (2) residents of nursing homes and other chronic care facilities, (3) adults and children with chronic disorders of the pulmonary and cardiovascular systems (including children with asthma) or with chronic metabolic diseases, (4) renal dysfunction or immunosuppression, (5) and children and teenagers who are receiving long-term aspirin therapy (and therefore may be at risk of developing Reye's syndrome after influenza). Healthcare workers and household members in close contact with high-risk individuals should also be vaccinated. Children less than 12 years of age should only be given the split-virus or purified surface antigen vaccines, because they have a lower potential to cause febrile reactions.

Influenza viruses have a high degree of strain specificity and of genetic instability. These factors require a continual reevaluation of the components of influenza virus vaccine and result in periodic infections of epidemic proportions even among immunized persons. Most available vaccines are bivalent and contain types A and B virus strains.

Poliomyelitis Vaccines

There are two forms of poliovirus vaccines, the oral vaccine (OPV; Sabin) that contains live attenuated virus and the inactivated virus vaccine (IPV, Salk) that is administered subcutaneously. The former creates an intestinal infection that provides long-lasting immunity in the intestine, the site of entry of the virus, whereas the latter creates serum antibodies. The oral Sabin vaccine is preferred for immunization of children; the Salk vaccine is preferred for adults, but some circumstances make it important to administer the Salk vaccine to children as well. The two vaccines are described below, and the factors influencing the choice of vaccine are discussed following the two descriptions.

Poliovirus vaccine inactivated (IPV; Salk) is a sterile suspension of inactivated poliomyelitis virus of types 1, 2, and 3. The virus strains are grown separately in primary cultures of Rhesus monkey kidney tissues bathed by a complex nutrient fluid containing more than 60 ingredients. After incubation, the virus is harvested by decanting the nutrient fluid that is clarified by filtration; then, formaldehyde in a concentration of 1:4000 is added. The formaldehyde-treated virus is maintained at 36° C at pH 7 until all viruses are killed. A series of elaborate tests is performed to ascertain that all viruses are inactivated. Following these quality-control tests, the formaldehyde is neutralized and a preservative is added. The three types of virus are then pooled, and the resultant mixture is the trivalent vaccine.

In addition to the three types of poliomyelitis virus that have been cultured and identified, other paralysis-producing strains undoubtedly exist. However, in general poliomyelitis epidemics of major proportions have been caused by type 1 (Brunhilde). Type 3 (Leon) has proved to be the etiologic agent in less frequent epidemics, and type 2 (Lansing) has been involved only in sporadic cases. Immunization with one type of virus does not offer protection against the other types; thus, the current vaccine is a trivalent preparation. Improved strains of the various viral types are the object of continuous selection studies; the type 1 Mahoney strain, type 2 MEF-

1 strain, and type 3 Saukett strain are now used in preparing poliomyelitis vaccines.

In 1908 Landsteiner and Popper first transmitted and isolated poliomyelitis virus experimentally in monkeys. It was subsequently ascertained that monkeys that had survived one attack of poliomyelitis were resistant to further attacks; furthermore, blood serum from such monkeys neutralized the virus *in vitro*. Still later, this observation resulted in the successful attempt to induce passive immunity through the use of serum obtained from immune donors.

During 1948, Dr. John F. Enders and his associates at Harvard University originated a method of cultivating polio virus *in vitro* on animal tissues other than nervous tissue. Then, in 1953, Dr. Jonas Salk and his coworkers at the University of Pittsburgh perfected the roller-tissue method of polio virus culture, as well as the final detoxified form of polio vaccine. The Nobel Prize was awarded to Dr. Enders for his achievement in virus cultivation; international acclaim was bestowed on Dr. Salk for his development of the vaccine and its success in the extensive inoculation tests.

Field trials using polio vaccine were conducted during 1954 on a total of 1.83 million schoolchildren, of whom 440,000 received one or more injections of the vaccine; 210,000 received placebo injections consisting of a nutrient medium similar to but not used for actual growth of the virus organisms; the remaining 1.18 million were observed as controls. Vaccination consisted of an initial intramuscular injection of 1 mL of vaccine followed by a second 1-mL injection 1 week later and a third 1-mL injection about 4 weeks after the second. (Note: *The time intervals for active immunization have changed.*) The mass inoculations covered a total of 217 selected areas in 44 states of the United States and 48 areas of Canada and Finland.

The results of this carefully controlled study encouraged the National Foundation for Infantile Paralysis to purchase sufficient vaccine to inoculate approximately 9 million schoolchildren during 1955. The success of the mass polio vaccinations in both 1954 and 1955 received international prominence, not only because of the enthusiastic response from the children's parents and for the cooperative spirit of the biologic manufacturers, but also because of the ingenuity and tireless efforts of Dr. Jonas Salk. (Poliovirus vaccine inactivated is more commonly referred to as Salk polio vaccine.)

Poliovirus vaccine inactivated (IPV) is an active immunizing agent that has definite value in creating active immunity to the disease. IPV is the preferred vaccine for adults, because the incidence of vaccine-associated paralysis is slightly higher with OPV in adults (but not children). The usual dose, given subcutaneously, is three injections of 1 mL, 4 or more weeks apart, and a fourth reinforcing dose of 1 mL, 6 to 12 months later. In circumstances in which time will not allow the three dose schedule, but between 4 and 8 weeks are available before protection is needed, two doses of IPV should be administered at least 4 weeks apart. If less than 4 weeks are available, OPV should be used as a single dose.

Poliovirus vaccine live oral is a preparation of one or a combination of the three types of live, attenuated polioviruses. The virus strains are grown separately in primary cultures of monkey kidney tissue. It has been manufactured and tested in a manner suited only for oral administration and is free from any known microbial agent other than the attenuated poliovirus or polioviruses intended to be present. This vaccine is commonly called **trivalent oral polio vaccine (TOPV)** and contains one or all of types 1, 2, or 3 Sabin poliovirus strains.

Three scientists working independently developed procedures for the manufacture of this vaccine: Dr. Albert Sabin of the University of Cincinnati, Dr. Harold Cox of Lederle Laboratories, and Dr. Hilary Koprowski of the Wistar Institute of Philadelphia. The results of large-scale trials extending over a period of several years indicated that oral polio vaccine has longer-lasting immunity, greater ease of administration, and presumably lower costs of production than the Salk polio vaccine. The tests involved more than 13 million people in countries outside of the United States. Extensive domestic trials were performed in the Dade County, FL; Minneapolis; Cincinnati; and Rochester, NY areas. In the Dade County field trials, the vaccine was incorporated into a cherry-flavored oral preparation that was designed to immunize against all three strains of poliomyelitis.

Safety tests conducted by the US Department of Public Health resulted in the announcement in August 1960 that the Sabin formula was the most "suitable for use in the United States." Licensed manufacture of this trivalent vaccine began early in 1963; quantity production was reached later that year.

The manufacture of poliovirus vaccine live oral is similar to that of poliovirus vaccine inactivated (Salk) because the virus strains are grown separately in monkey tissue cultures. However, the viruses are not killed by treatment with formaldehyde, as is done with Salk vaccine; instead, the viruses are attenuated. Therefore, the Sabin oral vaccine should never be administered parenterally.

Live poliovirus vaccines offer protection against strains of poliomyelitis virus that cause paralysis. The attenuated live virus, when present in the intestinal tract, multiplies and produces a localized resistance to reinfection by the same type of virus, thus stimulating the production of type-specific serum antibodies. The development of such localized resistance to the growth of the virus affords a protection that is independent of specific, circulating antibodies. Salk vaccine provides protection against paralytic poliomyelitis through the stimulation of serum antibodies specific for types 1, 2, and 3 poliovirus, but does not cause the inhibition of viral growth in the intestine that characterizes the Sabin vaccine.

Poliovirus vaccine live oral is generally frozen. When stored at a temperature of $-10°$ C, the expiration date is not later than 1 year after date of manufacture or date of issue. It may be thawed and refrozen not more than ten times, provided that the thawed material is kept refrigerated and the total cumulative duration of the thaw is not more than 24 hours.

Poliovirus vaccine live oral is an active immunizing agent. When administered orally, it effectively develops immunity to the poliovirus, Sabin strains types 1, 2, and 3. The usual administration schedule involves an initial administration of two doses at not less than 8-week intervals. A third, reinforcing dose is administered 8 to 12 months later. The volume of vaccine indicated on the label as representing one dose is generally placed on a cube of sugar, which is eaten by the individual to be immunized. The immunization schedule should be carried out in the winter and spring to avoid the summer peak of other intestinal enteroviruses that may interfere with the desired immunologic response.

The choice between OPV and IPV is influenced by circumstances and by the risk of developing vaccine-associated paralytic disease. As mentioned previously, unvaccinated adults should be administered IPV. Adults who have received less than a full primary course of either vaccine should receive the remaining required doses of either vaccine if they have increased risk of exposure to poliovirus. Adults who completed a course of primary immunization with OPV may be given an additional dose of OPV when faced with increased risk of exposure, but the need for the booster dose is not well established. If their primary course was administered with IPV, they may be given a booster of either IPV or OPV. OPV is preferred in children regardless of the immunization status of adult household contacts, unless the household contacts include a person with immunodeficiency (see below). There is a small risk (four cases reported out of 24 million doses) that an unimmunized adult will develop paralytic poliomyelitis when children in the household are given OPV. They should be informed of the risk, and if desired should be vaccinated with IPV before OPV is given to the child. Generally, pregnant women are not given either OPV or IPV unless immediate protection is needed; in such cases OPV is administered.

Another factor affecting the choice is immunodeficiency in either the patient being vaccinated or household contacts. Patients with immunodeficiency or their household contacts should not be given OPV because of the substantially increased risk of vaccine-associated disease; IPV is recommended. If the household contact of an immunodeficient patient is administered OPV, close contact between the two household members should be minimized for 1 month following administration of the vaccine, because that is the period of maximum virus excretion.

Measles Vaccines

Vaccines containing live attenuated rubeola (measles) and rubella (German measles) viruses are available for active immunization. Viruses for production of these vaccines are grown on cultures of either avian embryo tissue or human diploid cell tissue. The vaccines are available in a lyophilized form. They should be stored at a temperature of between 2 and 8° C and have a 1-year expiration date.

The vaccines should be kept in the dark and protected from light at all times, as light inactivates the viruses. The reconstituted vaccines may be stored in the refrigerator but should be discarded after 8 hours. The preferred product for routine administration of measles (rubeola) and rubella is the trivalent Measles, Mumps, and Rubella (MMR) vaccine.

Measles virus vaccine live or rubeola vaccine is prepared from attenuated viruses derived from the original Edmonston B strain. The Enders strain is a modified Edmonston strain, and it is claimed to have a high degree of antigenicity with a low incidence of adverse reactions; coadministration of immune globulin may not be necessary with vaccines employing this strain. The measles virus is grown on cultures of chicken embryo tissue. It produces a modified measles infection in susceptible individuals. The vaccine is highly immunogenic and antibody levels persist for more than 13 years without substantial decline. Because it is inducing an infection, fever and/or rash may occur, usually between the 5th and 12th days following immunization. Febrile or afebrile convulsions or seizures have been observed, but they are rare.

Rubeola vaccine is recommended for active immunization of children 15 months of age or older. Use in infants under 15 months of age is not recommended. Younger children may fail to respond because of residual circulating antibodies passively transferred from the child's mother.

Persons who are immunosuppressed because of HIV infection, cellular immune deficiencies, or hypogammaglobulinemias should not be vaccinated. Nevertheless, the Advisory Committee on Immunization Practices recommends that HIV-positive children who are asymptomatic be vaccinated. Patients who have had anaphylactic or severe allergic reactions to egg protein should not be vaccinated nor should pregnant women. Pregnancy should be avoided for 3 months following vaccination based on the association of adverse fetal effects with the natural measles virus. There is not a substantiated association with the vaccine virus, but caution is advisable. If exposure to measles occurs during pregnancy, the use of the immune serum is advised.

Rubella virus vaccine live is prepared from the Wistar Institute RA 27/3 strain grown on human diploid cell tissue. Rubella vaccine is recommended for active immunization against German measles for children aged 1 to puberty and for certain other individuals. Use in infants under 1 year of age is not recommended. This vaccine should not be administered to pregnant or immediate postpartum women, and special caution must be exercised if it is given to sexually active females. Rubella infection is associated with a congenital Rubella syndrome, and therefore vaccinating susceptible post-pubertal females confers protection against acquiring the disease when they are pregnant. However, precautions must be taken to eliminate the possibility of pregnancy in women of child-bearing age for at least 3 months following immunization. It is important to immunize children of pregnant females, because they are then less likely to acquire natural rubella and bring it into the household. Immunity is obtained with a single subcutaneous injection of not less than 1000 $TCID_{50}$ of the reconstituted vaccine. (The $TCID_{50}$ is the quantity of virus estimated to infect 50% of inoculated tissue cultures.)

The same warnings about immunization of pregnant and immunosuppressed patients as were described for the rubeola vaccine apply to the use of rubella vaccine. Immunization should be deferred during the course of any acute illness in children or adults.

Rubella vaccine is generally well-tolerated, but symptoms including rash, fever, headache, sore throat, malaise, polyneuritis, and arthralgias and arthritis occur occasionally. Guillain-Barrë syndrome, encephalitis, and other central nervous system (CNS) reactions, and optic neuritis occur rarely. Postpubertal females are more likely to experience self-limiting arthralgias or arthritis beginning 2 to 4 weeks after vaccination and should be advised of the possibility of those symptoms.

Mumps virus vaccine live is prepared with the B-level Jeryl Lynn strain of the virus, which is grown in cell cultures of chicken embryo tissue. It provides active immunity for at least 10 years after immunization and is particularly valuable to susceptible individuals approaching puberty and to adults. It is not recommended for infants less than 1 year old, because they may retain maternal mumps antibodies that may interfere with the immune response. The vaccine is available in a lyophilized form; immunization involves a single subcutaneous injection of not less than 20,000 $TCID_{50}$ of mumps virus vaccine. MMR is the preferred immunizing agent for mumps, as well as measles and rubella. Patients allergic to egg protein should be tested for hypersensitivity prior to injection, and it should be avoided in patients who report anaphylactic reactions to egg protein.

Hepatitis B vaccine is composed of chemically inactivated hepatitis B surface antigen (HBsAg) particles. The particles used to be obtained from the plasma of healthy chronic HBsAg carriers by plasmapheresis, separated from the infectious Dane particle by density gradient centrifugation, and absorbed on aluminum hydroxide. However, now the surface antigen proteins are produced in recombinant yeast cultures and are free of association with human blood or blood products (Recombivax HB and Engerix-B are the recombinant vaccines). Specific antibody (anti-HBs) develops in 93% to 99% of healthy persons less than age 40 who receive the recommended regimen; over age 40 the rate drops to between 88% to 89%. Studies have shown a lower response when the vaccine is administered in the buttock rather than in the deltoid muscle. Vaccine-induced antibody persists for at least 5 years; booster doses are not routinely recommended.

The hepatitis B virus causes hepatitis in hundreds of thousands of people each year in the United States. The initial infection is fatal only in a few cases, but others go on to develop chronic active hepatitis, cirrhosis, and hepatocellular cancer. In less-developed areas of the world, the incidence of all of these disorders is much higher; it has been estimated that 200 million are chronically infected with the hepatitis B virus.

Vaccination is recommended for individuals in high-risk categories as listed in Table 12–4. The vaccine is given intramuscularly in three doses of 1.0 mL (20 μg), with the first two doses 1 month apart and a booster dose administered 6 months after the first dose. For patients on dialysis and others who are immunocompromised, three doses of 2.0 mL (40 μg) should be used. For children under 10 years old, three doses of 0.5 mL (10 μg) are recommended. Infants born to hepatitis B surface-antigen-positive mothers are at risk of developing a chronic carrier state during the first year of life. Therefore, they are administered 0.5 mL of hepatitis B immune globulin at birth and three 0.5 mL doses of hepatitis B vaccine at age 1 to 7 days, 1 month, and 6 months.

Hepatitis A vaccine is now available in the United States. Hepatitis A virus infections occur through fecal-oral person-to-person transmission or by ingestion of contaminated food or water, particularly raw shellfish. The risk of exposure is highest in areas with poor sanitation. American Indian reservations and Alaskan Native villages have high rates of infection. Close contact (including sexual contact) with infected individuals is a main source of infection. Outbreaks in daycare centers also have been reported. The vaccine is recommended for travelers to endemic areas and other high risk groups.

The vaccine is an inactivated virus vaccine prepared in human cell culture. It confers protective levels of specific humoral antibodies in 96%

of adult recipients after 1 month, and antibody titers rise to 40 to 80 times the protective level after the booster. Protection is expected to last 10 years or more after the booster. Each mL of the vaccine contains 1,440 Elisa Units of viral antigen. It is administered in two doses for adults, a 1 mL intramuscular dose followed by a second dose 6 to 12 months later. For children 2 to 18 years old, two 0.05 mL intramuscular doses are administered 1 month apart followed by a booster dose 6 to 12 months later. If immediate protection is needed, immune globulin can be administered at the same time at separate injection sites.

Varicella virus vaccine live has recently been approved by the FDA for use in the United States. Until the vaccine's approval, chicken pox, caused by the varicella virus, was the principal childhood disease for which a vaccine was not generally available. Chicken pox in otherwise healthy young children is not a particularly risky or serious illness, although it is uncomfortable and causes lost school time and lost work time for parents. Also, it is a more serious disease in adolescence and adulthood. In addition, varicella zoster is a virus that integrates into the DNA of the cells and sometimes reemerges later in life, especially in immunosuppressed patients, as a painful skin condition called ''shingles'' or ''zoster,'' or even as central nervous disorders.

The vaccine is an attenuated live virus. The Oka/Merck strain used in the vaccine is attenuated by passage in human and embryonic guinea pig cell cultures. It is not 100% effective. The breakthrough rate for high-potency batches of the vaccine (some early batches were about half the potency of the current vaccine) is estimated at less than 1% annually for over a 3-year period. Among individuals in close contact with a person with the highly contagious disease, one study showed an absolute efficacy rate of 77%, with 20% developing a mild rash and 2% developing the full disease pattern; studies have shown it be a safe vaccine.

Final recommendations for use are still under development, but the current recommendations are that all healthy children 1 to 12 years old who have not had chicken pox receive a single subcutaneous dose of vaccine, and that those older than 12 years receive two doses 4 to 8 weeks apart; it is not recommended for children under 1 year of age, nor for pregnant women or immunosuppressed patients, including those with HIV infection. Because of the association between varicella, salicylates, and Reye's syn-

Table 12–4

Recommended Immunization Schedule for Adults

Immunizing Agent	Indications for Use	Dosage
Adsorbed tetanus and diphtheria toxoids for adult use (Td)	Every adult	Primary immunization: 0.5 ml, intramuscularly, repeated once after 4–8 weeks, then once 6–12 months later. Booster every 10 years
Live attenuated measles virus vaccine[1]	Unimmunized, born after 1956 and recipients of inactivated vaccine given 1963–1967	1000 $TCID_{50}$ [2] subcutaneously
Live rubella virus vaccine[1]	Unimmunized young women	1000 $TCID_{50}$ [2] subcutaneously
Influenza virus vaccine	Patients with diabetes or other metabolic diseases, severe anemia, or chronic pulmonary, cardiovascular, or renal disease, immunocompromised patients, those in chronic care facilities, and everyone over 65 years of age	0.5 mL intramuscularly annually
Polyvalent pneumococcal vaccine	Patients with chronic cardiac or pulmonary disease, alcoholism, cirrhosis, diabetes, Hodgkin's disease, nephrotic syndrome, renal failure, cerebrospinal fluid leaks, immunosuppression, asymptomatic or symptomatic HIV infection, and everyone over 65 years of age	0.5 mL subcutaneously or intramuscularly
Hepatitis B vaccine	Medical and laboratory workers with frequent exposure to blood or blood products, intravenous drug abusers, male homosexuals, dialysis patients, recipients of non-recombinant, blood-derived proteins, mortuary workers, residents and staff of institutions for the mentally retarded, and immunocompromised patients	1 mL intramuscularly in deltoid muscle, repeated after 4 weeks and again 6 months after first dose.
Hepatitis A vaccine	Travelers to endemic areas, other high risk patients	1 mL dose in deltoid muscle, repeated 6 to 12 months later
Varicella virus vaccine	Healthy adults who have not had varicella infection	Two doses 4 to 8 weeks apart

[1] May be given in bivalent vaccine.
[2] Quantity of virus estimated to infect 50% of inoculated tissue cultures $\times$ 1000.

drome, the manufacturer recommends avoiding salicylates for 6 weeks after vaccination. Post-marketing surveillance will help determine the need for boosters. Once the vaccine is widely used, unvaccinated children will be more likely than previously to remain susceptible until they reach adulthood, when the disease is much more severe.

Despite the safety and efficacy of the chicken pox vaccine, there was substantial controversy that delayed its approval. The controversy stems from the fact that the attenuated varicella virus, like the natural virus, remains in the patient's nerve cells for life, distinguishing this vaccine from other live virus vaccines that typically are shed from the body after a short time period. The worry is that the virus will be reactivated later in life or under conditions in which the patient is immunosuppressed to cause shingles or more severe complications. Thus far the concerns appear unfounded; in clinical trials, children who had received the vaccine and then developed leukemia (and were immunosuppressed) developed shingles with equivalent frequency and severity to those who had experienced natural chicken pox.

There are several other viruses for which vaccine development is underway, the most significant of which is **human immunodeficiency virus (HIV)**, which causes AIDS. There are many approaches being tested to develop a vaccine effective against human immunodeficiency virus. The development is difficult for several reasons; there currently is no good animal model for the human virus (primates are used with an analogous simian virus); our understanding of the parameters that confer immunity is inadequate; and there is substantial variation in the structure of key antigenic viral proteins. There also is concern that a vaccine not cause deleterious effects on the immune system (perhaps by inducing autoimmunity), and of course the use of live attenuated or killed whole cell vaccines is accompanied by grave concern for errors or unpredicted recombinations that would actually transmit the disease. Nevertheless, the benefit to be derived from a successful vaccine is enormous, and the search is continuing.

Attempts to develop a vaccine are focusing, at least in part, on the antigens that elicit neutralizing antibodies. Antibodies that neutralize HIV-1 *in vitro* are elicited by several surface glycoproteins (gp120 and gp41) and to some extent by internal proteins p17 and p51/66. The portion of the gp120 molecule that appears to be particularly important is the ''V3 loop'' (or the third variable region), which unfortunately varies in structure from strain to strain. Vaccine candidates are being developed based on these antigenic proteins or synthetic peptides that include only portions of the surface proteins rather than the entire protein. In some cases, these antigens are being expressed in live vectors of other viruses. One that has been most extensively studied is a vaccinia virus-gp120 construct in which the *env* gene of HIV-1 has been inserted into the thymidine kinase locus of the vaccinia

genome. Other investigations have involved killed whole HIV, which has evoked many safety concerns, and live attenuated virus that have been genetically altered to delete regulatory genes, resulting in a virus that will confer immunity but not be pathogenic. The advantage to a live attenuated vaccine would be long-lasting immunity, but again safety concerns are a major limiting factor in the testing of such a vaccine.

RICKETTSIAL VACCINES

Rickettsiae are cultured in chick embryos or in monkey kidney tissue cultures in a manner similar to that for viruses. They cannot be grown in artificial culture media and must be subjected to the same precautions as viruses. At the present time, rickettsial vaccines are not produced commercially in the United States. Murine typhus, tsutsugamushi fever, and rickettsial diseases as well as epidemic typhus are of considerable importance in other parts of the world. Vaccines are available in these problem areas for all of these rickettsial diseases.

BACTERIAL VACCINES

Bacterial vaccines consist of suspensions of attenuated or, more commonly, killed pathogenic bacteria in isotonic sodium chloride solution or other suitable diluents. Other bacterial vaccines involve antigenic portions of the bacteria, either isolated by chemical extraction or produced via biotechnology. Sometimes these antigens are conjugated to other proteins to increase immunogenicity. The strains of bacteria employed in preparation of the vaccines must be selected for high antigenicity, and a measure of the potency of a vaccine may be expressed as the number of organisms per unit volume or as biologic reference units. Suspensions of young, living organisms grown in standard culture media are killed chemically, by application of moist heat at a temperature slightly above the thermal deathpoint, or by exposure to ultraviolet light.

The smooth or ''S'' strains of bacteria are uniformly more antigenic than the rough or ''R'' strains. Occasionally, stock cultures lose their antigenic qualities, and care must be exercised in a biologic manufacturer's laboratory to ensure the use of suitable strains.

Good immunologic responses are obtained with the following bacterial vaccines: pertussis, plague, typhoid, diphtheria, tetanus, pneumococcal, and *Haemophilus influenzae* b. The effectiveness of BCG vaccine and meningitis vaccines are still being evaluated. New bacterial vaccines under development include improved cholera and tuberculosis vaccines, and a new leprosy vaccine. Many of these involve biotechnology in producing either altered (attenuated) bacteria through gene deletion or purified antigenic components of the bacterial pathogen.

Typhoid vaccine is estimated to be about 70% effective in preventing typhoid fever, an acute, febrile, enteric infection caused by *Salmonella typhi*, depending partly on the degree of exposure to the organism. Virulent strains of *S. typhi* pass through the stomach and colonize the intestinal tract; they then penetrate the lumen and enter the lymphatic system and blood stream. The ability of the organism to cause disease is dependent on the production of a complete lipopolysaccharide, but enough is formed to elicit a protective immune response. There is also a parenteral vaccine available that contains heat-phenol-inactivated *S. typhi* Ty-2. It is recommended for persons who have had household contact with a known typhoid carrier or for travelers going to areas of the world in which typhoid fever is endemic. Typhoid vaccination is not recommended in the United States or in areas of natural disaster. Travelers should be warned to avoid contact with or ingestion of contaminated water and foods even though they have been vaccinated, because the vaccine is not 100% effective.

The oral vaccine is available as enteric-coated capsules and should be taken in four doses on alternate days, and the series should be completed at least 1 week prior to potential exposure. The capsules should be stored in the refrigerator prior to ingestion and taken 1 hour before a meal with a cold or lukewarm drink. Sulfonamides and other antibiotics will inhibit bacterial multiplication in the intestine and prevent a protective immune response. The parenteral vaccine is administered in two doses at an interval of 4 weeks or more. The parenteral vaccine causes more side effects; almost all patients will experience local reactions (pain, erythema), and many will experience systemic reactions (fever, malaise, headache) beginning within 24 hours of administration. Nevertheless, the parenteral vaccine should only be used in children less than 10 years of age and in immunocompromised pa-

tients, including those with HIV infections. Booster doses for those at continued risk are necessary every 3 years for those patients receiving the parenteral vaccine, and the manufacturer recommends a complete series every 5 years for patients receiving the oral vaccine.

Cholera vaccine is a sterile suspension of killed cholera vibrios (*Vibrio cholerae*) in isotonic sodium chloride solution or other suitable diluent. It is prepared from equal portions of suspensions of cholera vibrios of the Inaba and Ogawa strains. The vaccine contains eight units of each serotype strain per milliliter of suspension. This vaccine should be stored at a temperature between 2 and 8° C, and the expiration date is not longer than 18 months from the date of issue.

Cholera vaccine is an active immunizing agent in the development of immunity to the disease. The vaccine is only about 50% effective and then only for 3 to 6 months. The World Health Organization no longer recommends cholera vaccine prior to travel to cholera-infected areas, because the risk of acquiring cholera is low. However, some countries still require vaccination as a condition of entry. The usual adult dose, given intradermally, is 0.2 mL, and 0.2 mL 1 to 4 weeks later; a 0.2 mL dose is repeated every 6 months, if necessary. Higher levels of antibody may be achieved in children less than 5 years old by using a subcutaneous or intramuscular route of injection.

Plague vaccine is a sterile suspension, in an isotonic sodium chloride solution or other suitable diluent, of killed plague bacilli (*Yersinia pestis*) of a strain selected for high antigenic efficiency.

The bacteria causing bubonic and pneumonic plague in humans are named *Yersinia*, in honor of the Swiss bacteriologist Yersin who was the first to isolate and identify the disease-causing organism. Rats serve as an animal reservoir for the organisms, but the disease is transmitted to humans through the bites of fleas that infest the rats. With rat control and large-scale vaccination, plague can be eliminated. In the United States, plague bacilli have been found in wild animals and their fleas in 15 western states.

Plague vaccine is an active immunizing agent and is used to produce immunity to the disease. Its use is generally restricted to travelers in known plague areas, including rural upland or mountainous areas of South America, Asia and Africa. It is also administered to persons who have frequent contact with wild rodents in plague enzootic areas in the United States, which include Arizona, California, Colorado, Idaho, Nevada, New Mexico, Oregon, and Utah. The usual immunization schedule involves two to three intramuscular injections, with the first dose of 1.0 mL followed in 1 to 3 months with a second dose of 0.2 mL. A third injection of 0.2 mL 3 to 6 months after the second injection is strongly recommended.

Pertussis vaccine (whole-cell; wP) is a sterile bacterial fraction or suspension of killed pertussis bacilli (*Bordetella pertussis*) of a strain or strains selected for high antigenic efficiency. There also is an acellular pertussis vaccine (aP) that consists of pertussis toxin and filamentous hemagglutinin inactivated with formaldehyde. The acellular form has fewer reported side effects than the whole-cell vaccine, especially local reactions at the injection site, as well as the fever, vomiting, and high-pitched unusual cry that sometimes accompanies the use of DTwP. However, the acellular form is currently licensed for only the fourth and fifth doses of the DTP series. Both the whole cell and acellular types of pertussis vaccine are only available in combination with diphtheria and tetanus toxoids.

A new acellular vaccine has recently been approved by the FDA. If it proves to be sufficiently immunogenic to be used for all doses in the immunization schedule, it will probably replace the whole-cell pertussis vaccine.

Bordetella pertussis is the organism that causes the disease known as whooping cough or pertussis. The cough is probably caused by a toxin in the bacterial body that also appears in filtrates of bacterial cultures. The organisms attach themselves to the cilia of epithelial cells in the trachea, and the irritation produced provokes the cough spasm.

Pertussis is highly communicable, with attack rates of over 75% reported for unimmunized household contacts, and causes severe disease, especially in infants and young children. The vaccine has the potential to cause some adverse effects (inconsolable crying, convulsions, collapse or shock, high fever) that led to considerable controversy about the use of the pertussis vaccine. However, a formal reevaluation in 1984 of its risks versus its benefits led to a recommendation for its continued use. A dose of acetaminophen at the time of vaccination appears to reduce the risk of high fever and febrile convulsions. The occurrence of any type of neurological symptoms following DTwP administration and the presence of any changing or evolving

CNS disorder (whether or not it is associated with the vaccine administration) are generally considered a contraindication against further doses of the pertussis component.

Because the incidence rate and severity of pertussis decrease with age and because the vaccine may cause side effects and adverse reactions, pertussis immunization is not recommended for children after their 7th birthday. The recommended dosage schedule for primary immunization is 0.5 mL, intramuscularly, beginning at 6 weeks with two more doses at 4 to 8 week intervals. A reinforcing dose is given 1 year after the third dose, and a fifth dose is recommended at age 4 to 6 years of age (as the child enters school). The acellular vaccine may be used for the fourth and fifth doses. The Department of Health and Human Services has a Vaccine Adverse Event Reporting System and the following adverse effects should be reported: anaphylaxis within 24 hours, encephalopathy within 7 days, hypotonic-hyporesponsive collapse within 7 days, residual seizure disorder, any acute complication or sequelae of the above events, or any side effects which according to the manufacturer contraindicate further doses (e.g., convulsions). Initial reporting is by health providers to the city, county, or state health department. Although the reporting requirement is particularly relevant to the DTwP preparation, it applies to most vaccines and reportable side effects can be found in manufacturer's package inserts.

One can expect that a recombinant acellular vaccine would be substantially safer than the whole-cell vaccine, so a highly immunogenic recombinant acellular vaccine would be highly desirable and would eliminate the concerns and controversy surrounding pertussis vaccination.

Tuberculosis Vaccines

Studies of the effectiveness of vaccines to produce immunity to tuberculosis are constantly in progress. The vaccine known as BCG (prepared from Bacillus Calmette-Guérin) is a freeze-dried preparation of the culture of an attenuated strain of bovine tuberculosis originally isolated by the two bacteriologists Calmette and Guérin. This vaccine has provided bacteriologists and immunologists with a subject of controversy for years. The chief point of difference concerned the relative safety of the vaccine, but refinements in the processing and improvements in the testing have now assured a safe, nontoxic product for human use.

BCG vaccine is a dried, living culture of the bacillus Calmette-Guérin strain of *Mycobacterium tuberculosis* var. *bovis*. The culture is grown in a suitable medium from a seed strain of known history that has been maintained to preserve its capacity for conferring immunity.

The expiration date of BCG vaccine is up to 1 year if it is stored at 5° C. This vaccine should be used within 2 hours after reconstitution. BCG vaccine has been accepted by European physicians for a number of years, and endorsement by American investigators was forthcoming during the 1950s. Immunologic protection against tuberculosis is only relative and is not permanent or predictable. The vaccine is recommended primarily for use in infants and children with risk of intimate and prolonged exposure to persistently untreated or ineffectively treated individuals with pulmonary tuberculosis. It should be used only with individuals who have a negative tuberculin skin test. It is no longer recommended for healthcare workers at risk of repeated exposure; tuberculin skin testing surveillance and isoniazid prophylaxis when appropriate are recommended instead.

It is administered intradermally as the reconstituted vaccine in doses of 0.2 to 0.3 mL. Potential adverse effects include lymphadenopathy, osteomyelitis, lupoid reactions, disseminated BCG disease, and death. Lymphadenopathy occurs occasionally; all the other side effects are rare.

Interestingly, BCG is also used for carcinoma of the urinary bladder. Intravesical injection causes a local inflammatory reaction that causes a reduction or elimination of superficial cancerous lesions of the urinary bladder.

Meningococcal polysaccharide vaccines contain the specific bacterial capsular polysaccharides for *Neisseria meningitidis* serogroups A, C, Y, and W-135. The presence in human serum of antibodies to meningococcal polysaccharide antigens is strongly correlated with immunity to meningococcal meningitis. The use of meningococcal polysaccharide vaccine is indicated for military recruits, household or institutional contacts of meningococcal disease (adjunct to antibiotic prophylaxis), terminal complement component deficient patients, anatomically or functionally asplenic patients, and adults and children over 2 years of age at risk in epidemic areas.

Routine vaccination is not recommended in the United States for the following reasons: (1) the disease is infrequent, (2) no vaccine exists against serogroup B which accounts for 50% of the cases in the United States, and (3) the vaccine is not efficacious in children under 2 years of age, who account for about a third of the serogroup C cases.

The immunizing dose is a single subcutaneous injection of 0.5 mL, containing 50 μg of meningococcal polysaccharide.

Pneumococcal vaccine polyvalent affords protection against the 23 most prevalent capsular types of pneumococci, which account for at least 90% of pneumococcal disease. It is prepared by isolating and purifying the polysaccharide antigens from strains of *Streptococcus pneumoniae* that contain these serotypes. Its use is indicated for those 2 years of age or older in whom there is an increased risk of morbidity and mortality from pneumococcal pneumonia. This includes (1) immunocompetent adults who are at increased risk of developing pneumococcal disease or its complications because of chronic illnesses (e.g., cardiovascular or pulmonary disease, cirrhosis, diabetes mellitus), (2) adults older than 65 years of age, (3) immunocompromised children and adults (e.g., those with splenic dysfunction, Hodgkin's disease, lymphoma, multiple myeloma, chronic renal failure, or organ transplants), (4) children with sickle cell disease, and (5) asymptomatic or symptomatic HIV infected patients older than 2 years of age. Even with current antibiotic therapy, the mortality rate in high-risk patients hospitalized with pneumococcal infection has remained higher than 25%, thus supporting the use of a vaccine.

The vaccine is administered as a single dose given either subcutaneously or intramuscularly (preferably in the deltoid muscle or lateral mid-thigh). Severe local reactions have occurred after a second dose; therefore, more than one dose is not recommended, even for patients who received an older vaccine that contained fewer pneumococcal types. Some groups of patients at a high risk of developing pneumococcal pneumonia, such as children with sickle cell disease or nephrotic syndrome, may have lower peak levels of antibody response or more rapid rates of antibody decline. However, reimmunization is not recommended currently.

The vaccine is used directly as supplied (no reconstitution or dilution). It should be refrigerated but is stable at room temperature for several days (PnuImune 23) to 1 month (Pneumovax 23).

Haemophilus b conjugate vaccine (HibCV) is composed of the purified, capsular polysaccharide of *Haemophilus influenzae* type b (Hib), covalently bonded to either diphtheria toxoid, diphtheria CRM$_{197}$ protein, or to the OMPC (outer membrane complex) of *Neisseria meningitidis* serogroup B. The development of stable humoral immunity requires recognition of foreign material by both B-lymphocytes and T-lymphocytes. The Hib polysaccharides alone stimulate a T-independent response that is short-lived. By covalently bonding the polysaccharide to the protein, the polysaccharide is presented as a T-dependent antigen and both enhanced antibody response and an immunologic memory result. Antibodies to this antigen correlate with protection against invasive disease. Virtually all cases of *Haemophilus influenzae* meningitis among children are caused by strains of Hib. Despite effective antimicrobial therapy, the mortality rate from *Haemophilus* meningitis ranges from 5 to 10%, and about one third of the survivors have some form of permanent injury to the CNS. In addition, Hib can cause epiglottitis, osteomyelitis, arthritis, cellulitis, and pneumonia in children.

The first conjugate vaccine developed was ProHIBIT in which the polysaccharide is conjugated to the diphtheria toxoid. This product should not be used in children less than 18 months of age, because they do not develop an adequate immune response before that age. The later vaccines (HibTITER, OmniHIB, and Ped-vaxHIB) are recommended for routine use with normal infants who should receive their first dose at 2 months of age. They should receive three doses at 2-month intervals and then a booster dose at 15 months of age. Unvaccinated children less than 24 months of age who have had invasive *Haemophilus influenzae* b disease should still receive the vaccine, as many children that age fail to develop immunity following natural disease. Most unimmunized children over 6 years old and most adults have protective titers of naturally acquired antibodies. The vaccine is administered intramuscularly (0.5 mL dose) in the midthigh or deltoid muscle. The HibTITER vaccine (conjugated with diphtheria CRM$_{197}$ protein) is also available combined with DTwP (Tetramune). Use of this preparation will decrease the number of separate injections a child must receive. However, the acellular pertussis vaccine is preferred for the fourth and fifth doses; Hib vaccine is not yet available combined with that vaccine, so the DTwP-Hib should be used for the first three doses only.

TOXINS AND TOXOIDS

Toxins are bacterial waste products that are considered poisonous to the animal body. Nevertheless, they act as antigens because of their power to stimulate certain cells of the body to produce antibodies called antitoxins. In practice, toxins are modified to inactivate the toxicophore group of the molecule, leaving the antigenic group unchanged.

When toxins are excreted from the bacterial cells producing them and are dissolved in the surrounding culture medium, they are referred to as **exotoxins**. In other cases, when they are retained within the bacterial body, they are called **endotoxins**.

To produce a solution of exotoxins commercially, the highly virulent organisms are cultured in beef broth medium and then killed by appropriate means. The organisms are removed by filtration through a bacterial filter, and the filtrate that contains the toxins and other products of growth is standardized on a suitable animal to determine the minimum lethal dose. This dose represents the smallest amount of the toxin that will kill a majority of a series of guinea pigs within 96 hours after subcutaneous administration. Commercial toxins serve as a starting point for the manufacture of antitoxins, as described below.

The source of "the most poisonous poison" is *Clostridium botulinum*, a microorganism generally unable to grow in the body of a warm-blooded animal but capable of causing death if its exotoxins are ingested. Thus, botulism is a matter of food poisoning. When the toxins produced by this bacterium are compared with other types of protein poisons (diphtheria toxin and snake venom), their potencies range from 10 to 1000 times higher. Five kinds of neurotoxins have been determined; food poisoning in humans commonly is produced by types A, B, and E.

Treating exotoxins with formaldehyde reduces or eliminates the toxic properties without affecting the antigenic properties. These products detoxified in this manner are called **fluid toxoids**, and they are used to induce artificial active immunity in susceptible individuals. By precipitating or adsorbing the fluid toxoid with alum, aluminum hydroxide, or aluminum phosphate, an **adsorbed toxoid** is produced which, when administered, results in a slower release of the antigen from the site of injection and a subsequent production of higher and more prolonged antibody titers. However, the adsorbed toxoids are more prone to produce local reactions at the site of injection than are fluid toxoids. To avoid this, adsorbed toxoids should be administered by deep intramuscular injection, whereas the fluid toxoid may be administered subcutaneously.

Both fluid and adsorbed toxoids are used to produce active immunity against diphtheria and tetanus. They are used alone and in combination. In young children, **diphtheria and tetanus toxoid combined with pertussis vaccine** is often used, and the combination is commonly known as triple antigen or DTwP or DTaP, depending whether the whole cell or acellular pertussis vaccine is included.

Repeated immunization with diphtheria and tetanus toxoids may result in increasingly severe local reactions. Diphtheria antigen in absorbed diphtheria and tetanus toxoids for adult use (Td) is therefore fourfold to tenfold less than in adsorbed diphtheria and tetanus toxoids for pediatric use (DT) and in DTP. Also, a lower frequency of booster immunization for tetanus is now recommended.

Tetanus is acquired through contaminated deep wounds. Wound cleaning and debridement when necessary are first line preventive measures. The need for tetanus toxoid (active immunization) with or without tetanus immune globulin (passive immunization) depends on the condition of the wound and the patient's immunization history. Tetanus occurs rarely in patients with a documented series of primary immunization with the toxoid. Boosters are recommended every 10 years for adults, and patients with wounds who have a documented booster within 5 years do not need to receive toxoid. Patients with wounds with an incomplete or uncertain history of tetanus immunization should receive the tetanus immune globulin along with a booster dose of tetanus toxoid (if a primary series is certain) or the first dose of a primary immunization series (if no tetanus immunization has been received). Antitoxin antibodies will rise rapidly in patients who have completed a primary immunization series.

The toxoids alone and in combination with pertussis vaccine should be stored at a temperature of between 2 and 8° C. The expiration date is not later than 2 years after the date of issue.

DIAGNOSTIC ANTIGENS

A number of antigen-containing preparations are employed as diagnostic aids to determine whether an individual has developed hypersensitivity to certain types of organisms. Hypersensitivity is usually the result of a previous infection caused by the specific etiologic agent. Small quantities of the diagnostic preparations are usually injected intradermally, and the developing reaction is usually read at 48 hours, although observations at 24 hours and at 72 hours are often helpful. The usual type of positive response is a localized, well-defined wheal accompanied by erythema.

Antigen-containing diagnostic preparations that are commonly available include the tuberculins, histoplasmin, coccidioidin, diphtheria toxin, and mumps skin test antigen. Other preparations that are occasionally used for diagnostic purposes are formulated and employed according to the same basic principles.

PASSIVE IMMUNOLOGICALS

Passive immunologicals are antibodies that have been preformed in response to exposure to a given organism and have been isolated from the producing animal (or human). They are injected into patients requiring instant, but short-lived immunity to a specific organism, or into patients who are unable to mount their own immune response. Because the antibodies are foreign proteins, hypersensitivity reactions are a frequent problem, especially when the antibodies are prepared from horses or other nonhuman sources (called "antiserums"). Human antibody preparations are called "immune serums."

Antitoxins are prepared from the blood of animals, usually horses, that have been immunized by repeated injections of specific bacterial exotoxins. The toxin, in constantly increasing doses, induces the formation of antitoxin in the blood of the injected animal. After tests have been conducted to determine the antitoxin titer of the serum, the animal is bled, the clot is permitted to form, and the clear supernatant serum is separated for processing.

In the past, diphtheria antitoxin consisted of unprocessed serum that when injected often caused numerous cases of sensitivity to horse serum proteins. Today, depending on the manufacturer, one of two methods of processing is employed. The first involves a series of precipitations using varying concentrations of ammonium sulfate. During this process, the euglobulin and fibrinogen fractions are initially "salted" out, followed by the pseudoglobulin fraction that contains the antitoxin. The latter fraction is re-dissolved, dialyzed, and filtered. The second method uses a pepsin solution to digest the plasma, thus removing up to 80% of the protein; however, a loss of about 20% in antitoxin content occurs also. The digested material is then treated with ammonium sulfate solution, redis-solved, dialyzed, and filtered. Both of these methods aim to eliminate the proteins of horse serum and the resulting serum sickness.

Antitoxins are standardized in terms of ''anti-toxin units.'' The international unit of diphtheria antitoxin is the same as that of the American or National Institutes of Health unit: that amount of antitoxin that is contained in 1/6000 g of a certain dried, unconcentrated horse serum anti-toxin that has been maintained since 1905 at the National Institutes of Health, Bethesda, MD. On the other hand, the international unit of tetanus antitoxin is equivalent to only one half the po-tency of the American or National Institutes of Health unit: that amount of antitoxin that is con-tained in 0.00015 g of a dried, unconcentrated horse serum antitoxin maintained since 1907, 3000 international units being equivalent to 1500 American units.

No antitoxin, antivenin, or antiserum prepared from horse serum should be given without care-fully inquiring about prior exposure to horse serum or about allergic response upon exposure to horses. Whenever these products are adminis-tered, a syringe containing epinephrine injection (1:1000) and a tourniquet should be available to counter an anaphylactic reaction. Also, sensitiv-ity testing should be performed before adminis-tration, either by injecting intracutaneously 0.02 mL of a 1:100 dilution of the product to be ad-ministered or by instilling a drop of 1:100 dilu-tion of the product into the conjunctival sac. A drop of sodium chloride injection, USP, placed in the opposite eye, provides a control.

The hypersensitivity reactions that can arise from the injection of biologics prepared from horse serum can range in severity from acute anaphylaxis and death, occurring almost imme-diately after injection, to serum sickness, which may arise hours to weeks following treatment. Typical manifestations of serum sickness in-clude fever, urticaria, adenopathy, and arthritis.

Diphtheria antitoxin is a sterile, nonpyro-genic solution of the refined and concentrated proteins, chiefly globulins, containing antitoxic antibodies obtained from the blood serum or plasma of healthy horses that have been immu-nized against diphtheria toxin or toxoid. It has

a potency of not less than 500 antitoxin units/mL.

The expiration date with a 20% excess of po-tency is not later than 5 years after the date of manufacture or the date of issue. Diphtheria anti-toxin should be stored at a temperature of be-tween 2 and 8° C.

Diphtheria antitoxin is a passive immunizing agent capable of inducing passive immunity against diphtheria. It is a valuable curative agent when used in sufficient amount to neutralize the pathogenic effects of the toxin formed in the pa-tient. This is especially true when the antitoxin is used early in the disease and before the detri-mental effects are too far advanced. Any person with clinical symptoms of diphtheria should re-ceive the antitoxin at once without waiting for bacteriologic confirmation. The usual prophy-lactic dose, intramuscularly or intravenously, is 1000 to 10,000 units; the therapeutic dose is 20,000 units to 120,000 units.

Although penicillin and other antibiotics kill the diphtheria organisms, they have no effect on the toxins.

Tetanus antitoxin is a sterile, nonpyrogenic solution of the refined and concentrated pro-teins, chiefly globulins, containing antitoxic an-tibodies obtained from the blood serum or plasma of healthy horses that have been immu-nized against tetanus toxin or toxoid. It has a potency of not less than 400 antitoxin units/mL.

Tetanus antitoxin should be stored at a tem-perature of between 2 and 8° C. The expiration date of the liquid antitoxin is not later than 5 years after the date of manufacture or issue with a 20% excess of potency.

Tetanus antitoxin is employed in the treatment and prophylaxis of tetanus if (and only if) teta-nus immune globulin is not available. It creates passive immunity to tetanus. Like diphtheria antitoxin, it is a valuable therapeutic agent when used early in the disease. Prophylactic doses should be given to individuals who have had two or fewer injections of tetanus toxoid and who have tetanus-prone injuries that are more than 24 hours old. Tetanus toxoid should also be ad-ministered at a different site on the patient. The usual prophylactic dose, intramuscularly or sub-cutaneously, is 1500 to 5000 units; the therapeu-tic dose is 50,000 to 100,000 units or more, with at least part of the dose given intravenously.

Botulism antitoxin is a sterile, nonpyrogenic solution of the refined and concentrated anti-toxic antibodies, chiefly globulins, obtained from the blood serum or plasma of healthy horses that have been immunized against the toxins produced by both the type A and type B and/or type E strains of *Clostridium botulinum*. This antitoxin contains not more than 20% of solids and should be stored at a temperature of between 2 and 8° C. The expiration date is not later than 5 years after the date of issue.

This multivalent antitoxin is used to treat all cases of toxemia caused by the types of botulinus bacteria used in its preparation. A multivalent antitoxin is advantageous because the prescribing physician is not required to wait for a determination of the type of the causative organism.

Botulism antitoxin is classed as a passive immunizing agent to be used in the treatment of botulism. The usual dose is 20,000 units intravenously, repeated at 2- to 4-hour intervals as necessary. It is not available commercially but can be obtained from the CDC.

Venoms are poisonous excretions produced by animals; they can be compared with the toxic waste products of bacteria (exotoxins). The detrimental effects developed in humans and animals following the bite of poisonous snakes (rattlesnake, copperhead, moccasin, cobra, and others) have been known for many years. About 10,000 people are bitten by poisonous snakes every year in the United States. Poisonous snakebites often cause severe pain and can lead to tissue necrosis, amputation, and death. The venom of the rattlesnake is a complex mixture, containing mostly proteins, many of which have enzymatic activity and a nonenzymatic neurotoxic fraction. Similarly, the venoms of the tarantula, scorpion, black widow spider, honeybee, wasp, and other arthropods produce various deleterious effects, depending on the amount, time of year, and other conditions. Chemical examinations of the poisons of toads have revealed that both skin and glandular secretions possess toxic substances called bufotoxins. The chemical structures of the bufotoxins are somewhat similar to those of the aglycones of the cardiac glycosides; in fact, the bufotoxins appear to have a similar pharmacologic effect.

Snake venins or venoms are obtained by holding a poisonous snake over a conical glass container covered with a sheet of thin rubber that the snake penetrates with its fangs, whereupon the semi-liquid venom is ejected into the container.

Mixtures of venins from the poisonous snakes of a locality, country, or continent are prepared and used in the preparation of polyvalent antivenins (antisnakebite serums).

Treatment of a snakebite is controversial, but most authorities believe that early administration of antivenin is the therapy of choice. The location of antivenins for rare species and names and telephone numbers of experts on venomous bites can be obtained at any hour from the Arizona Poison Control Center (telephone number, 602-626-6016).

Antivenin (Crotalidae) polyvalent or North and South American antisnakebite serum is a sterile, nonpyrogenic preparation derived by drying a frozen solution of specific venom-neutralizing globulins obtained from the serum of healthy horses immunized against venoms of four species of pit vipers. These are *Crotalus atrox* (Western diamondback), *C. adamanteus* (Florida diamondback), *C. durissus terrificus* (South American rattlesnake), and *Bothrops atrox* (South American fer-de-lance) (Fam. Crotalidae).

This antivenin is standardized by biologic assay on mice in terms of venom neutralization. It should be protected against exposure to excessive heat. The expiration date for antivenin (Crotalidae) polyvalent with a 10% excess of potency is not more than 5 years after date of issue.

Antivenin (Crotalidae) polyvalent is a passive immunizing agent used for treating snakebite of the species indicated. The preferred route of administration is intravenous infusion, as a 1:1 to 1:10 dilution of antivenin in sodium chloride injection or 5% dextrose injection, after testing for sensitivity to horse serum.

In general, antivenins are prepared in the same manner as antitoxins. The specific venin is injected into horses in gradually increasing doses until the blood titer reaches the desired strength. The animal is then bled, and the blood serum is subjected to the required processing. Antivenins have been prepared for use in many parts of the world. In addition to antivenin (Crotalidae) polyvalent, univalent or bivalent antivenins are available to protect against the copperhead (*Agkistrodon*) alone, or combined with antivenin against the rattlesnake (*Crotalus*) in the United States and other snakes in other countries, such as the bushmaster and palm vipers of tropical America and the boomslang, cobra, puff adder, and gaboon viper of Africa.

Antivenin (*Micrurus fulvius*) or North American coral snake antivenin is the sterile, nonpyrogenic preparation derived by drying a frozen solution of specific venom-neutralizing globulins obtained from the serum of healthy horses that have been immunized with the venom of *Micrurus fulvius*, the eastern coral snake. This preparation also neutralizes the venom of *M. fulvius tenere* (Texas coral snake), but does not neutralize the venom of *Micruroides euryxanthus* (Arizona or Sonoran coral snake).

Antivenin (*Latrodectus mactans*) or black widow spider antivenin is prepared from the serum obtained from horses immunized against the venom of the black widow spider (*Latrodectus mactans*). It is available in a lyophilized form and is recommended as a specific treatment of the effects of venom from the bites of this spider. It may be given intramuscularly or intravenously over a 15-minute period when diluted in 10 to 50 mL of saline solution.

Immune globulins are immunizing biologics that contain specific antibodies derived from the blood of humans who have survived an attack of a specific disease or who have been immunized in some other manner. Chances of sensitization are less with human serum derivatives than with immune serums from animal sources (called "antiserums").

Immune globulins may be obtained from the plasma or serum pool of a large number of random donors or from a limited number of individuals who have been hyperimmunized against a specific antigenic material. Preparations derived from a large, random source contain a general spectrum of antibodies and may be used for many diverse purposes. Standardization of the globulin fractions for specific antibodies provides specialty preparations for specific use. Preparations such as pertussis immune globulin and tetanus immune globulin, which are obtained from hyperimmunized sources, contain high titers of specific antibodies and are intended for specific use. Standard immune globulins contain approximately 16.5% gamma globulin and cause rapid immunity that lasts 1 to 3 months.

This type of preparation should be stored at a temperature of between 2 and 8° C. The expiration date is usually not more than 3 years after the date of issue. Serum globulins offer rapid protection (artificial passive immunity) and are administered intramuscularly, except for immune globulin intravenous. Live virus vaccines should be administered 2 weeks before or 3 months after immune globulin administration, because antibodies in the globulin preparation may interfere with the immune response to the vaccination. Some other vaccines can be given at a different site but at the same time as the immune globulin as specified by the manufacturer (e.g., tetanus toxoid and tetanus immune globulin).

Immune globulin, immune serum globulin (human), immune globulin intramuscular, or gamma globulin is a sterile, nonpyrogenic solution of globulins and contains many antibodies normally present in adult human blood. Each lot of immune globulin is prepared by pooling approximately equal amounts of material (source blood, plasma, serum, or placentas) from at least 1000 individuals.

Immune globulin has some prophylactic value in chicken pox, hepatitis A, rubella, and other diseases. In many instances, serum globulin offers no benefit after onset of disease symptoms. However, measles can be modified by using this preparation.

Immune globulin is a passive immunizing agent. The dosage is based on body weight and varies with the intended use. The usual intramuscular dose is 0.2 mL/kg for measles prophylaxis and 0.02 mL/kg for prophylaxis against hepatitis A. It is also administered to treat gamma globulin deficiency for the prevention of recurrent infections.

Immune globulin intravenous (IGIV) provides immediate antibody levels, whereas intramuscular administration involves a 2- to 5-day delay before adequate serum levels are attained. It is used in the treatment of immunodeficiency syndrome, especially in patients who require an immediate increase in immunoglobulin blood levels. There are many products available. The usual doses in immunodeficiency disease are 100 mg/kg to 400 mg/kg (depending on the product) administered monthly by intravenous infusion. The infusion rate needs to be carefully controlled.

Tetanus immune globulin or tetanus immune globulin (human) is a sterile, nonpyrogenic solution of globulins derived from the blood plasma of adult human donors who have been immunized with tetanus toxoid.

This immune globulin is especially useful for passive immunization against tetanus in individuals with wounds that may have been contaminated with tetanus microorganisms. It is intended particularly for persons who have not previously received tetanus toxoid for active immunization. It is indicated in contaminated or serious wounds in patients whose immunization history is uncertain or for whom the primary immunization series has not been completed. Because it is derived from humans, tetanus immune globulin is much safer than tetanus antitoxin, which is also available. A single injection is usually sufficient.

Rabies immune globulin is a sterile, nonpyrogenic solution of antirabies gamma globulin concentrated by cold alcohol fractionation from plasma of donors hyperimmunized with rabies vaccine.

Rabies immune globulin is indicated for passive protection against rabies in persons suspected of exposure to rabies, particularly in cases of severe exposure. After initiation of the vaccine series, it takes approximately 1 week to develop immunity to rabies; therefore, the value of immediate passive immunization is important for successful prevention of the disease. Its use is preferred to antirabies serum because it is of human origin, and therefore, possesses the added advantage of removing the risk of serum sickness.

It is recommended that rabies immune globulin be used in combination with rabies vaccine as the best postexposure prophylaxis. The usual dose is a single administration of 0.133 mL/kg of body weight at the time of the first vaccine dose. Up to half the dose should be used to infiltrate the wound and the rest administered intramuscularly. Repeating the dose may interfere with maximum active immunity expected from the vaccine.

Hepatitis B immune globulin is a sterile, nonpyrogenic solution of immunoglobulin prepared from pooled plasma obtained from donors with high titers of antibody to hepatitis B surface (HBs) antigen. Administration is indicated for postexposure prophylaxis following accidental exposure to hepatitis-B-contaminated materials. The exposure can be either parenteral, through direct mucous membrane contact, or through oral ingestion. The materials most often involved are blood, plasma, or serum that is positive for HBs antigen. Injections should be given intramuscularly not later than 7 days after exposure. Infants born to hepatitis-antigen-positive mothers should receive 0.5 mL intramuscularly into the anterolateral thigh, preferably within 12 hours of birth.

Varicella-zoster immune globulin is the globulin fraction of human plasma, primarily immunoglobulin G, found in routine screening of normal volunteer blood donors. When absorbed into the circulation, the antibodies persist for 1 month or longer and are sufficient to mitigate or prevent varicella infection. It has its greatest effectiveness when administered within 96 hours of exposure to the varicella virus. Because supplies of the varicella-zoster immune globulin are limited, it is recommended that its use be restricted to susceptible immunodeficient individuals with no history of varicella, and with definite exposure to the virus. The dose range is 125 units/10 kg body weight, up to a maximum of 625 units administered by deep intramuscular injection in the gluteal muscle or in another large muscle mass.

$Rh_o(D)$ immune globulin is a sterile, nonpyrogenic concentrated solution of globulins derived from human blood plasma containing antibody to the erythrocyte factor $Rh_o(D)$. This antibody neutralizes the antigen in Rh-positive blood, which sensitizes Rh-negative women and results in Rh hemolytic disease of the newborn in subsequent pregnancies.

This preparation is recommended for administration to unsensitized Rh-negative women who give birth to Rh_o (D)- or D^u-positive infants. It should be administered within 72 hours of Rh-incompatible delivery, miscarriage, abortion, or transfusion, and the usual dose is the entire content of one vial (containing 300 μg of antibody) given intramuscularly. The antibody neutralizes any antigen introduced into the mother as a result of mixing of fetal and maternal blood during childbirth, and thus prevents sensitization.

Lymphocyte immune globulin or antithymocyte globulin (equine) is a lymphocyte selective immunosuppressant that is prepared by immunizing horses with human thymus cells and then isolating the equine gamma globulin. It is thought that it alters the function of the T-lymphocytes, which are responsible in part for cell-mediated immunity, and therefore it is indicated for use in organ transplant.

When administered with conventional immunosuppressive therapy at the time of rejection in allograft renal transplant patients, it increases the frequency of resolution of the acute rejection episode. The usual adult dose is 10 to 30 mg/kg/day administered by intravenous infusion.

Cytomegalovirus immune globulin intravenous (CMV-IGIV) is used for the attenuation of primary cytomegalovirus disease in patients who have received a kidney transplant. It is particularly indicated for use in CMV negative patients who receive a CMV-seropositive kidney. In these patients cytomegalovirus infection is often observed as pneumonia or hepatitis. The immune globulin reduces the incidence of these infections by about 50% (from 75% of such patients to 36% of such patients in one trial).

The CMV-IGIV is administered intravenously within 72 hours post-transplantation and is administered every 2 weeks up to 16 weeks post-transplantation.

MONOCLONAL ANTIBODIES

The preparation and general uses of monoclonal antibodies is presented in Chapter 2. Monoclonal antibodies present the opportunity to provide passive immunization with antibodies grown in culture instead of isolated from animals or humans. Perhaps, more importantly, monoclonal antibodies can be developed to target specific protein targets in the body to block that protein or carry therapeutic agents to it. Such is the case with two monoclonal antibody products currently on the market for their therapeutic (rather than diagnostic) effects. These antibody preparations are muromonab-CD3 (Orthoclone OKT3), and abciximab (ReoPro).

Muromonab-CD3 is a murine (mouse-derived) monoclonal antibody to the CD3 antigen of human T cells. It is a biochemically purified IgG immunoglobulin. The antibody reacts with and blocks the function of the CD3 protein in the membrane of T cells. CD3 is associated with antigen recognition and is essential for signal transduction within the T cell. When it is blocked, immunosuppression occurs and specifically graft rejection is reversed, because CD3-positive T cells play a major role in graft rejection in renal, cardiac, and hepatic transplant patients. A decrease in numbers of circulating CD3-, CD4-, and CD8-positive T cells is observed within minutes after administering the antibody. Between day 2 and day 7 of treatment, circulating CD4 and CD8 cells reappear (although CD3 cells do not). Sometimes CD3 cells will reappear during week 2 of therapy, presumably because of the development of neutralizing antibodies. Circulating CD3-positive T cells reappear rapidly after therapy termination.

Muromonab-CD3 is used only after signs of rejection have occurred. In clinical trials it was found to reverse 94% of the rejections compared to 75% with the conventional high-dose steroid treatment. It also was effective in reversing 65% of the acute renal allograft rejections in cases in which steroid and lymphocyte immune globulin therapy was contraindicated or was unsuccessful.

Muromonab-CD3 is administered intravenously as an IV bolus in less than 1 minute.

Serum levels of the antibody can be measured with an ELISA assay. Circulating serum levels greater than 0.8 mcg/mL block the function of cytotoxic T cells. It is administered in doses of 5 mg/day for 10 to 14 days, beginning when allograft rejection is diagnosed. In cardiac and hepatic transplants (but not renal transplants), its use is limited to situations in which it is determined that rejection has not been reversed by standard corticosteroid therapy.

There are significant adverse effects associated with the use of muromonab-CD3. In addition to the potential for hypersensitivity reactions one anticipates with proteinaceous drugs, there is a syndrome called cytokine release syndrome (CRS) that causes high, spiking fevers, chills and rigors, headache, tremor, nausea and vomiting, abdominal pain, malaise and joint pains, generalized weakness, and less frequently, cardiopulmonary and neuropsychiatric adverse events. CRS is associated with the first two to three doses of the drug and is attributed to the release of cytokines by lymphocytes or monocytes. The manifestations of CRS can be minimized by pretreatment with 8 mg/kg of methylprednisolone administered 1 to 4 hours prior to the first dose of muromonab-CD3. If it occurs, intensive supportive treatment may be required.

Because muromonab-CD3 is a protein, it must be handled with care. No other drugs should be administered in the same intravenous line. The product should be refrigerated and should not be frozen or shaken. No bacteriostatic agent is included; therefore, unused portions of an ampule should be discarded.

Abciximab is a Fab (fragment antigen binding) fragment of the chimeric human-murine monoclonal antibody 7E3, that has recently been approved for use as an adjunct to percutaneous transluminal angioplasty to prevent abrupt closure of the treated coronary vessel. Platelets can cause abrupt closure of blood vessels after angioplasty by adhering to the wall of the blood vessel damaged by the angioplasty procedure. Aggregated platelets can then serve as a focal point for deposition of fibrin, leading to vessel reocclusion. Abciximab prevents platelet aggregation by binding to the platelet glycoprotein IIb/IIIa receptor and thus preventing adhesive glycoproteins from binding to the surface of activated platelets. Evaluation of the clinical efficacy of abciximab has shown that it statistically reduces the incidence of reocclusion compared to placebo but doubles the risk of bleeding.

Whether the benefit is great enough to offset the risk and the high cost of the drug remains to be determined.

Abciximab is administered as a bolus intravenously, followed by an intravenous infusion for 12 hours. Marked inhibition of platelet function is observed during infusion, but bleeding times return to normal within 12 hours of the end of infusion in most patients.

IMMUNOMODULATORS

Immunomodulators, which are also known as "biological response modifiers," are substances that modify the immune response in the body. The broad term includes such chemicals as corticosteroids, which can lead to immunosuppression, but for the purposes of this chapter, we will focus upon proteins that are involved in regulating the development of the myeloid cell lines in the bone marrow, proteins involved in regulation of various aspects of the immune function, and some natural products used as immunosuppressants. Specifically the substances to be addressed fall into the following categories: colony-stimulating factors, interleukins, interferons, and the immunosuppressants, cyclosporin and FK506 (also known as tacrolimus).

The **colony-stimulating factors** (CSFs) are proteins involved in the production and differentiation of stem cells in the bone marrow into various types of blood cells. Currently we know of five colony-stimulating factors, named by the type of cell they stimulate: granulocyte stimulating factor (GSF), granulocyte-macrophage stimulating factor (GM-CSF), macrophage stimulating factor (M-CSF), interleukin-3 or multicolony-stimulating factor, and erythropoietin, which stimulates the formation of red blood cells (erythrocytes). Several of these have been produced via recombinant technology and have been approved for use by the FDA. The current uses will be described; however, there may be further uses approved in the future as we gain a more complete understanding of their effects and interactions.

G-CSF is a 174-amino-acid residue glycoprotein normally produced in the body by monocytes, fibroblasts, and endothelial cells. The product used medicinally is produced by recombinant *Escherichia coli* and is not glycosylated. It also has an *N*-terminal methionine to permit bacterial protein synthesis. Its generic name is filgrastim and it is sold as Neupogen. G-CSF stimulates neutrophil differentiation and function by binding to specific receptors on the hematopoietic cell surface, leading to a shortening of the maturation period. It has little effect on other cell types.

Filgrastim is approved for use in the recovery from neutropenia following cancer chemotherapy in nonmyeloid cancers. It is usually administered in a dose of 5 mcg/kg/day subcutaneously or intravenously, starting the day following the end of chemotherapy and continuing with daily therapy for up to 2 weeks or until the absolute neutrophil count reaches 10,000/mm^3. A fall in neutrophils by about 50% is to be expected once therapy is discontinued. Filgrastim has been shown to decrease hospitalization, decrease the use of intravenous antibiotics, and prevent infection when compared to placebo. It is generally well tolerated with bone pain, which occurs in about a quarter of patients, as the only consistently observed adverse effect.

The protein product should be stored in the refrigerator and not frozen. However, it is stable at room temperature for 6 hours. Shaking should be avoided. The vial is a single use vial and any remaining drug should be discarded, because microbial contamination from the first entry could lead to proteolysis and bacterial growth.

GM-CSF is a 127-amino acid residue glycoprotein whose generic name is sargramostim. It is manufactured as recombinant protein in yeast and bacteria. The yeast form is a mixture of three *N*-glycosylated species and is not *O*-glycosylated, in contrast to the native human protein, which is both *N*- and *O*-glycosylated. The recombinant form has a leucine at position 23 in place of an arginine residue that was labile to proteases. The yeast form is sold as Prokine and Leukine. The bacterial form (produced in *E. coli* and non-glycosylated) is called Leucomax. The various forms have somewhat different specific activities (units per mg) *in vitro,* but all are effective *in vivo.*

GM-CSF stimulates hematopoietic cells in the granulocyte-macrophage pathways to divide and differentiate, and also stimulates and activates mature macrophages and granulocytes. It is approved for use in myeloid reconstitution after autologous bone marrow transplantation such as is used in patients with Hodgkin's disease, non-Hodgkin's lymphoma, and acute lymphoblastic leukemia. It reduces the time to engraftment, decreases the incidence of infectious episodes, reduces the need for antibiotics, and decreases the length of hospitalization. It may also be useful for enhancing neutrophil recovery in other patients undergoing bone marrow transplantation, for correcting neutropenia in patients with aplastic anemia, and for reducing the nadir of myelosuppression in patients undergoing cytotoxic chemotherapy, but all these uses are off-label for now. The use in AIDS patients is controversial, but in combination with zidovudine, it appears to raise the numbers of monocytes, neutrophils, and eosinophils.

GM-CSF is usually administered daily at doses of 250 mcg/m^2/day in a 2-hour infusion, beginning 2 to 4 hours after bone marrow infusion and continuing for 21 days. Monitoring includes twice weekly blood counts and therapy is discontinued if the neutrophil count reaches 20,000/mm^3.

Adverse effects with GM-CSF are more common and more severe than with G-CSF. Toxicity also occurs more frequently with intravenous than with subcutaneous administration. There often is a reaction with the first dose that can involve flushing, hypotension, tachycardia, dyspnea, myalgias, and nausea and vomiting. Other side effects observed include fever and chills, bone pain, anorexia, and rash; at higher doses fluid retention, pleural and pericardial infusions, and venous thrombosis have been observed.

The protein product must be reconstituted prior to use. It should be swirled to dissolve rather than shaken, and dilute solutions should have human albumin added to them to prevent adsorption to intravenous delivery bags and lines (the albumin will compete for adsorption sites). No preservative is added so the vials should be used once and then discarded.

Erythropoietin (Epoietin alfa) is a glycoprotein normally produced in the kidney that stimulates the division and differentiation of erythroid precursor cells in the bone marrow. Epoietin alfa is a recombinant protein produced in mammalian cells so that it has the identical 165-residue amino acid sequence and glycosylation pattern as the native human protein. It is sold as Epogen or Procrit. Epoietin alfa is used to treat anemia in patients with chronic renal failure, whether or not they are undergoing kidney dialysis. It also is used to treat anemia related to ziduvudine therapy in AIDS patients and in cancer patients on chemotherapy. It is not intended for immediate treatment of severe anemia and is not a substitute for emergency transfusion. It also, of course, cannot treat anemias caused by iron or folate deficiencies, and anemias resulting from hemo-

lysis or bleeding should be treated appropriately with other approaches.

Erythropoietin dosage is individualized to achieve a target hematocrit. The starting dosage is usually 50 to 100 units/kg three times a week until the target hematocrit of 30% to 33% is reached. Then a maintenance dose is individualized to maintain the hematocrit within the target range. Erythropoietin is usually well tolerated. Adverse effects include hypertension, headache, tachycardia, nausea and vomiting, some flulike symptoms, and allergic reactions. Seizures have been reported, but they are rare. The patient's iron stores should be evaluated during therapy.

Like the other colony-stimulating factors, erythropoietin may be denatured by shaking, should be refrigerated and not frozen, and material remaining in a vial should be discarded after a single entry. It may be administered intravenously or subcutaneously.

The **interleukins** are a family of cytokines that are critical to the communication network between cells involved in the immune response. There now are about eleven interleukins that have been identified, and the list is growing. The physiological effects of each of these are still being explored, and their exploitation for pharmacological purposes is still in its infancy. The use of only one interleukin, **interleukin-2** (aldesleukin), is currently approved by the FDA. Aldesleukin (sold as Proleukin) is approved for use in metastatic renal cell carcinoma. It is being investigated for use in Kaposi's sarcoma in combination with zidovudine and for malignant melanoma, colorectal cancer, and non-Hodgkin's lymphoma.

Aldesleukin is produced by recombinant DNA technology in *Escherichia coli*. It differs in several ways from the native interleukin-2: (1) it is nonglycosylated, (2) it does not have the *N*-terminal alanine found in the native protein, (3) it has a serine substituted for cysteine at amino acid position 125 to increase stability, and (4) it exists in microaggregates of 27 interleukin-2 molecules. However, aldesleukin retains the native immunoregulatory biological activity of interleukin-2 including enhancement of lymphocyte mitogenesis and cytotoxicity, induction of killer cell activity, and induction of interferon-γ production. It inhibits tumor growth although the exact mechanism is unknown.

Adverse effects with aldesleukin are frequent, often serious, and sometimes fatal. Monitoring should occur prior to and during administration and daily during therapy. Most patients will experience fever and chills, pruritus, and gastrointestinal side effects upon administration. More serious adverse effects include cardiac and pulmonary toxicities (including myocardial infarction), bowel perforation, CNS effects including coma and seizures, and renal and liver dysfunction. They generally will reverse when drug treatment is stopped. Dexamethasone may ameliorate life-threatening toxicities but will result in a loss of therapeutic effect of aldesleukin.

For metastatic renal carcinoma, aldesleukin is administered by 15-minute intravenous infusion every 8 hours. Each course of treatment consists of two 5-day treatment cycles separated by a rest period, unless severe toxicities cause a discontinuation of therapy. The product must be reconstituted with sterile water and should be a clear, slightly yellow liquid. It should be swirled rather than shaken. Dilution is with sterile water; bacteriostatic water or normal saline can increase aggregation. Albumin should not be added to the product, and in-line filters should be avoided. The product should be stored at refrigerator temperatures and administered within 48 hours of reconstitution. Any unused portions must be discarded as the product contains no preservative.

Interferons are protein cytokines with molecular weights ranging from 15,000 to 21,000 daltons produced by a variety of cell types in response to a variety of stimuli, including viral infections, bacterial toxins, and some intracellular pathogens. They play a complex role in the immune system, often augmenting the effects of the interleukins. There are three main types of interferon—interferon-α, interferon-β, and interferon-γ—but there are many subtypes controlled by different genes. For instance, we now know of 17 different human genes for interferon-α. There is overlap and synergism among the various types and subtypes, and the activities of each of these different proteins is still being elucidated. In general, interferon-α (all subtypes) is produced primarily by leukocytes, and its activity is primarily antiviral; interferon-β is produced primarily by fibroblasts and has both antiviral and immunoregulatory activities; interferon-γ is produced by T lymphocytes and is an activator of macrophages and mediates local inflammation. Recombinant forms of subtypes of all three types are now approved for limited uses. As our understanding of the interferons and their actions increase, there undoubtedly will be further pharmacological uses of these proteins.

Interferon-α is not directly antiviral. It is released in response to viral infection or other stimuli. It then binds to cell surfaces at receptors shared by interferon-α and interferon-β, and increases gene transcription of over 20 cellular proteins, some of which specifically inhibit specific steps in virus replication. The specific biochemical effects are varied and include inhibition of penetration, uncoating, transcription, and translation of viral proteins and/or viral assembly and release.

Interferon-α is actually a family of related proteins with about 70% sequence homology. At present three forms of interferon-α are available for therapeutic use. These are recombinant **interferon alfa-2a** (Roferon A), recombinant **interferon alfa-2b** (Intron A), and natural **interferon alfa-n3** (Alferon N), a mixture of α interferons produced from activated human leukocytes. Interferon alfa-2a is produced by recombinant *Escherichia coli* and is approved for use in hairy cell leukemia and AIDS-related Kaposi's sarcoma. Interferon alfa-2b is also produced by recombinant *E. coli* and is approved for the same uses plus condylomata acuminata (genital warts), chronic hepatitis non-A, non-B/C, and chronic hepatitis B. Both have been used for a variety of other viral diseases (including cytomegalovirus, rhinovirus, herpesvirus, and vaccinia virus infections) and cancers, especially leukemias and lymphomas; clinical trials are underway to establish safety and efficacy. The mechanism of the antiproliferative, antitumor activity is not well understood, but it may involve both a direct antiproliferative effect on cancer cells and a modulation of the immune system. Interferon alfa-n3 is currently approved for use in condylomata acuminata and is also being tested for other viral diseases and tumors.

Interferon-α (including the subtypes) is administered intralesionally for genital warts and has been tested as a nasal spray for rhinovirus, but generally it is administered systemically by the subcutaneous or intramuscular route. Adverse effects from systemic administration are related to a flu-like syndrome that is dose-related and can be ameliorated to some degree by preadministration of acetaminophen or a nonsteroidal anti-inflammatory agent. Tolerance to these effects usually develops over time, especially at lower doses. More severe side effects may develop in patients receiving higher doses and include neuropsychiatric problems (e.g., depression, confusion), bone marrow suppression, cardiac and pulmonary problems, dermatologic reactions, and hepatic abnormalities. Drug interactions may also occur because of inhibition of cytochrome P-450 enzymes (specifically observed with aminophylline), and there may be synergistic adverse effects on the bone marrow when administered with zidovudine.

Like other protein products, these should not be shaken nor frozen. However, the solution is stable for about 1 month following reconstitution, and the vials may be reentered.

Interferon beta-1b (Betaseron) is manufactured using recombinant *E. coli* containing a human gene obtained from human fibroblasts. The engineered gene replaces cysteine in position 17 with a serine to increase protein stability. The protein has 165 amino acids and a molecular weight of 18,500 daltons and differs from the native protein in that it is nonglycosylated. It has both antiviral and immunoregulatory properties, but it is currently approved only for use in relapsing-remitting multiple sclerosis. Multiple sclerosis is characterized by recurrent attacks of neurologic dysfunction followed by complete or incomplete recovery and interferon beta-1b has been shown to reduce the frequency of clinical exacerbations. The mechanism is not completely understood, but it is thought to intervene with an autoimmune demyelination reaction that is involved in the pathogenesis of the disease. It is also being investigated for use in AIDS, AIDS-related Kaposi's sarcoma, metastatic renal cell carcinoma, malignant melanoma, and acute non-A/non-B hepatitis.

For multiple sclerosis, interferon beta-1b is administered subcutaneously every other day continuously. Like the other interferons, there is a wide range of side effects that illustrate what broad effects these proteins have in the body. Again, flu-like symptoms are common during the initiation of therapy and can be relieved to some degree with acetaminophen. Patients need to be cautioned about the photosensitivity, the possibility of depression, and its potential as an abortifacient. Adverse events have been observed in association with almost every system in the body and include cardiovascular, neurologic, gastrointestinal, endocrine, metabolic, hematologic, and musculoskeletal abnormalities.

Interferon beta-1b is sold as a powder for injection. Each vial contains 0.3 mg of interferon beta-1b and 15 mg of albumin and 15 mg dextrose. It is reconstituted with 1.2 mL of diluent and 1 mL (0.25 mg of drug) is injected subcutaneously. The product contains no preservative, so it must be discarded following a single use. It should be stored at refrigerator temperatures before and after reconstitution and should be used within 3 hours of reconstitution.

Interferon gamma-1b (Actimmune) is a 140 amino acid lymphokine also produced using recombinant *E. coli*. In contrast to the other types of interferons, interferon γ has potent phagocyte activating properties, including the generation of toxic oxygen species within phagocytes that mediate the killing of intracellular pathogens such as *Staphylococcus aureus, Toxoplasma, Leishmania, Listeria*, and *Mycobacterium avium-intracellulare*. It also enhances antibody-dependent cellular cytotoxicity and natural killer cell activity. It interacts with other lymphokines such as interleukin-2 and forms part of a complex lymphocyte regulatory network.

Pharmacologically, its only currently approved indication is for chronic granulomatous disease, an inherited disorder characterized by deficient phagocyte oxidative metabolism. However, it is being investigated as adjunctive therapy in patients with a variety of chronic intracellular infections. It is administered in doses of 50 mcg/m^2 subcutaneously three times a week. Vials contain no preservative and, therefore, are suitable only for single use. The solution should not be frozen nor shaken and should be stored at refrigerator temperatures prior to use. Adverse effects at these doses include the typical flu-like syndrome observed with interferons and CNS disturbances, including decreased mental status, gait disturbances, and dizziness. At higher doses cardiovascular effects, reversible neutropenia, and elevation of hepatic enzymes were observed in some patients.

Cyclosporin A and **Tacrolimus** (or **FK506**) are immunosuppressants used in prophylaxis of organ rejection. Cyclosporin A is a cyclic polypeptide consisting of 11 amino acids produced as a secondary metabolite of the fungi *Tolypocladium inflatum* or *Cylindrocarpon lucidum*. It is highly stable, very lipophilic, and essentially not soluble in water; it is administered intravenously in a polyethoxylated castor oil and ethanol vehicle or orally in olive oil and ethanol. Tacrolimus is a macrolide molecule produced by *Streptomyces tsukubaensis*.

Both drugs are used to inhibit T-lymphocytes and prevent rejection of transplanted organs. Cyclosporin A principally inhibits the T-helper cells, but the T-suppressor cells may also be suppressed. It inhibits lymphokine production and release including interleukin-2; it does not cause bone marrow suppression. It is effective for prophylaxis of organ rejection in kidney, liver, and heart transplants, and has had limited but successful use with other transplant procedures including pancreas, bone marrow, and heart/lung. Because it is an inhibitor of chronic immune-mediated inflammation, it also shows promise for treatment of a variety of autoimmune diseases. Nephrotoxicity is the major side effect, and hypertension is sometimes observed. It has a broad range of drug interactions because of the fact that it is metabolized by P-450 liver enzymes.

Tacrolimus (FK506) is a newer agent that inhibits T-lymphocyte activation. It is currently approved for use in liver transplant and is being investigated for other transplant procedures and treatment of autoimmune diseases. It is administered intravenously and then orally. The principal adverse effects are tremor, headache, nausea and diarrhea, hypertension, and nephrotoxicity. Hypersensitivity reactions including anaphylaxis have been reported. Increased susceptibility to infection and lymphoma development may result. It also is metabolized by P-450 enzymes and has many drug interactions. Tacrolimus and cyclosporin A should not be used concurrently.

SUGGESTED READINGS

Ad Hoc Working Group for the Development of Standards for Pediatric Immunization Practices. Standards for Pediatric Immunization Practices. J. Amer. Med. Assoc., *269*:1817, 1993.

Adams, W.G., Deaver, K.A., Cochi, S.L., Plikaytis, B.D., Zell, E.R., Broome, C.V., Wenger, J.D.: Decline of Childhood *Hemophilus influenzae* Type b (Hib) Disease in the Hib Vaccine Era. J. Amer. Med. Assoc., *269*:221, 1993.

American College of Physicians. *Task Force on Adult Immunization: Guide for Adult Immunization*. 2nd ed., Philadelphia, American College of Physicians, 1990.

Anon.: Interferon Beta-1b for Multiple Sclerosis. Med. Lett. Drugs Ther., *35*:61, 1993.

Anon.: Tetramune—a Combined Vaccine for Infants. Med. Lett. Drugs Ther., *35*:104, 1993.

Anon.: Varicella Vaccine. Med. Lett. Drugs Ther., *37*:55,1995.

Anon.: Hepatitis A Vaccine. Med. Lett. Drugs Ther., *37*:51,1995.

Borel, J.F.: Pharmacology of Cyclosporine (Sandimmune). Pharmcol. Rev., *41*:240, 1989.

Centers for Disease Control and Prevention. Recommendation of the Immunization Practices Advisory Committee (ACIP): General Recommendations on Immunization. MMWR *43*:RR-1, 1994.

Cimons, M.: FDA Approves, Pediatricians Endorse Chicken Pox Vaccine. Amer. Soc. Microbiol. News, *61*:291, 1995.

Cohen, J.: Bumps on the Vaccine Road. Science, *265*: 1371, 1994.

Coleman, R.M., Lombard, M.F., Sicard, R.E.: *Fundamental Immunology*, 2nd ed., Dubuque, Iowa, William C. Brown, 1992.

Conte, J.E. Jr., Barriere, S.L.: *Manual of Antibiotics and Infectious Diseases*. 7th ed., Philadelphia, Lea & Febiger, 1993.

Dolin, R., Keefer, M.C.: Chapter 106. Vaccines for HIV-1 Infection. In *Mandell, Douglas, and Bennett's Principles and Practice of Infectious Diseases*, 4th ed., Mandell, G.L., Bennett, J.E., Dolin, R., eds., New York, Churchill Livingstone, 1995.

Fleischman, R.A.: Southwestern Internal Medicine Conference: Clinical Use of Hematopoietic Growth Factors. Am. J. Med. Sci., *305*:248, 1993.

Frank, M.O., Mandell, G.L.: Chapter 33. Immunomodulators. In *Mandell, Douglas, and Bennett's Principles and Practice of Infectious Diseases*, 4th ed., Mandell, G.L., Bennett, J.E., Dolin, R., eds., New York, Churchill Livingstone, 1995.

Hinan, A.R., Koplan, J.P.: Pertussis and Pertussis Vaccine: Reanalysis of Benefits, Risks and Costs. J. Amer. Med. Assoc., *251*:309, 1984.

Olin, B.R., Hebel, S.K., Gremp, J.L., Hubert, M.K., eds.: *Drug Facts and Comparisons*, 1995 ed., St. Louis, Facts and Comparisons, 1995.

Orenstein, W.A., Hinman, A.R., Bart, K.J., Hadler, S.C.: Chapter 300. Immunization. In *Mandell, Douglas, and Bennett's Principles and Practice of Infectious Diseases*, 4th ed., Mandell, G.L., Bennett, J.E., Dolin, R., eds., New York, Churchill Livingstone, 1995.

Roilides, E., Pizzo, P.A.: Modulation of Host Defenses by Cytokines: EvolvingAdjuncts in Prevention and Treatment of Serious Infections in Immunocompromised Hosts. Clin. Infect. Dis., *15*:508, 1992.

Sigal, N.H., Dumont, F.J.: Cyclosporin A, FK-506 and Rapamycin: Pharmacological Probes of Lymphocyte Signal Transduction. Annu. Rev. Immunol., *10*:519, 1992.

Index

317